1990

Yearbook of Science and the Future

1990

Yearbook of Science and the Future

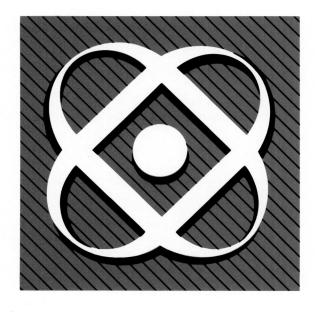

Encyclopædia

Britannica, Inc.

Chicago
Auckland
Geneva
London
Madrid
Manila
Paris
Rome
Seoul
Sydney
Tokyo
Toronto

1990

Yearbook
of Science
and the
Future

The University of Chicago
The Yearbook of Science and the Future is published with the editorial advice of the faculties of the University of Chicago.

Encyclopædia Britannica, Inc.

Editor
David Calhoun

Associate Editor
Charles Cegielski

Editorial Staff
Daphne Daume, Karen Justin, Arthur Latham

Art Director
Cynthia Peterson

Planning Analyst
Marsha Check

Senior Picture Editor
Kathy Nakamura

Layout Artist
Dale Horn

Illustrators
Anne H. Becker, John L. Draves, Curtis E. Hardy

Art Production Supervisor
Richard A. Roiniotis

Art Staff
Amy I. Brown, Daniel M. Delgado, Patricia A. Henle, Kathy Kalinowski

Manager, Copy Department
Anita Wolff

Senior Copy Editors
Julian Ronning, Barbara Whitney

Copy Staff
Elizabeth A. Blowers, Ellen Finkelstein, Lawrence D. Kowalski, Thomas J. Riggs, Peter Shrock

Manager, Production Control
Mary C. Srodon

Production Control Staff
Marilyn L. Barton, Vernetta McCoy, Yvonne G. Pua

Manager, Composition and Page Makeup
Melvin Stagner

Coordinator, Composition and Page Makeup
Philip Rehmer

Composition Staff
Duangnetra Debhavalya, Morna Freund, John Krom, Jr., Thomas Mulligan, Gwen Rosenberg, Tammy Tsou

Page Makeup Staff
Michael Born, Jr., Griselda Cháidez, Arnell Reed, Danette Wetterer

Contents

Feature Articles

Encyclopædia Britannica Science Update

The Science Year in Review

A Science Classic

Institutions of Science

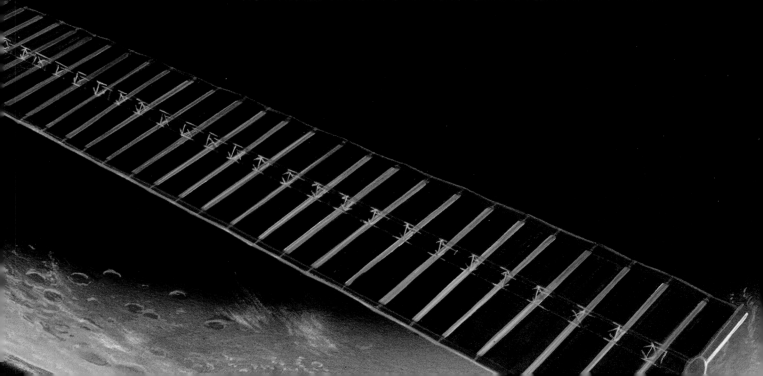

IN QUEST
OF
MARS

BY J. KELLY BEATTY

DESPITE A FLURRY OF EXPLORATORY MISSIONS IN THE 1960s AND 1970s,
MARS HAS NOT BEEN VISITED BY EARTH'S SPACECRAFT FOR MORE THAN A DECADE.
NOW THE RED PLANET IS ONCE AGAIN GETTING PLENTY OF ATTENTION.

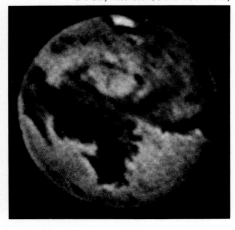

Stephen Larson, Lunar and Planetary Laboratory, and Gary Rosenbaum, Steward Observatory

Throughout recorded history no planet has so captured the human imagination as Mars. Gleaming brightly in the night sky, Mars's baleful red color sets it apart from all the solar system's other worlds. The Earth and Mars are close planetary neighbors, and as they circle the Sun, they swing past each other every 26 months or so. Because its orbit is not circular, the Red Planet comes particularly close to the Earth—roughly 57 million kilometers—at intervals of 15 or 17 years. (One kilometer is about 0.62 mile.) Such was the case during the summer and early autumn of 1988, when Mars was a dazzling and unmistakable beacon in the evening sky. In fact, for astronomers in the Northern Hemisphere, the planet was then seen at its best since 1875, and not until the year 2025 will it again be so close to Earth and so high above the horizon for American viewers.

For Mars, 1988 was a watershed year for another reason. On July 7 and again five days later, spacecraft from Earth rocketed off in its direction for the first time in 13 years. The nearly identical spacecraft, called Phobos 1 and Phobos 2, were named after one of the planet's two small moons (the other moon is Deimos), and they were built by scientists and engineers in the Soviet Union. The last spacecraft sent to Mars were the U.S. Viking space probes, which departed Earth in 1975 and arrived at Mars the following summer.

A legacy of mixed success

Why have so many years passed between these missions to the Red Planet? The situation was very different in the 1960s and particularly in the 1970s. During this period the U.S. and U.S.S.R. together sent a score of spacecraft to study Mars, usually dispatching them every other year to take advantage of the times when Earth and Mars were close to each other.

Many factors have slowed the pace of planetary exploration over the last decade. Not insignificant was the fact that, once the rush of initial

J. KELLY BEATTY, Senior Editor of Sky & Telescope *magazine, specializes in solar system exploration and the Soviet space program.*

(Overleaf) Illustration by Pat Rawlings, Eagle Engineering

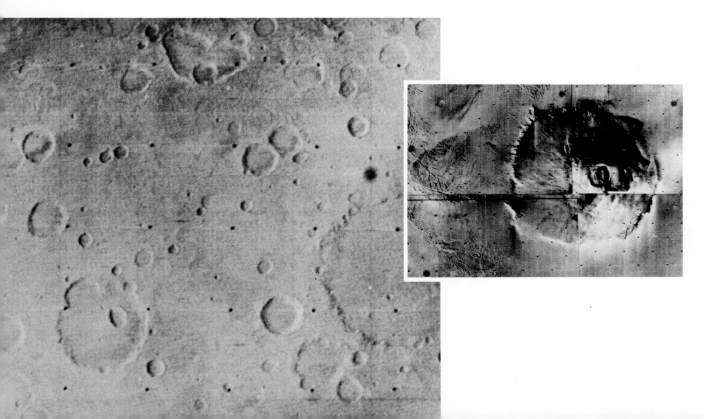

discoveries was over, scientists needed time to carefully analyze the data already collected by past missions before deciding on designs for the next ones. The task proved especially difficult because scientists' perceptions of Mars were changing rapidly. When Mariner 4, a U.S. craft, swept past the planet in July 1965, it returned 22 crude but useful television images of a desolate, cratered landscape that looked remarkably like the Moon. This impression was reinforced by views obtained in 1969 by Mariners 6 and 7, which also determined that the planet's warmest days approached room temperature, its nighttime temperatures plummeted below 200 kelvins (200 K; −73° C or −100° F), and the ice at its south pole was a frigid 148 K (−125° C or −193° F).

The notion that Mars was a static, "dead" world changed again in 1971, when Mariner 9 became the first spacecraft to orbit Mars (or any planet other than Earth). Over the next 12 months, the 7,329 images it relayed to Earth showed that Mars is far from being geologically uninteresting. Instead, the planet was seen to sport huge dormant volcanoes, vast canyons, and ancient river beds. Through Mariner 9's television eyes, people on Earth watched dust storms rage across the Martian plains and wispy white clouds form atop its mountain peaks.

Mars had become interesting again, but still lacking was the answer to a question that had been pondered for centuries: Does life exist on the Red Planet? Long before spacecraft coursed across interplanetary space, telescopes had shown astronomers that Mars is surrounded by a thin atmosphere, has icy white polar caps, and experiences seasonal changes in its surface markings. Some observers even thought they could discern a global network of vegetation-lined canals, presumably built by the planet's inhabitants. By the late 19th century, the notion that intelligent beings lived on Mars was widespread. In fact, a turn-of-the-century contest, which could be won by anyone who could establish communication with another celestial body, specifically excluded the Red Planet because talking to Martians was considered too easy.

The close approach of Mars to the Earth in 1988 treated observers in the Northern Hemisphere to the best views of the planet in more than a century. Representative of the detail obtained from Earth-based telescopes is the image of Mars at the top of the opposite page, photographed electronically in early October with a CCD (charge coupled device) array through the Steward Observatory's 1.55-meter (61-inch) reflector in Arizona. Scientists' perceptions of Mars changed during the 1960s and 1970s as increasingly sophisticated space missions returned ever better data and video images of the surface. The "dead world" impression conveyed by Mariners 4, 6, and 7 (opposite page, bottom left; from Mariner 6 in 1969) was overturned by the visit in 1971–72 of Mariner 9, which revealed a geologically varied planet with giant dormant volcanoes (opposite page, bottom right), vast canyons (below), and ancient riverbeds.

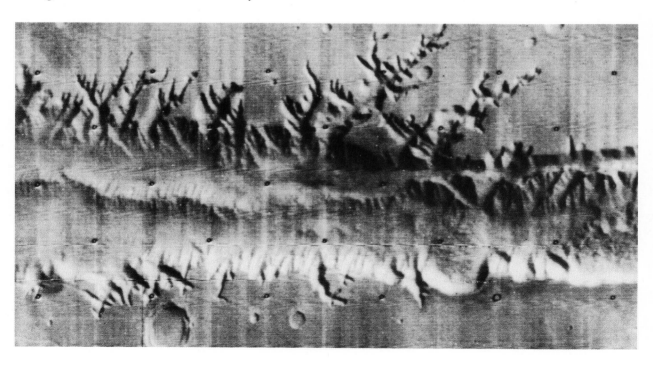

To settle the matter of life on Mars, the U.S. sent two Viking spacecraft, each consisting of an orbiter and a lander. Bristling with instruments, Viking 1's lander plopped down onto Mars's Chryse Planitia ("Plain of Gold") on July 20, 1976; Viking 2's lander touched down on Utopia Planitia ("Utopian Plain"), 1,500 kilometers away, on September 3. Although each carried a quartet of sophisticated, automated laboratories designed specifically to search for life in the soil and thin atmosphere of Mars, they found none. The Viking program itself, however, was fabulously successful, and for years all four component spacecraft returned useful scientific data to scientists.

Throughout the era of the Mariners and Vikings, the U.S.S.R. struggled to establish its own program of Mars exploration. That nation's first attempt, in 1960, and as many as seven more over the next decade all failed. Not until the twin orbiter-lander spacecraft called Mars 2 and

Missions to Mars—U.S.

spacecraft	date launched	mission	results
Mariner 3	11/5/64	flyby	Failed to reach Mars after leaving Earth parking orbit.
Mariner 4	11/28/64	flyby	Flew by Mars 7/14/65; returned images.
Mariner 6	2/24/69	flyby	Flew by Mars 7/31/69; returned images.
Mariner 7	3/27/69	flyby	Flew by Mars 8/5/69; returned images.
Mariner 8	5/8/71	orbiter	Failed to achieve Earth orbit.
Mariner 9	5/30/71	orbiter	Entered Mars orbit 11/13/71; mapped surface and returned first images of Martian moons.
Viking 1	8/20/75	orbiter/ lander	Entered Mars orbit 6/19/76; lander set down 7/20; conducted long-term tests and observations in orbit and on surface.
Viking 2	9/9/75	orbiter/ lander	Entered Mars orbit 8/7/76; lander set down 9/3; conducted long-term tests and observations in orbit and on surface.

12

Mars 3 arrived there in November and December 1971 could Soviet scientists claim some success. Both began orbiting the planet as planned, but Mars 2's landing craft somehow malfunctioned during descent. The lander from Mars 3 did touch down successfully on Dec. 2, 1971, beating Viking 1 to the Martian surface by 4½ years. Inexplicably, however, its radio transmissions ceased after only 110 seconds. Mars 2 and 3 had the misfortune to arrive during a raging, planetwide dust storm, which rendered the orbiters' cameras virtually useless and may have doomed both landers. The U.S.S.R. launched two more pairs of separate Mars orbiters and landers in 1973, but its run of bad luck continued. One orbiter and one lander sped past the planet without slowing down, and the second lander stopped transmitting moments before reaching the surface. Of the four, only the Mars 5 orbiter accomplished its mission as planned.

The quest resumes: Project Phobos

After the Vikings completed their scrutiny of Mars, no other spacecraft were sent to the planet until the U.S.S.R. launched its Phobos probes in 1988. One reason for the hiatus was that planetary exploration had become very expensive (the Viking mission, for example, cost more than $1 billion). A second and perhaps more important reason was that by the late 1970s the attention of space planners had turned elsewhere; U.S. scientists were exploring the outer solar system with their Pioneers and Voyagers, and their Soviet counterparts had become preoccupied with Venus, where exploratory craft from the U.S.S.R. were enjoying considerably more success than they had at Mars. Thus, in a sense, only recently has it become Mars's "turn" again. From now through the

In the late 19th and early 20th centuries, it was widely believed that the surface of Mars was crisscrossed with a network of canals built by intelligent life. An illustration from a fictional work in the November 1916 issue of The Electrical Experimenter portrays a Martian construction crew fabricating a canal with the aid of disintegration beams. Realistic attempts to settle the matter of Martian life had to wait for the arrival of the U.S. Viking missions in 1976. The images assembled into the rendition of Mars shown below were taken in June 1976 when Viking 1 was about 560,000 kilometers from the planet. Tables (opposite page and this page) summarize past U.S. and Soviet Mars exploration programs.

(Below) photo, NASA

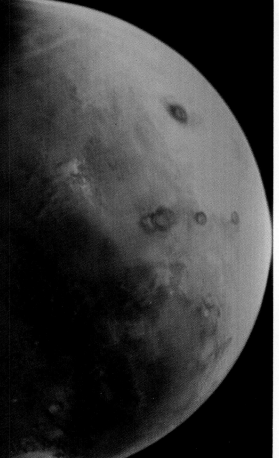

Missions to Mars—U.S.S.R.

spacecraft	date launched	mission	results
unannounced	10/10/60	flyby	Failed to achieve Earth orbit.
unannounced	10/14/60	flyby	Failed to achieve Earth orbit.
unannounced	10/24/62	flyby	Failed to leave Earth orbit.
Mars 1	11/1/62	flyby	Communications failed 3/21/63 at distance of 106 million km.
unannounced	11/4/62	flyby	Failed to leave Earth orbit.
Zond 2	11/30/64	flyby	Communications failed 5/65.
Zond 3	7/18/65	test	Photographed far side of Moon; passed Mars orbit; communications failed 3/66.
unannounced	3/27/67	lander?	Rumored launch failure of second-generation Mars probes.
Kosmos 419	5/10/71	orbiter/ lander	Failed to leave Earth orbit.
Mars 2	5/19/71	orbiter/ lander	Orbiter entered Mars orbit 11/27 and returned data; lander crashed.
Mars 3	5/28/71	orbiter/ lander	Orbiter entered Mars orbit 12/2 and returned data; lander survived 110 seconds on surface.
Mars 4	7/21/73	orbiter	Engine malfunction prevented craft from entering Mars orbit; flew by 2/10/74.
Mars 5	7/25/73	orbiter	Entered Mars orbit 2/12/74 and returned images.
Mars 6	8/5/73	lander	Contact lost seconds before landing 5/12/74; measured Martian atmosphere during descent.
Mars 7	8/9/73	lander	Engine malfunction caused lander to miss planet 3/9/74.

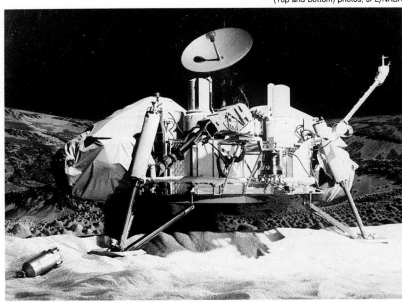

The Viking 1 and Viking 2 spacecraft each carried a lander (right) designed to study the Martian surface and to search for life on the planet. Separated by 1,500 kilometers, the landers scooped soil samples into onboard automated laboratories for chemical and biological analyses, but no encouraging sign of life was found. The surface sampler of Viking 1's lander (below) hangs in the foreground of the ruddy Martian landscape. The Viking program achieved enormous success, returning over 50,000 images of Mars and transmitting useful data to scientists for more than six years.

1990s, U.S. and Soviet deep-space exploration efforts will focus heavily on the Red Planet.

As its name implies, the objectives of Project Phobos included not only Mars but also its satellites. Conceived in the early 1980s by scientists at the Space Research Institute, Moscow, the two spacecraft represented the first use of a new, larger, and more sophisticated design than had been employed for previous Soviet interplanetary craft. In particular, they were equipped to approach the Martian moons and hover quite

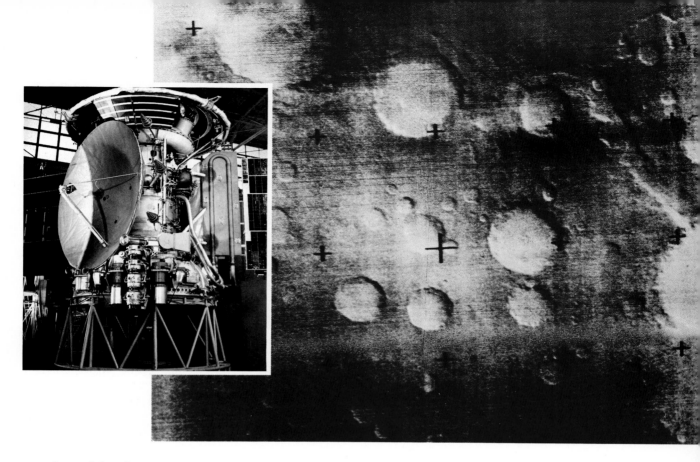

near them while taking measurements. To do this, they needed advanced stabilization systems and "intelligent" computerized sensors to navigate the craft over large obstacles. All together, the 6,220-kilogram (13,700-pound) craft carried two dozen different experiments—many supplied by both Eastern and Western European countries. Scientists consider Phobos and Deimos particularly interesting objects because their size and color are similar to those of many asteroids. Both moons could, in fact, be asteroids that long ago ventured too near Mars and were forced into orbits around the planet by its strong gravity.

Early in 1988 the completed spacecraft were shipped to the Baykonur Cosmodrome, a Soviet launch facility located roughly 100 kilometers east of the Aral Sea. Despite two picture-perfect launches by powerful Proton rockets, one of the spacecraft was soon irretrievably lost. Flawed commands transmitted to Phobos 1 in late August 1988 apparently caused it to break its radio link with Earth, and communication with the hapless probe could not be reestablished. Moreover, Phobos 2 temporarily lost the use of part of its camera system and other electronic systems during the seven-month journey to Mars, thus jeopardizing what remained of the mission.

Arriving at Mars on Jan. 29, 1989, Phobos 2 fired its rocket engine to slow down and be captured into an orbit around Mars. It then spent the next two months examining both the Martian landscape below and the prime target, Phobos. To take pictures, Phobos 2 first had to break its communication link with Earth, then swing to one side until its cameras were in position, and finally return to its previous orientation in order to

A frustrating run of failures and limited successes plagued the Soviet Mars program during the 1960s and early 1970s. The landing craft of Mars 3 (above left) did touch down on the Martian surface in 1971, beating Viking 1 by 4½ years, but its radio transmissions stopped less than two minutes after landing. One of the few unqualified successes was the Mars 5 orbiter, which reached the planet in early 1974 and returned useful images (above right).

Photos, Tass/Sovfoto

15

Phobos 2's namesake, the Martian moon Phobos (above), was photographed by the spacecraft about a month after the craft had entered orbit around Mars in late January. Illustration (opposite page, bottom) shows the general design of the Phobos 1 and 2 craft, while the accompanying table (below) lists the international contributions to the project's scientific payload. Weight limitations prevented equipping both spacecraft with all of the experiments.

regain contact with Earth. All of this activity was controlled by an onboard computer. Several maneuvers took the craft ever closer to the moon, which is irregularly shaped and 27 kilometers across at its widest point. The mission's most critical encounter was to take place in early April, at which time Phobos 2 would ease to within 50 meters of the moon's cratered surface and spend about 15 minutes slowly passing over the terrain. (One meter is about 3.3 feet.) But with only two weeks to go, a mysterious malfunction brought the mission to an abrupt and disappointing conclusion. Apparently something happened during the photography session on March 27 that prevented the spacecraft from reestablishing its vital radio link. Phobos 2 was never heard from again.

Had it performed the daring flyby as planned, the spacecraft would have fired at the moon many dozens of times with a small laser called LIMA-D and an ion beam called DION. These energetic pulses were to destroy tiny bits of the dusty surface, and when the resulting vaporized rock reached the hovering spacecraft, it would be analyzed by onboard instruments. All the while, Phobos 2's cameras would record details no larger than softballs in and around the target areas. The craft would also have used its many other instruments to learn a great deal about the general mineralogical composition of the surface. Of particular interest would have been measurements of how much water is bound to the minerals.

Near the end of its brush with Phobos, the spacecraft was to drop two small instrumented packages onto the surface. One would conduct

Project Phobos Scientific Payload

Experiment	Description	Participants
orbiter		
AEG-F	Low-energy ion and electron spectrometer	Hungary, U.S.S.R.
APV-F	Magnetometer and plasma-wave analyzer	Czechoslovakia, ESA[3], Poland, U.S.S.R.
ASPERA	Ion and electron mass spectrometer	Finland, Sweden, U.S.S.R.
AUGUST	Spectrometer (atmospheric analysis)	France, U.S.S.R.
DION	Secondary ion generator and analyzer	Austria, Finland, France, U.S.S.R.
FREGAT	Multi-wavelength CCD camera	Bulgaria, East Germany, U.S.S.R.
FGMM	Magnetometer	East Germany, U.S.S.R.
GRUNT	Low-frequency radar (subsurface sounding)	U.S.S.R.
GS-14	Gamma-ray spectrometer (rock composition)	U.S.S.R.
IPHIR	Photometer (solar-constant monitor)	ESA[3], France, Switzerland, U.S.S.R.
IPNM[1]	Neutron spectrometer (rocks' H_2O content)	U.S.S.R.
ISM	Infrared spectrometer (rock mineralogy)	France, U.S.S.R.
KRFM	Thermal-infrared radiometer (mineralogy)	
LET	High-energy solar cosmic-ray detector	ESA[3], Hungary, U.S.S.R., West Germany
LILAS	Low-energy gamma-ray burst detector	France, U.S.S.R.
LIMA-D	Laser-aided mass spectrometer (remote analysis of surface composition)	Austria, Bulgaria, Czechoslovakia, East and West Germany, Finland, U.S.S.R.
MAGMA	Magnetometer	Austria, U.S.S.R.
PLASMA	Ionospheric studies (uses GRUNT antenna)	U.S.S.R.
RF-15	X-ray spectrometer	Czechoslovakia, U.S.S.R.
SLED	Low-energy solar cosmic-ray detector	Hungary, U.S.S.R., West Germany
SOVIKOMS	Ion mass spectrometer (solar wind)	Austria, Hungary, U.S.S.R., West Germany
SUFR[1]	Extreme-ultraviolet solar detector	U.S.S.R.
TAUS	Proton and alpha-particle spectrometer	Austria, Hungary, U.S.S.R., West Germany
TEREK[1]	Solar X-ray telescope and coronograph	Czechoslovakia, U.S.S.R.
TERMOSKAN[2]	Infrared spectrometer and radiometer	U.S.S.R.
VGS	High-energy gamma-ray burst detector	France, U.S.S.R.
long-duration automated lander (LAS)		France, Hungary, U.S., U.S.S.R., West Germany
"hopper" lander[2]		U.S.S.R.

[1]Carried aboard Phobos 1 only.   [2]Carried aboard Phobos 2 only.   [3]European Space Agency.

experiments for many months using a television camera, a seismometer, a penetrator tipped with a thermometer, and an instrument that employs high-energy radiation to deduce the approximate chemical composition of the ground beneath it. The second package did not carry as many instruments as the first, but it had a spring-powered "foot" that could push against the ground and cause the package to hop—and gently bounce—to a new location 20–40 meters away. After the flyby Phobos 2 would have been moved to a higher orbit to avoid a collision with its target

Plans for Phobos 2's active exploration of the moon Phobos are diagramed above. Closing to within 50 meters of the satellite, the spacecraft probes beneath its cratered surface with radar (far left) and vaporizes bits of the surface with laser and ion beams (left and center) for onboard analysis. Near the end of its encounter, Phobos 2 releases two landers: one a fixed station (right) designed to conduct long-duration experiments and transmit results directly to Earth, the other a mobile package (far right) able to hop to new locations by means of a spring-powered "foot."

(Top) CNES document; illustration by David Ducros; (bottom and opposite page) adapted from information obtained from *Sky & Telescope*, used with permission

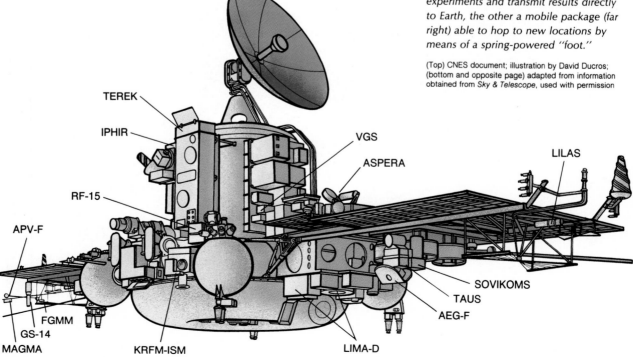

TEREK

IPHIR

VGS

ASPERA

LILAS

RF-15

APV-F

SOVIKOMS

TAUS

AEG-F

FGMM

GS-14

MAGMA

KRFM-ISM

LIMA-D

Airframe-integrated concept for scramjet-powered craft is apparent in the design above. A number of combustors arranged side by side girdle the aircraft's underside. Forward of the combustors, the gently curved surface is designed to cause the airflow approaching the combustors to change direction, resulting in effective compression at supersonic speeds. Behind the combustors, the sharply sloped underside acts as a nozzle, allowing expansion of the hot exhaust leaving the combustors. Airframe-integrated designs also produce increased pressures over much of the underside, giving the aircraft lift and the ability to fly with wings either reduced in size or completely absent.

NASA, Langley

engine efficiency would rise because the airflow would not be subjected to such violent changes in speed. The basic concept of the scramjet is reflected in the phrase that the name stands for: supersonic-combustion ramjet. However, this strategy at once immerses the designer in a host of difficulties. High-speed inlets tend to be temperamental. They can readily "unstart," or allow their flow to break down, so that flame shoots from the front of the engine. In addition, injecting fuel into a supersonic airflow is not an easy task. The fuel may blow out the back before it has time to burn. Other issues arise that are at least as daunting.

To accelerate an aircraft to orbital speed, scramjets must generate considerably more thrust than the drag that tends to slow the craft down. At the moderate speeds of turbojets, drag can be effectively reduced by streamlining the plane's design, using thin swept wings, and similar means. Above Mach 6, however, two new and powerful sources of drag come into play. The first is the boundary layer, a layer of slow air that clings to the skin of the aircraft. It thickens at very high speeds, producing aerodynamic friction that gives rise both to additional drag and to severe aerodynamic heating. The second is the intense shock wave, or sonic boom, that the plane produces in flight. This boom is unavoidable and produces an effect called wave drag that contributes to slowing the aircraft.

Overcoming these additional sources of drag requires the scramjets to produce even more thrust. This, in turn, means larger engines to scoop up more incoming air, but larger engines produce more drag. The designer thus is threatened with a vicious cycle. To break free it is necessary to reexamine the very concept of airplane design on the basis of its fundamentals.

Drag results when the aircraft disturbs the air that flows past it. For the engines of conventional jet aircraft to provide enough thrust, it is sufficient that they intercept only a modest part of the airflow. Scramjets, however, must do more. They must intercept most if not all of the air that flows past. In other words, the same air disturbed by the plane, which produces drag, needs to flow through its scramjets to give thrust. What emerges from this design requirement is an airframe-integrated scramjet, wherein the aircraft fuselage serves as part of the engine installation. Such a concept breaks with the usual practice of designing engines separately from an airframe, then mounting them in place. Instead, the entire aircraft becomes indistinguishable from its propulsion system.

How can this be accomplished? Typical designs for scramjet-powered craft put a number of combustors side by side, forming a belt that girdles the aircraft's underside. Forward of these combustors the underside forms a gently sloping curved shape that tapers to a point at the nose. The shape causes the incoming flow to change direction when approaching the combustors. According to well-established principles of high-speed aerodynamics, this turning compresses the flow with surprising effectiveness. The forward underside thus acts as an inlet. To the rear of the combustors the underside slopes sharply upward toward the tail of the aircraft. The slope allows that part of the underside to act as a nozzle, which causes the flow from the combustors to expand and to yield thrust.

Model of a scramjet-powered aircraft design (below left) and a mock-up of a scramjet combustor (below) are readied by NASA technicians for wind-tunnel testing at several times the speed of sound. Wind tunnels that simulate speeds above Mach 8 have not yet proved feasible to build. Consequently, computer simulations of aerodynamic flows have come to the fore as major tools for evaluating designs meant to reach toward orbital speed.

Photos, © John Madere

The airframe-integrated arrangement has a second benefit. It produces increased pressures over much of the underside, both forward and aft of the combustors. The increased pressures, in turn, constitute lift. Even without the use of wings, the aircraft not only can fly but indeed also can gain altitude. The Air Force has conducted flight tests of a variety of such lifting-body shapes, showing that they can be made to fly adequately during takeoff and landing as well as at high speed. By dispensing with wings or reducing them to small nubs at the sides of the aircraft, airframe integration gives both high thrust and reduced weight and drag.

Computational fluid dynamics

Despite the major design benefits of the airframe-integrated scramjet, the designer still faces a particularly severe difficulty. The design must be treated as a whole, with the recognition that whatever is done for the sake of aerodynamics affects the propulsion—and vice versa. It is subject to many technical uncertainties involving boundary layers, shock waves, aerodynamic heating and drag, and mixing and combustion of fuel. Moreover, these uncertainties grow worse as one proceeds to higher speeds.

The traditional way to deal with those issues has been to test engines and models of the aircraft in high-speed wind tunnels. For an airframe-integrated scramjet this is not feasible. Testing models gives little useful information; the technical issues are so intricate that only studies of a full-size aircraft will do. In addition, no test facilities exist that can accommodate anything larger than a few meters in diameter. What is worse, wind tunnels that sustain airflows above Mach 8 for hours or even minutes at a time have not yet proved feasible to build. Instead there are shock tunnels, which use explosives to produce high-velocity airflows for a fraction of a second. These limitations in test facilities stymied early efforts to develop scramjet engines during the 1960s.

Within the past decade, however, computer simulations have come to the fore as a major supplement to wind-tunnel tests. Tunnel tests, if they could be conducted, would evaluate a design by measuring lift, drag, engine thrust, and values of the pressure, temperature, velocity, and chemical composition at numerous points about an aircraft and its engines. In theory, all this information can be computed from physical principles by solving the basic equations of aerodynamics, known as the Navier-Stokes equations. Such solutions are far from straightforward; they have served to test the capabilities of the most powerful supercomputers. Specialists in the field continue to demand yet more computing power, along with better computer programs.

Despite its current limitations, computational fluid dynamics—the use of computers to solve the Navier-Stokes equations and thus to simulate aerodynamic flows—has proved to be of real benefit in the design of airframe-integrated scramjets. It also has given an entirely new role to wind and shock tunnels. Rather than being employed for direct tests and evaluations of proposed designs, these ground facilities now validate the computer programs, providing data to assess the correctness of the computations. In validating a fluid dynamics program, the computer is asked

(Opposite page) Two views of a generic X-30 NASP design—oblique underside (top) and head on (bottom)—were created on a Cray X-MP supercomputer at NASA's Ames Research Center in California. Colors on the surface of the craft define airflow pressure levels predicted by a computational fluid dynamics program solving the Navier-Stokes equations for the given airframe design at a speed of Mach 12. Green and blue areas represent lower pressures, and red and magenta higher pressures. The effect of the curved underside in compressing the airflow can be seen in the rearward progression of colors from green to yellow and then to red near the location of the combustor inlets. The surrounding colored halo depicts a cross section of the shock wave near the tail of the aircraft.

Photos, NASA, Ames

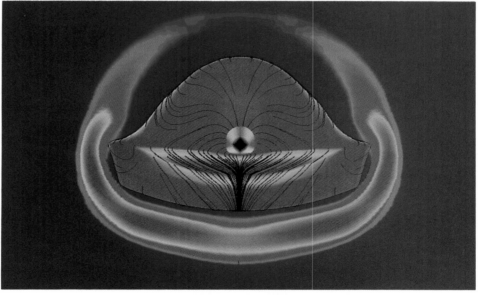

Worker at Pratt & Whitney, West Palm Beach, Florida, collects advanced metal alloy powder formed by rapid quenching techniques. Such materials, particularly the lightweight, heat-resistant titanium aluminides, are being studied as alternatives to denser nickel alloys in construction of the National Aerospace Plane.

The titanium aluminide powder, which resembles a gray flour, then can be loaded into a press and heated anew, causing the individual grains to weld together. The billets so formed can be rolled into sheet stock. Such sheets, in turn, lend themselves to superplastic forming, a process that yields complex shapes with great accuracy. In this process the sheets are heated to a temperature at which they can be shaped within a die using gas pressure, almost as if they were sheets of cloth being draped on a form. Several sheets arranged in layers can form honeycomb or sandwich structures, the sheets welding together strongly where they touch. Titanium aluminide structures offer useful strength at temperatures as high as 980° C (1,800° F).

Moreover, such metal powders are to be used in a different class of materials, the metal-matrix composites. These materials feature fibers or particles embedded within a matrix, or surrounding mass, of metal. The fibers can be of carbon, boron, or silicon carbide; the particles may be compounds of boron. While these substances have greater strength and heat resistance than the metal and are lighter in weight, they cannot by themselves be fabricated into structural parts. The metal thus acts as a

38

binder to hold the fibers or particles together so that the designer can take advantage of their properties.

Three other classes of advanced materials are also being developed within NASP. Advanced carbon-carbon composites are made of carbon fibers held within a surrounding carbon matrix that is obtained by the breakdown of pitch at high temperatures. Such carbon-carbon composites are to withstand temperatures as high as 1,925° C (3,500° F) with the help of suitable coatings to prevent oxidation. The NASP effort also is developing materials having high heat conductivity, such as a metal-matrix composite of copper and carbon fibers. These will serve within the hot parts of the engines, where the ability to remove heat rapidly will be at a premium. Yet another class of materials under development is intended to resist a high-temperature deformation known as creep. These too will serve in the engines, which must stand up to numerous repeated uses without damage.

Active cooling

Despite the benefits of advanced materials, flight to orbit will impose aerodynamic heating so severe as to demand more than the best materials can offer. It will be necessary to provide for active cooling of the engines and of the hot areas of the aircraft exterior. Thus, liquid hydrogen must serve as a coolant as well as fuel, being circulated through appropriate heat exchangers so as to bring the temperatures of the aircraft under control.

For cooling the exterior, it is not possible to use the thermal-insulation approach of the space shuttle, wherein insulating tiles of lightweight silica overlie a "cold," conventional aluminum structure. Though that approach is simple in concept, it still took years to make it work. The cooling requirements of NASP, by contrast, are far more complex and call for an approach that has never flown to orbit—the "hot" structure. This engineering miracle demands a temperature-resistant metal skin that is robust enough to bear the stresses of flight. In addition, the hot structure must be integrated with heat exchangers for active cooling over the hottest parts of its surface.

In designing the heat exchangers, an obvious approach is to circulate liquid hydrogen through channels under the skin. The properties of hydrogen, however, require that as a coolant it flow at high speed and pressure through large numbers of small tubes. This arrangement is an open invitation to leaks. As an alternative the NASP craft is likely to rely on heat pipes—tubes that transfer heat in quantity without moving parts by means of the cyclical evaporation and condensation of an appropriate liquid. Arrays of heat pipes might carry heat to a central heat-transfer loop, which would unload the heat on the hydrogen fuel making its way to the engines.

Why is all this complexity necessary? It is indeed essential, but not only to prevent the aircraft from overheating. Burning hydrogen fuel in an airflow to produce thrust while overcoming drag is not readily accomplished at very high speeds, such as Mach 15 or 20. The airframe may glow brightly owing to heat from aerodynamic friction. The glow represents prodigious radiation of energy—the energy of motion converted into heat and light—which can be made up only by burning fuel. This energy loss is a form of drag that makes it more difficult to accelerate to higher speeds. Moreover, within the engines rising temperatures can bring the same performance limitations that restrict the conventional ramjet at lower speeds. Once again, the energy of the fuel may be tied up in unburned molecular fragments rather than being released as heat. If one tries to overcome this problem by providing for a speedier and therefore cooler airflow within the scramjets, one finds it achievable only at the cost of reducing the pressure buildup within the inlet. Without adequate pressure within the scramjet, performance again falls off.

An active cooling system that uses hydrogen to cool the aircraft exterior addresses both of these issues. A cooler exterior radiates less heat and thus wastes less fuel. At the same time, the hydrogen fuel circulation through the skin has absorbed energy and become warmer; when burned, it gives more thrust. And this same hydrogen, when added copiously to the airflow within the scramjets, limits the temperature rise of that air, so that the engines can continue to burn fuel effectively. At Mach 20 or 25 it is actually desirable for the engines to receive as much as four to six times more hydrogen than can be burned in the available air. This fuel-rich operation produces valuable thrust simply by having the hydrogen become hot and expand as a gas. And the more hydrogen fuel that passes through the aircraft on its way to the engines, the greater the opportunity to cool large areas of the aerodynamically heated outer skin.

Flight to orbit will subject NASP to heating so severe as to require active cooling of the engines and hottest parts of its surface. A computer simulation of the airflow around a generic X-30 design flying at Mach 19 uses colored contour lines to display skin-surface temperatures, with the color scale expressed in multiples of atmospheric temperature. Vivid blues identify the extremely hot areas most in need of active cooling.

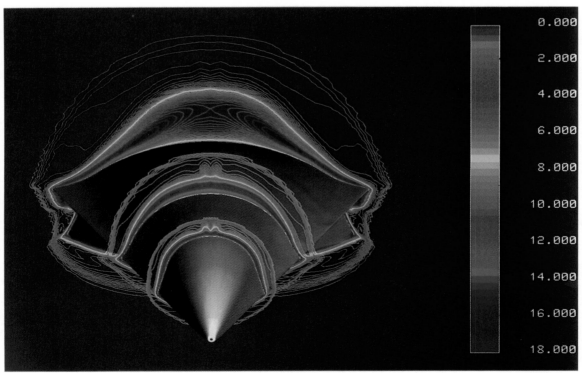

Getting into orbit

As NASP designers demand ever more speed from current technology, the technical uncertainties grow increasingly severe. Their approaches begin amounting to strategies that must be pushed as far as they will go in hopes of building a scramjet-powered craft that can fly to orbit. Nevertheless, at some point in the flight a rocket will be needed for the final boost into orbit. An orbit, after all, is flight outside the atmosphere, and even the best scramjet can give no thrust where there is no air. In addition, technical uncertainties in scramjet operation may make it desirable to cut in the rocket somewhat earlier—a hedge against the possibility that the scramjets will be unable to go all the way.

To deal with these uncertainties, NASP plans call for installing a rocket able to take the experimental X-30 aircraft to orbital speed and altitude from as low as Mach 15. If future scramjets appear to be truly capable of Mach 25, then the final-ascent rocket may be comparatively small, perhaps a part of the overall engine package itself. The ejector of an ejector scramjet, for instance, might provide a final boost in a straightforward way, but if more rocket thrust is necessary, a separately installed engine, with its additional weight, might be added.

Applications

The initial use of the technology developed in the National Aerospace Plane program will be in building the X-30. Current plans call for selecting a set of designs and awarding contracts for construction in late 1990. Construction is to begin in 1992 and flight testing to be conducted during 1994–96. The X-30's mission is explicit: to fly to orbit on scramjets.

It will not do so, however, on the first flight. It may not do so on the 50th. Instead its pilots will nudge it faster and higher in small steps. Moreover, these flights will be conducted for the purpose of basic engineering research, to learn about the performance of such an aircraft in flight. For instance, there may be high-speed missions in which the scramjets will not serve to power the craft. An onboard rocket may take the X-30 to near-orbital speed while the scramjets are operated experimentally at low thrust to provide performance data.

After each flight NASP scientists and engineers will turn to their supercomputers, using computational fluid dynamics to study the flight results. A good match between computation and flight data will mean that matters are reasonably well understood and that the X-30 can advance to a more demanding flight. A poor match will mean that the flight has turned up surprises, which must be understood in detail before tests can advance.

If the X-30 succeeds in reaching orbit with its scramjets, the way will be open to a new generation of aircraft. The high-temperature materials, the cooling systems, the scramjets, the computational fluid dynamics— all will have been proved through experimental test and thus will be ready for use in operational designs. A manned launch vehicle similar in purpose to the space shuttle is likely to be an early project.

One such concept, studied at McDonnell Douglas in 1985, projects a loaded weight on the runway of 181,000 kilograms (400,000 pounds), less than that of a DC-10 airliner. Its fuel load would be 96,000 kilograms (211,000 pounds). It would weigh 68,000 kilograms (150,000 pounds) empty and would carry 13,600 kilograms (30,000 pounds) to orbit. This would contrast with the shuttle, which weighs 1.95 million kilograms (4.3 million pounds) at lift-off and carries a maximum payload of 21,300 kilograms (47,000 pounds). More recent studies of post–X-30 launchers, carried out in 1988, give loaded weights of 181,000 to 227,000 kilograms (400,000 to 500,000 pounds), of which 60–65% would be fuel. Payload would be 29,500 kilograms (65,000 pounds). Cost per flight would be $1 million to $9 million, leading to a cost per kilogram in orbit of $35 to $310 ($15 to $140 per pound). This compares with $6,600 per kilogram ($3,000 per pound) or more for the shuttle.

These, of course, are merely projections from studies carried out on paper, and they must be taken with a grain of salt. When the shuttle itself was at a comparable stage in its design, engineers projected that it would carry 29,500 kilograms for $110–$220 per kilogram ($50–$100 per pound) in orbit. Still, today there is no firm basis for assuming that a post–X-30 launch vehicle would go the way of the shuttle, and few would doubt that such low costs, if achieved, indeed would revolutionize prospects for spaceflight. For instance, the hotel entrepreneur Barron Hilton stated in 1967 that if costs would be cut to what in money of the late 1980s would be $44 per kilogram ($20 per pound) in orbit, he would build a hotel in space.

NASP technology may also find its way into the airline industry. The burgeoning Pacific Rim has brought a surge in trans-Pacific travel, yet such flights are grueling, having a duration of 15 hours even when nonstop. Market forecasts at Boeing and McDonnell Douglas anticipate that by the year 2000 there will be opportunity to build some 400 high-speed commercial jet aircraft to serve these travelers, at a cost of some $200 billion. Who will build them—the U.S. or Japan? Will they fly at Mach 3, for which the needed technology is reasonably foreseeable, or at Mach 5, which could offer compelling advantages? Success with the X-30 is likely to provide technology that will influence the answers to these questions. The result may be the Orient Express to which President Reagan referred in his address.

There also are potential military applications. Gen. Lawrence Skantze, who gave strong support to NASP when he headed the U.S. Air Force Systems Command, described NASP-type aircraft as offering "the speed of an ICBM and the flexibility and reliability of a bomber." Such an aircraft "can scramble, get into orbit, and change orbit so the Soviets can't get a reading accurate enough to shoot at it. It offers strategic force survivability," because a fleet of them "could sit alert like B-52s." Another official was even more explicit: "We're not looking for a cargo machine. We're looking for a killer Air Force weapon that can go out and get the enemy."

For the moment, all such projected applications are premature. It will be necessary to carry the NASP program to completion, to build and fly the X-30, and to learn where the real problems and prospects lie as the pertinent technologies develop and mature. If the NASP effort fulfills the high hopes of its backers and if the scramjet achieves its promise, a fourth era in aerospace well may dawn. The low-cost and straightforward access to space would help humankind learn what can truly be done in orbit and understand the real significance of space for the future. If NASP can do that—and, along the way, contribute to tomorrow's high-speed airliners that may turn the Pacific into a lake—then it is certain to stand out as a pathbreaking and a memorable adventure.

FOR ADDITIONAL READING

Griffin Y. Anderson, Daniel P. Bencze, and Bobby W. Sanders, "Ground Tests Confirm the Promise of Hypersonic Propulsion," *Aerospace America* (September 1987, pp. 38–42).

John V. Becker, "Prospects for Actively Cooled Hypersonic Transports," *Astronautics & Aeronautics* (August 1971, pp. 32–39).

T. A. Heppenheimer, "Launching the Aerospace Plane," *High Technology* (July 1986, pp. 46–51).

T. A. Heppenheimer, "Little Giants Win Space-Plane Contracts," *High Technology Business* (February 1988, pp. 24–27).

T. A. Heppenheimer, *The National Aerospace Plane—1989 Edition* (Pasha Publication, 1989).

Patrick J. Johnson, Allen H. Whitehead, and Gary T. Chapman, "Fitting Aerodynamics and Propulsion into the Puzzle," *Aerospace America* (September 1987, pp. 32–37, 42).

Robert A. Jones and Paul W. Huber, "Toward Scramjet Aircraft," *Astronautics & Aeronautics* (February 1978, pp. 38–48).

Robert M. Williams, "National Aero-Space Plane: Technology for America's Future," *Aerospace America* (November 1986, pp. 18–22).

THE ARROW OF TIME

by Stephen Hawking

*What is the difference between the past and the future?
Why do we remember the past but not the future?
And how is this connected with
the study of the universe?*

there is no resistance. On the other hand, if there is no current, the loop will continue without a current.

One can label the two states of the memory 1 and 0. Before an item is recorded in the memory, the memory is a disordered state with equal probabilities for 1 and 0. After the memory interacts with the system to be remembered, though, it will definitely be in one state or the other. Thus, the memory passes from a disordered state to an ordered one. However, in order to make sure that the memory is in the right state, it is necessary to use a certain amount of energy. This energy is dissipated as heat and increases the amount of disorder in the universe. One can show that this increase of disorder is greater than the increase in the order of the memory. Therefore, when a computer records an item in memory, the total amount of disorder in the universe increases. Thus, the direction of time in which a computer remembers the past is the same as that in which disorder increases.

Consequently, our subjective sense of the direction of time, the Psychological Arrow of Time, is determined by the Thermodynamic Arrow of Time. Disorder increases with time because we measure time in the direction in which disorder increases. You cannot have a safer bet than that!

Cosmological Arrow

But why should the universe be in a state of high order at one end of time, the end that we call the past? Why was it not in a state of complete disorder at all times? After all, this might seem more probable. And why is the direction of time in which disorder increases the same as that in which the universe expands? One possible answer is that God simply chose that the universe should be in a smooth and ordered state at the beginning of the expansion phase. We should not try to understand why or question His reasons because the beginning of the universe was the work of God. But the whole history of the universe can be said to be the work of God. It appears that the universe evolves according to well-defined laws. These laws may or may not be ordained by God, but it seems that we can discover and understand them. Is it, therefore, unreasonable to think that the same or similar laws may also hold at the beginning of the universe?

In the classical theory of general relativity, which describes gravity and the space-time structure of the universe, the beginning of the universe has to be a singularity of infinite density and space-time curvature. Under such conditions all the known laws of physics would break down. Thus, one could not use them to predict how the universe would begin. The universe could have started out in a very smooth and ordered state. This would have led to well-defined Thermodynamic and Cosmological Arrows of Time, like those we observe, but it could equally well have started out in a very lumpy and disordered state. In that case the universe would already be in a state of complete disorder, and so disorder could not increase with time. It would either stay constant, in which case there would be no well-defined Thermodynamic Arrow of Time, or decrease,

Conditions suitable for the development of intelligent beings are made possible only when the three arrows of time—Thermodynamic, Psychological, and Cosmological—all point in the same direction.

48

in which case the Thermodynamic Arrow of Time would point in the opposite direction to the Cosmological Arrow. Neither of these possibilities would agree with what we observe.

As stated above, the classical theory of general relativity predicts that the universe should begin with a singularity where the curvature of space-time is infinite. In fact, this means that the theory predicts its own downfall. When the curvature of space-time becomes large, quantum gravitational effects will become important and the classical theory will cease to be a good description of the universe. One has to use a quantum theory of gravity to understand how the universe began.

We do not yet know the exact form of the correct quantum theory of gravity. However, there are certain features that we expect to be present in any viable theory. One of these is Einstein's idea that the gravitational field, and maybe other fields as well, can be represented by a curved space-time that is warped or distorted by the mass and energy in it. Objects try to follow the closest thing to a straight path through space-time but, because space-time is curved, their paths appear to be bent by a gravitational field.

Another idea that is expected to be part of any ultimate theory is Richard Feynman's proposal that quantum theory can be formulated as a "sum over histories." In its simplest form, this idea proposes that a particle has every possible path, or "history," in space. Each history has a "probability" that can be calculated from the way in which the particle traverses the path. For this idea to work, one has to pretend that space-time is "Euclidean"; that is, that time is just like another direction in space. One adds up the probabilities for all the particle histories with certain properties, such as passing through certain points at certain times. One then has to extrapolate the result back to the real space-time, in which time is different from the directions in space. This is not the most familiar approach to quantum theory, but it gives the same results as other methods.

In the case of quantum gravity, Feynman's idea of a "sum over histories" would involve summing over different possible histories–different Euclidean curved space-times—for the universe. One has to decide how the space-times that one includes in the sum behave at early and late times. This will determine how the universe starts and finishes—whether it starts or finishes in a state of order or disorder. This, in turn, will determine whether there is a well-defined Thermodynamic Arrow of Time and whether it agrees with the Cosmological Arrow.

"No boundary" proposal
In classical general relativity there are only three possible behaviors of the universe in time: (1) it may exist for an infinite time in the past and the future; (2) it may have a beginning or an end at a finite time; or (3) it may be periodic in time. In fact, work that Roger Penrose and I did about 20 years ago showed that if one made certain reasonable assumptions, the second possibility was the correct one. The universe would have begun at a singularity of infinite curvature about 15 billion

years ago. As I explained, one could not predict how the universe would start or what the Thermodynamic Arrow of Time would do because the laws of physics would break down at the singularity.

However, in a quantum theory of gravity there is another possible way for the universe to behave in time. In the Feynman "sum over histories" one uses curved space-times that are Euclidean; that is, time is on the same footing as directions in space. In this case it is possible for the curved space-time manifold to be finite in extent but without any boundaries or edges in time or space. It would resemble the surface of the Earth but with two more dimensions. The surface of the Earth is finite in extent but does not have any boundaries or edges. Sailing off into the sunset does not result in falling over an edge or running up against a barrier.

In 1983 James Hartle and I proposed that the boundary condition of the universe is that it has no boundary. Under this condition, the universe would be completely self-contained. Consequently, it would not need any external agency to set it going or to choose the way in which it began. The laws of physics would hold at every point and would not break down anywhere. Thus, they would determine completely how the universe behaved.

Space-time could be like the surface of the Earth, with time analogous to degrees of latitude. The circles of latitude start at a single point at the North Pole. As one goes south, these circles get bigger. This is like the universe starting at a single point and expanding. The universe would reach a maximum size at its equator and would contract again to its south pole. Even though the North and South Poles are the beginning and end of degrees of latitude, they are perfectly ordinary points on the Earth's surface. There is no edge or singularity at either pole. Similarly, the beginning and end of time would be ordinary points of space-time at which the laws of physics held.

If the "no boundary" proposal is correct, the laws of physics should determine how the universe began. Of course, it would be very difficult to work this out exactly, especially because no one is sure of the precise laws that govern quantum gravity. However, Jonathan Halliwell and I have made an approximate calculation that indicates that the universe would have begun its expansion in a very smooth and ordered state. The expansion could not have been completely uniform in space, though, because that would violate the uncertainty principle of quantum theory. There had to be small fluctuations in density and velocity. However, the "no boundary" condition implied that these fluctuations were in their ground state; that is, they were as small as they could be, consistent with the uncertainty principle.

The universe would have started off with a period of exponential or "inflationary" expansion in which it would have increased its size by a very large factor. During this expansion the fluctuations in density would have stayed small at first, but they would later have started to grow. Regions in which the density was slightly higher than average would have had their expansion slowed down by the gravitational attraction of the extra mass. Eventually, that region would stop expanding and collapse to form galaxies, stars, and beings like us. The universe thus would start in a smooth and ordered state and would become lumpy and disordered. This would explain the existence of the Thermodynamic Arrow of Time. (See *1986 Yearbook of Science and the Future* Feature Article: THE INFLATIONARY UNIVERSE.)

But what would happen if and when the universe stopped expanding and began to contract? Would the Thermodynamic Arrow reverse and disorder begin to decrease with time? Such a situation would lead to all sorts of science-fictionlike possibilities for people who survived from the expanding to the contracting phase. Would they see broken cups gathering themselves together off the floor and jumping back on the table? Would they be able to remember tomorrow's prices and make a fortune on the stock market?

Until recently, I believed that disorder would decrease when the universe recollapsed. This was because I thought that the universe had to return to a smooth and ordered state when it became small again. However, work by Don Page and a student of mine, Raymond Laflamme, caused me to change my mind. I now think that the "no boundary" condition implies that disorder will continue to increase in the contracting phase. The Thermodynamic Arrow of Time will not reverse. It will continue to point in the same direction.

Weak anthropic principle

There remains the question Why do the Thermodynamic and Cosmological Arrows point in the same direction? Why does disorder increase in the same direction of time as that in which the universe expands? If one believes that the universe will expand and then contract, as the "no boundary" proposal seems to imply, this becomes a question of why we should be in the expanding rather than in the contracting phase.

One can answer this question on the basis of the weak anthropic principle. This states that conditions in the contracting phase would not be suitable for the existence of intelligent beings who could ask the question Why is disorder increasing in the same direction of time as that in which the universe is expanding? The inflation in the early stages of the universe implies that the universe will not recollapse for a very long time. By then all the stars will have burned out and the baryons in them will probably have decayed into light particles and radiation. The universe would be in a state of almost complete disorder or thermal equilibrium. There would be no Thermodynamic Arrow of Time. Disorder could not increase because the universe would be in a state of complete disorder already. However, a well-defined Thermodynamic Arrow is necessary for intelligent life to operate. Human beings must consume food, which is an ordered form of energy, and convert it into heat, which is a disordered form of energy. Thus, intelligent life could not exist in the contracting phase of the universe. This is the explanation of why we observe that the Thermodynamic and Cosmological Arrows of Time point in the same direction.

52

Conclusions

To summarize, the laws of physics do not distinguish between the forward and backward directions of time. However, there are at least three "arrows" that point in a direction in time and that distinguish the past from the future. They are the Thermodynamic Arrow, the direction of time in which disorder increases; the Psychological Arrow, the direction of time in which we remember the past and not the future; and the Cosmological Arrow, the direction of time in which the universe expands rather than contracts.

I showed that the Psychological Arrow was determined by the Thermodynamic Arrow and that the two would always point in the same direction. The "no boundary" proposal for the universe implies that there is a well-defined Thermodynamic Arrow of Time because the universe started in a smooth and ordered state. The reason we observe this Thermodynamic Arrow to agree with the Cosmological Arrow is that intelligent beings can exist only in the expanding phase. The contracting phase will be unsuitable because it does not have a well-defined Thermodynamic Arrow of Time.

If you have remembered every word I have written, your memory will have recorded about 150,000 bits of information. Thus, the order in your brain will have increased by about 150,000 units. However, while you have been reading, you will have converted about 300,000 joules of ordered energy, in the form of food, into disordered energy, in the form of heat that you lose to the air around you by convection and sweat. This will increase the disorder of the universe by about 20 million million million times the increase in order that took place because you remembered this article.

Chaos:
Does God Play Dice?

by Ian Stewart

Much apparently random behavior in nature is now known to possess hidden patterns governed by mathematical rules and geometric forms. Researchers in many branches of science are working to understand the patterns and exploit them.

Albert Einstein did not believe that "God plays dice." He was deeply convinced that the universe is governed by precise laws rather than by chance. Within the past 15 years or so, however, mathematicians and scientists have discovered that systems obeying precise laws can nevertheless behave in a random fashion. Perhaps God can play dice—and create a universe of complete law and order—in the same stroke.

This startling possibility is a consequence of a new, exciting area of mathematics, the theory of chaos, which shows that systems obeying precise and simple laws do not always act in regular and predictable ways. The mathematics of chaos has been applied to irregularities of the heartbeat, disease epidemics, the motion of moons, and hundreds of other problems in all branches of science. This astonishing theory reveals a strange universe, one in which the fluttering of a butterfly's wing can change the weather or the gravitational attraction of spectators can change the result of a billiard shot. It is an entirely new world, a new kind of mathematics, a fundamental insight into the irregularities of nature.

Time and tide . . .

Scientists can predict the tides, so why do they have so much trouble predicting the weather? Accurate tables of the time of high or low tide can be worked out months or even years ahead. Weather forecasts often go wrong within a few days, sometimes even within a few hours. People are so accustomed to this difference that they are not in the least surprised when the promised heat wave turns out to be a blizzard. In contrast, if the tide table predicted a low tide but the beach was under water, there would probably be a riot.

IAN STEWART is Reader in Mathematics at the Mathematics Institute, University of Warwick, Coventry, England.

(Overleaf) Illustration by Dale Horn

The unpredictability of weather on the Great Plains (top) contrasts dramatically with the regular ebb and flow of the tide in Canada's Bay of Fundy (bottom). The physical system that gives rise to weather involves no more variables than that which gives rise to tides, yet one phenomenon is chaotic and the other ordered. Once it seemed reasonable to assert that the variables of a chaotic system, if not especially numerous, must be highly complex in their interactions. Today scientists and mathematicians are finding that chaos can be fundamentally simple.

Of course, the two systems are rather different. The weather is extremely complex; it involves dozens of such quantities as temperature, air pressure, humidity, wind speed, and cloud cover. Tides are much simpler. Or are they?

Tides are perceived to be simpler because they can be easily predicted. In reality, the system that gives rise to tides involves just as many variables—the shape of the coastline, the temperature of the sea, its salinity, its pressure, the waves on its surface, the positions of the Sun and Moon, and so on—as that which gives rise to weather. Somehow, however, those variables interact in a regular and predictable fashion. The tides are a phenomenon of order. Weather, on the other hand, is not. There the variables interact in an irregular and unpredictable way. Weather is, in a word, chaotic.

But what causes the difference between order and chaos? Not so long ago the answer seemed straightforward. The weather is a much more complex system than the tides. Although both involve many different factors, the factors interact in a much more complicated way in the weather system than they do for tides. In general, complexity causes chaos. The answer is simple—except that today it appears to be wrong. Mathematicians and scientists in many different disciplines believe that something more subtle, more interesting, and much more fundamental is going on. Chaos can be simple, too.

Randomness and predictability

The central task of science is to make the world comprehensible and, in particular, predictable. Astronomers can compute many features of planetary motion—but, as will be shown, not all features—for millions of years into the future. The ebb and flow of the tides, the flight of

Science strives to make the world predictable. The destination of a batted ball, the force exerted by a roller coaster ride, and the orbits of planets are examples of behavior that can be determined in advance from known physical laws. Like the underlying mechanism of an orrery (below), which neatly accounts for the clockwork motions of its model solar system, the laws that so successfully predict many features of nature once led scientists to believe confidently in a clockwork universe of order and predictability. Over the centuries, however, it has become clear that the behavior of some systems cannot be predicted even if the laws are known.

a javelin, the flow of an electric current, the pressure patterns on an aircraft's wing—all these things likewise can be predicted in advance.

Nevertheless, despite the best computers that money can buy, the secrets of accurate weather forecasting more than a few days ahead remain a mystery. The ups and downs of the stock market resemble a lottery more than a science. For such systems, people resort to statistics and speak of "random" effects. Yet, where does randomness come from?

Over the centuries scientists have been led to distinguish two types of physical systems. First, there are systems with a small number of variables, such as a single particle moving under the influence of gravity, whose laws are known exactly and whose behavior is predictable. Second, there are complicated systems with a huge number of variables, such as a trillion colliding molecules in a tiny quantity of gas, which are unpredictable even if the laws are known because it is impossible to carry out the necessary computations in a reasonable time. For this second type of

A grand orrery, or planetarium, of English origin, maker unknown, mid-eighteenth century; Adler number A-61; courtesy of the Adler Planetarium, Chicago

57

system only statistical predictions are feasible. Thus, there has arisen a fundamental distinction between deterministic systems, whose behavior is specified by precise laws and can in principle be predicted exactly and forever, and stochastic systems, whose behavior seems random.

But is the distinction really fundamental? What is meant by such terms as predictable and random? Are they really so different?

Celestial potato

One of the most unusual planets in the solar system is Saturn, not just because of its spectacular rings but because of one of its satellites, Hyperion. Hyperion is irregularly shaped, a celestial potato. As it orbits Saturn, it tumbles end over end. The orbit is precise and regular, but the tumbling is not. It is possible to predict Hyperion's position in orbit thousands of years ahead, but the direction in which it will point is unpredictable even a few months ahead. Most heavenly bodies roll along like soccer balls on a flat playing field, but Hyperion more resembles a football bouncing over a battlefield.

The traditional picture of order and chaos would lead one to assume that these two aspects of the motion are governed by very different physical laws: deterministic for the position, stochastic for the direction. Perhaps random effects such as interplanetary gas clouds or the solar wind are affecting the direction in which Hyperion points? But, no, it turns out that the same laws, Newton's laws of motion and gravitation, explain both the regular and the irregular features of Hyperion's movements.

Hyperion's irregular motion was described in 1983 by Jack Wisdom, an astronomer at the Massachusetts Institute of Technology, and his colleagues Stanton Peale and François Mignard. They set up a mathematical model incorporating Newton's laws and solved it with the aid of a fast computer. To visualize the results, they drew a picture showing the direction in which Hyperion is pointing and the rate at which that

Mixing colors of paint (above) seems a disorderly process, and the behavior of the stock market (right) resembles a lottery more than a science. For such systems the term random is used, to distinguish them from deterministic, predictable systems. But the distinction is not as fundamental as it may seem, for within certain random-appearing behavior lies a secret inner regularity.

Photos, JPL/NASA

direction is changing. To simplify the results further, they instructed the computer to plot one variable against the other, direction versus rate, on a two-dimensional graph every time Hyperion passed through some fixed position in orbit. The result resembled a series of superimposed snapshots: a black dot, representing Hyperion, hopping about on a sheet of paper, each hop representing one orbit.

If the direction in which Hyperion is pointing changes regularly, then this dot will also move regularly in some simple pattern. For example, if the direction changes periodically in a repetitive cycle, then the point will hop through a series of positions, eventually returning to where it started. If the direction changes irregularly, however, then the moving point eventually will smear itself out over the paper in a field of random dots.

They found that the pattern of dots depends on the energy with which Hyperion moves. For some energies, the moving dot does indeed trace out simple, regular patterns in the form of closed curves, "islands" of predictable motion. For other energies, however, it traces out rather shapeless regions stippled with random dots. The equations are the same in both cases, but changing just one quantity—energy—switches the behavior from predictable regularity to unpredictable chaos.

In the distant past, Hyperion's rotational period (its "day") was much faster than its orbital period (its "year"). Its motion was then regular. Over aeons of time, Saturn's gravitational pull slowed the rotation, and Hyperion stood up on end like a spinning top. It continued to lose energy through tidal friction until it reached an energy level corresponding to irregular motion. Then the consistency of millions of years was undone in a few days. Within three or four orbits, Hyperion began to tumble randomly in all directions.

This kind of story is not unique to Hyperion. In fact, as investigators are now finding out, almost any system of deterministic laws can generate apparently irregular and unpredictable motion. Chaos in this sense is not mere purposeless erratic behavior; it is random-appearing behavior with a secret inner regularity.

Modeling the world

To understand the origins of chaos, one must answer another question: how do scientists predict the behavior of a natural system? They set up a mathematical model consisting of equations, which often look very technical and forbidding. In principle, however, the way they work is simple. The equations specify what the system will do a little later in terms of what it is doing now. For example, the equations that model weather specify how to start with the weather's present state and calculate what it will be doing in a minute's time. A forecast one minute ahead may not seem useful, but by repeating the process 60 times, one can predict the weather an hour ahead. By repeating that process 24 times, one obtains a prediction one day ahead, and by repeating that process 365 times, one predicts the weather a year ahead. It requires many tedious and repetitive calculations, but modern computers are very good at those. On a supercomputer a ten-day forecast can be performed in less than

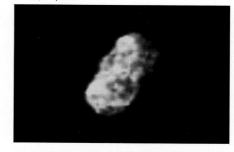

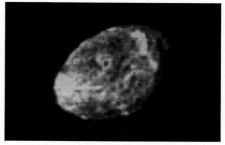

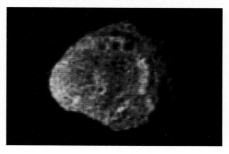

Saturn's moon Hyperion was photographed sequentially by the Voyager 2 spacecraft in 1981. As it orbits its parent planet, it tumbles end over end in a way that is unpredictable even months in advance, although the laws that describe its tumbling are no different from those that account for its very predictable orbit around Saturn. Hyperion's tumbling was found to depend on the energy with which it moves. For certain energy levels, including higher ones that it had in the distant past, its tumbling is regular and predictable. For others, including its present energy level, Hyperion turns chaotically.

Nonlinearity

Mathematicians divide equations that model physical systems into two types: linear and nonlinear. Chaos occurs only in nonlinear systems.

The physical difference between the two types is that distinct solutions of a linear equation can be added together, or superimposed, to obtain another solution. For nonlinear equations, superimposition is not possible. For example, shallow water waves obey the linear "wave equation"; interference patterns can be obtained by superimposing two distinct circular patterns of ripples; that is, by adding two solutions. Large waves do not add in this way, making their interactions more complicated. In suitable circumstances, two large waves can combine to create one that is higher than the individual waves put together, as nonlinear effects amplify the size. At sea such nonlinear interaction can lead to ocean waves large enough to sink a supertanker.

The mathematical distinction is that linear equations are easier to solve than nonlinear ones, and it is often possible to write down explicit formulas for the solutions. Historically, linear systems have been given undue prominence for this pragmatic reason. Most natural systems, however, are best modeled by nonlinear equations. With modern computers and new mathematical tools from geometry and topology, nonlinear equations can be investigated. Because chaos does not occur in linear systems, the experience gained from linear models has been in some respects misleading.

an hour. Nevertheless, weather services do not publish predictions for a year ahead, so it is obviously not that easy.

Tides, on the other hand, depend largely on the positions of the Sun and Moon relative to the Earth, and the same kind of step-by-step calculation does indeed predict those positions not just years ahead but centuries. Therefore, almanacs can include the times of sunrise and sunset and the phases of the Moon, while tide tables based on those facts can be published years ahead.

Still, why are the two cases so different?

Mathematical dough

The answer lies in a mathematical principle of enormous power and generality—the idea that dynamics can be visualized pictorially. A picture is worth a thousand words; in dynamics it is worth a million numbers. Modern dynamics uses sophisticated computer graphics to represent complicated series of observations. The results are often breathtaking, the deep inner beauty of mathematics revealed as art.

The common mathematical feature of all models of physical systems is the repetitive application of a single, fixed rule: how to get from behavior at one instant to behavior an instant later. This rule is applied repeatedly, with the output from one step becoming the input for the next. The process that transforms input into output, *i.e.*, the "law of nature," is identical at each step.

Computers work with numbers, but another model may be more friendly—a lump of dough. To see how a single point of the dough moves at each stage, one can put a very tiny raisin in it. Then the dough is transformed repeatedly according to some selected rule, and the raisin is watched. Where it goes depends on how the dough is transformed and can vary wildly. Despite this variability, one can distinguish three very common and very different types of behavior. Here are three examples, one for each type.

The first rule for transforming the dough is "Shrink it to half its size." If that rule is repeated again and again, the dough shrinks to a quarter of its original size, then one-eighth, one-sixteenth—and soon one is looking at a rapidly diminishing speck of dough. The raisin moves toward the middle of the diminishing lump, rather quickly at first but soon apparently not at all, unless one observes through a powerful microscope.

The shrinking dough is an example of a process that produces no significant changes in the long run. It corresponds to a physical system that settles down toward some steady state and stays there. For example, a young animal grows to adulthood and then, until the grim reaper intervenes, remains pretty much the same. Hyperion sits on end, spinning steadily like a top, and without tidal friction would continue to do so forever. A vat of vegetable oil and chemicals producing margarine warms up as the chemical reaction gets going but settles to a steady, comfortable working temperature.

The second rule is "Rotate through a right angle." As the dough undergoes pure rotation, with no shrinking, one watches the raisin. It turns

Three simple rules are applied repeatedly to a lump of dough containing a small raisin. In each case the raisin exhibits a very different and very common type of behavior. See pages 60–62.

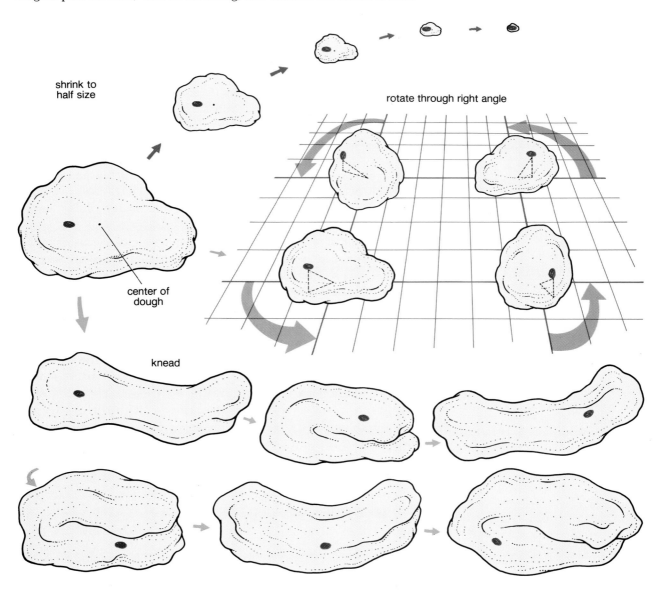

shrink to half size

rotate through right angle

center of dough

knead

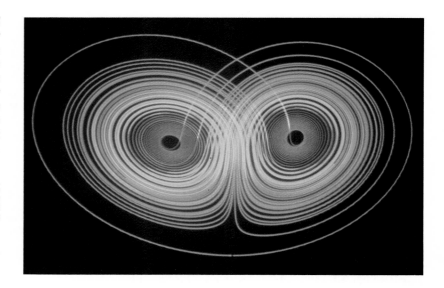

mathematical space, and it has its own multidimensional geometry. In particular, the state of an evolving system again corresponds to a curve in phase space.

The lump of dough is a metaphor for phase space. A raisin in the dough represents a particular point in phase space; that is, a particular set of values for the variables. The path that the raisin follows as one manipulates the dough corresponds to the development of the system in time. And the rule for transforming the dough corresponds to the underlying equations of the system, the "laws of nature," which specify how the point in phase space moves.

This insight answers the original question about weather and tides. The process that produces weather is not more complex mathematically than that which controls the tides, nor is it specified by a more random transformation. But it happens to be much better at mixing things up.

The butterfly effect

A dramatic version of this phenomenon was noticed in the early 1960s by U.S. meteorologist Edward Lorenz, who called it the butterfly effect. He was using a computer to simulate a simplified model of a weather system, and he stopped the machine in the middle of a run. When he restarted it, he did so with slightly different numbers. He expected to get results identical to those from a run that used the original numbers, but instead the computer was soon making totally different predictions. "The flapping of a butterfly's wing," he said in reference to the slight alteration in starting values, "can change the weather."

In terms of the image of kneading dough, Lorenz was modeling the paths of two raisins that begin a very tiny distance apart. However close they are to begin with, each stretch operation moves them farther apart. Eventually one of them starts to be folded up in a way different from the other, after which they move independently. This is the reason that the dough becomes thoroughly mixed.

64

In other words, small differences in initial data can lead to completely divergent predictions. Lorenz's model was very simple, but meteorologists have confirmed that butterfly effect in the more sophisticated models that they use for forecasting. Of course, real weather is not determined by the flap of a wing. While one butterfly in Paris is busy creating a hurricane over New Orleans, another butterfly in Tokyo may be destroying it again. Real weather is influenced by the combined effects of billions of different, tiny, uncontrollable, and unpredictable movements of the atmosphere. The butterfly effect is important, though, because it dramatizes the reasons why weather sometimes can be unpredictable. The dynamics of models of the weather can amplify tiny errors of measurement and completely change the resulting forecasts.

"Good evening; this is Annie Cyclone with the weather. Because of the butterfly effect, there is no forecast this evening. The atmosphere is in an unstable state, making it impossible to take accurate measurements for our computer models. However, we expect it to stabilize by Friday, when we will give you the prediction for the weekend." Unless meteorologists can find some cunning way around the butterfly effect, this may be the least misleading weather forecast of the future.

Patterns of chaos

The butterfly effect is the bad news about chaos. There are fundamental limits to certain kinds of predictability, limits that are inherent in the mathematical nature of deterministic systems. Moreover, the butterfly effect does not apply solely to weather prediction. There is, for example, the motion of a billiard ball. In principle, very tiny forces—such as the gravitational attraction of a nearby spectator—produce very tiny changes

The underlying reason that chaotic systems lead to unpredictability is that they are especially good at mixing things up. Such mixing can quickly amplify small differences in initial measurements or starting values into completely divergent predictions, a phenomenon that Lorenz named the butterfly effect. A strange attractor called the Ikeda map (top left) represents a certain iterated mathematical expression, one whose solution for some starting value is repeatedly substituted back into the equation to obtain new values. When two starting values differing only in the 14th decimal place—so close in fact as to be indistinguishable (top right, marked with a single asterisk)—are tracked through the iterative process, they soon become widely separated. The end points of the numbered lines show the amount of the divergence after the 26th through 29th calculations.

65

Recently developed mathematical models of the heartbeat have shown laws hidden within the apparent chaos of the irregular beating sometimes seen in diseased hearts. Mathematically the heart is a forced oscillator; its natural rhythm interacts in a complex way with a driving frequency from the brain such that the two types of oscillation lock together at certain specific driving frequencies to produce the final frequency that the heartbeat assumes. The relation of the final frequency to the driving impulses is given by a mathematical graph called the Devil's staircase (below). Each step on the staircase corresponds to a final frequency of the heartbeat, while the height of each step above the base represents the ratio of the final and driving frequencies. Some possible ratios are indicated. Each step is flat, which shows that the two frequencies stay locked at a constant value even when the driving frequency (shown by the graph's horizontal axis) changes, as long as it remains within the range of that particular step. Were the heartbeat to be represented by a linear mathematical model rather than by the nonlinear staircase, the ratio would change constantly with the driving frequency, and the graph would be a smooth slope.

in the way the ball moves after being struck. In practice, of course, the changes are so small as to be unobservable. Nevertheless, these changes can be amplified by the butterfly effect so that they become visible to the unaided eye. If 20 billiard balls are lined up in a row such that each collides into the next, then the change in gravitational force caused by one spectator moving seats can alter the direction of the 20th ball by an angle of 30° or more. In practice it is impossible to reproduce the exact initial conditions accurately enough to demonstrate this effect in an experiment, but it can be confirmed mathematically or by computer models. Thus, it is not always possible to predict the long-term behavior of a system, given its state at some particular instant.

This is not the only useful type of information, however. A more important message is that chaotic systems have strong hidden patterns governed by fixed mathematical rules and archetypal geometric forms. These hidden laws within chaos often permit making other kinds of prediction or deducing other kinds of order. There is thus an optimistic message: complicated effects may have simple causes. If people can understand the newly discovered patterns of chaos, they can learn to exploit them.

For example, chaos may be responsible for fluctuations in the populations of animals, insects, or viruses. Are plagues of locusts or epidemic diseases manifestations of chaos? If so, entomologists and epidemiologists can concentrate on the regular laws that govern population dynamics

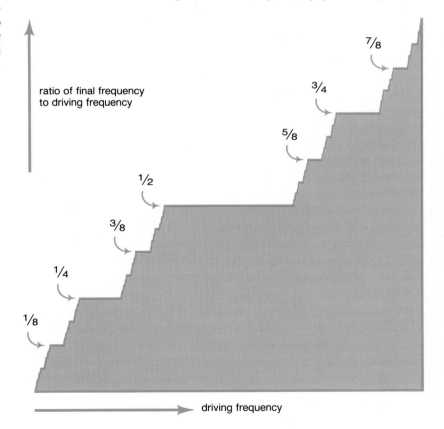

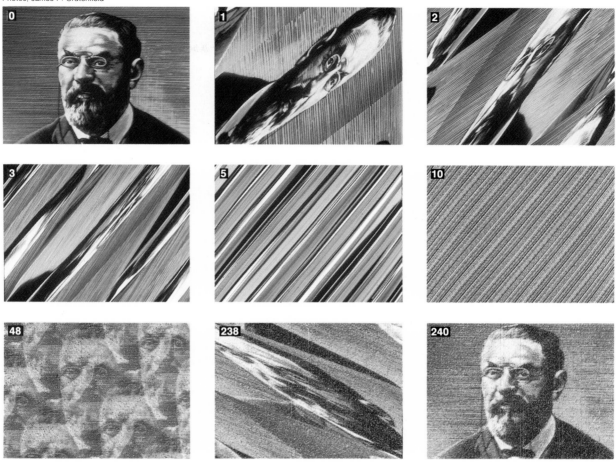

rather than having to worry about possible external effects; this makes the scientific task a great deal more straightforward.

Chaos opens up new ways of analyzing experimental data. In particular it has inspired a technique known as phase space reconstruction, which makes it possible to plot out the underlying geometry of the dynamic transformations. Given measurements of the motion of a raisin in a lump of dough, for instance, this method rapidly reconstructs the stretch-and-fold operation responsible for its apparently random path.

William M. Schaffer and Mark Kot of the University of Arizona have applied phase space reconstruction to historical data on epidemics of mumps, measles, and chicken pox. They deduced an underlying dynamic that, mathematically speaking, is very similar to the stretch-and-fold process for kneading dough. They thereby discovered hidden laws in what had hitherto been thought of as a random process. Such patterns might lead to better methods of disease control. Robert May of Princeton University is currently using chaotic dynamics to model some features of the spread of AIDS.

Patterns of chaos also occur in the activity of the human heart. The normal heart beats in a regular rhythmic pattern—a paradigm for or-

Digitized portrait of Henri Poincaré illustrates the emergence of chaos in an operation similar to the stretch-and-fold process of kneading dough. A simple transformation done by computer stretches the image diagonally. Where the stretched image exceeds its original shape it is wrapped around to the other side and cut, as seen in image 1. The process is repeated; the number on each image indicates how often the transformation has been made. Gradually the portrait is scrambled into a seeming jumble of points (images 1–10). As the transformations proceed, some points in certain images return near their original locations, and recognizable pictures appear (images 48, 238, and 240). These reappearances show that the underlying structure is not lost, just hidden, even when all looks random.

67

Turbulent flows, which can generate complex structures completely different from those of slow, smooth flows, have been studied for signs of chaos. The image at right is a computer reconstruction of a water jet squirting from a circular nozzle into still water. The water in the jet carries a dye that fluoresces under laser light, allowing the jet to be photographed electronically with a light-sensitive CCD (charge coupled device) array. The digitized image so obtained is color-coded over a range from deep blue to red according to the intensity of the fluorescence, which is directly proportional to the dye concentration. The turbulence recorded in the image appears to be made up of superposed fractal structures.

R. R. Prasad and K. R. Sreenivasan

dered dynamics. A diseased heart can beat irregularly, however, and this behavior is often fatal. Leon Glass of McGill University, Montreal, and colleagues have developed mathematical models of the heartbeat, revealing the hidden laws within the apparent chaos. Mathematically, the heart is a forced oscillator. Whereas it vibrates with a natural rhythm, this motion is modified by electrical impulses originating in the brain. The two types of oscillation do not just add up; instead they interact in a complex manner, and the component oscillations lock together at certain specific frequencies at which the heart is driven. The relation between the frequency of the heartbeat and that of the driving impulses from the brain is given by the Devil's staircase, a mathematical graph having infinitely many horizontal steps. Each step corresponds to a particular frequency that the heartbeat can assume. In 1987 Dante Chialvo and Jose Jalife of the State University of New York at Syracuse confirmed the occurrence of the Devil's staircase in muscle fibers from the hearts of sheep.

The Devil's staircase has its own secret pattern. Each step corresponds to a fraction that describes how the frequencies lock. For example, the fraction $5/8$ indicates that five cycles of the heartbeat occur for every eight cycles of the stimulus from the brain.

The fractions on the steps of the Devil's staircase obey intricate number-theoretic laws. Number theory used to be considered the ultimate in ivory towers, pure as the driven snow and about as practical. The dynamics of the heart are but one of its many recent applications. The study of chaos is breaking down many boundaries within science. Countless curious items lie folded neatly away in the pure mathematician's chest

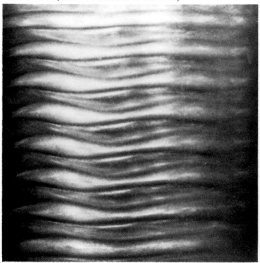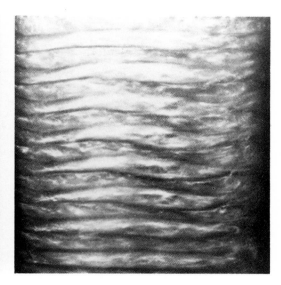

of drawers, bearing a faded label: Fascinating but Useless. The advancement of medical and scientific knowledge is making investigators bring them out into the open air, dust them off, and wear them with pride.

Footprints of chaos

Research into chaos can be traced back to 1890, when Henri Poincaré studied the stability of the solar system. Will the planets continue in roughly their present courses, or might one of them (the Earth?) wander off into eternal darkness or crash into the Sun? He did not find the answer, but he found a new method—the geometry of dynamics. Today his ideas have grown into the subject called topology; that is, "rubber-sheet geometry," the geometry of continuous deformations. Poincaré invented topology to reach places that mere formulas could not and thereby made the first discovery of chaos, in the orbital motion of three bodies under gravity.

Others followed Poincaré's pioneering trail. In the Soviet Union the mathematician Andrey Kolmogorov of Moscow State University made basic advances in the irregular features of dynamics. By the 1960s an American mathematician, Stephen Smale of the University of California at Berkeley, had formulated a plan to classify all typical kinds of dynamic behavior. Chaos found a place within Smale's worldview as a natural phenomenon, completely on a par with such regular behavior as periodic cycles.

Applications followed. For example, sometimes a fluid flows smoothly, but sometimes it becomes turbulent and irregular. In attempting to explain why, two European mathematicians, David Ruelle of the Institut des Hautes Études Scientifiques, Bures-sur-Yvette, France, and Floris Takens of the State University at Groningen, The Netherlands, suggested in 1970 that turbulent flow might be an example of dynamic chaos. At about this time chaos escaped the mathematicians' net and became fair game for everyone. Experimental physicists, notably Harry Swinney,

Fluid flow between two concentric cylinders, the inner one rotating and pulling the fluid around with it, is recorded in the photos above. For moderate rotation rates, the flow pattern is highly ordered and predictable, resembling a stack of stretched doughnuts (left). As the rotation rate is increased, small eddies appear and the doughnuts ripple, undergoing an abrupt transition to turbulence (right). Such studies have provided a way to look at the onset of turbulence in fluids. They indicate that weak turbulence created between the cylinders is well described by chaotic models.

69

then at the City College of New York, Jerry Gollub, then at Haverford (Pennsylvania) College, and Albert Libchaber, then at the École Normal Supérieure, Paris, showed that Ruelle and Takens were partly right, partly wrong. Chaos does occur in turbulent flow but not in precisely the way they suggested.

This work raised two important questions: how can chaotic models be tested experimentally, and how can different types of chaos be distinguished? The usual technique for testing a theory is to make a long series of observations and compare it with the theoretical predictions. With chaos, however, the butterfly effect gets in the way; slight errors in the observations will give widely varying results.

Chaos is something like the abominable snowman—the attempt to track it down frightens it away. Still, an elusive quarry may leave tracks in the snow. Scientists are learning to recognize chaos from its footprints.

One of the most dramatic footprints was discovered in 1975 by physicist Mitchell Feigenbaum, then at Los Alamos (New Mexico) National

Period-doubling cascades

U.S. physicist Mitchell Feigenbaum discovered a remarkable numerical regularity in the behavior of chaotic systems. It occurs in physical systems that change at fixed intervals of time according to some fixed dynamical rule and shows how rapidly the equations that model these systems transform from order to chaos when the parameters are varied. In many such systems, as some parameter is changed, a single steady state becomes periodic, of period 2; that is, a single point attractor splits apart, or bifurcates, into a pair of points, and the system hops alternately from one to the other. As the parameter is further varied, this splitting repeats, leading to attractors of period 4, 8, 16, . . . , doubling infinitely often. This can be seen in the accompanying figure as the repeated branching of the tree-shaped left-hand portion. The random, speckled bands in the right-hand portion represent chaos. This behavior, called a period-doubling cascade, is a standard route of transition from order to chaos.

Successive bifurcations of the attractor occur for smaller and smaller changes of the parameter; in other words, successive "twigs" in the diagram split ever more rapidly. Feigenbaum showed that whenever a period-doubling cascade occurs, each new bifurcation comes more quickly than the preceding one by a factor that approaches ever closer to the number 4.669201609. . . . This "magic number" does not depend on the specific equations or on the "law of nature" that the equations describe. Represented by the symbol delta (δ), it is a new fundamental constant, on a par with pi (π), the ratio of the circumference of a circle to its diameter.

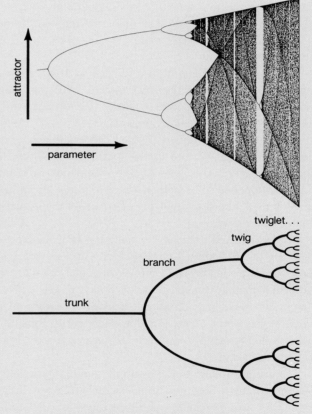

In the period-doubling cascade (top), as some parameter is varied, the attractor splits repeatedly in two. Regardless of the physical system in which the cascade appears, the ratio of sizes of trunk to branch, branch to twig, and so on, always gets closer to the same "magic number" δ.

Laboratory. It is a number approximately equal to 4.6692016, a constant as fundamental as pi or *e*. This number is associated with a particular transition from order to chaos known as a period-doubling cascade, and the identical number occurs in every period-doubling cascade. It is universal. Feigenbaum's discovery was the first of many footprints by which the tracks of chaos are now recognized. One can measure the Feigenbaum number without following the tiny details of the motion of individual points, thus sidestepping the butterfly effect. It has been observed in systems as varied as the dripping of a faucet, the oscillations of liquid helium, and the fluctuations of gypsy moth populations. The Feigenbaum number is a predictable constant in a world of chaos.

A new unity

If chaos is so ubiquitous, why was it not found sooner? Until recently, scientists were having enough problems with the regularities of nature, let alone the irregularities. More seriously, they lacked effective techniques, other than statistics, for studying irregularities. The invention of fast computers changed all that. Without computers no one could perform the millions of calculations needed to observe the patterns of chaos. With computers, especially computer graphics, it is almost impossible not to stumble into them at every turn.

Mere calculation is not enough, however. New mathematics is needed to help understand what the computer reveals, and the geometry of dynamics is the key. In Poincaré's hands this insight led to topology, and then to Smale's program, but other investigators derived different, equally valuable, insights. Benoit Mandelbrot of the IBM Thomas J. Watson Research Center, Yorktown Heights, New York, has become famous for his discovery of fractals, intricate geometric objects with infinitely fine structure. The geometric forms associated with chaos turn out to be fractals, a curious case of parallel evolution in scientific research.

Chaos shows the value of dialogue across scientific disciplines and the utility of blue-sky research, aimed not at a particular technological goal but at broad understanding of basic phenomena. It shows that ideas from pure mathematics, developed because of the subject's own internal imperatives, can have important applications to the real world. And it is leading to a new scientific unity. Today's chaos theorist works with a heady brew of new and old mathematics, applied science, and powerful technology. It is interdisciplinary research at its best.

Designer chaos

Chaos teaches many lessons. Its prime message is simple: do not jump to conclusions. Irregular phenomena do not require complicated equations or equations with random terms. Simple causes may have complicated effects. Small changes may produce vast consequences.

On the loss side of the balance sheet is the revelation that even if the laws of nature are known, one may not be able to predict what will happen. Whether something is complex depends not so much on how it is described but on what questions are asked and from what point of view.

71

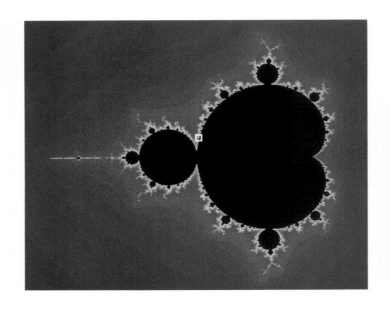

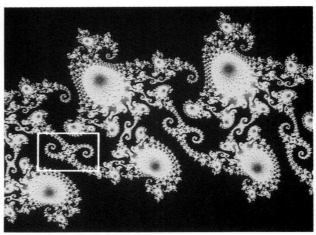

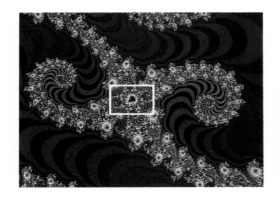

On the profit side, things that look complicated may turn out to be simple if one can find the right way to look at them. This is "designer chaos," exploiting the universal geometry of dynamic systems to build plausible and illuminating models of irregularities in the universe. The heartbeat, measles epidemics, Hyperion—in these cases designer chaos works beautifully. There are hundreds of other examples from every corner of the scientific enterprise. They include the stability of magnetically confined plasma in experimental fusion reactors, turbulence in fluids, reversals of the Earth's magnetic field, the dripping of a faucet, the progress of chemical reactions, the wobbles of soap bubbles, corrosion in batteries, the transmission of nerve impulses, the motion of a ship moored to a buoy, the structure of metal ores, the formation of soot, the behavior of electronic circuits, and the way in which meteorites that reach Earth are transferred from the asteroid belt.

In the case of the weather, things are not as clear. Here the main impact of chaos is to cast severe doubts on the practical feasibility of long-term weather prediction. Forecasts a few days ahead are fine, but is accuracy a month in the future too much to expect? Tomorrow some genius may cut through the difficulties with a revolutionary idea, but present approaches seem doomed to failure by their own internal laws.

Finally, what of Einstein's question? Does God play dice after all? Through the eyes of chaos, the metaphor takes on a new aspect. Despite their associations with games of chance, dice are deterministic. If the speed and position of a rolling die could be measured accurately enough, then its future would be predetermined. With a fast computer and a video camera, one could predict the outcome before the die stopped moving. However, one simply cannot measure the speed and position accurately enough. The butterfly effect amplifies tiny errors, and predictions fail. This example illustrates just one of several ways in which a theoretically deterministic system can behave unpredictably; that is, "at random."

Einstein objected to random chance; he believed in a universe of complete law and order. But now research into chaos shows that exact laws automatically generate random effects as well as regular ones. Thus, the question changes. It is not so much whether God plays dice . . . as how.

Fractals are intricate geometric objects having infinitely fine structure. No matter how much they are magnified, more and more worlds of detail emerge. The fractal known as the Mandelbrot set (opposite page, top left) is perhaps the most complex object in mathematics. As the computer-generated images reveal, a journey through successively higher levels of magnification (left to right, top to bottom) uncovers a never-ending pageant of shepherd's crooks, lace eyes, and shapes resembling the entire set. The strange attractors of chaos, which typically are composed of infinitely many thin layers fitted together, turn out to be fractals.

Images by H. Jürgens, H.-O. Peitgen, and D. Saupe, © copyright The Beauty of Fractals by H.-O. Peitgen and P. Richter, Springer-Verlag, Heidelberg, 1986, and The Science of Fractal Images by H.-O. Peitgen and D. Saupe (eds.), Springer-Verlag, N.Y., 1988

FOR ADDITIONAL READING

Ralph Abraham and Christopher D. Shaw, *Dynamics: The Geometry of Behavior,* 4 vols. (Aerial Press, 1982–88).

James P. Crutchfield, J. Doyne Farmer, Norman H. Packard, and Robert S. Shaw, "Chaos," *Scientific American* (December 1986, pp. 46–57).

Ivar Ekeland, *Mathematics and the Unexpected* (University of Chicago Press, 1988).

James Gleick, *Chaos: Making a New Science* (Viking Press, 1987).

Heinz-Otto Peitgen and Peter H. Richter, *The Beauty of Fractals* (Springer-Verlag, 1986).

Ian Stewart, *The Problems of Mathematics* (Oxford University Press, 1987).

Ian Stewart, *Does God Play Dice?* (Basil Blackwell, 1989).

THE TRUTH ABOUT

SHARKS

by Noel D. Vietmeyer

Contrary to *Jaws*, most sharks are small and harmless to humans. They come in a great variety of shapes and sizes, and their remarkable resistance to cancer is now being studied by many scientists.

(Top) Ron & Valerie Taylor—Australasian Nature Transparencies; (bottom) Steve Early—Animals Animals

NOEL D. VIETMEYER *is a Professional Associate with the National Research Council in Washington, D.C.*

(Overleaf) Sand tiger shark; photograph, Tom McHugh—Photo Researchers

Sharks are an enigma. Scientists have little idea how fast they grow, how long they live, how often they eat, how much they rest, exactly where they live, or how many of them there are. For most species scientists are even unsure of the gestation period and how many young they produce.

Nonetheless, progress in understanding sharks' secrets is being made. Using scuba gear, submersibles, telemetry, and sensitive modern instrumentation, scientists—from ecologists to pharmacologists—are stripping away the outer veils of mystery. The result is a growing admiration of these fish. Sharks are not dim-witted eating machines but physiological wonders—perhaps the best-built organisms in all the natural world. Specialists now speak of these fishes' abilities almost with awe.

This growing body of knowledge is also proving that most of what people fear about sharks is unfounded. Indeed, it is laying the basis for a

probable major change in public attitudes. Soon the idea that the shark is an enemy to be utterly destroyed could disappear—as did fears of wolves, dragons, vampires, sea serpents, and other former "monsters" when the unvarnished truth was exposed.

Moreover, scientists are proving that sharks contribute so much to the world that, by and large, these killer fish are more our friends than our enemies. In fact, given new findings in the field of medicine, sharks might soon be saving more human lives than they have taken in all of history.

Shark species

Most of us know what a shark looks like, but our vision is that of just one branch of the shark family—mainly the swift-swimming, open-ocean branch. Many lesser-known species come in a multitude of unusual shapes and sizes. Among the family eccentrics are the thresher shark with a tail as long as its body; the angel shark, as flat as a flounder; the saw shark with a nose like a chain saw; and the hammerhead, whose T-shaped head is perhaps the oddest found on any animal.

Sharks are distinguished from other fish by the presence of sexual organs called claspers, multiple gill slits, cartilaginous skeletons, and tooth-covered skins. ("Normal" fish have single gill openings, bony skeletons, and scaly or smooth skins.) They range in size from dwarf sharks, between 10 and 15 centimeters (4 and 6 inches) in length when fully grown, to the whale shark, more than 13 meters (43 feet) long, the biggest fish in the sea.

The differences demonstrate what theoretical ecologists call "adaptive radiation." Starting from a common ancestor some 400 million years ago, the shark diversified in form and function and spilled out ("radiated") to fill vastly different ecological niches. Though many think of it as the quintessential predator, among shark species are scavengers,

A wide variety of shapes characterizes the 350 species of sharks. The hammerhead (opposite page, top) has one of the most unusual heads of any animal, and the angel shark (opposite page, bottom) is flat. The horn shark (below) has a mouth adapted for a diet of mollusks, sea urchins, and crustaceans.

© David Doubilet

77

parasites, plankton feeders, and bottom feeders that live on shellfish and crustaceans. There are exquisitely streamlined species that annually migrate across the oceans, and there are sedentary varieties that hug the ocean floor. There is even a "freshwater" shark: the bull shark, a coastal species that wanders up rivers. In the Orinoco River in Venezuela, one was found more than 1,600 kilometers (1,000 miles) from the ocean, and another bull shark was reportedly found 2,818 kilometers (1,750 miles) up the Mississippi, in Alton, Illinois.

In only about the last 20 years, approximately one-third of the 350 shark species have been discovered. These have included a whole new world of sharks in the ocean's deepest recesses, in some cases more than a kilometer below the surface. One newly found deep-water species, the "cookie cutter," demonstrates the great variety of sharks. It is eel shaped and about the size of a policeman's billy club. With its sucking mouth, it attaches itself to the sides of fish and reams out neat round plugs of skin and flesh that are the size of Vanilla Wafers. It gained particular notoriety a few years ago when nuclear submarines surfaced with mysterious perforations in their rubber-coated sonar domes. The cause was not attempted espionage, just cookie cutters seeking supper.

Another oddity was discovered off Hawaii in 1976 when a U.S. Navy research ship pulled up a sea anchor and found that it had accidentally snagged a fish that had never before been seen. It was dubbed "megamouth" because its head and mouth were enormous. It was a male with weak, loose skin, flabby muscles, and soft cartilage. It had tiny teeth and strange gill structures like those that whales use to filter masses of minuscule food organisms out of the ocean. Leighton Taylor at Honolulu's Waikiki Aquarium found its stomach filled with soupy red plankton, consisting mainly of tiny shrimp and jellyfish. In 1984 a second male was captured near Los Angeles, and in the summer of 1988 a third megamouth washed up on a beach at Mandurah, south of Perth in Western Australia.

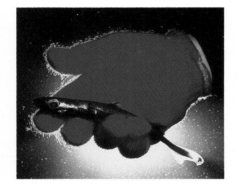

Basic physiology

In the study of shark physiology fascinating discoveries have been made. For example, Francis Carey, a marine physiologist at the Woods Hole (Massachusetts) Oceanographic Institution, has been taking sharks' temperatures for almost 30 years. He found that at least four species—including the terrifying mako and the great white of *Jaws* fame—are actually warm-blooded.

Like all organisms, sharks generate heat in their muscles, brains, digestive tracts, and other body parts. However, unlike most fish, the four warm-blooded sharks have a system of intertwined blood vessels that acts as a "heat exchanger." By means of a countercurrent flow, the arteries recover heat from the veins before the venous blood can reach the gills, where it comes so close to the cold sea that it loses any surplus heat. As a result of this recycling, these sharks can be warmer than the ocean around them by approximately 10° C (18° F). The extra heat boosts the animal's speed, endurance, power, and rate of digestion.

Samuel Gruber of the University of Miami, Florida, discovered another striking physiological trait: many sharks are long-lived and slow to mature. A lemon shark three meters (ten feet) long, for example, can be 30 to 50 years old. Some larger sharks are thought to be more than 100 years old. In addition, lemon sharks (they are yellow in color) require just over 13 years to reach sexual maturity. And many, perhaps most, other well-known species must be more than two decades old before they can reproduce.

Gruber's conclusions were based on the fact that a shark's vertebrae produce rings in much the same way as does a tree. They are not, however, annual rings, and to determine their periodicity, Gruber caught more than 1,000 sharks, injected them with the yellow-colored antibiotic tetracycline hydrochloride, tagged them, and released them. Tetracycline binds to calcium and is deposited in the vertebrae, where it can be seen to fluoresce a bright golden yellow under ultraviolet light. Gruber counted the rings in sharks that were recaptured. Lemon sharks, he found, follow a lunar cycle and add roughly a ring a month.

Round hole in the flesh of a dolphin (above left) was made by the bite of a "cookie cutter" shark (above). The species named "megamouth" because of its huge head and mouth was discovered in 1976. A second male (below) was captured near Los Angeles in 1984.

(Top left) Chris Newbert/© 1985 DISCOVER PUBLICATIONS; (top right) © David Doubilet

Natural History Museum of Los Angeles County

79

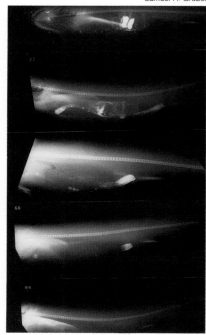

Samuel H. Gruber

Sharks may seem like the ultimate aliens, but in surprising ways the physiology of many species parallels that of humans. Warm-bloodedness and comparable life-spans (about 70 years) are two examples. The reproductive systems reveal even more striking similarities. For example, all sharks use internal fertilization; the male has two copulatory organs called claspers; and most sharks are born alive. In some species females incubate free-floating embryos in a chamber inside their bodies. (In at least one genus, the biggest embryos swim around gobbling up their smaller siblings as well as all new eggs that appear.) However, in other species—including the gray sharks (Carcharhinidae) and hammerheads (Sphyrnidae)—the embryos attach to a uterus and are fed through a placenta and umbilical cord like human embryos.

Sensory systems

It once was thought that sharks were automatons that mindlessly followed trails of blood. However, modern instruments have shown that they use an array of sensory organs of almost incredible sensitivity. For example, lines of small pores running along their flanks detect vibrations traveling through the water. Sharks are most attracted by low-frequency vibrations, probably because those are the sound signatures of an animal writhing in distress. Although 600 cycles per second is the frequency to which sharks are most sensitive, during the Mercury space program engineers found that sharks are also attracted to sound pulses of about 200 cycles per second—the frequency transmitted by a helicopter's beating blades. Thus, while divers were attaching flotation collars to the space capsules bobbing in the Pacific, helicopters overhead were ringing the dinner gong for all the sharks in the neighborhood.

"Swimming nose" is an apt description of a shark's sense of smell. Head swinging from side to side, a shark continually monitors the various smells and tastes as the water flows through its nostrils and mouth. Electrodes implanted in the sensory nerves have shown that sharks detect

Series of X-ray images of the gut of a shark reveals that food (made visible to X-rays by being laced with barium sulfate) requires more than 80 hours to move through the animal's digestive tract. Most fish digest their food in 16–24 hours, and the comparative slowness of sharks may explain why some grow so slowly and take so long to reach maturity.

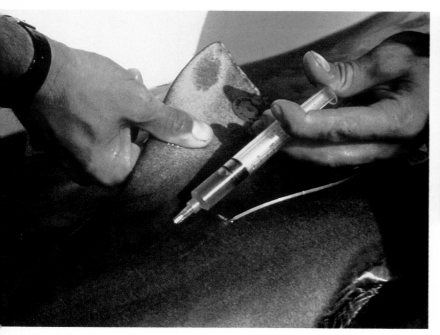

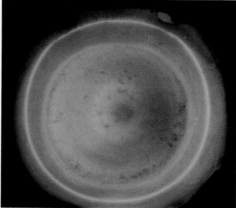

scents of blood and decaying flesh as dilute as one part in a million or more parts of water.

Contrary to a commonly held earlier belief, sharks are not almost blind. In the open-water species, at least, the eye is backed by the tapetum, a lining of mirrorlike cells. Light passing through the retina bounces off the tapetum and returns through the retina. This double stimulation probably doubles the visual sensitivity of these sharks in the darkness of night or of the deep ocean. Some of the reflected light passes out as "eyeshine" like that seen in cats. In deep-sea species this shine is green, while in others it is blue or gold.

Although adapted for dim light, many shark eyes must also handle the dazzling brilliance of surface waters. Unlike the staring eyes of regular fish, these have pupils that contract to tiny slits or points in bright light. Also, pigments spread out and temporarily block the reflection of the tapetum, which is reminiscent of the sunglasses that darken when exposed to sunlight.

Perhaps the most amazing sense of sharks is a sort of "radar" that detects minute electric currents. Adrianus Kalmijn of the University of California Scripps Institution of Oceanography at San Diego determined that sharks can detect electric fields as low as 0.001 microvolts per centimeter, the best electrical acuity of any animal. Thus, sharks would detect electric fields equivalent to the voltage of a 1.5-volt flashlight battery spread over a distance of 3,200 kilometers (2,000 miles). Or, put another way, the minimum amount of electricity it takes to just tingle one's fingers is 100 million times more than the minimum amount a shark can detect.

Sharks use this ability to seek out invisible prey. They can detect a flounder buried beneath the sand by emissions from the electrochemical and physiological processes in its body. (Such emissions are what physicians measure when taking an electrocardiogram of the heart.) In addition, chemicals in the mucous membranes of the mouths, gills, and skins of fish (especially when damaged) react with the salt water to emit tiny currents that can also be sensed by sharks.

Embryo of a swell shark with a yolk sac that it uses for nourishment (above left) floats inside an egg case laid by its mother. The swell shark hatchling (above) has a double row of enlarged spiky denticles that help it force its way out of the case. Other species of sharks produce living young rather than eggs.

A tagged lemon shark is injected with a chemical that glows in ultraviolet light (opposite page, bottom). The chemical becomes incorporated in the growing portions of the hard parts of a shark's body. Consequently, a cross section of the recaptured shark's spinal column later viewed in ultraviolet light (opposite page, right) reveals a glowing ring at the place where spinal tissue was being formed when the shark was injected. This allowed researchers to determine that lemon sharks add about one ring per month.

Kalmijn obtained evidence that sharks may use their electrical acuity for navigation. A swimming shark cuts the Earth's magnetic field, inducing minute electric currents around itself. The direction in which it swims affects the direction of the induced current. Thus, sharks have the equipment for a built-in electromagnetic compass, and almost certainly they use it.

Locomotion

By tagging sharks, researchers have found that some species are among the greatest of all globe-trotters, migrating as far as many birds. John Casey of the Northeast Fishery Center of the National Marine Fisheries Service in Narragansett, Rhode Island, began clamping tags onto sharks off the east coast of the United States more than 20 years ago. His tags have been returned by fishermen from almost all corners of the Atlantic. The distance record as of mid-1988 was held by a blue shark tagged off the east coast of the U.S. that was caught again off Africa, 5,800 kilometers (3,500 miles) away. The longevity record was held by two sandbar sharks that Casey had tagged in 1965 and that were recaptured 22 years later.

From such studies it is now known that the common dogfishes that summer off New England winter off Georgia. Some go as far as Brazil. Big oceanic sharks, such as blue sharks and tiger sharks, follow the great ocean currents and make regular circuits of 16,000 kilometers (10,000 miles) or more.

It is puzzling that sharks are among the strongest swimmers in the oceans. Their bodies are supported by mere cartilage, the soft, gristly material that makes up a human's ears. However, Stephen Wainwright of Duke University, Durham, North Carolina, found that these boneless swimmers rely on their skins. This horny sheath pulling the muscles from the outside substitutes for a skeleton pushing them from the inside. Acting like a huge tendon, the skin gives the shark its sinuous move-

Electrodes are connected to the olfactory (sense of smell) organs of a lemon shark and the shark is stimulated with chemical substances (above). When the subsequent electrical activity is recorded, certain chemicals that attract the shark produce characteristic changes in the olfactory organs and brain. A dogfish (below) bites an electrically simulated prey in an experiment which revealed that sharks can detect electric fields as low as 0.001 microvolts per centimeter, the best electrical acuity of any animal.

ment, powerful whiplash thrust, and great speed. Mako sharks have been clocked at almost 48 kilometers (30 miles) per hour, an amazing speed for underwater travel.

H. David Baldridge of Sarasota, Florida, a longtime U.S. Navy shark expert, noted that sharks actually "fly" like airplanes. The airfoil shape of their pectoral fins, which they hold out like wings, provides lift. The tail (caudal) fin helps provide roll control. Also, in some species the body (especially the snout) performs as a lifting surface for achieving attitude control.

Nature has condemned most sharks to life without sleep or even rest. To begin with, they lack the gas bladder with which most other fish achieve neutral buoyancy at different depths. Huge oil-filled livers provide some buoyancy but not enough for complete flotation. Baldridge once measured a 460-kilogram (1,015-pound) tiger shark and found that although its 78-kilogram (171-pound) liver buoyed it up, its apparent weight in seawater was still 3.3 kilograms (7.3 pounds).

Because of their heaviness, sharks must literally swim or sink. Like airplanes, sharks "stall" if they stop moving. Baldridge measured the stall speed at about 0.76 meters (2.5 feet) per second. When a shark stalls, its nose goes up, and the fish falls tail first through the water.

Another reason sharks stay awake is that, like other fish, they require the constant passage of water over their gill systems in order to maintain respiration but, unlike other fish, most sharks cannot pump water over their gills by muscular action. As a result, they must literally swim to

Ophthalmologist Stanley Spielman examines the eye of a hammerhead shark with an ophthalmoscope. The shark is strapped to an underwater operating table, and its eyelid is temporarily sewn open. Unlike other fish, sharks have eyes with pupils that contract to tiny slits or points in bright light.

Gary Montenori

83

breathe, a vulnerable aspect of their physiological design contributing to the difficulty of keeping sharks alive in the laboratory.

Intelligence

Enough has been learned to lay to rest forever the once-common notion that sharks are lazy, cowardly, clumsy, and stupid. More than 30 years ago Eugenie Clark, a marine biologist now at the University of Maryland, presented lemon sharks with targets of various shapes, rewarding them with food when they pressed their snouts against one and punishing them by tapping their snouts when they pressed the other. The sharks learned quickly to discriminate between square- and diamond-shaped targets as well as between red and white ones. However, the difference between a circle and a square was beyond their capacity to distinguish.

They proved to have good memories, too. After "hibernating" through the winter, these sharks remembered all they had learned the previous fall. Clark guessed that they remember things for years, if not for the rest of their lives.

Trainers at the Naval Ocean Systems Center in San Diego taught nurse sharks to retrieve hoops and perform other tasks. They used the same techniques that work with porpoises. They taught the sharks to nudge a fist and to respond to buzzers, and they discovered that the fish rebelled if the lessons were too hard. A frustrated shark would bash its head on the gate to get out of the "classroom tank" and back to the less stressful "homeroom."

Fall of the monster myth

There is a special helpless horror created by the thought of being attacked and eaten by a huge shark. The image of a mindless monster that malevolently seeks out humans for a quick meal is a recent phenomenon, however. Throughout most of history people correctly considered sharks to be like lions or bears—predators that would eat humans but were hardly terrifying demons with an insatiable desire for human flesh.

The motion picture *Jaws* had much to do with stimulating public fear. Since the 1975 movie, many beachgoers have stayed out of the surf or at least have continually worried while there. Although based on a freak series of attacks along the coast of New Jersey in 1916, in which there were five incidents of shark attacks in ten days, *Jaws* is mostly science fiction, and the shark in the film a creature almost entirely of imagination. Even along the California coast, with one of the highest attack rates in the world, a great white kills only one person every eight years on average.

Of the 350 or so shark species, only about a dozen have been firmly implicated in attacks on humans, with the great white and tiger sharks leading the lists. Despite common beliefs, most sharks are small and harmless to humans. In 1981 Leonard Compagno of San Francisco State University assessed 296 shark species and found that half were less than one meter (3.3 feet) long and 82% were under 2 meters; he determined that about 50 species are potentially dangerous.

If sharks were truly man-eaters, there would have been many more fatalities during recent years because the sport of scuba diving is sky-rocketing in popularity and thousands of scuba divers are encountering sharks underwater. (There are even some famed dive sites where seeing or feeding sharks is the main attraction.) Although several divers who were holding speared fish have been fatally attacked, few unprovoked attacks have ended fatally. Eugenie Clark reported that during more than 30 years of research throughout the world, she made hundreds of dives with sharks and found them to be timid. Unless she took deep breaths and was careful to be absolutely quiet, they became alarmed and swam away.

Indeed, Clark tracked down several of the tales of shark attack and found that they resulted from gross negligence or even downright false-hood. One widely publicized experience turned out to be the result of a famous shark catcher cornering a lemon shark in a pen; he had speared it several times before it bit off his calf. Another person had been ille-gally mining coral, lost his leg to dynamite, and blamed a shark to cover up his misdeeds.

Shark attack

Sharks can be lethal to people, but why they attack is poorly understood. It is difficult to keep them in captivity and even more difficult to study them in their natural habitats.

Donald Nelson of California State University at Long Beach studied attacks by gray reef sharks at Enewetak in the Marshall Islands. He recorded that nearly all attacks by this species were preceded by an exaggerated display of "body language." The sinuous, graceful creature transformed into a tense, stiff, zigzag shape, with the back arched, the snout high, and the pectoral fins pointed downward. The jaws sometimes

Close-up of a nurse shark reveals that its skin is covered with dermal denticles. These are modified teeth that give the skin a texture similar to sandpaper. Scientists have suggested that the alignment of the denticles channels water, resulting in a streamlined flow that reduces friction as the shark swims. The denticles of sharks (such as the mako shark) that swim in the open sea are smaller and more efficiently shaped for streamlined flow than those of the more sluggish species (such as the nurse shark) that live near the ocean floor.

Guido Dingerkus

85

opened and shut in rapid succession, and the shark often rolled sideways in a contorted posture.

To induce confrontations Nelson constructed a submersible shaped somewhat like a shark. When he piloted it in Enewetak Lagoon, it elicited the attack display and several attacks. (Luckily, it was bite-proof.) When he cornered a shark or followed its every move, it would slow down, intensify its display, and, when the sub was about two meters away, attack with lightning speed. In one attack that was filmed, the shark took only 0.33 second to hit the sub, biting the forward motor and tearing up the plastic propeller.

Nelson noted that the attacks were not brought on by hunger; no predator forewarns its prey of its intent to kill. This display, therefore, is a warning that the shark is displeased and the intruder should leave.

Scientists have compiled and analyzed the data on shark attacks over a period of several decades. There are fewer than 100 shark attacks worldwide each year, and the number has been closer to 50 in recent years. The mortality rate of the victims ranges from 17 to 35%.

While some attacks appear to be based on aggression, few seem to be for food. More often than not the human victims are not eaten. Indeed, the shark often flees at high speed. Sometimes it just bumps the person with its snout and runs, perhaps because of curiosity rather than as an invitation to participate in dinner.

Some attacks in northern California appear to be cases of mistaken identity. The problem is that sharks cannot distinguish between seals and surfers in black wet suits. One scientist explains that if you look like a seal and go swimming in the shark's dining room, you can end up as the main course.

Attacks on boats have been considered a sign of innate aggression, but the weak galvanic fields created by metallic objects in seawater

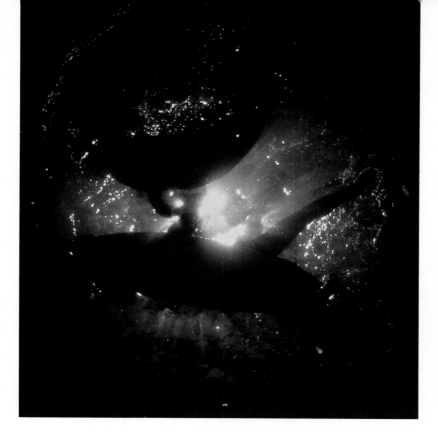

A seal (top) and a surfer in a wet suit (bottom) look much the same in the water. Sharks can not distinguish between the two, and so some attacks by sharks on surfers in wet suits may be cases of mistaken identity in which the human was perceived as a seal—a favorite meal for a shark.

may attract or confuse the sharks. Bright colors may also be powerful attractants. For example, in 1971 Scott Johnson and Ernest McFadden of the U.S. Naval Undersea Research and Development Center in San Diego dressed dummies in life vests of different colors and offered them up as "taste tests." Mako and blue sharks showed a clear preference for International Orange, the color that had been selected to be seen easily by rescue aircraft and ships. As a result shark researchers sometimes refer to International Orange as "yum-yum yellow," and recently it has been replaced on the bottoms of life rafts with black.

Shark repellents have been sought since World War II. There is still no sure protection from sharks in open water, but some interesting discoveries have been made. For example, Eugenie Clark found a Red Sea fish, the Moses sole, that produces a chemical so repellent that sharks cannot bring themselves to bite into the fish. In experiments two hungry sharks

Moses sole produces a chemical that repels hungry sharks from biting into it. The repellent is a protein with detergent action, and later tests demonstrated that an ingredient of industrial cleaning agents is just as effective.

repeatedly attacked a Moses sole in their tank for 28 hours, but the little fish repelled them every time. The repellent compound, isolated by Gruber and Zlotkin, proved to be a protein with detergent action. Tests have since shown that a common ingredient of industrial cleaning agents is just as effective.

Anatomy of a shark bite

Since the 1960s photographers standing inside steel cages have filmed sharks—usually great whites—mauling large chunks of meat. Run in slow motion, the films show how elegant and complex the process is.

Often the great white starts by viewing the scene above the surface—perhaps the only fish to lift its head into the air and peer around. Then it lunges. The teeth lie flat on the inside of the mouth—retracted for maximum streamlining. A flap of skin covers the eyes for protection. The lower jawbone is thrust forward, and the snout draws back to bring the mouth to the front of the body and erect the teeth. The ring of jaws then slides forward like loose dentures so that the shark can anchor its teeth deeply into a large victim. Then the jaws close, and the animal violently shakes the entire forward part of its body until chunks of tissue, as much as 18 kilograms (40 pounds) of flesh and bone, have been torn out. Then it swims away still jerking its head.

With its eyes covered, the animal is blind when it bites. Probably at this point it uses its electrical acuity. This is better than sight because in the last few meters of an attack blood and turbulence often cloud the

Great white shark (above) is considered to be more dangerous to humans than any other shark. Growing to a maximum length of about 7 meters (21 feet), it is perhaps the only fish to lift its head into the air and look around (opposite page, top). Its huge jaws (opposite page, bottom left) crash together with several thousand kilograms of force. The teeth are triangular and serrated (opposite page, bottom right), and the top ones slash down into the spaces between those on the bottom.

water and also because their mouths are on the underside of the head and sharks thus cannot "look" food into them.

A great white's jaws crash together with several thousand kilograms of force. The teeth are triangular, serrated like steak knives, and so sharp that one could shave with them. The top ones slash down into the spaces between the bottom ones, slicing together like scissor blades. In the process a dozen front teeth may break or tear out. However, the teeth are anchored in a layer of tough connective tissue rather than in jaw sockets, and within about two weeks a new row marches forward to take up position in the front lines.

Saving lives

Sharks are extraordinarily healthy. Lunging at prey, they often slice their bodies open and, during mating, males clasp females with their teeth, savagely tearing their back, flanks, and tail area. Nonetheless, even the most massive wounds seem to heal without lingering problems. Sharks obviously have very effective ways of warding off infections.

University of Miami researchers showed in 1981 that sharks' blood contains antibodies that destroy an almost unbelievable array of bacteria, viruses, and other living pathogens, as well as many chemicals. Also, they reported, a backup immune system adds an extra layer of protection, providing the shark with a remarkable—possibly unique—natural immunity to disease.

Several research teams began exploring these qualities. Gary Litman of the Showa University Research Institute in St. Petersburg, Florida, reported that the horn shark's immune system includes a separate subsystem that protects T cells. Because T cells are the targets of the AIDS virus, this discovery could have far-reaching consequences for humans.

Rosemary Chastney—Ocean Images, Inc.

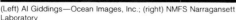

(Left) Al Giddings—Ocean Images, Inc.; (right) NMFS Narragansett Laboratory

For about 20 years researchers have suspected that sharks are one of the few animals that are essentially cancer-free, and Carl Luer of the Mote Marine Laboratory in Sarasota, Florida, has been trying to find out if this is true. Since 1981 he has been feeding certain species of shark with fish containing packages of aflatoxin, one of the most effective cancer-inducing agents known. He sometimes even injects sharks with the deadly chemical. After seven years of experiments, he had not been able to induce a single tumor. Without exception, all other laboratory animals undergoing the same treatment develop tumors.

Probably the shark's unusual immune system has something to do with its resistance to cancer, but in 1981 Judah Folkman at Children's Hospital in Boston and Robert Langer at the Massachusetts Institute of Technology began probing yet another possibility. Several years earlier Folkman had demonstrated that tumors secrete chemicals called growth factors that encourage blood vessels to grow toward them. Eventually the two fuse, and the cancerous mass gains nourishment and voids waste products through the host's blood vessels. Folkman hypothesized that if this process could be blocked, tumors would be unable to grow. Then he found that solid tumors (the type that infect tissues and bone, as opposed to liquids such as blood and lymph) stopped at a line of cartilage. Working in collaboration, Folkman and Langer isolated and purified proteins in the cartilage that inhibited the tumor. The proteins did not have to come from shark cartilage, but sharks have far more cartilage than other animals.

Materials purified from shark cartilage are also undergoing advanced clinical trials as an artificial skin to protect victims of severe burns

Carl Luer of the Mote Marine Laboratory in Sarasota, Florida, examines a dead nurse shark that had been long exposed to aflatoxin, a powerful cancer-inducing chemical. After seven years of such experiments no evidence of cancer was found in any of the sharks.

Carl A. Luer, Mote Marine Laboratory, Sarasota, Florida

against their biggest enemy—infections. Compared with other foreign proteins, the sheets of cartilage "skin" are less likely to be rejected by the human body.

The future

Sharks are among the oldest vertebrates. Their lineage can be traced back some 400 million years. Some of today's species seem to have remained virtually unchanged for 60 million years. They saw the dinosaurs, ichthyosaurs, and pterosaurs come and go. Sharks may not survive much longer, however. Increasingly, scientists are concerned that certain species may soon disappear.

With reproductive strategies like those of whales—low fecundity, slow growth, and delayed maturity—sharks have the same vulnerability to overharvesting. Nevertheless, each year an estimated 100 million sharks are killed—some for food, some for sport, some in senseless anger. Because of this a number of species are being destroyed at alarming rates. The spiny dogfish—one of the most common ingredients in England's beloved fish-and-chips—became virtually extinct in Scotland and Norway in 1968. The school shark was hunted to near extinction in parts of Australia decades ago. The porbeagle in Norwegian waters is no longer available in commercial quantities. California's soupfin shark was so heavily fished in the 1930s and 1940s—when scientists found that its liver had more vitamin A than any other source and many millions of people drank what was euphemistically called "cod-liver" oil—that it has never recovered. Even great whites are threatened with extinction in some areas because their teeth are being sold for jewelry.

It seems unlikely that protest marchers or international boycotts will be organized to save the shark. Sharks play a vital role in the oceans, however. They are the major predators—with no natural predators of their own—and their actions influence all the species in the seas. They are what theoretical ecologists call a "keystone species," one whose presence is necessary to support the tenuous web of interrelationships known as the food chain.

Already some breakdowns may be occurring because of reduced shark numbers. In eastern Canada, for example, there has been a geometric increase in the numbers of cod carrying a parasitic worm that makes them unmarketable. One explanation is that this is related to the increased population of seals that carry one life stage of the cod parasite, an increase made possible by the declining number of shark predators. On the western coasts of the United States and Canada, fishermen are complaining that the rising numbers of seals, sea lions, and sea otters are eating into their catch.

In sum, the wave of new research demonstrates that the shark is still an enigma. It is strange, unpredictable, and dangerous; it attacks not merely out of the depths of the ocean but out of the depths of prehistory. For all that, it is no mindless machine, automatically attacking and devouring anything that gets in its way. Indeed, it is a magnificent organism and a crucial link supporting the oceanic food chain.

Pollen:

Nature's Fingerprints of Plants

by Vaughn M. Bryant, Jr.

Bees eat it, plants need it to reproduce, and millions of sneezing people endure it. But to scientists who study it, pollen is a source of fascinating stories about the Earth, ancient cultures, and modern criminals.

At a murder trial a defendant claims he had never been in the mountains where the victim was killed. Investigators have found a pair of muddy boots in the defendant's house, and the prosecutor wonders if the mud came from the dirt road at the scene of the crime.

The U.S. Department of Agriculture purchases 200 barrels of domestic honey as part of America's farm-subsidy program. Because the price paid will be much higher than the cost of imported honey, the USDA wishes to certify the true source of the honey it is receiving.

On an offshore platform in the North Sea, where drilling costs run more than $15,000 per meter (about 3.3 feet), a geologist wants to know if drilling has already passed through the oil-bearing zone and if she should recommend abandoning the site as a dry hole.

These three scenarios have one thing in common: the needed information can be determined through examination of the pollen present in the mud, the honey, or the bedrock in question. In fact, over the past 75 years the study of pollen has helped solve numerous problems in plant evolution, geology, archaeology, and climatology, as well as in modern detective work.

More than meets the nose

Palynology, the discipline concerned with the study of pollen and spores, is not a word recognized by most people, yet the health problems caused by airborne pollen and spores are well known. An estimated 15 million Americans suffer from hay fever, and some spend months in misery each year. Pollen and spores are rich in proteins that are released when the grains come in contact with the moist membranes in the human nose and lungs. To the immune system of those persons unfortunate enough to be sensitive, these proteins are foreign substances that call for a full response. Part of the immune system consists of mast cells, which line the walls of the respiratory passages and release histamines and other biologically active compounds into the bloodstream as a defense. It is the body's reaction to these compounds that causes the symptoms of congestion, itching, and sneezing.

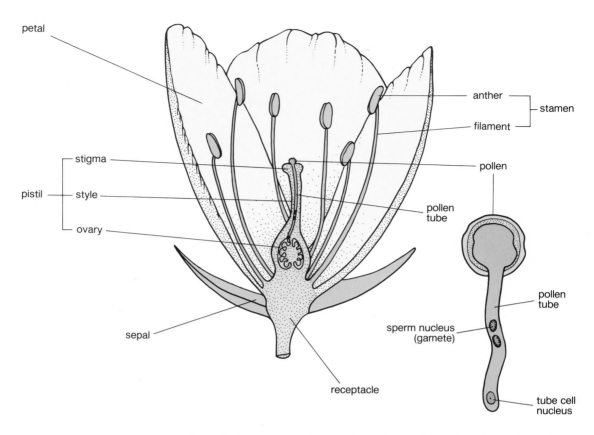

- petal
- anther
- stamen
- filament
- stigma
- pistil
- style
- pollen
- ovary
- pollen tube
- sepal
- receptacle
- pollen
- pollen tube
- sperm nucleus (gamete)
- tube cell nucleus

VAUGHN M. BRYANT, JR., is Professor and Department Head, Department of Anthropology, Texas A&M University, College Station.

(Page 92) Catkins (flower clusters) of hybrid black poplar, shedding pollen; photograph, © Alastair Shay—Oxford Scientific Films

In technical terms microscopic pollen is defined as the multinucleate gametophyte generation of flowering plants. In simple terms its most important function is to carry the male gametes—*i.e.*, the male sex cells—needed for plant reproduction. Each minute pollen grain is formed in the anther, the male apparatus, of seed-bearing plants for eventual transport to the pistil, the female apparatus, where fertilization—the fusion of male and female gametes—occurs. Spores, on the other hand, refer to the asexual reproductive bodies of lower vascular plants, such as ferns, and of nonvascular plants such as algae, fungi, and mosses. Unlike

pollen, spores are capable of developing into new individual organisms without first fusing with another reproductive cell. Spores and pollen, however, do have similarities; they are about the same size, both remain preserved in sediments for millions of years, and both are often produced in great quantity.

The ancients knew that plants produced a yellow powder. "Pollen," in fact, is the Latin word for "fine dust." Whereas these people observed that at certain times of the year plants emitted clouds of yellow dust, few understood its importance. Today it is fairly certain that the Assyrians at least recognized that after the yellow dust from a male date palm was shaken above the flowers of a female date palm, yields of fruit increased. Assyrian murals in the palace of Ashurnasirpal II dating from as early as 860 BC show a winged god dusting palm flowers with pollen. A similar motif is repeated in a number of other Assyrian murals, including one on display in the Metropolitan Museum of Art, New York City.

In his writings during the 5th century BC, the Greek traveler Herodotus reported that the date palm had two sexes and that coating the female flowers with the yellow dust increased the yield of fruit. Herodotus' observations, however, were dismissed as being incorrect; by the middle of the next century, Aristotle had categorically denied the existence of sex in plants. After all, he questioned, are not plants fixed in place by their roots and therefore unable to move about in search of a mate?

With the invention in the middle 1600s of sufficiently powerful lenses for microscopy came the first view of a pollen grain. By the 1680s an Englishman, Nehemiah Grew, and an Italian, Marcello Malpighi, had both published studies of pollen grains complete with drawings and descriptions. Although each knew nothing about the other's research, both hinted that pollen may be the transporter of sperm.

For the next two centuries botanists continued to look at pollen grains, studying their morphological features—*i.e.*, their form and structure—

Diagram (opposite page, top) illustrates the principal parts and the fertilization of a typical flower. Pollen, which contains the sperm cells, or male gametes, is formed in the anther for eventual transport to the pistil, the female apparatus. Once a pollen grain adheres to the pistil's sticky tip, or stigma, it germinates, sending out a pollen tube that grows down through the style. Reaching the ovary, the tube delivers its sperm nuclei to the egg cells, or female gametes. The inner structure of a coral hibiscus flower (opposite page, bottom left) comprises a striking array of pollen-laden stamens topped with a five-branched style that ends in tufted stigmas. Scanning electron micrograph (opposite page, bottom right) shows a cluster of pollen grains bursting from a coleus anther.

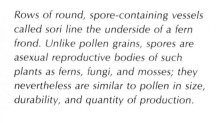

Rows of round, spore-containing vessels called sori line the underside of a fern frond. Unlike pollen grains, spores are asexual reproductive bodies of such plants as ferns, fungi, and mosses; they nevertheless are similar to pollen in size, durability, and quantity of production.

Alabaster relief from ancient Calah (now in Iraq) depicts a winged god pollinating a female palm tree. Together with similar murals it strongly suggests that the relation of pollen to fruit yields was recognized by the Assyrians as early as the 9th century BC.

and establishing their vital role in plant reproduction. They noted also that some plants dispersed great volumes of pollen that was carried by the wind, while other plants produced little pollen and instead relied on insects or birds to carry it from the male to the female flower. Little other use for pollen, aside from its role in plant reproduction and as a food for bees, was realized until the early part of the 20th century. In the 1830s Christian Ehrenberg had reported that fossil pollen and spores remained preserved in sedimentary rocks of great age and had even hinted that they might prove to be useful as indicators of past environmental conditions. At the time, unfortunately, no one paid much attention to Ehrenberg's observations.

Beginnings of modern palynology

By the early 1900s interest in learning about past geologic events was running high. Scientists began to look at plant materials that had been preserved in peat bogs in hopes of finding clues to sequences of past climatic change. Their major concern was the identification of seeds, leaves, and wood in peat deposits, but a few, such as Swedish botanist Gustav Lagerheim, also took an interest in the many fossil pollen grains preserved in the deposits. Lagerheim suggested that fossil pollen might be useful in identifying past vegetation, but he did not offer an effective way to use that information. Then, in a lecture presented in 1916 at a meeting of Scandinavian scientists, E. J. Lennart von Post, a Norwegian geologist who was influenced by Lagerheim, shocked his colleagues by asserting that the recovery of pollen from buried sediments was the most precise method available for determining cycles of past vegetational change. As he lectured, von Post set forth the basic theory of pollen analysis and explained why pollen was the ideal tool for studying changes in past vegetation and, by inference, climate.

96

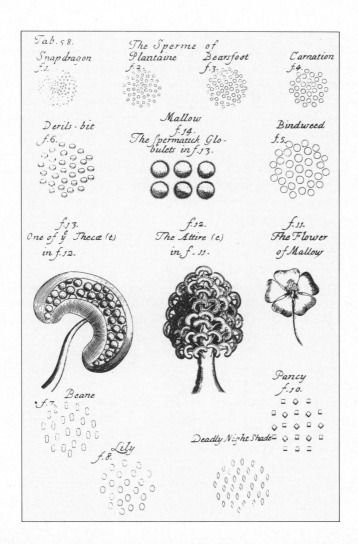

Tab. 58.

Snapdragon f.1.

The Sperme of Plantaine f.2. Bearsfoot f.3.

Carnation f.4.

Devils-bit f.6.

Mallow f.14. The Spermatick Globulets in f.13.

Bindweed f.5.

f.13. One of ỹ Thecæ (t) in f.12.

f.12. The Attire (e) in f.11.

f.11. The Flower of Mallow

Beane f.7.

Lily f.8.

Deadly Night Shade

Pancy f.10.

Within decades of the invention of sufficiently powerful microscope lenses in the middle 1600s, naturalists in England and Italy published illustrated studies of pollen grains. The set of engravings at left is from Nehemiah Grew's The Anatomy of Plants (1682). In the early 20th century Norwegian geologist E. J. Lennart von Post (below) set forth the theory of pollen analysis in the form of five basic principles, which have been amply validated by subsequent research.

First, he pointed out, many plants produce great quantities of pollen or spores, which are dispersed by wind currents. Second, pollen and spores have very durable outer walls that can survive for long periods of time. Third, the morphological features of pollen and spores remain consistent within each species, yet each different species produces its own unique form. Fourth, each pollen- or spore-producing plant is restricted in its distribution by ecological conditions such as moisture, temperature, and soil type. As such, each species is most plentiful in areas that best meet the plant's needs. And fifth, most wind-borne pollen tends to fall to the Earth's surface within a small radius, roughly 50–100 kilometers (30–60 miles), of where it is dispersed. Using the principles he set forth, von Post showed how his pollen analysis of bog deposits in central Sweden revealed the precise sequence of vegetational change beginning thousands of years ago with the pioneer plants that grew immediately after the continental glaciers receded and ending with the present spruce forests. Subsequent research has amply confirmed the validity of each of von Post's statements.

97

Pollen dispersal

Many plants rely on the wind to carry spores or pollen to their intended destinations, yet wind pollination is an inefficient method. Thus, to ensure fertilization, plants must produce great volumes of pollen in order that at least a small fraction will find its intended destination. The magnitude of pollen production by some plants staggers the imagination. For example, scientists in Sweden estimate that their spruce forests in the southern third of the country annually liberate more than 75,000 tons of microscopic pollen into the atmosphere. Plants such as marijuana produce over 70,000 pollen grains per anther; a single plant shoot can generate more than 500 million pollen grains. Today the illegal growing of marijuana in parts of the southern and western U.S. has created a serious health hazard for thousands of residents who suffer from hay fever.

A larger number of plants possess more efficient methods of pollen dispersal and therefore need make only small numbers of pollen grains. Clover, for example, generates only 220 pollen grains per anther, while maple produces around 1,000 grains per anther. Such plants rely on insects, birds, or bats to carry out pollination. Unlike wind-pollinated plants, which have only tiny flowers, pollinator-dependent plants produce large, showy, fragrant flowers and rich nectars for luring pollinators. As the animals collect nectar and pollen, pollen adheres to the hairs around the face and body and to the legs. On the pollinators' visit to the next flower, some of the pollen brushes off and completes fertilization. For millions of years many plants, such as the orchids, and their pollinators have evolved together in such a complex manner that today neither could survive without the other. Living in the tropical regions of Central America, for example, are 20 species of bucket orchids and 20 species of euglossine bees. Of these, each species of bee is adapted to pollinating only one species of bucket orchid.

Plants that rely on pollination by the wind must produce pollen in great volumes to ensure that some will reach its intended destination. When shaken, a cypress pine (above) disperses pollen clouds into the air. (Below) A vast accumulation of pollen rides the waves at Crater Lake, Oregon, during the summer when the surrounding forest trees pollinate.

(Top) Jen and Des Bartlett—Bruce Coleman Inc.;
(bottom) Martha Cooper—Peter Arnold, Inc.

Pollinator-dependent plants trade off heavy pollen production for large showy flowers and sweet nectars that attract bats, birds, and insects. A greater short-nosed fruit bat (top left) feeds from the flower of a banana plant; pollen on its fur will be transported to the next banana trees it visits. A soldier beetle pollinates a primrose willow blossom (top right). Certain Central American orchid species and their euglossine bee pollinators have co-evolved in such a complex way that each bee species is adapted to pollinate only one orchid species (bottom left). A euglossine bee in the throat of a bucket orchid (bottom right) carries a pair of pollen sacs (pollinia) implanted on it during an earlier visit to another orchid. When the bee leaves, specialized hooks on the flower will strip the pollinia from the bee's back.

Almost all of the pollen von Post found in his analysis of Swedish peat deposits was from wind-pollinated plants. Herein lies one of the limitations of pollen analysis. Pollen records are excellent capsules of information about which wind-pollinated species once lived in a region, yet they tell almost nothing about insect-pollinated plants, which of course were also present. Fortunately for scientists using fossil pollen to reconstruct ancient environments and trace the long evolution of plants, insect pollination began comparatively recently, around 100 million years ago.

Durability of pollen

Von Post's second point was that pollen and spores survived well in sediments. He was not the first to realize this, for scientists in the early 1800s had already reported that pollen and spores remained preserved in deposits long after most other organic components, such as seeds, leaves, wood, shell, and bones, had decayed. It was not until a century later, however, that the question of why the walls of pollen grains and spores were so durable began to be answered. Between 1928 and 1937 chemist Fritz Zetzsche of the University of Bern, Switzerland, and his co-workers made a series of important discoveries. They learned (1) that a unique chemical compound found in modern spores and pollen, which they named sporopollenin, was also present in spores and pollen millions of years old; (2) that sporopollenin is so durable because it resists destruction by acids; (3) that the walls of pollen and spores are composed of two main compounds, sporopollenin and cellulose; and (4) that the ratio of cellulose to sporopollenin in the walls of pollen and spores

99

varied greatly from one plant species to the next. Other scientists later refined Zetzsche's early conclusions and determined that sporopollenin is durable because it is composed of oxidative copolymers of carotenoid and carotenoid esters.

For decades sporopollenin was thought to be restricted only to the walls of spores and pollen. It is now known that a number of microscopic aquatic organisms, including dinoflagellates, acritarchs, and chitinozoans, as well as some species of algae, also produce acid-resistant outer walls that seem to contain sporopollenin.

Reliable identifiers of plant species

Von Post's third essential point addressed the reliability of using pollen and spore morphology as a key to the plants that produced them. Beginning in the late 1600s with the research of Grew and Malpighi and continuing for the next 200 years, many botanists studied the morphology of pollen and spores. Their combined efforts left a convincing record showing that pollen produced by each species is the same regardless of where the plant grows. Subsequent research revealed that minor size differences do occur within the pollen or spores of a single species, yet all grains are morphologically identical. Thus, for purposes of identification, the pollen of each species is as reliable as a human fingerprint.

Accurate indicators of habitat and change

The last two points made by von Post have also been proved correct. The first is obvious: plants occur in the greatest numbers in areas of their optimum habitat. Spruce trees, for example, proliferate on cold, alpine slopes, where few other trees can survive. Similarly, cacti are common in desert regions, where they are well adapted to very dry conditions.

Centuries of pollen studies reveal considerable variation among plant species in the shapes and sizes of their pollen grains. They also show convincingly that the grains produced by each species are morphologically identical regardless of where the plant grows and thus are as reliable for the purpose of identification as a human fingerprint. In the scanning electron micrograph below, pollen grains from several different plants are compared: (a) phlox, (b) rooster comb, (c) chrysanthemum, (d and e) two species of smartweed, and (f) geranium.

Martha Cooper—Peter Arnold, Inc.

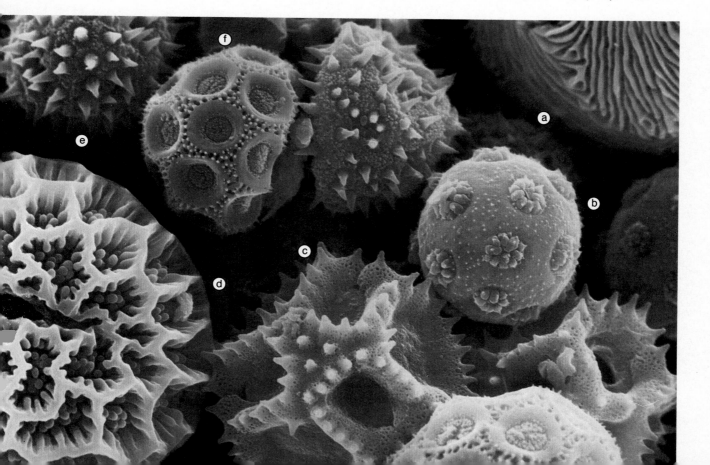

In gross terms, the greater the density of a given plant in a region, the greater the abundance of that plant's pollen in the soils of the same region. Although a number of variables prevent a one-to-one correlation from being exactly correct, it is still useful as a general rule.

The final point made by von Post was that fossil pollen is an accurate reflection of the changes in regional vegetation. Today scientists know that many factors determine if the pollen found at a given locale is an accurate reflection of even the wind-pollinated plants living within a 50–100-kilometer radius of the site. Such factors as pollen production, the speed at which different pollen types fall to the ground, selective decay of some pollen types over others, and the potential recycling of previously deposited pollen are just a few of the concerns that must be addressed. In spite of these problems, von Post's original conclusion is still basically correct. In many regions of the world, and especially in the region of central Sweden where he conducted his initial study, the pollen that falls to the ground is a reliable indication of the wind-pollinated plants living within a comparatively small radius.

In looking back, it is apparent that what separated von Post's approach from previous studies was his use of mathematics. Von Post developed a way to quantify the percentages of each pollen type present and then compare the changes in fossil pollen percentages from one time period to the next. From this simple beginning developed the field of pollen analysis.

Modern palynologists know much more about pollen than was even dreamed about in the early 1900s. Microscopes are more powerful, and some, like the electron microscope, allow study of the way pollen grains are formed and develop. Computers enable scientists to test in seconds ideas and theories about fossil pollen data that once would have taken months or years to calculate. Most importantly, the applications of pollen studies have reached far beyond the use first proposed by von Post.

Pollen and petroleum exploration

Economically, one of the most important applications of palynology is in the field of petroleum geology. In the first third of the 20th century,

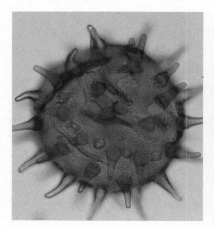
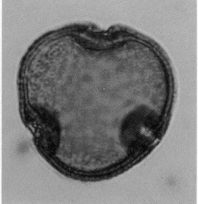

The distinctive shapes of pollen grains are easily studied under the ordinary light microscope; shown are stained single grains of the American linden (left) and a species of hibiscus (far left). The visible outer layer of the pollen grain is an extremely durable substance that can remain preserved in sediments for millions of years.

Photos, Vaughn M. Bryant, Jr.

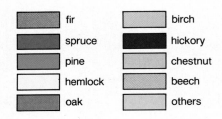

fir		birch	
spruce		hickory	
pine		chestnut	
hemlock		beech	
oak		others	

In many parts of the world, the pollen found at a given locale is a reliable indicator of the wind-pollinated plants living within a comparatively small radius. Variation in the fossil pollen record at that locale accurately reflects the changes in local vegetation and, by inference, in climate. In the example diagramed, sediment taken from a lake bottom (top) will be found to contain pollen from various tree species in the region. If a vertical core through several layers is examined, the relative amount of pollen from each species at each layer will vary. The width of each colored area at a particular depth in the diagram reflects the proportion of pollen collected from one tree species compared with the total; a percentage scale is added at the top. From the types and amounts of pollen found at each level, palynologists can infer the vegetation and thus the general climatic conditions that prevailed when the pollen was deposited in the lake. By extension, the same analysis can be applied to the pollen in the sediments of an extinct lake (bottom).

Adapted from "Radiocarbon Dating," Edward S. Deevey, Jr. Copyright © February 1952 by Scientific American, Inc. All rights reserved.

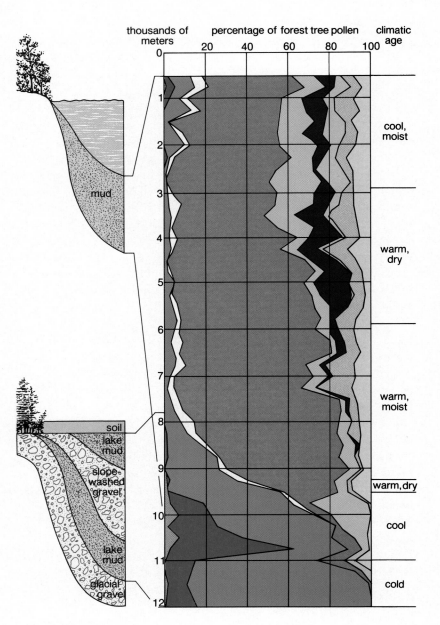

petroleum exploration concentrated on the recovery of oil and gas from shallow deposits. In many cases drilling was based on a knowledge that oil and gas are lighter than water and tend to flow upward through sediments until they reach an impervious layer. Potential underground sources were identified by surface and exposed geologic features that revealed such structures as faults, salt domes, and anticlines. Correlations of oil-bearing zones in rock strata were based on the similarities and differences from one zone to the next in the composition of the strata and the types of tiny silicate-walled or silicate-shelled sea organisms that are present as fossils in the rock. These approaches worked fairly well until the mid-1930s, when companies began drilling deeper wells and exploring new regions.

102

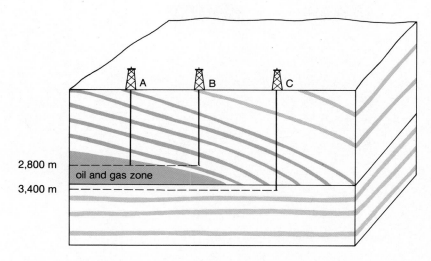

Geologists working for the Royal Dutch/Shell Corp. were among the first to encounter problems while exploring for petroleum in Mexico. They soon discovered that they were unable to use previous methods to identify the Mexican subsurface stratigraphy needed to locate oil and gas deposits. Out of frustration one of the Shell geologists, T. F. Grimsdale, suggested using fossil pollen as stratigraphic indicators for the Mexican deposits. Subsequent attempts to use fossil pollen for stratigraphic correlation at oil-well sites in Mexico, Venezuela, and Colombia proved useful and led Shell to become the first petroleum company to incorporate pollen analysis as one of its basic exploration techniques.

In the late 1940s and early 1950s, oil companies conducted a frantic search for palynologists. Large sums of money were poured into the few academic centers that trained palynologists. Stratigraphers already employed by oil companies were sent back to college to be retrained as palynologists, and every new graduate in palynology was guaranteed a job with the petroleum industry. Meanwhile, at the many new petroleum research centers, money was being spent to develop local, regional, and worldwide pollen guides for the different geologic time periods ranging from the present Cenozoic to the Paleozoic, which began more than a half billion years ago. Because of the highly competitive nature of the petroleum industry, a cloud of secrecy soon covered their pollen studies, resulting in much repetition. Today, more than 50 years after Grimsdale first suggested using fossil pollen data in petroleum exploration, few petroleum companies would feel comfortable without access to pollen data. Also, for obvious reasons, most petroleum companies still do not allow their palynologists to publish company research data or give lectures about their new pollen discoveries.

Applications in archaeology

Like the petroleum industry, the field of archaeology was slow to realize the potential value of pollen data. During the first part of the 1900s, before the development of radiocarbon dating, a few European archaeologists used fossil pollen as a dating tool. By correlating similarities in the

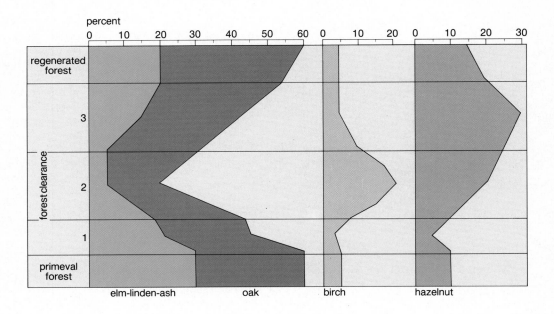

percent

regenerated forest

3

forest clearance

2

1

primeval forest

elm-linden-ash   oak   birch   hazelnut

Diagram (above and opposite page) shows the way in which fossil pollen collected in cores from a Danish bog records the effects of the introduction of agriculture into Denmark thousands of years ago. This pollen record, from a period between 2 500 and 2 300 BC, is almost identical to one found in bog sediments at the Barkaer site dating from 4 000 BC. The width of each colored area in the diagram represents the percentage of pollen from one species or a group of species compared with the total, with scales given at the top. Tree species appear on the left, while the category of herbaceous plants, with a breakdown, appears on the right. In the older, primeval forest elm, linden, and ash together accounted for 30% of the pollen, oak 30%, birch 5%, and hazelnut 10%. During three successive stages of forest clearance, the pollen distribution changed. (Opposite page, bottom) Researchers take core samples from the Boriack bog in Texas for pollen analysis and other studies.

fossil pollen record of archaeological sites with well-dated pollen records of nearby bog and lake deposits, archaeologists were sometimes able to date specific events in the past. Successful examples of this early work include the dating of an 18-meter (60-foot) boat found in a Danish peat bog at about 2,400 years old, the dating of an early Polish village to about 700 BC, and the dating of a man buried in a Danish peat bog to about 2,000 years ago. Beyond this type of application, however, little was done to apply pollen data to archaeology.

Johannes Iversen, a Danish geologist, became the "Grimsdale of archaeology," awakening the discipline to the potential value of pollen studies as Grimsdale had done for the petroleum industry. In 1941 Iversen was asked for help by Peter Glob, an archaeologist who for several years had been excavating an area of ancient human habitation in northern Denmark called the Barkaer site. Like other archaeologists of that time, Glob suspected that groups of people with a knowledge of farming and animal husbandry had migrated into Denmark from the south and had introduced these new ideas to others living in the region. Danish archaeological records indicated that soon after the migrant farmers arrived, other cultures living in northern Europe quickly converted from hunting and gathering to agriculture and animal domestication. The problem facing Glob was how to pinpoint when and in what way this change to farming had occurred.

Today the Barkaer site is located on a low hill, but it once had been a small island. As the land rose, the lake surrounding the island became increasingly shallow, finally filling in to become a bog. By examining fossil pollen collected in core samples from the bog, Iversen determined how the local transformation from hunting and gathering to agriculture had occurred and also dated the change. He based his conclusions on several observations. First, the pollen record around 4000 BC showed a

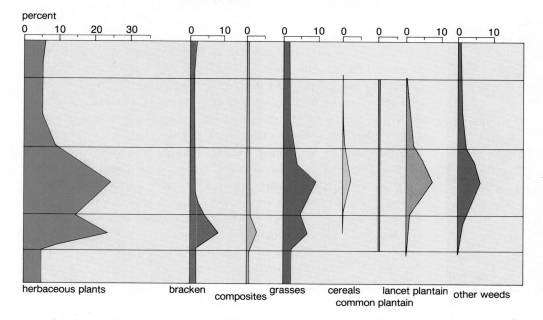

percent

herbaceous plants · bracken · composites · grasses · cereals · common plantain · lancet plantain · other weeds

sudden decline in pollen from elm and other trees, indicating that the nearby forest had been felled quickly to prepare the area for planting. Second, the appearance of numerous microscopic flecks of charcoal in the same peat deposits suggested that the fallen trees and brush had been burned to clear the land. And third, the record showed that immediately after the forest disappeared, fossil pollen from domestic cereal crops and pasture plants such as clover appeared—convincing evidence that the inhabitants were now farming and raising domestic animals. Iversen dated the precise time of these events by comparing the fossil pollen record of the Barkaer site with other nearby fossil pollen chronologies that already had been dated.

Iversen's dramatic discoveries were impressive. Even so, it was not until the 1960s that pollen studies were conducted with any degree of

Bonfire Shelter (top) in southwestern Texas, although far south of the normal prehistoric grazing range of bison, is famous for being the southernmost site in North America where prehistoric hunters had driven large bison herds off cliff edges to their death. Studies of fossil pollen collected from deposits at Bonfire Shelter and nearby sites helped establish that climatic conditions favored such a southerly presence of bison herds only twice in the past 12,000 years, at times that coincided with two groups of killing drives separated by 7,500 years. Bison skeleton (above) lies in one of the bone beds unearthed at Bonfire Shelter.

ing flowers as food. Palynologists can make such statements with some confidence because experiments show that eating either flowers or large quantities of honey is the only way that sizable amounts of pollen from insect-pollinated plants can enter the digestive system. Honey, however, does not seem a likely source in ancient Texas since honeybees were not introduced into the Americas until the 1600s.

Some modern health-food enthusiasts believe the ancients recognized something that has since been forgotten: the food value and health benefits of flowers and pollen. Today selling pollen has become a big business. In Sweden and other countries, stores offer vitamins, toothpaste, face cream, lipstick, and even pet food made from pollen; athletes eat pollen daily in the belief that it gives them added strength; and elderly people regularly down pollen pills with their meals in hopes of staving off the effects of old age. Unfortunately, scientific tests conducted at Louisiana State University by Ralph Stehen have shown that athletes on high-pollen diets perform no better than others. Furthermore, his studies indicate that although pollen grains are rich in vitamins and proteins, they are no better than a healthful diet of other natural foods.

Like the discoveries made by Iversen at the Barkaer site in Denmark, pollen records from deposits at Bonfire Shelter and Devil's Mouth site, both located in southwestern Texas, solved puzzling archaeological questions. Bonfire Shelter is a unique site. Although it is located hundreds of kilometers south of the Great Plains and the normal prehistoric grazing range of bison, it is famous for being the southernmost site in North America where prehistoric hunters had driven large herds of bison over cliffs to their death.

When excavated, Bonfire Shelter presented a problem. The site's deposits contained only two discrete zones of fossil bison bones, and within

108

each zone evidence showed that at least three separate killing drives had taken place within a 50–100-year period. Between the earlier zone, dating from the Paleo Indian period around 10,000 years ago, and the second zone, dating from about 2,500 years ago, the site was not used or occupied by prehistoric humans. Why, archaeologists asked, was the site used for killing bison only for two short periods and not for the 7,500 years in between?

Fossil pollen studies from deposits in Bonfire Shelter and nearby sites revealed that over the past 12,000 years climatic conditions in south-western Texas favored a maximum amount of grass cover only twice. In other words, local grazing conditions were ideally suited for supporting large bison herds only during two brief intervals in that time, and those intervals coincided with the two zones of bison bones at Bonfire Shelter. The absence of continuing signs of human presence suggests that the bison were stampeded to their death by skilled hunters who probably did not even live in the area. Archaeologists now believe that northern hunters followed the grazing bison herds south and twice discovered that Bonfire Shelter was an ideal location for a bison drive.

During early excavations at Devil's Mouth site, located only 100 kilometers southeast of Bonfire Shelter, the lack of suitable materials made it impossible to carry out accurate radiocarbon dating of the upper strata at the site. Instead, fossil pollen in the upper zones was compared with the fossil pollen record of nearby Bonfire Shelter. By matching similarities in the two pollen records, archaeologists succeeded in dating strata 8 and 9 at the Devil's Mouth site to about 1000 BC on the basis of well-dated strata at Bonfire Shelter. Years later, new excavations at Devil's Mouth uncovered charcoal deposits, which could be dated by the radiocarbon method, in the upper levels of the site. The radiocarbon date from the bottom of stratum 9 was 850 BC and fell within 150 years of the date previously assigned by pollen analysis. Fossil pollen cross dating of archaeological sites does not always work this well, but when it does it is impressive.

Storage vessels called amphoras (below) that are gathered from sunken wrecks of ancient ships often contain pollen in their bottom sediments. Once analyzed, the pollen can yield clues as to the types of cargoes—wine, grapes, dates, or spices, for example—that the ships traded. Similarly, pollen found in sediments taken from the bilge area of a sunken ship (below left) can help identify the ship's home port or its ports of call; in some cases the pollen may suggest what kinds of loose cargo—hay, wood, fruit, or other plant products—the ship carried. The bilge was commonly used as the ship's garbage dump and consequently is often rich in pollen. Photos are of the Kyrenia shipwreck (fourth century BC) off the north coast of Cyprus.

Photos, M. L. Katzev, Institute of Nautical Archaeology

Soil from a boot is collected at a police crime laboratory. Analysis of the pollen mixture in the sample may yield information about the past or present whereabouts of a criminal or victim.

New ways to use pollen data continue to be developed. Within the last decade underwater archaeologists have begun searching the sunken wrecks of ancient Greek, Roman, and Phoenician ships in the Mediterranean Sea for traces of old pollen in amphoras and other cargo containers that once carried wines, spices, cereal grains, and other trade goods. Like the pollen found in the pottery at American Pueblo sites, pollen from underwater storage containers may hold the only clues yet remaining as to the types of ancient cargoes being shipped. Also, by taking pollen trapped along the inside bilge area of a sunken ship and comparing it with collections of airborne pollen gathered from various ports, investigators can determine the ship's home port.

Palynologic detective work

Detectives and palynologists have at least two things in common: both search for clues, and occasionally both are involved in solving crimes. Many police agencies have yet to learn that fossil pollen can provide valuable clues in criminal cases. Although numerous examples exist, one of the best known comes from Austria, where pollen data helped solve a murder case in 1959.

A man on a journey down the Danube River disappeared near Vienna, but his body could not be found. Another man, with a motive for killing him, was arrested and charged with murder. Without a confession or a body, however, the prosecutor's case seemed hopeless. As the investigation proceeded, mud found on a pair of the defendant's shoes was given to palynologist Wilhelm Klaus of the University of Vienna for analysis. Klaus determined that the mud contained spruce, willow, and alder pollen as well as a fossil hickory pollen grain 20 million years old from exposed Miocene-age deposits. Only one small area 20 kilometers (12 miles) north of Vienna along the Danube Valley has soils that contain this mixture of pollen. When confronted with the identity of this location, the shocked defendant confessed his crime and showed authorities where he had buried the body, which indeed was in the region pinpointed by Klaus.

In recent years pollen analysis has been enlisted to foil dishonest honey producers. As part of the federal farm-subsidy program, the USDA buys U.S.-produced honey at a fixed price, which is higher than the open-market value of imported honey. The purpose is to encourage American farmers to raise honeybees needed for proper pollination of fruit and vegetable crops. Occasionally, a honey producer will buy tons of foreign honey and attempt to resell it to the federal government as domestic honey. This is where palynologic detective work becomes important.

Honeybees collect nectar and pollen and use both to make honey. Since their collecting relies on local plants, the pollen in the honey becomes a perfect key to the geographic region where the hive is located. Furthermore, attempts to "doctor" foreign honey with domestic pollen types will not mask the true origin of the honey, because it is the pollen already present in the honey that reveals its origin. Companies that market honey for commercial sale also conduct pollen tests to make sure that the beekeepers who supply their clover honey or orange blossom

110

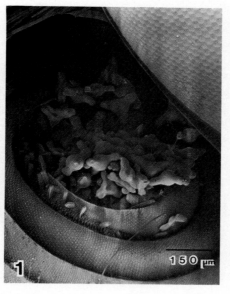

Every year large numbers of adult moths of the agriculturally destructive bollworm (far left) feed on nectar and pollen at distant breeding areas before traveling to the central and southeastern U.S. to mate and lay eggs. By studying the pollen stuck to the moths' bodies, palynologists can locate their outside breeding areas and identify the plants they use for food—information important to developing control measures. Adherent pollen grains evident in the scanning electron micrograph of the proboscis of a bollworm moth (left) reveal that the moth had been feeding on flowers of the evening primrose.

(Left) Runk/Schoenberger—Grant Heilman Photography, Inc.; (right) Mike Pendleton, Texas A&M University, College Station

honey are providing a product that really does come from clover plants or orange blossoms.

Pollen detective work is also part of a current plan to reduce the crop damage done by the bollworm (*Heliothis zea*). Each spring millions of adult bollworm moths arrive in the central and southeastern U.S. from outside breeding areas. The adults feed on nectar and pollen before mating and laying eggs. After the eggs hatch, the larval stage destroys millions of dollars' worth of cotton, corn, and soybeans. Insecticides are expensive to use and ecologically unsafe and have not been effective in controlling the migrations of this pest.

Palynologists are helping to find another approach to controlling the bollworm. By capturing adults and identifying the pollen stuck to their bodies, they are learning what plants the moths use for food and where many of their distant breeding areas are located. Their work has revealed, for example, that moths arriving in Arkansas carry pollen from plants native only to southern Texas and northern Mexico, suggesting a migration route nearly 1,600 kilometers (1,000 miles) long. Also, by knowing what plants the moths use as food, scientists hope to find ways to trap the adults at their feeding sources.

A paean for pollen

Even though pollen is responsible for the sneezes and watery eyes of hay fever season, there are reasons to be grateful. Without its ubiquitous presence there would probably be less gasoline for transportation and less oil and natural gas for home heating and electrical generation. Scientists would be more in doubt about the sequence of climatic changes that the Earth has experienced and would know much less about the diets of prehistoric cultures. Humankind would also be more ignorant about the origins and spread of agriculture. In short, without pollen, the world would likely be a poorer place.

ISLANDS

Natural Laboratories for Biologists

by Kenneth L. Crowell

How have flightless mammals made their way to some islands and not others, and why do they flourish on some and decline on others? Biologists, using the new discipline of island biogeography, are seeking the answers to these and other questions.

Why are there no native mammals on oceanic islands such as Bermuda or the Hawaiian Islands? Why does Ireland lack not only snakes but most land mammals? Why does Newfoundland have only one-third as many mammal species as the smaller Canadian province of New Brunswick or the U.S. state of Maine? Why have the national parks of western North America steadily lost species since their founding? These are all questions that have been addressed by the discipline of island biogeography.

Because islands have fewer species than comparable areas on mainlands, they can serve as natural laboratories in which to study such processes as population growth and regulation, competition between species, predator-prey interactions, and speciation. Indeed, the unique faunas of islands helped Charles Darwin and his contemporary Alfred Wallace formulate their theory of natural selection.

The land masses of the Earth can be divided into three classes: continents; continental or landbridge islands, which were once connected to a continent; and oceanic islands, which have always been isolated. By comparing the number and kinds of species on these different land masses, biogeographers can make inferences about how animals reach islands and how they respond to the insular environment. The best-known studies of island life have dealt with birds, but because their powers of dispersal are so limited, mammals demonstrate the complementary processes of colonization and extinction much more dramatically than do plants, insects, and birds.

Picture a volcano rising out of the sea. How soon will life appear on it? This natural experiment has taken place during the past century with the eruption of Krakatoa 21 kilometers (13 miles) off the coast of Java in the South Pacific in 1883. After just three years 11 species of ferns and 15 flowering plants had become established on Krakatoa, and after 50 years there were not only 271 plant species but also 7 kinds of reptiles (1 crocodile, a python, and 5 lizards), 28 birds, 3 species of bats, and a rat. From studies of other Philippine islands of a similar size, ten species of terrestrial mammals can be expected; so however they cross the water barrier, additional animal species will certainly continue to colonize Krakatoa until its ark is full.

KENNETH L. CROWELL is a Professor of Biology at St. Lawrence University, Canton, New York.

(Overleaf) Illustration by John Zielinski

113

Now imagine a small peninsula near Borneo in Southeast Asia during the late Pleistocene Epoch (ended 10,000 years ago), when sea levels were much lower than at present. Slowly the sea rises as the glaciers and polar ice caps melt. One day the peninsula becomes an island. On that day some 50 species of mammals inhabit the area. At first the water is very shallow, and a tiger or a herd of elephants leave for the mainland, but some species avoid the water and others are unaware of their increasing isolation. Noah's Ark not withstanding, two of a kind is not enough, and over the years most species die out. Large carnivores like the leopard cannot find sufficient prey; ungulates (hoofed animals) such as the rhinoceros may find the shrinking habitat inadequate. Eventually, through selective extinction, the mammal species on the island become a sustainable and balanced community consisting of half a dozen kinds of rodents and some combination of a shrew, tarsier, monkey, or perhaps a deer.

How different are the histories of these two islands. Nevertheless, biogeographers believe that, given sufficient time and stable environmental conditions, oceanic and landbridge islands of equal area will attain the same number of species.

114

Crossing the water barrier

The first question most people ask is how animals get to islands. Clearly wings are a big advantage, and bats, like birds, are well represented on islands—even on such isolated ones as Bermuda, Hawaii, and New Zealand, which lack other native mammals. Nonetheless, the fact that nonflying mammals do occur on oceanic islands is incontrovertible evidence that they do cross water barriers. Natural modes of immigration include both the active means of swimming and crossing ice bridges and passive waif dispersal—rafting on vegetation or ice floes.

Many mammals reach islands by swimming. Aquatic species such as the North American beaver, the mink, and the river otter are found on islands as far as 40 kilometers (25 miles) offshore. White-tailed deer and moose are frequently observed swimming between the coastal islands of Maine—one deer swam more than 11 kilometers (7 miles) across open water. The many Bear Islands off the coast of Maine imply that the black bear once traveled freely between them. Likewise, deer, elephants, and hippos were once found on islands in the Mediterranean Sea and off the coast of Japan.

Mice and shrews are common on small coastal islands. Indeed, mice have been observed swimming distances of almost one kilometer (0.6 mile) between islands in the frigid waters of Labrador. Keeping warm is a problem—just as it is for humans swimming the English Channel, and so water temperature is a factor limiting the distance. Because small objects have a greater surface area relative to their mass, small mammals lose heat faster. Thus, Finnish workers found that larger species of shrews were able to reach more distant islands in lakes.

There is, however, another method that enables small animals to traverse longer distances—rafting. Mammalogists at the University of British Columbia proposed that rafts of timber formed by landslides on the rugged coast might transport animals to islands. On Cape Breton

Islands contain fewer species of animals than comparable areas on mainlands and therefore serve as natural laboratories in which to study such processes as population growth, competition between species, and interactions between predators and their prey. On the opposite page is Moorea in the Society Islands of the South Pacific.

White-tailed deer are among the many kinds of flightless mammals that reach islands by swimming.

Leonard Lee Rue III—Animals Animals

Kenneth L. Crowell

Island in the Gulf of St. Lawrence, the late Austin Cameron of McGill University, Montreal, observed "islands . . . of vegetated soil carried seaward on floating ice" when overhanging bluffs gave way during spring thawing. He attributed the presence of small mammals on such isolated islands as Anticosti and Newfoundland to this process. The most impressive evidence for the efficacy of rafting is the presence of several forms of rice rat (many now extinct) on the Galápagos, some 1,000 kilometers (600 miles) off the coast of Ecuador.

In northern regions ice rafts and ice bridges provide another means of dispersal. The arrivals of Arctic foxes and polar bears on the northeastern coast of Newfoundland by ice floe have been witnessed, and it is presumed that the Arctic hare, ermine, and wolf also reached the island in this way. Strong currents in the 19-kilometer (12-mile) Strait of Belle Isle, which separates Newfoundland from the Ungava Peninsula of Quebec, prevent the formation of an ice bridge, but in the sheltered bays of coastal Maine ice bridges several kilometers wide form every decade or two, allowing such species as the red fox to cross to the larger

M. R. Rosenzweig

Mammals can reach islands by rafting on ice floes (opposite page, top). Highway bridge from the mainland to Deer Isle in Maine (left) allowed the island to be colonized by skunks, raccoons, and porcupines.

islands. In the Thousand Island region of the St. Lawrence River between New York State and Ontario, Mark Lomolino, now at the University of Northern Arizona, Flagstaff, tracked mammals on ice and found that in the spring as many as 13 species, including small shrews, moles, and rodents, traveled distances of more than one kilometer. Again the physiology of the animals was a limiting factor, and Lomolino found that the larger species, such as coyotes and deer, traveled farther.

Circumstantial evidence for the importance of swimming and crossing ice bridges is provided by the uniform absence of certain species from islands. Among animals that shun water—at least the cold water of the North Atlantic—and are not found on islands are the porcupine, the gray squirrel, and, surprisingly, the raccoon. Hibernating species such as the woodchuck, the striped skunk, and the eastern chipmunk are also absent from all but the least isolated of the islands of eastern North America, suggesting that their winter sleep prevents the use of ice bridges. Highway bridges constructed in this century to the large Maine islands have allowed colonization by the porcupine, the skunk, and the raccoon. This

The Arctic fox and polar bear (opposite page, bottom) have been observed rafting to the northeastern coast of the island of Newfoundland on ice floes, and researchers believe that the Arctic hare and wolf (below) arrived at the island in the same way.

(Opposite page, left) E. R. Degginger—Animals Animals; (right) Sven Gillsater—Bruce Coleman Inc.; (this page) photos, Bruce Coleman Inc.; (left) F. Erize; (right) Jack Couffer

The meadow vole is the most common mammal on the islands of eastern North America. It is a proficient swimmer, can live in a wide variety of habitats, and can produce a large litter every few weeks.

demonstrates that, once there, those species can multiply on islands, but they will not cross the water barrier by either swimming or crossing ice.

Usually an animal community consists of several trophic levels: herbivores such as rodents, rabbits, and hoofed grazers; carnivores of several sizes; and insectivores, which prey on invertebrates. By contrast, because colonization of islands is such a chancy process, the faunas of oceanic islands are unbalanced. For example, the island of Anticosti in the Gulf of St. Lawrence has only one mouse and five carnivores, presumably those most able to take advantage of opportunities for dispersal. Only four orders of land mammals have been recorded from the entire West Indies: insectivores, rodents, edentates (sloths, armadillos, and anteaters), and primates—and the latter two categories are now extinct. There are no marsupials, rabbits, carnivores, or ungulates, though these are all represented on the nearby mainland.

The kinds of animals found on isolated islands are primarily determined by their capacity for colonization. (Strictly speaking, immigration is the arrival of a new species, while colonization implies subsequent success of the population.) Although large mammals such as bears, deer, elephants, and hippos are found in several groups of offshore islands, rodents predominate in the impoverished faunas of distant oceanic islands. Not only are rodents good dispersers but they also appear to be superbly adapted to setting up housekeeping on arrival. Being herbivores—or indeed, omnivores—rodents have a broad diet and a prodigious capacity to reproduce. Thus, a few colonists, or perhaps even one pregnant female, can rapidly populate an island. For example, the meadow vole, the most common mammal on the islands of eastern North America, is a proficient swimmer, occupies a wide range of habitats, and can produce a large litter every few weeks.

Where distances between islands and the mainland are short, immigration rates are relatively high, and the number of species will depend on the proximity to the mainland. Currents surely influence direction and distance in both swimming and waif dispersal, and other islands often serve as stepping-stones from source areas. Thus, elephants once island-hopped 320 kilometers (200 miles) across the Bay of Bengal.

The rate of colonization can sometimes be determined from historic records. Kenneth Crowell of St. Lawrence University, Canton, New York, documented rates at which new species became established during the past 100 years on coastal islands of Maine, where distances ranged from about 100 meters to 8 kilometers (330 feet to 5 miles). For such species as the white-footed mouse, the beaver, the white-tailed deer, the black bear, and the red fox, the average rate was one species every 50 years. The minimum rate of colonization for longer time periods can be estimated by dividing the number of known native species, including extinct forms documented by fossils, by the age of the island. Thus, the 12 land mammals native to Newfoundland can have arrived there only after deglaciation 12,000 years ago, making the mean colonization rate about one species per 1,000 years. In the more isolated islands in the West Indies and the Philippines, which are tens of millions of years old,

118

colonization rates have been estimated to be only one every 250,000 to 1.5 million years. Because colonization of remote islands is so rare, the evolution of new species makes a major contribution to their diversity.

Landbridge islands

More than 100 years ago Alfred R. Wallace observed that many groups of mammals found in southeastern Asia and the islands of Borneo, Sumatra, and Java were not found on the islands to the east. The line demarcating the two regions is now known as Wallace's Line; it separates the islands of the continental shelf from the oceanic Philippines. Indeed, 12 families of mammals and most of the species belonging to 15 others do not cross the line. In his classic book, *The Malay Archipelago,* Wallace wrote that the mammals of the Sunda (continental) shelf provide "evidence of a very striking character that these great islands must once have formed a part of the continent, and could only have been separated at a very recent geologic epoch." In fact, landbridge islands owe their existence primarily to the worldwide rise in sea levels since the last glaciation, when sea level was 115 meters (365 feet) lower than at present.

In contrast to oceanic islands, which must rely on dispersal across the water barrier, landbridge islands receive a legacy of species from their past. That is, as part of the mainland before they were isolated by rising sea levels or crustal movements, these islands possessed as many species as any comparable continental area. In the Gulf of St. Lawrence, Cape Breton and Prince Edward islands lie close to mainland Nova Scotia and were connected to it in postglacial times. Mainland Nova Scotia has 38

Wallace's Line and Weber's Line mark the limits of habitation of animals on, respectively, the Asian and Australian-New Guinea continental shelves. Thomas Huxley later added a correction to the northern end of Wallace's Line. Between the lines lie oceanic islands that have not had land bridges for the past 150,000 years.

Adapted from *Island Life* by Sherwin Carlquist; copyright © Sherwin Carlquist, The Natural History Press, Garden City, N.Y.

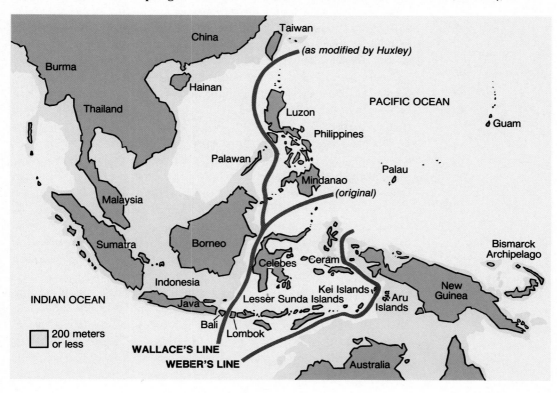

kinds of terrestrial mammals, and these landbridge islands support 24 and 31 species, respectively. By contrast, the much larger oceanic island of Newfoundland has only 12 native mammals. Similarly, the West Indian landbridge island of Tobago has nine living nonflying mammal species, while most of the oceanic Lesser Antillean islands of the West Indies have none.

The animal populations of landbridge islands are more diverse than the small and unbalanced assemblages of oceanic islands. For example, the animals native to Ireland include a frog, a salamander, and 11 species of mammals—including the hedgehog, a shrew, the Arctic hare, the red deer, and the stoat. This is far too extensive and balanced a community to be accounted for by waif dispersal, and Ireland must therefore have been connected to Britain by a landbridge in early postglacial times. The fact that Ireland possesses only 40% as many vertebrate species as Britain may indicate that it was cut off from Britain before the latter was severed from continental Europe.

The distribution of the larger animals is usually limited by island size. On the Sunda shelf of Malaysia, the number of carnivore species is related to island size, with tigers, leopards, bears, and wild dogs restricted to the largest islands and elephants, rhinoceroses, and tapirs absent from all but the three largest islands (Borneo, Sumatra, and Java). Similarly, of approximately 25 islands in the Gulf of California, only the four largest landbridge islands are inhabited by the jackrabbit, the deer, the coyote, and the gray fox. This scarcity of large mammals on islands is primarily a result of their larger home ranges. Large animals require more energy and, therefore, greater living space than do small ones; this is especially so for carnivores at the top of the food chain. Larger home ranges demand a larger area to support a viable population, and larger areas also offer a greater variety of habitats. Thus, there is a direct relationship between the size of an island and the number of species it supports. A number of lines of evidence indicate that the primary reason for this is the selective extinction over time of large and specialized species from smaller landbridge islands.

This phenomenon of area-based extinction has important implications for conservation biology. It was first described by James H. Brown of the University of New Mexico, who was not studying islands at all but was studying the mountains of the southwestern United States. These forest-clad mountains of the Basin and Range region are separated by inhospitable desert, making them analogous to islands. Brown observed that the smaller ranges boast fewer species and deduced that these are populations that have been isolated there since the late Pleistocene Epoch (10,000–15,000 years ago), when the climate was cooler and wetter. Since that time each range has lost extinction-prone species (those with larger body size, especially carnivores) just as on the landbridge islands discussed above. Bruce Patterson of the Field Museum of Natural History in Chicago noticed that if the mountains are ranked in order of decreasing area, species drop out in a predictable order, and he found the same to hold for true landbridge islands such as those of the Gulf of California.

Insular equilibrium theory

Ecologists have long recognized that there is a direct relationship between number of species and area, and this holds for whole continents as well as mountains and islands. E. O. Wilson of Harvard University and the late Robert MacArthur of Princeton University recognized the complementary roles of colonization and extinction in the formulation of their landmark insular equilibrium theory. This theory predicts that because small islands will have higher rates of extinction than large ones, they will support fewer species, and because distant islands will have lower rates of colonization than less isolated ones, these will also have fewer species. At some point the rates of colonization and extinction will become equal, and the number of species will stabilize. Over time the particular species on an island may vary but, given stable conditions, the number of species will remain approximately constant.

The significance of this theory is that it provides a dynamic explanation for the species-area effect and a new approach for studying the distribution of plants and animals. Like all good theories, both its power and its shortcomings lie in its simplicity. By exploring situations in which the theory's assumptions are violated or its predictions fail, ecologists have broadened their understanding of the processes controlling species diversity.

It is now apparent that immigration plays a dominant role in determining the composition of oceanic islands, whereas extinction predominates on landbridge islands. Because mammals are not able to disperse easily, most oceanic islands are depauperate—their ark is not yet full—while, because of their recent origin, landbridge islands may still be supersaturated with species. Furthermore, for mammals the processes of colonization and extinction require very long periods of time. Therefore, environmental conditions may well change before equilibrium is attained. That is, climatic or geologic changes may alter the rules before the game is over; therefore, mammals may really achieve equilibrium only on small coastal islands.

Evolution and relict species

Mammals have not undergone the impressive evolution exhibited by the birds, plants, and insects of the Hawaiian or Galápagos archipelagos. Nevertheless, mammalian speciation is still taking place on isolated islands, and subspecies or geographic races of mammals are recognized on islands throughout the world. Older or more isolated islands such as the Antilles and the Philippines often have their own endemic, or unique, species. For example, almost three-quarters of the mammals native to the Philippine island of Luzon are endemic. Such differentiation is more frequent on distant islands because there is less gene flow from populations from other areas. Indeed, on oceanic islands the rate of speciation may exceed the rate of colonization by new species.

How rapidly does evolution take place? By studying the house mouse on islands throughout the world, R. J. Berry of University College, London, found that populations only 40 years old were as distinct as those founded

For 22 islands near the eastern coast of North America there is a direct relationship between the size of the island and the number of species of animals that inhabit it.

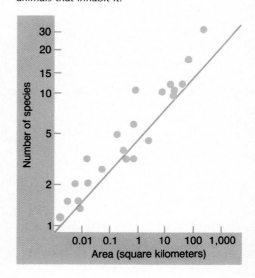

121

Tarsier (opposite page, top left) has disappeared from continents but persists on islands of southeastern Asia. The Virginia opossum (opposite page, top right) is a descendant of marsupials that inhabited South America before the emergence of the Central American landbridge less than ten million years ago. Ring-tailed lemur (opposite page, bottom) lives on Madagascar, the largest oceanic island in the world. There it occupies an environmental niche that on a continent would be filled by other animals.

(Opposite page, top left) Tierbilder Okapia, Frankfurt am Main; (top right) © Joe McDonald—Bruce Coleman Inc.; (bottom) Dale & Marian Zimmerman—Bruce Coleman Inc.

200 years ago. In northern latitudes distinct subspecies have evolved on islands that were formed after the last glaciation, 12,000 years ago, but the formation of entirely new species may require five to ten times that long. The primary cause of differentiation in insular populations appears to be "founder effect"—the fact that these populations are derived from only a few individuals endowed with a biased sample of genes.

Populations smaller than a few hundred individuals tend to lose genes randomly through the process of genetic drift. Many islands have such populations and thus serve as laboratories in which processes of population genetics and their relevance to the conservation of rare and endangered species can be studied.

The species-poor island community provides a major impetus for new adaptations. First there is release from the normal pressures of predation and competition between species. At the same time restricted space puts a premium on innovation. This is most often expressed as shifts in behavioral niches. For example, freshwater habitats are often scarce on islands. On some shrubby islands off the coast of Maine, the muskrat, a marsh species, has invaded upland habitats—apparently filling the niche of the absent rabbit. With time such behavioral adaptations may be accompanied by changes in the physical structure of the animals.

The most striking evolutionary change in insular mammals is change in size, first noted by J. Bristol Foster. He noted that on islands throughout the world small mammals, especially rodents, tend to become larger, while insular races of large species, which are apt to be grazers and carnivores, are generally smaller. To explain these widespread trends biologists argue that in the absence of the mammalian predators, small mammals may find large size advantageous in thwarting attacks by birds of prey. Moreover, very small animals are limited in their choice of foods, and so being slightly larger would allow individuals a more varied diet. This would be enhanced by the absence of close competitors in the impoverished insular fauna. Large animals, on the other hand, are limited by their total caloric intake and would find smaller size an advantage.

The now-extinct Pleistocene fauna of the islands of the Mediterranean

Among living species, the yellow-footed marsupial mouse of Australia most closely resembles the ancestral marsupials that managed to reach the continent, perhaps by land or possibly by crossing narrow channels of seawater. It exemplifies the speciation that continues to take place in relatively isolated areas.

Keith Gillett—Animals Animals

demonstrated both these trends in the form of giant rodents and dwarf elephants, hippos, and deer. According to P. Y. Sondaar of the Geological Institute in Utrecht, The Netherlands, there were "rabbit-sized mice, pony-sized elephants and pig-sized hippos." The smaller stature of the elephants and hippos reduced their requirements for food and home range, allowing more individuals to be supported. The absence of predators permitted shortening of the limbs, which facilitated the exploitation of upland habitats on the mountainous islands. These changes clearly occurred on the islands—not in the mainland ancestors—and the ability of these adapted animals to disperse was subsequently lost because their limbs were too short for swimming. The fact that similar changes took place on several islands indicates that natural selection was responding to similar environmental pressures or opportunities. In effect, these experiments yield similar results, indicating a common mechanism.

Many forms of life have persisted on islands after they disappeared from the continental mainstream. Tarsiers, nocturnal primates that feed on insects, are now restricted to the islands of southeastern Asia. Most landbridge islands are usually of relatively recent origin, but a few islands and the island continents are of ancient origin and may harbor "living fossils." For example, two species of solenodon, a shrewlike insectivore, are found only on the West Indian islands of Cuba and Hispaniola, but fossils reveal several species of solenodon and a closely related form from these islands, Puerto Rico, and others. In a controversial hypothesis Bruce MacFadden of the Florida State Museum proposed that these animals did not reach the islands by swimming or rafting but are descended from ancestors separated from mainland populations by tectonic movements of the Earth's crust. That is, they were already aboard protoislands when seafloor spreading decoupled the Caribbean and North American plates in the early Cenozoic Era, some 50 million years ago.

Ringed plover approaches its nest. Such ground-nesting birds are among the animals that have suffered from the introduction of mammals into their habitats, in this case from trampling by pigs and nest robbing by rats, stoats, ferrets, and mongooses.

In 24 national parks of western North America the number of species of nonflying mammals increases directly with the area of the park.

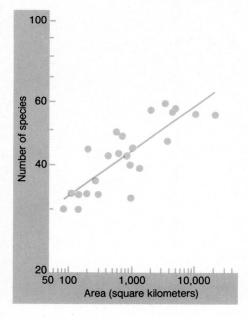

Certainly the presence of marsupials in Africa, Australia, and South America can be explained by continental drift after the breakup of the supercontinent Pangaea about 150 million years ago. Before the emergence of the Central American landbridge less than ten million years ago, the fauna of South America included an array of marsupials and archaic ungulates. The opportunistic Virginia opossum is one successful descendant from that epoch.

Isolated on Australia, marsupials radiated into niches that on most continents are occupied by placental mammals. This development of ecological equivalents in unrelated forms is called convergent evolution. Madagascar, which broke away from Africa more than 75 million years ago, is the largest oceanic island in the world. Its endemic families of lemurs and tenrecs (small insectivores) have also undergone limited convergent evolution.

It is ironic that islands, which have so few species to lose, have lost many of their unique forms to introductions of animals from other places. One-third of all extinctions taking place during historic times have been on islands, and most of these have been caused by introduced species. Although mammals are poorly represented on islands, their introduction has wreaked havoc on insular ecosystems. This occurs precisely because other forms of life, in the absence of mammals, have not evolved normal defense mechanisms against them. Many plants that lack spines and toxic compounds are exposed to overbrowsing by sheep, goats, rabbits, and deer. Ground-nesting birds are vulnerable to trampling by pigs and predation or nest robbing by rats, stoats, ferrets, and mongooses. In the West Indies the mongoose was first introduced to Jamaica in 1872 to control snakes in sugarcane plantations. It is now found on all but two of the major islands and has been responsible for the extermination of several species of endemic birds and lizards. The Spaniards often intro-

124

duced pigs and goats—and, inadvertently, rats—to uninhabited islands to provide food to shipwrecked sailors. Thus, populations of ground-nesting birds on Bermuda were decimated decades before its colonization by the British in 1612. Not all introductions were made by Europeans, however. During the past 2,000 years the Polynesians have carried cats, dogs, pigs, and the Polynesian rat throughout the South Pacific with disastrous consequences for the native animals. Unfortunately, most efforts to remove introduced species from islands have failed. When dealing with fragile island ecosystems, an ounce of prevention is truly worth a pound of cure.

Parks as islands

The work of Brown and Patterson on species loss in the isolated mountain ranges of the U.S. Southwest was especially significant because these are not real islands, yet deserts proved as formidable a barrier to dispersal as oceans. Island effects have also been described for such diverse systems as invertebrates in caves, fish in Canadian lakes, and birds in forest fragments throughout the world. In each case habitat "islands" are isolated by inhospitable environments.

William Newmark of the University of Michigan recently completed a study on the mammals of the parks of western North America. Fourteen parks located in seven states and two Canadian provinces ranged in area from 144 to 20,800 square kilometers (56 to 8,000 square miles) and contained from 33 to 59 species. Not surprisingly, there was a strong correlation between the number of species and park size, but Newmark was able to document extinctions occurring since the establishment of each park. On the average each park experienced one extinction every two years, but the rate of extinction was greater in smaller parks and also in older ones. The rarer species, those with lower population densities, were most likely to be lost. These were usually the larger or more specialized animals such as the mountain goat, cougar, and grizzly bear—precisely the ones most in need of protection. This confirmed the predictions of island biogeographers that parks are like landbridge islands—once isolated by human exploitation of surrounding areas, they will inevitably lose species.

These findings present serious challenges for the future management of even the largest nature reserves. Forms of human disturbance such as roads or clear-cuts (removals of trees) have been shown to inhibit the movement of mammals, thus reducing recolonization of isolated habitats; therefore, whenever possible, planners should enlarge wilderness areas and preserve natural corridors interconnecting protected areas. As parks become increasingly isolated by a matrix of agriculture, housing, or asphalt, park managers will have to be alert against the inroads of invasive species and disease. At the same time, they will also have to bolster populations of rare species through periodic reintroductions.

Islands are often regarded as areas with specialized, even unique, environments. Today, however, biologists return from them with valuable insights into the evolution and distribution of animals throughout the world.

125

Costa Rica's Fight for the Tropics

by Alvaro F. Umaña Quesada

A Latin-American country the size of West Virginia is attracting worldwide interest in its struggle to protect and manage its rich, but seriously threatened, biologic diversity.

Costa Rica's biologic diversity is outstanding in the Americas, as well as in the tropical world. The country's geographic location makes it a bridge between continents and between oceans; its rugged topography includes mountains of many sizes; and its land bears two different seasonal regimes that contribute to its extremely varied habitats. The combination of these elements gives Costa Rica's territory of 51,100 square kilometers, which is about three ten-thousandths of the Earth's surface, nearly 5% of all the plant and animal species known to exist on the planet. (A kilometer is about 0.62 mile; a square kilometer is about 0.39 square mile.) Partly for this reason the country is one of the largest centers of tropical research in the world.

Dense vegetation and abundant wildlife once covered nearly all of Costa Rica. Today only fragments of that richness remain. The transformation of the land reflects what has been taking place throughout the tropics—the destruction of habitats through deforestation for agriculture, livestock raising, and commercial logging, which in turn is leading to the loss of countless species of plants and animals. It is estimated that human activity accounts for the disappearance worldwide of more than 100,000 square kilometers of mature tropical forest each year.

Costa Rica has long been conscious of the need to protect its biologic heritage and of its potential for exerting a positive influence on the fate of the tropics. Its enjoyment of a stable democratic government for nearly a century, absence of a national army for the past 40 years, large middle class, and high literacy rate have fostered a sustained, aggressively led grass-roots conservation movement as well as an inviting climate for international participation and scientific research. Consequently, despite limited financial resources, the country has been in the forefront of tropical preservation efforts.

In recent years Costa Rica's conservation leaders have come to realize that biologic preservation programs in Central America cannot succeed

ALVARO F. UMAÑA QUESADA is Minister of Natural Resources, Energy, and Mines for the Republic of Costa Rica.

(Overleaf) Photograph, © Michael K. Nichols—Magnum

Like other tropical nations, Costa Rica has lost vast areas of its forests to agriculture, cattle raising, and lumbering. Despite legal protections, burning of the forest to make charcoal or to clear land for farming persists (top). Near Poás Volcano dairy fields stretch where a cloud forest once stood (right). Even after the forest is gone, ranching continues to degrade the land; the cattle eat saplings and dig up the soil with their hooves (opposite page, top).

in isolation from economic development. They foresee that expanding population in Costa Rica and its neighbors and other social pressures will drive people to exploit natural resources for farming and lumbering despite the most stringent legal protections. In response, Costa Rica is vigorously pursuing the concept of sustainable management within its protected areas and forest reserves, whereby conservation needs would be integrated with the livelihoods of the local residents. To help support this new approach of sustaining both people and nature, Costa Rica has recently reorganized its system of protected areas and embarked on a bold financial strategy for attracting funds.

Land, climate, and life

Costa Rica is located about 10° north of the Equator, in the Central American isthmus, between Nicaragua and Panama. Less than 150 kilometers separate the coastal plains, and the country lies on a long axis with a northwest-southeast direction. Complex volcanic and sedimentary mountain ranges that rise nearly four kilometers above sea level also lie along this axis. The volcanic mountain ranges of the north meet with the uplift ranges of the south in a Valle Central that is home to about half of the country's 2.7 million people and includes the national capital of San José.

Tectonic plate movements have generated the geologic history of Costa Rica, whose rocks are very young. The region emerged as a result of the parting of the North and South American plates. Interaction between several Pacific plates and the Caribbean Plate led to the uplifting of most of the country, most likely during the Miocene Epoch (between 7 million and 26 million years ago). The configuration of Central America

Photos, Oxford Scientific Films; (top) D. H. Thompson; (bottom) © Peter Ryley

has changed markedly during the last 50 million years, with part of the area now occupied by Costa Rica having been an archipelago or situated elsewhere. The rise and consolidation of the mountainous backbone of Costa Rica was accompanied by intense volcanic activity. The resulting igneous material covers more than half of the country today. The continuous land connection between North and South America has been in existence for only about three million years.

As a new land bridge, the Central American isthmus contains portions of the plants, animals, and, more recently, the human cultures of North and South America. For example, until about three million years ago, Central American mammals reflected primarily North American forms including deer, wildcats, otters, and foxes. Their interchange with South American mammals—anteaters, sloths, agoutis, pacas, opossums, ground sloths, armadillos, and monkeys—is a very new phenomenon. About two million years ago humid tropical forests became widespread in Central America, slowing the two-way trek of life in the isthmus and leading to its distinctive present biotic characteristics.

The average temperature of Costa Rica's warmest month does not exceed that of the coolest month by more than 5° C (9° F) at a given site. The mean annual temperature oscillates between 26° and 27.8° C (78.8° and 82° F) in the Atlantic and Pacific lowlands and falls as low as 4.5° C (40.1° F) on the highest peaks. Trade winds of the Atlantic strongly influence Costa Rica's climate, and no point is more than 80 kilometers from a large water mass. In general, seasonally predictable weather disturbances account for most of the rainfall in the Central American tropics, and large amounts of rain are generated by moisture-rich air that is pushed up the mountains by trade winds and then cooled. Rainfall is

D. H. Thompson—Oxford Scientific Films

Major elements of Costa Rica's system of parks and reserves are located on the map below. National parks are identified on the body of the map, while names of other features appear on a numbered legend. Creation of the present system began in the early 1970s, initially through executive decrees that were later ratified by law.

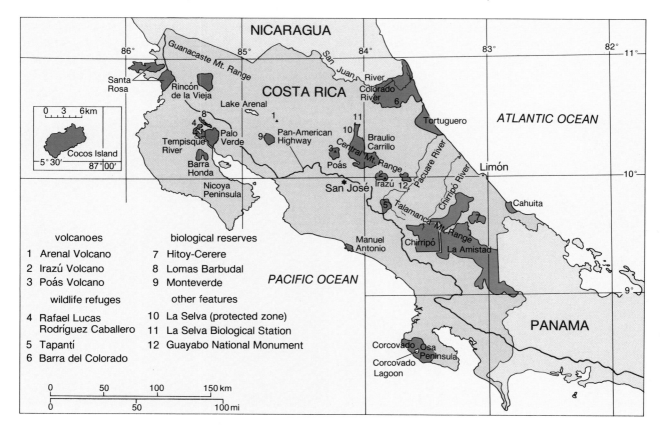

volcanoes
1 Arenal Volcano
2 Irazú Volcano
3 Poás Volcano

wildlife refuges
4 Rafael Lucas Rodríguez Caballero
5 Tapantí
6 Barra del Colorado

biological reserves
7 Hitoy-Cerere
8 Lomas Barbudal
9 Monteverde

other features
10 La Selva (protected zone)
11 La Selva Biological Station
12 Guayabo National Monument

abundant in Costa Rica, ranging from more than 6,500 millimeters (255 inches) per year to less than 1,500 millimeters (60 inches) in certain regions and averaging over 3,000 millimeters (120 inches) yearly.

All these factors contribute to the country's diverse mosaic of habitats and ecosystems, which include tropical dry and seasonally deciduous forests, rain forests and cloud forests (temperate, cloud-enshrouded rain forests on mountain slopes), paramos (equatorial mountain grasslands), and mangrove swamps. These habitats contain as many as one million species of organisms. Viewed as repositories of biologic diversity, they are among the world's most species-rich ecosystems and give Costa Rica one of the highest densities of species per unit area on Earth.

From Columbus to the 19th century

Christopher Columbus arrived in Cariay (Cariari), which is now called Limón, in 1502 on his fourth trip. Impressed by the abundance of gold gifts he received, he named the territory Costa Rica ("Rich Coast"). Although the country still has ample gold resources, its name now applies more properly to its biologic endowment.

In the early 1520s, when the first conquerors and settlers arrived, they found natural forests from coast to coast. Extensive fixed farmlands of indigenous Indian tribes mixed with dry forest prevailed in the Nicoya Peninsula of the northwest. In wetter areas, shifting agricultural systems were widespread, and their common characteristic was that they allowed the forest to grow back. The arrival of the Spanish settlers, largely imperial and of limited agronomic ability, had little effect for several centuries except to decimate the indigenous cultures through war and introduced diseases. As Spanish culture slowly began to dominate most of Costa Rica, the agronomy of the native cultures was abandoned. Only in areas like the northern plains and the Talamanca mountain range in the south were the native tribes able to maintain control. Armed revolts in the Talamancas in 1610 and 1709 kept the Spanish away for many years. This region, comprising the entire mountain system of southern Costa Rica, is the most important undisturbed area remaining in the country.

A mist-draped cloud forest at 1,600 meters (5,250 feet) in the Monteverde Biological Reserve (left) and the lowland marsh of the Palo Verde National Park (right) offer some idea of Costa Rica's diversity of habitats, which are home to as many as one million different species of organisms.

Mountains of the Talamanca range rise behind some of Costa Rica's many coffee plantations. The development of coffee agriculture and penetration into European coffee markets in the 19th century ended the nation's cultural isolation. The consequent integration of Costa Rica into the world economy brought contact with naturalists and explorers, whose accounts of their visits to the country stimulated scientific interest.

© Max & Bea Hunn—D. Donne Bryant Stock Photo

Before the arrival of the Spanish, Costa Rica's population was estimated to be in the hundreds of thousands. Afterward, the impact of land theft and disease was so catastrophic that the indigenous population had shrunk to 17,000 by 1569 and to 8,000 by 1801. Living primarily in the valleys and plateaus of the interior, this diminished, mixed population remained isolated and poor.

Toward the middle of the 19th century, the fertile Valle Central was almost completely occupied, and colonists moved up into the mountains. Waves of settlers and immigrants destroyed large tracts of the country's forests and started a cultural tradition that persists today among much of the rural population. Commercial exploitation of forest without replanting, coupled with the beliefs that all land is good for agriculture and that to remove the forest is to "improve" it, remain obstacles that must be overcome if the country's existing biodiversity is to be preserved.

Two other critical events took place during the mid-1800s—ones that eventually put an end to Costa Rica's colonial isolation and cultural deprivation. The development of coffee agriculture on the land's fertile volcanic soil and the initial penetration into European coffee markets caused a major social transformation and initiated the process of integrating Costa Rica into the world economy. Ever since, trade has been a critical element for the nation's small economy. Trade also brought with it important cultural and scientific contacts. A number of European naturalists and explorers visited Costa Rica and published accounts of their travels, creating further interest. In addition, the California gold rush of 1848 generated an international effort to find the most favorable route across the Central American isthmus on the journey from the U.S. East Coast to San Francisco. From 1851 to 1856 approximately 2,000 passengers per month traveled up the San Juan River and across Lake Nicaragua.

Scientific awakening

Danish naturalist and physicist Anders Ørsted visited the country from 1846 to 1848 and made the first systematic meteorologic observations

131

Establishment of protected areas

The need to preserve key examples of Costa Rica's extraordinary natural resources began to be felt by the middle of the 19th century after settlers had colonized a major portion of the Valle Central. Early decrees introduced the concept of inalienable areas (areas that cannot be privately owned), and in 1913 the crater and lake of Poás Volcano were protected. In 1945 "national park" appeared for the first time in Costa Rican legislation, which gave that designation to two kilometers on each side of the Pan-American Highway. In 1955 a law created the Institute of Tourism and gave it the right to establish and maintain national parks; at the same time, the law declared that those areas within a radius of two kilometers around all volcanic craters were also parks. These early measures were not well enforced, primarily owing to lack of resources. The oak forests near the Pan-American Highway have long disappeared, having been converted to charcoal by local residents.

In 1969 a new forestry law established a National Parks Department. Efforts to create and manage a system of parks and reserves have been supported by all subsequent governments. The administration of José Figueres Ferrer (1970–74) created the Cahuita, Santa Rosa, Poás, Irazú, Manuel Antonio, and Rincón de la Vieja parks as well as the Guayabo National Monument, the only archaeological park in Costa Rica. A series of reforms gave greater independence to the National Parks Service during the Daniel Oduber Quirós administration (1974–78), and many key elements were added to the system: the Barra Honda, Chirripó, Corcovado, Tortuguero, and Braulio Carrillo parks and the biologic reserves of Hitoy-Cerere, Carara, and Caño Island. The conservation effort was continued during the Rodrigo Carazo Odio administration (1978–82), which added Cocos Island, Palo Verde, and La Amistad national parks. La Amistad, located in the Talamanca region along the border with Panama, is the largest national park (almost 2,000 square kilometers) and is part of the Talamanca Biospheric Reserve. Many of the parks, originally created

by executive decree, were ratified by law during the presidency of Luis Alberto Monge Álvarez (1982–86). Also decreed during that period were several protected zones such as La Selva, which extended Braulio Carrillo down to the northern plains, and the Pacuare River, a major white-water attraction now threatened by hydroelectric development.

Whereas the present administration of Oscar Arias Sánchez has added further key elements, including Guanacaste and Arenal parks, primary efforts have concentrated on an overall evaluation of the system of protected areas, as well as the creation of an integrated network of regional projects.

Costa Rica's present system of national parks and reserves protects the nation's most outstanding examples of its natural and cultural heritage. The parks and reserves, which represent over 6,000 square kilometers, or 12% of the country's land area, constitute the core of the system. An additional 15% of territory falls under such categories of protection as forest reserves, protected zones, wildlife refuges, and Indian reserves. All these wilderness areas provide shelter for most of the 208 species of mammals, 850 species of birds, 160 species of amphibians, 220 species of reptiles, and 130 species of freshwater fish that have been discovered in the country, as well as an estimated 35,000 insect species. At the same time, they preserve almost all of the approximately 9,000 vascular plants identified to date. Together they are a refuge for numerous plant and animal species that are in danger of extinction or that are endemic to Costa Rica; *i.e.*, found nowhere else.

The forest reserves and additional protected areas are multiple-use zones that carry varying degrees of restrictions. This portion of the country, which is often populated, generally privately owned, and of high forestry potential, experiences the most serious management problems.

Forest reserves, almost entirely privately owned, account for nearly 4,000 square kilometers. Their primary purpose according to present

135

highest point, 634 meters (2,080 feet) above sea level. The generally rugged terrain leads to the formation of spectacular waterfalls. The waters surrounding the island are unusually transparent and are filled with abundant marine life, including very high populations of sharks.

Central Volcanic Mountain Range

This project, known as Foresta, is to be supported jointly by Costa Rica and the U.S. Agency for International Development. It will develop forestry and agroforestry as economically and ecologically appropriate land uses in the buffer zones around the Braulio Carrillo, Poás, and Irazú national parks and support the permanent management of these areas. The project comprises a total of 1,460 square kilometers, including over 500 square kilometers of national parks, nearly 750 square kilometers of forest reserves, and over 80 square kilometers of protected zones.

Poás and Irazú national parks surround two of the most spectacular volcanoes in the country, each rising over 3,000 meters (9,850 feet) and both active. This area lies north of San José and is contiguous with the most densely populated part of Costa Rica. It has exceptional economic and ecological importance, partly because it supplies much of the water, wood, and agricultural produce for the Valle Central and partly because its diverse landscape contains unusual biologic diversity and tourist attractions. A major highway to the Atlantic coast transects Braulio Carrillo, providing easy access and magnificent panoramic views.

In 1985 a land corridor connecting Braulio Carrillo and the La Selva Biological Station was added, providing a protected migration route for animals from the top of the central mountain range to the lowlands. Many species, including birds that depend on seasonally available fruit and nectar, must migrate up and down these slopes to survive. The new project will attempt to widen the corridor and promote sustainable forestry management in adjoining areas.

Another aim of Foresta is the creation of an independent Foundation for the Development of the Central Volcanic Cordillera that ultimately will provide countrywide direction, technical assistance, coordination, and funding for improved management of the national parks; promote sustainable management of natural forests in buffer zones; and provide sound development alternatives for local populations. The project itself will have a life of seven years, but the foundation it creates will operate indefinitely through a permanent endowment.

Arenal

Arenal National Park, which bears the name of an active volcano in the Guanacaste mountain range, is still in the planning and financing stage. Expected to be legally established by mid-1989, it will include parts of the Tenorio and Arenal forest reserves, which surround the man-made reservoir for the Arenal Hydroelectric Project. The Arenal megapark will also include the 120-square kilometer Monteverde Biological Reserve and the area between Monteverde and Lake Arenal. Nearly three-fourths of the annual flow of water into the reservoir comes from tributaries in

Poás National Park possesses one of the few active volcanic craters in the Americas accessible by road (above) and is among the most frequently visited parks in Costa Rica. The stunted forest cloaking the volcano of Irazú National Park (opposite page) is home to rabbits, coyotes, armadillos, Mexican tree porcupines, and various bird species. Both parks lie quite near San José and have exceptional economic and ecological importance.

by executive decree, were ratified by law during the presidency of Luis Alberto Monge Álvarez (1982–86). Also decreed during that period were several protected zones such as La Selva, which extended Braulio Carrillo down to the northern plains, and the Pacuare River, a major white-water attraction now threatened by hydroelectric development.

Whereas the present administration of Oscar Arias Sánchez has added further key elements, including Guanacaste and Arenal parks, primary efforts have concentrated on an overall evaluation of the system of protected areas, as well as the creation of an integrated network of regional projects.

Costa Rica's present system of national parks and reserves protects the nation's most outstanding examples of its natural and cultural heritage. The parks and reserves, which represent over 6,000 square kilometers, or 12% of the country's land area, constitute the core of the system. An additional 15% of territory falls under such categories of protection as forest reserves, protected zones, wildlife refuges, and Indian reserves. All these wilderness areas provide shelter for most of the 208 species of mammals, 850 species of birds, 160 species of amphibians, 220 species of reptiles, and 130 species of freshwater fish that have been discovered in the country, as well as an estimated 35,000 insect species. At the same time, they preserve almost all of the approximately 9,000 vascular plants identified to date. Together they are a refuge for numerous plant and animal species that are in danger of extinction or that are endemic to Costa Rica; *i.e.*, found nowhere else.

The forest reserves and additional protected areas are multiple-use zones that carry varying degrees of restrictions. This portion of the country, which is often populated, generally privately owned, and of high forestry potential, experiences the most serious management problems.

Forest reserves, almost entirely privately owned, account for nearly 4,000 square kilometers. Their primary purpose according to present

135

A flowering leaf cactus (above), a strikingly colored poison dart frog (below), a crab at Manuel Antonio National Park on the Pacific coast (bottom), a three-toed sloth from the Limón area (below center), and a toucan in the Guanacaste region (below right) represent a minute fraction of the beauty and variety of Costa Rica's biologic heritage.

law is timber production. So far, their exploitation has not provided for procedures such as replanting that would ensure replacement of the portion harvested. When properly managed to guarantee renewability, these areas can supply much more than timber; for example, watershed protection, hydroelectric energy, habitats for plants and animals, and sites for scientific research and ecotourism (nature tourism). To the forest reserves can be added Indian reserves and multiple-use protected zones, which account for 2,790 and 1,400 square kilometers, respectively.

Sustainable management and reorganization

The zones that surround such absolute protection areas as parks and reserves play a highly significant role in conservation efforts and preservation of biodiversity. These "buffer" zones can become positive or negative influences on the parks, depending on how they are managed. Today, in tropical less developed countries, the concept of conservation as the absolute preservation of nature in which humans have no place, has become obsolete. Replacing it is sustainable development, a concept for managing national resources that sees conservation and economic development as compatible and complementary. This approach was highlighted in a 1987 report of the UN World Commission on Environment and Development, which defined sustainable development as that "which meets the needs of the present without compromising the ability of future generations to meet their own needs."

Accordingly, the people who live in the buffer zones are seen as a critical element in sustainable management, not only in protecting the areas they inhabit but also in the success of the entire system. Unless the needs of the local inhabitants can be integrated and accommodated in resource-management programs, unless they can be given alternatives

for generating income without destroying the forest, and unless they can be taught to understand the natural history around them, there appears only a small chance that the country's biologic resources can be saved. On the other hand, successful sustainable management of the mosaic of parks, reserves, and inhabited protected areas would assure conservation of nearly 95% of Costa Rica's biodiversity and of most of its habitats and ecosystems.

Until recently, the main priority in Costa Rica's conservation efforts was legal protection. Parallel efforts to secure the funds to compensate owners for their land have not kept pace. About 20% of the national parks still consist of inholdings (privately owned land), much of which belongs to small farmers and peasants who are not allowed to work their land, a situation that causes persistent conflicts.

Among the more dramatic illustrations of the problems of conservation in the tropics was the invasion of Corcovado National Park by hundreds of gold panners in 1985. They were subsequently moved out of the park and compensated at significant expense to the government, but invasions of the park continue. This example demonstrates how the social pressures affecting local populations can become a serious threat to fragile conservation areas nearby. Accommodating the needs of local populations thus has become a fundamental principle in Costa Rica's present efforts to reorganize the management of protected areas.

Other principles, such as integrated management of the mosaic of protected areas and regional organization to promote decentralized decision-making, also guide the reorganization. In addition, planners have sought mechanisms for the proper representation of local nongovernmental organizations, scientific research, environmental education, tourism, and other interests. They have also tried to strike a balance between private and public interest so that private support from international and local groups is properly channeled.

There are seen to be three imperative steps for the preservation and management of tropical diversity: save it, explore it, and harvest it. Whereas the progression of emphasis should be in the order given—*i.e.*, preserve, census, and produce—the three steps must take place simultaneously to some degree. Different regions of the country have their own unique characteristics and are at different points in the progression.

In line with these imperatives, a central objective of Costa Rica's system of protected areas is to preserve its biodiversity as part of its national and global heritage for the benefit of present and future generations. At the same time, the system promotes the use of the areas as centers for scientific research, environmental education, and ecotourism. Assessing the biodiversity of Costa Rica has been identified as an important ongoing program that will be strengthened. Grass-roots inventories of birds, plants, and insects are at various stages of completion throughout the country. A ten-year effort, based on local collection efforts but involving scientists throughout the world, is now under way to gather and catalog about one million species of organisms believed to exist in the country. A parallel effort to educate the public—both within the country and

Courtesy, Organization for Tropical Studies; photo, Catherine M. Pringle.

Local schoolchildren learn about the tropical forest at La Selva as part of an environmental education program that brings students to the research station for field trips and other activities. In Costa Rica's program of sustainable management, teaching the people who live near protected areas to understand the natural history around them and the benefits of its preservation is crucial to saving the country's biologic resources.

internationally—about the economic and social benefits of preservation is critical.

On the basis of these general principles and objectives, eight major conservation and sustainable development regions have been established, encompassing the entire spectrum of protected areas. The National Parks Service and Forestry and Wildlife directorates operate jointly in each of these regional projects with the support of the National Parks Foundation (established in 1979 to raise funds to purchase parkland and help manage the parks) and many international nongovernmental organizations. For each of these regions a management committee in which scientific and local interests are represented holds the basic decision-making power over the way in which the regional project is developed and administered. Although differences exist from region to region in the formulation and implementation of such plans, decentralized administration is becoming a reality.

Debt-for-nature swaps

Crucial to the success of this effort has been new financing provided to conservation through so-called debt-for-nature swaps. With the support of the Swedish and Dutch governments, as well as many international conservation groups, a variety of transactions were approved by the end of 1988. Donations and grants totaling less than $12 million were used to purchase titles to more than $75 million of Costa Rica's debt to foreign banks, which sold off the debt at a large discount to get it off their hands. In exchange for the titles, the Central Bank of Costa Rica returned more than $35 million to the donors in the form of local currency bonds whose earnings are accrued through investment in conservation and sustainable development projects. This funding plan, which will continue to be encouraged and expanded, is a needed complement to budgeted allocations and affords the only opportunity to hire additional people and provide training and improved working conditions for local personnel.

It is noteworthy that the debt-for-nature swaps ultimately have allowed Costa Rica to triple the amount of donations received while providing local currency bonds that constitute an endowment for future management. The National Parks Foundation, in turn, has become a "conservation bank," and it will eventually handle endowment funds for most of the eight conservation regions.

A legal reform that became valid in 1989 gives the same rights and duties to employees hired by private conservation organizations as are enjoyed by government personnel. In addition, it allows for the creation of a fund to provide additional training and to distribute benefits to the entire system. A balanced mix of governmental and private support, both local and international, has been found to be the only viable way to guarantee sustainability.

The work to bring the mosaic of protected areas into a system of integrated management under local jurisdiction has led to the creation of the eight regional conservation and development projects, or "megaparks," discussed below.

138

Guanacaste

Tropical dry forest is one of the most endangered life zones in Mesoamerica, and the establishment of Guanacaste National Park in the northwest will protect the largest remaining tract of dry forest from California to Panama. The project will include what is presently Santa Rosa National Park on the Pacific coast, as well as the territory to the east between the Pan-American Highway and the Atlantic side of the Guanacaste mountain range. Eventually it may link other protected areas of this important volcanic range from the town of Orosí to the Arenal project. It will establish a total of 826 square kilometers of wilderness areas and will provide a corridor of protected areas from the mountain peaks all the way to the Pacific Ocean. In addition, it is designed to be a "user friendly" social and cultural institution that contributes to the daily life of the local residents, and it provides for ecological and cultural restoration of areas that have been degraded by cattle raising.

Guanacaste will be large enough to maintain habitats for healthy populations of all animals and plants that are known to have originally occupied the region and to contain enough duplicate habitats to allow intensive use of some areas by visitors and researchers. The restoration of large areas of species-rich and habitat-rich tropical dry forest will depend primarily on fire control by managers, grass control by cattle, and tree-seed dispersal by wild and domestic animals. In addition to being a major cultural resource, the park will also contribute scientifically and economically in a variety of other ways, serving as gene and seed banks for dry-forest plants and animals, watershed protection, examples of reforestation technology, and sites for ecotourism and conventional tourism.

Recent work to integrate the management of Costa Rica's mosaic of protected areas has led to the creation of eight regional projects, or megaparks. The approximate boundaries of the projects and their relation to the previously established parks and reserves are shown on the map below.

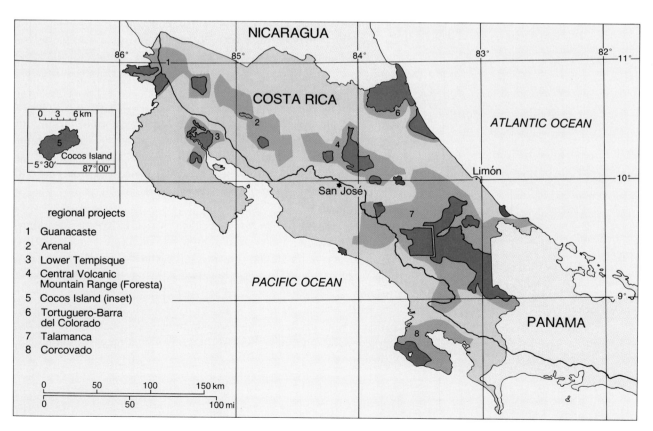

regional projects

1 Guanacaste
2 Arenal
3 Lower Tempisque
4 Central Volcanic Mountain Range (Foresta)
5 Cocos Island (inset)
6 Tortuguero-Barra del Colorado
7 Talamanca
8 Corcovado

Lower Tempisque

This regional project, also in the northwest, will join the Lomas Barbudal Biological Reserve (23 square kilometers) with Palo Verde National Park (57 square kilometers) and the Rafael Lucas Rodríguez Caballero National Wildlife Refuge (74 square kilometers). The resulting biogeographic unit is one of the regions of greatest ecological variety in the country, containing perhaps 15 distinct habitats. They include lakes, freshwater and brackish swamps, mangrove swamps, grasslands, thorn scrubs, lowland deciduous forests, hillside mixed forests, savannah woodlands, riparian (riverbank) forests, and evergreen forests. About 70% of Lomas Barbudal is covered with deciduous and riparian forests, savannah woodlands, and gallery forests (riverbank forests in otherwise treeless areas). Oak forests and extremely dry areas rich in cactus plants are also present.

Palo Verde is subject to seasonal flooding, and its natural network of waterways provides ideal conditions for the largest concentration of waterfowl and wading birds in Central America. Seasonally, hundreds of thousands of herons, storks, egrets, grebes, ibis, ducks, and jacanas flock there to feed and mate. The area could contain as many as 300 species of birds. Monkeys, both howler and white-faced, and white-tailed deer are common.

Lomas Barbudal is rich in insect species, particularly bees, wasps, butterflies, and moths, and it shelters numerous vertebrates, including 130 observed species of birds. Four endangered species of trees—mahogany, Panama redwood, gonzalo alves, and rosewood—grow in abundance in the reserve.

The area encompassed by the Lower Tempisque project faces persistent threats from dry-season fires. Furthermore, it soon will be subjected to pesticides and other pollutants from a large adjoining irrigation project being planned.

Corcovado National Park, on the Osa Peninsula, comprises at least 13 different ecosystems including herbaceous swamps and holillo forests (pictured above). Its enormous biologic diversity has made it an important international research center for the study of tropical rain forest ecology. Among the park's protected life are (opposite page, top to bottom) heliconia, a tropical herb; species of saddleback caterpillar and tarantula; and hermit crabs.

Corcovado

Corcovado National Park, comprising 418 square kilometers on the Osa Peninsula in the southern Pacific region, constitutes a prime example of wet tropical forests. Rainfall in the interior of the peninsula is estimated at 5,000–6,000 millimeters (200–240 inches) per year on the highest peaks, with averages of 3,000–4,000 millimeters (120–160 inches) per year for the entire park. About 13 different ecosystems have been described, among them rocky and sandy intertidal zones, mangroves, a freshwater herbaceous swamp (Corcovado Lagoon), swamp and holillo forests, alluvial-plain forests, and a variety of montane and cloud forests that cover about half of the park area.

More than 500 species of trees grow in the park at a density of more than 100 different species per hectare (0.01 square kilometer). Corcovado contains more than one-fourth of all the tree species known to exist in the country, including some of the largest trees of the tropical forest, towering 50 meters (165 feet) above the ground. The park is home to 140 species of mammals, 367 of birds, 117 of amphibians and reptiles, and 40 of freshwater fish. Over 6,000 insect species live there, including 123 species of butterflies identified to date. Corcovado protects such endangered mammals as the tapir, cougar, ocelot, jaguar, and giant anteater and contains the largest population of scarlet macaws in the country.

Corcovado National Park is surrounded by the Golfo Dulce Forest Reserve (800 square kilometers), which is inhabited by about 5,000 families. The entire peninsula, including Corcovado, is rich in placer gold deposits, whose exploitation by gold panners has been a persistent problem for the government. The Corcovado project poses one of the most difficult challenges to sustainable management of tropical forests.

Talamanca

The Talamanca complex—encompassing La Amistad and Chirripó national parks (1,900 and 500 square kilometers, respectively), adjoining Indian reserves, protected zones, forest reserves, and the Tapantí National Wildlife Refuge—accounts for more than 10% (5,000 square kilometers) of Costa Rica's land area. Bordering Panama on the southeast, it is the largest, most diverse regional project and the only one containing the remaining native populations. The area holds the greatest biologic wealth and variety and protects the largest remaining blocks of virgin forest in the country.

Wide variations in altitude, which range from near sea level to the highest peaks in the country, and differences in soil type, climate, and topography contribute to the extraordinary number of habitats found in Talamanca. They include paramos, swamps, oak forests, madrono forests, fern groves, and different kinds of mixed forests. Tall, damp cloud forests cover a significant part of the area and are extremely complex. Huge oak forests covered by epiphytic plants are common, and madrono forests are prevalent at the higher elevations. The paramos, which begin at nearly 3,000 meters (9,850 feet), consist of mixed shrubs, grasses, and perennial herbaceous plants. The enormous variety of wildlife has not yet been properly assessed. There are over 400 species of birds, over 265 of amphibians, and many endangered mammals.

More than 20,000 Indians of the Bribrí and Cabecar cultures inhabit Talamanca, and many settlers encroach upon the area. Inholdings are still a serious problem in both La Amistad and Chirripó, and management of Indian reserves is also difficult, particularly because of logging pressures and expansion of the road network.

Talamanca's unique cultural and biologic characteristics, as well as its size and complexity, contribute to making it one of the highest priorities for Costa Rican conservation. The region was declared a biospheric reserve by Unesco in 1982 and a world heritage site in 1983.

Tortuguero-Barra del Colorado

This regional project, on the Atlantic coast, includes Tortuguero National Park (190 square kilometers), Barra del Colorado National Wildlife Refuge (920 square kilometers), and a coastal link between them. Tortuguero's beaches are an important nesting site for the green turtle, which can reach 1.2 meters (3.9 feet) in length and 375 kilograms (825 pounds) in weight. Other species of sea turtles that nest in the park are leatherbacks and hawksbills. The area receives some of Costa Rica's heaviest rainfall, ranging between 5,000 and 6,000 millimeters (200 and 240 inches) per year. The wildlife refuge, which borders Nicaragua, is a mosaic of swamp forests, swamp palm forests, and mixed forests. The park to the south contains littoral (shoreside) woodlands rich in grasses, cyperaceous plants, and coconut palms; high rain forests; swamp forests; holillo forests; and herbaceous swamps and marshes.

The area supports a wealth of wildlife, including such endangered species as the West Indian manatee, tapir, cougar, jaguar, ocelot, and crocodile. Tortuguero is especially rich in monkeys, fish, frogs and toads, and birds. A natural network of canals and waterways crosses Tortuguero, while Barra del Colorado can be navigated readily on the waters of the San Juan and Colorado rivers, making it easy to observe waterfowl, river turtles, monkeys, sloths, and other wildlife of the banks and shores.

The refuge is inhabited by about 4,000 families, and the area is subject to persistent invasion by Nicaraguan refugees. Logging pressures and

A natural network of navigable waterways crosses Tortuguero National Park (below), offering habitats for several species of turtles, the West Indian manatee, a species of crocodile, and numerous freshwater fish and allowing easy observation of waterfowl, monkeys, and sloths along the banks. The park is also the most important nesting site in the western Caribbean for the green turtle (below right).

Cocos Island National Park, located about 500 kilometers (300 miles) southwest of Costa Rica, juts steeply from the ocean, the only outcrop of a marine mountain range. Its distance from the mainland makes it a natural laboratory for the study of plant and animal evolution. The island is also famous for stories of pirate treasure supposedly buried there between the 17th and the 19th century.

agricultural expansion in northern Costa Rica are also significant threats. Finding sustainable development alternatives incorporating tourism, wildlife management, and agroforestry (a mixture of agriculture and silviculture) are critical to preserving the area. The project is also part of a system of "protected areas for peace" established with Nicaragua.

Cocos Island

Cocos Island, located in the Pacific about 500 kilometers southwest of the Osa Peninsula, sits on the tectonic plate that bears its name. It is the only outcrop of Cocos Ridge, a marine mountain range rising nearly 3,000 meters (9,900 feet) above the seafloor. The ridge is made up of a chain of volcanoes that stretches from Costa Rica nearly to the Galápagos Islands. Cocos Island's isolation from the mainland, like that of the Galápagos, makes it a unique laboratory for studies of evolution. The island is economically important to Costa Rica because it adds about ten times more area to the nation's territorial waters.

Formerly a pirate haven, Cocos Island is famous for stories about several treasures supposedly buried there between 1684 and 1821. Hundreds of searches have been conducted thus far without success. Robert Louis Stevenson is believed to have based the locale for his novel *Treasure Island* (1881) on the Cocos Island tales.

The island's unique biology has attracted international attention. Of the 235 plant species identified to date, 70 are endemic. Three species of birds and two of reptiles also exist nowhere else. In addition, there are more than 200 species of fish, 118 sea mollusks, and 362 species of insects (65 endemic) that live on or near the island. A surrounding reef includes 18 species of corals.

The island receives an enormous annual rainfall, about 7,000 millimeters (275 inches), and is completely covered by a South-American-type evergreen forest, which becomes a cloud forest at the island's

143

Poás National Park possesses one of the few active volcanic craters in the Americas accessible by road (above) and is among the most frequently visited parks in Costa Rica. The stunted forest cloaking the volcano of Irazú National Park (opposite page) is home to rabbits, coyotes, armadillos, Mexican tree porcupines, and various bird species. Both parks lie quite near San José and have exceptional economic and ecological importance.

highest point, 634 meters (2,080 feet) above sea level. The generally rugged terrain leads to the formation of spectacular waterfalls. The waters surrounding the island are unusually transparent and are filled with abundant marine life, including very high populations of sharks.

Central Volcanic Mountain Range

This project, known as Foresta, is to be supported jointly by Costa Rica and the U.S. Agency for International Development. It will develop forestry and agroforestry as economically and ecologically appropriate land uses in the buffer zones around the Braulio Carrillo, Poás, and Irazú national parks and support the permanent management of these areas. The project comprises a total of 1,460 square kilometers, including over 500 square kilometers of national parks, nearly 750 square kilometers of forest reserves, and over 80 square kilometers of protected zones.

Poás and Irazú national parks surround two of the most spectacular volcanoes in the country, each rising over 3,000 meters (9,850 feet) and both active. This area lies north of San José and is contiguous with the most densely populated part of Costa Rica. It has exceptional economic and ecological importance, partly because it supplies much of the water, wood, and agricultural produce for the Valle Central and partly because its diverse landscape contains unusual biologic diversity and tourist attractions. A major highway to the Atlantic coast transects Braulio Carrillo, providing easy access and magnificent panoramic views.

In 1985 a land corridor connecting Braulio Carrillo and the La Selva Biological Station was added, providing a protected migration route for animals from the top of the central mountain range to the lowlands. Many species, including birds that depend on seasonally available fruit and nectar, must migrate up and down these slopes to survive. The new project will attempt to widen the corridor and promote sustainable forestry management in adjoining areas.

Another aim of Foresta is the creation of an independent Foundation for the Development of the Central Volcanic Cordillera that ultimately will provide countrywide direction, technical assistance, coordination, and funding for improved management of the national parks; promote sustainable management of natural forests in buffer zones; and provide sound development alternatives for local populations. The project itself will have a life of seven years, but the foundation it creates will operate indefinitely through a permanent endowment.

Arenal

Arenal National Park, which bears the name of an active volcano in the Guanacaste mountain range, is still in the planning and financing stage. Expected to be legally established by mid-1989, it will include parts of the Tenorio and Arenal forest reserves, which surround the man-made reservoir for the Arenal Hydroelectric Project. The Arenal megapark will also include the 120-square kilometer Monteverde Biological Reserve and the area between Monteverde and Lake Arenal. Nearly three-fourths of the annual flow of water into the reservoir comes from tributaries in

144

this area. Finally, Arenal will connect the Monteverde and San Ramón reserves to provide a total of nearly 500 square kilometers.

The Arenal project has been called Costa Rica's "last" national park since it represents one of the only remaining valuable and unique habitats of significant dimensions still unprotected. It is also the conclusion of a long effort begun by Quakers who emigrated from the U.S. in 1949 when they learned that Costa Rica had abolished its army. In the early 1970s a hydroelectric project was built in the region, but tragically no provision was made to protect the watershed. Today the electric utility has become a full partner in the effort to establish Arenal.

Many interrelated factors account for Costa Rica's success in protecting its biologic heritage. An openness to foreign visitors and scientists, over 120 years of free and compulsory education, a century of democratic life, and the absence of military influence in government have permitted a strong spirit of conservation to develop in Costa Rica's citizens and have attracted people from all corners of the planet. Their cooperative work, carried out in a highly propitious social environment, is giving encouragement to the rest of the tropics that some of the most unique fragments of the biosphere can truly be saved.

FOR ADDITIONAL READING

Mario A. Boza, *Costa Rica National Parks* (INCAFO, 1987).

Mario A. Boza and Rolando Mendoza, *The National Parks of Costa Rica* (INCAFO, 1988).

Gro Harlem Brundtland *et al.*, *Our Common Future,* a report of the World Commission on Environment and Development (United Nations, 1987).

Gary S. Hartshorn *et al.*, *Costa Rica: Country Environmental Profile* (Tropical Science Center, San José, Costa Rica, 1982).

Daniel Janzen (ed.), *Costa Rican Natural History* (University of Chicago Press, 1983).

Daniel Janzen, *Costa Rica: Cornerstone of the Tropical Biodiversity Edifice* (informal paper, 1988).

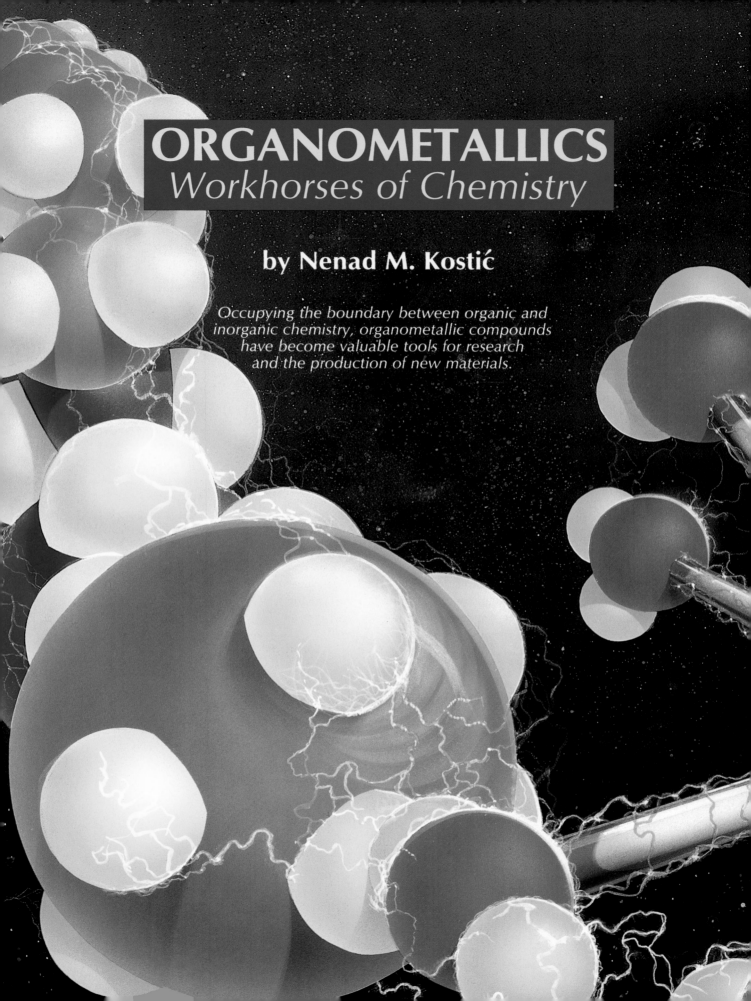

ORGANOMETALLICS
Workhorses of Chemistry

by Nenad M. Kostić

Occupying the boundary between organic and inorganic chemistry, organometallic compounds have become valuable tools for research and the production of new materials.

MACHINES OF INNER SPACE

by K. Eric Drexler

Taking cues from chemistry and biology, scientists and engineers are boldly sketching futuristic machines smaller than living cells—some no larger than proteins—that could literally build matter atom by atom.

K. ERIC DREXLER is a Visiting Scholar at Stanford University and President, Foresight Institute, Palo Alto, California.

(Pages 160–161) Illustration by Leon Bishop

(Pages 160–161) Within an artery of a human being of the future, three types of nanomachines of different size scales carry out their medical assignments. In the extreme foreground an immune-system augmentor has located an invading virus and extends arms tipped with receptor proteins toward its target. Farther back, at the upper left, an oncogene exciser has fastened itself above the nucleus of an endothelial cell that lines the blood vessel. It injects the nucleus with enzymes tailored to snip out a potential cancer-causing gene from the cell's DNA. Still farther in the background, at the lower left, a mass of atherosclerotic plaque on the arterial lining will soon be cut away by atherectomy machines that are gathering at the lesion. (Below) A nanometer is a billionth of a meter, or about 40 billionths of an inch. Atoms are about a third of a nanometer in diameter; 176 carbon atoms locked in the crystalline lattice of diamond fill a volume of one cubic nanometer.

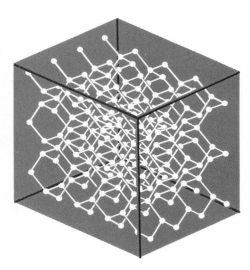

diamond: one cubic nanometer, 176 atoms

Human beings live in bodies made of atoms in a world made of atoms, and the way those atoms are arranged makes all the difference. To be healthy is to have tissues and cells composed of correctly patterned sets of atoms. To have wealth is, in large measure, to control collections of atoms organized in the form of useful objects, whether foodstuffs, housing, or spacecraft. If people could arrange atoms as they pleased, they would gain effectively complete control of the structure of matter. Nanotechnology offers to provide this control, bringing with it possibilities for health, wealth, and capabilities beyond most past imaginings. This sort of dominion over matter will not arrive overnight but will come only after years of hard work in various enabling technologies. Nonetheless, examples from chemistry and biology already demonstrate many of the basic possibilities.

Chemists have long known that atoms bond together to form molecules. Every diamond, for example, is a single, huge molecule made of carbon atoms. Every breath of air contains pairs of nitrogen and oxygen atoms, each pair a small molecule. Whether large or small, molecules are objects. Each has such properties as size, shape, mass, strength, and stiffness. Nanotechnology envisions using molecular-scale objects as components of molecular machines.

Nature shows that molecules can serve as machines because living things work by means of such machinery. Enzymes are molecular machines that make, break, and rearrange the bonds holding other molecules together. Muscles are driven by molecular machines that haul fibers past one another. DNA serves as a data-storage system, transmitting digital instructions to molecular machines, the ribosomes, that manufacture protein molecules. And these protein molecules, in turn, make up most of the molecular machinery just described. Nanotechnology aims to exploit a similar strategy, using programmable molecular machines termed assemblers to build things, including more molecular machines. Assemblers will work like tiny industrial robots, directing chemical reactions by positioning molecular tools to build complex structures atom by atom.

Microtechnology enables construction on a scale of micrometers, or millionths of a meter. Nanotechnology will enable construction on a scale of nanometers, or billionths of a meter. The term nanotechnology is sometimes used (especially in the U.K.) to refer to any technology giving some control of matter on a nanometer scale. This definition would seem to include glass polishing, the manufacture of thin films, and ordinary chemistry. As used in this article, however, the term describes a technology giving nearly complete control of the structure of matter on a nanometer scale. Since atoms are themselves about a third of a nanometer in diameter, this sort of nanotechnology will require a general ability to control the arrangement of atoms.

Even this control will not allow what the alchemists sought—a way to turn lead into gold. In essence, nanotechnology will be a vast elaboration of ordinary chemistry and biology. It will move atoms around as in chemical reactions, not fuse them or split them as in nuclear reactions. To transform one element into another will be beyond its ability.

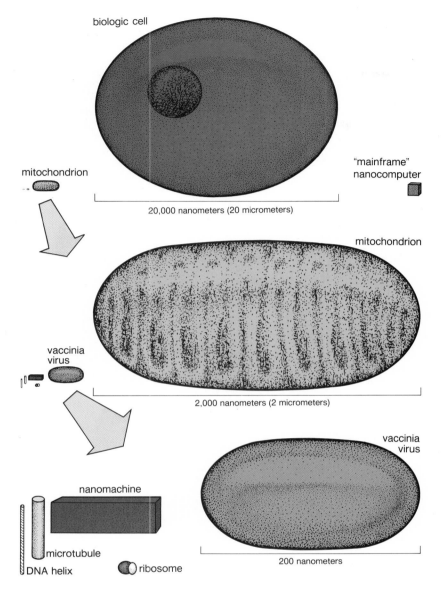

biologic cell

mitochondrion

"mainframe" nanocomputer

20,000 nanometers (20 micrometers)

mitochondrion

vaccinia virus

2,000 nanometers (2 micrometers)

vaccinia virus

nanomachine

microtubule

DNA helix   ribosome

200 nanometers

Microscopic components of the biologic world and artificial molecular devices are compared at successive levels of magnification to suggest the scale of nanomachines. In the world of nanotechnology a mechanical computer can be the size of a cellular mitochondrion, while a small programmable machine capable of, for example, helping in the repair of a damaged cell, can be smaller than a virus.

How might one bridge the gap between present abilities and nanotechnology? Two very different paths are being pursued today; one is a top-down strategy of miniaturizing current technologies, while the other is a bottom-up strategy of building ever more complex molecular devices, atom by atom.

The top-down approach

The top-down strategy sees the problem as one of scale, of pushing back the frontier of miniaturization. Such is the tradition of the watchmaker and the manufacturer of integrated circuits. The 20th century has seen great progress in miniaturization—from the shrinking of clockwork into fingernail-sized boxes to the shrinking of computers onto fingernail-sized chips—and this progress continues.

163

Photos, AT&T Bell Laboratories, Holmdel, N.J.

The same deposition and etching techniques used for fabricating thousands of semiconductor components on a single chip recently have allowed researchers to build simple mechanical micromachines. A pair of microtongs (this page, top) converts linear motion to rotary motion; length of the white reference dashes near the top is 100 micrometers (100,000 nanometers). A gearbox (center) comprises three interlocking gears having diameters of 180, 125, and 125 micrometers, left to right; individual teeth are about 20 micrometers wide, roughly the diameter of a living cell. A turbine 125 micrometers in diameter (bottom) can be rotated at high speed with jets of air sent through one of the connecting channels. On the opposite page, an electric micromotor (top) has a rotor 60 micrometers in diameter that can be driven by electrostatic forces. A four-joint crank (center) has a total length of 150 micrometers; the two inner joints are free from the substrate, while the two outer ones are pinned. Spiral springs (bottom) are each 100 micrometers in diameter.

Photos, Berkeley Sensor & Actuator
Center, University of California, Berkeley

One of the great visionaries of the top-down strategy was physicist Richard Feynman. In 1959 he gave a talk in which he proposed that large machines could be used to make smaller machines, and those to make machines still smaller, working step-by-step toward molecular dimensions. He envisioned microscopic lathes and described problems with building microscopic automobiles for mites. At the end of his talk, however, he turned to the molecular-size scale and hinted at the need for a bottom-up approach. "The principles of physics, as far as I can see," he said, "do not speak against the possibility of maneuvering things atom by atom." He went on to remark, "But it is interesting that it would be, in principle, possible (I think) for a physicist to synthesize any chemical substance that the chemist writes down. Give the orders, and the physicist synthesizes it. How? Put the atoms down where the chemist says, and so you make the substance." Nevertheless, Feynman suggested that these substance-synthesizing machines "will be really useless" because chemists will be able to make whatever they want without them.

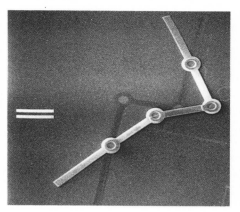

Modern microtechnology has followed a different path, also discussed by Feynman in his talk. Microtechnologists use beams of light or electrons to make patterns on surfaces and then apply such techniques as selective chemical etching or the deposition of thin films of metals, oxides, and semiconductors to develop those patterns into structures. The patterns can be micrometers or fractions of a micrometer across, and the structures can be wires and transistors or even mechanical devices.

Microtechnology as applied to electronics is an old yet fast-developing story; it has provided modern computer technology. Microtechnology for machines is more recent and is still in the research phase. Investigators have deposited patterned films of silicon over films of oxide and then dissolved the oxide to release silicon parts. Using clever patterns of deposition, Kaigham Gabriel and William Trimmer of AT&T Bell Laboratories, Holmdel, New Jersey, have shaped interlocking silicon gears, trapped against the surface by silicon flanges but left free to rotate. Streams of air can spin these gears like turbines at over 15,000 revolutions per minute. Richard Muller of the University of California at Berkeley has made the first electrostatic micromotors using a similar technology.

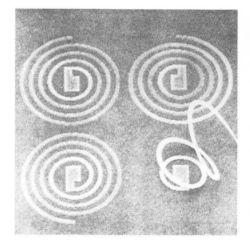

Silicon micromachining is pushing back the frontier of miniaturization, but how close has the top-down approach come to nanotechnology? In scale, it remains vastly different. Microgears and micromotors are now tens of micrometers in diameter, but nanogears and nanomotors will often be tens of nanometers in diameter or less—a thousandth the linear dimension and a billionth the volume of current micromachines. This is analogous to the difference between a truck and an integrated circuit.

More fundamental, however, is the difference in quality of construction. Micromachining, whether with microlathes or with etched patterns, can only shape materials from the outside. It cannot build them from the inside, from the bottom up, and so it cannot give complete control of the structure of matter. These top-down technologies have many uses (consider microcomputers) and may even yield nanoscale devices, but they cannot evolve into true molecular nanotechnology.

165

The bottom-up approach

In contrast with the top-down strategy, the bottom-up strategy sees no problem with making things small; chemists and biochemists already make small molecules with ease and in abundance. From this perspective the problem is to make things large while keeping detailed, molecular control of structure.

The bottom-up strategy was originally inspired by chemistry and molecular biology. For more than a century, chemists have understood molecules as small three-dimensional objects to be broken down and built up. In 1926 physicist Erwin Schrödinger supplied the foundations for a quantum mechanical theory of molecules and chemical bonding. In 1944 he wrote a book, *What Is Life?*, that correctly viewed life as based on molecular objects and machines. In 1953 James Watson and Francis Crick determined the three-dimensional structure of DNA, and four years later J. C. Kendrew and his colleagues in England were the first to describe the three-dimensional structure of a protein. Since then, molecular biologists have detailed the structures and functions of molecular devices at an ever increasing rate.

It was the existence of a wide range of natural molecular machines (*see* Table) that led me to propose artificial molecular machines, ultimately including such things as molecular assemblers, assembler-based replicators, mechanical nanocomputers, and cell-repair machines. Molecular machines in nature showed that a bottom-up approach to nanotechnology would work. Indeed, the most clearly workable bottom-up approach begins by mimicking nature, by designing new protein-based devices.

Proteins are polymers made by joining many smaller molecules—amino acid monomers—to form linear chains. The amino acids of protein chains form specific sequences, like the letters in a specific sentence. The sequence of amino acids in a protein likewise has a special significance: it determines how the chain will fold, or coil back on itself, to form a compact three-dimensional object. A folded protein can be as stiff as a piece of wood or engineering plastic. Furthermore, depending on its shape, surface properties, and so on, a folded protein can do things; for example, it can serve as an enzyme, as a structural element, or even

Macroscopic and Molecular Components		
technology	function	molecular examples
struts, beams, casings	transmit force, hold positions	cell walls, microtubules
cables	transmit tension	collagen, silk
fasteners, glue	connect parts	intermolecular forces
solenoids, actuators	move things	muscle actin, myosin
motors	turn shafts	flagellar motor
drive shafts	transmit torque	bacterial flagella
bearings	support moving parts	single bonds
clamps	hold workpieces	enzymatic binding sites
tools	modify workpieces	enzymes, reactive molecules
production lines	construct devices	enzyme systems, ribosomes
numerical control systems	store and read programs	genetic system

Adapted from K. E. Drexler, *Proceedings of the National Academy of Sciences*, vol. 78, pp. 5275–78, 1981

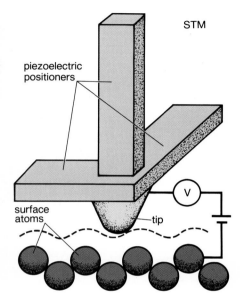

as part of a molecular motor. Just as a protein chain can fold up to form an object, so can a collection of proteins stick together to form a larger, more complex object, thus enabling construction of complex molecular machines.

Nonmolecular machines may also be of use in nanotechnology. In 1982 Gerd Binnig and Heinrich Rohrer at IBM's research laboratory in Zürich, Switzerland, announced their development of a device called the scanning tunneling microscope (STM). Like its younger relative, the atomic force microscope (AFM), the scanning tunneling microscope can move a sharp tip over a surface with atomic precision. This capability immediately suggested a modified bottom-up strategy for developing nanotechnology, using the STM tip to position molecular tools for precise molecular construction.

In the long term, the approach used to reach nanotechnology will make no difference because the early, clumsy technologies will swiftly be left behind. In the short term, however, the rates of progress in different approaches will be decisive, determining not only which approach pays off but how fast nanotechnology itself arrives.

Building with molecules

Various bottom-up approaches have produced experimental results. Bare STM tips, those without molecular tools, have made molecular-scale modifications on surfaces. At AT&T Bell Laboratories, Murray Hill, New

Small enough to be held in the hand, the scanning tunneling microscope, or STM (above left), can image surface detail down to the level of individual atoms. In its operation (above) a sharp metal tip is scanned within a few nanometers of the sample surface with piezoelectric positioners, while a voltage is applied between the tip and the sample. By means of a quantum mechanical process called tunneling, electrons flow across the gap between the tip and the sample surface. The positioners, which are materials that expand or contract with changes in electric voltage, respond to this flow by continually readjusting the tip height to maintain a constant gap distance as the tip scans the surface. A computer translates the movement of the positioners into a topographic map of the surface. The ability of the STM to scan a surface with atomic precision suggests an approach to nanotechnology—using the STM to position molecular tools for precise molecular construction.

167

J. S. Foster, J. E. Frommer, and P. C. Arnett, IBM Almaden Research Center, San Jose, Calif.

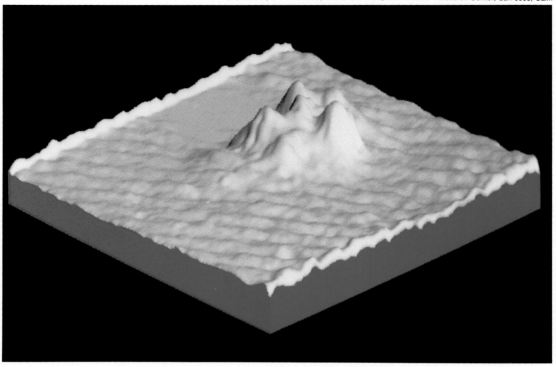

A bottom-up strategy for developing nanotechnology with the STM has been encouraged by recent experiments in which bare STM tips were used to make molecular-scale modifications on surfaces. In the STM image above, the mountainous peaks rising above a flat plain represent an organic molecule pinned to a clean graphite surface by an electrical pulse from the STM tip. Other images revealed that application of a second pulse caused such peaks to disappear completely or partially, as if the molecule had been either removed or cut into two pieces. Thus far, however, such manipulation has not produced the consistent, controllable results needed for building nanomachines.

Jersey, R. S. Becker, J. A. Golovchenko, and B. S. Swartzentruber have produced what appear in STM images as atom-sized bumps on germanium crystal surfaces, apparently accomplished by evaporating single atoms of germanium from the tip of the STM. At IBM's Almaden Research Center, San Jose, California, J. S. Foster, J. E. Frommer, and P. C. Arnett produced bumps on graphite crystals, chemically pinning fragments of single molecules to the crystals' surfaces using current from an STM tip. The presence and absence of such bumps might be used one day to store the ones and zeros of binary-coded computer data, crowding many trillions of bits into a square millimeter.

Thus far, however, such experiments have failed to produce specific, controllable molecular changes; the detailed nature of the bumps has been unpredictable. It seems unlikely that bare STM tips, even those ending in a single atom, can provide the precise, molecular control needed for building nanomechanisms. Whether or not nanotechnologists use STM or AFM devices for positioning, they will likely need molecular tools to construct the first generation of nanomachines.

In the long run, nanotechnology probably will use robotlike molecule-sized assemblers to position molecular tools, but assemblers are not necessary to begin building with molecules. Instead, one can use self-assembly to form larger structures from molecular components suspended in solution, using principles familiar to chemists and molecular biologists. Even assembler-style positioning using STM or AFM tips, if the technique becomes useful, will probably begin by the use of a self-assembly process to cap those tips with molecular tools.

168

Self-assembly differs radically from ordinary manufacturing techniques. It involves small pieces joining together automatically to form larger objects. Making a molecular device this way will be much like growing a crystal, whereby a solid, three-dimensional object is built up by adding layer after layer of molecules to its surface. Whereas crystals have simple, regular structures made of only a few kinds of molecules, molecular machines will be complex, irregular structures made of many different kinds. The component molecules themselves could be made by chemical synthesis, by mixing reactive compounds together in the right order under the right conditions.

Chemical synthesis and self-assembly have real advantages over atom-by-atom positioning. Using these methods to synthesize even a thousandth of a gram of a typical protein (a modest amount, by current standards) results in more than a million billion (10^{15}) molecular components, without the need for performing some billion billion (10^{18}) molecular assembly operations. In making a gram of devices, each self-assembled from a thousand molecular components, one would again make 10^{15} molecular objects and save another 10^{18} individual assembly operations. To pull cost numbers out of the air, at a millionth of a cent per assembly operation, this would mean a savings of $10 billion. Also, unlike alternatives, this kind of synthesis and assembly is already known to work in the laboratory and in nature.

How, though, can self-assembly work for molecules when it does not for cars or computers? The key principles are selective stickiness and thermal motion. Proteins and other large molecules can have complex shapes and surface properties. Two such molecules can fit like pieces in a jigsaw puzzle, having not only complementary shapes but complementary patterns of attractive forces; for example, electrical charge. They will stick to each other but not to molecules that lack this complementarity—this is selective stickiness. Warm molecules bounce about (which is the reason the molecules in air do not fall to the floor and stay there). In a liquid these thermal motions affect everything, including large molecules

Self-assembly involves small pieces coming together automatically to form larger objects. In the case of biologic components, its effectiveness has been demonstrated in the construction of natural structures as large and complex as bacterial ribosomes, which function to translate bacterial genetic material into proteins. When 55 different proteins and 3 different RNA molecules are brought together in a test tube under the right conditions, they spontaneously assemble into a functional ribosome capable of carrying out protein synthesis. Whether making cellular components or nanomachines, the key principles of self-assembly are the same: selective stickiness and thermal motion—i.e., molecules having complementary shapes and forces plus a constant mixing that quickly brings complementary molecules together.

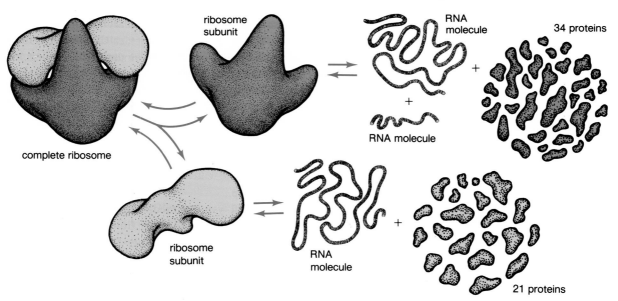

complete ribosome

ribosome subunit

ribosome subunit

RNA molecule

RNA molecule

RNA molecule

34 proteins

21 proteins

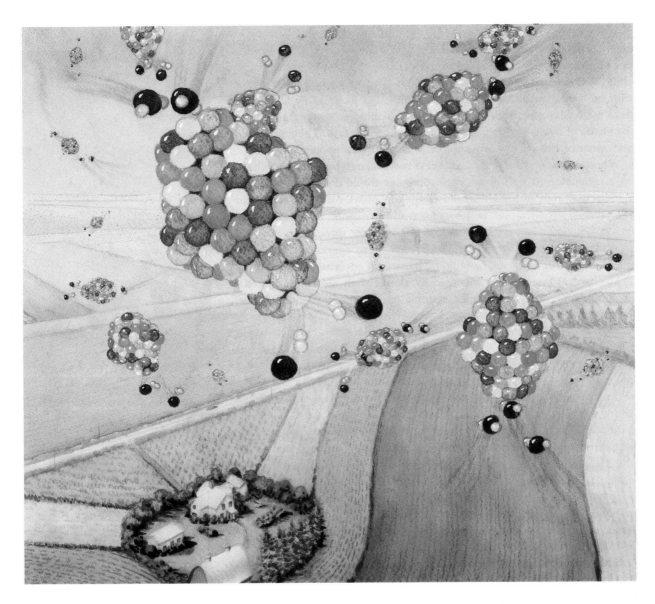

In this fanciful conception of an approach for counteracting environmental degradation, nanomachines suspended in the air like volcanic dust work to break down atmospheric pollutants into harmless compounds. Nanomachines may prove to be inexpensive, efficient alternatives to more conventional solutions for many problems in industry, medicine, and the environment.

Illustration by Leon Bishop

will become possible. Inexpensive fuel and efficient spacecraft made by nanomachines, for example, should eventually make spaceflight less expensive than air travel is today.

Parallels with other products of natural molecular machinery suggest further applications. For example, plants gave Earth its oxygen atmosphere and accumulated the carbon found in coal and oil. Today people fear that rising atmospheric carbon dioxide levels from the burning of fossil fuels may overheat the Earth through the greenhouse effect. If the solution does not come first in some other way (perhaps by the planting of more trees), solar-powered nanomechanisms could reverse the carbon dioxide buildup, taking a few years of operation to turn all the excess carbon dioxide back into carbon and oxygen.

Nanomachines, with their broad ability to rearrange atoms, will be able to recycle almost anything. Using nothing but sunlight and common materials, and with no by-products other than waste heat, they will produce a wide range of products. With production costs similar to those of plants, they will enable the clean, rapid production of an abundance of material goods. The benefits could be especially dramatic for the third world.

Potential medical applications also show that small systems can have big effects. Cells and tissues in the human body are built and maintained by molecular machinery, but sometimes that machinery proves inadequate: viruses multiply, cancer cells spread, or systems age and deteriorate. As one might expect, new molecular machines and computers of subcellular size could support the body's own mechanisms. Devices containing nanocomputers interfaced to molecular sensors and effectors could serve as an augmented immune system, searching out and destroying viruses and cancer cells. Similar devices programmed as repair machines could enter living cells to edit out viral DNA sequences and repair molecular damage. Such machines would bring surgical control to the molecular level, opening broad new horizons in medicine.

While contemplating the potential benefits of nanotechnology, though, one would be well advised to spend time contemplating its potential harm. The chief danger is not likely to be that of runaway accidents; replicators, for example, need no more have the ability to function in a natural environment than an automobile has the ability to refuel from tree sap. Deliberate abuse is another matter. One need only consider the prospect of programmable "germs" for biological warfare to see the seriousness of the problem.

Nanotechnology will let humankind control the structure of matter, but who will control nanotechnology? The chief danger is not a great accident but a great abuse of power. In a competitive world, nanotechnology will surely be developed. If democratic institutions are to guide its use, it must be developed by groups within the political reach of those institutions. To keep nanotechnology from being wrapped in military secrecy, it seems wise to emphasize its value in medicine, in the economy, and in restoring the environment. Nanotechnology must be developed openly to serve the general welfare. Society will have years to shape policies for its beneficial use, but it is not too soon to begin the effort.

FOR ADDITIONAL READING

A. K. Dewdney, "Nanotechnology," *Scientific American* (January 1988, pp. 100–103).

K. Eric Drexler, *Engines of Creation* (Anchor/Doubleday, 1986).

K. Eric Drexler, "Exploring Future Technologies," in *The Reality Club*, John Brockman, ed. (Lynx, 1988).

Richard Feynman, "There's Plenty of Room at the Bottom," in *Miniaturization*, H. D. Gilbert, ed. (Reinhold, 1961).

Foresight Update (Foresight Institute, Box 61058, Palo Alto, CA, 94306).

Jean-Marie Lehn, "Supramolecular Chemistry," *Angewandte Chemie, International English Edition* (vol. 27, 1988, pp. 90–112).

Shawna Vogel, "The Shape of Proteins to Come," *Discover* (October 1988, pp. 38–43).

PROFILING THE

EARTH'S

INTERIOR

by Drum H. Matthews

Using powerful new remote-sensing techniques,
geologists are making new discoveries about
the structures too deep beneath the Earth's
surface to be studied in any other way.

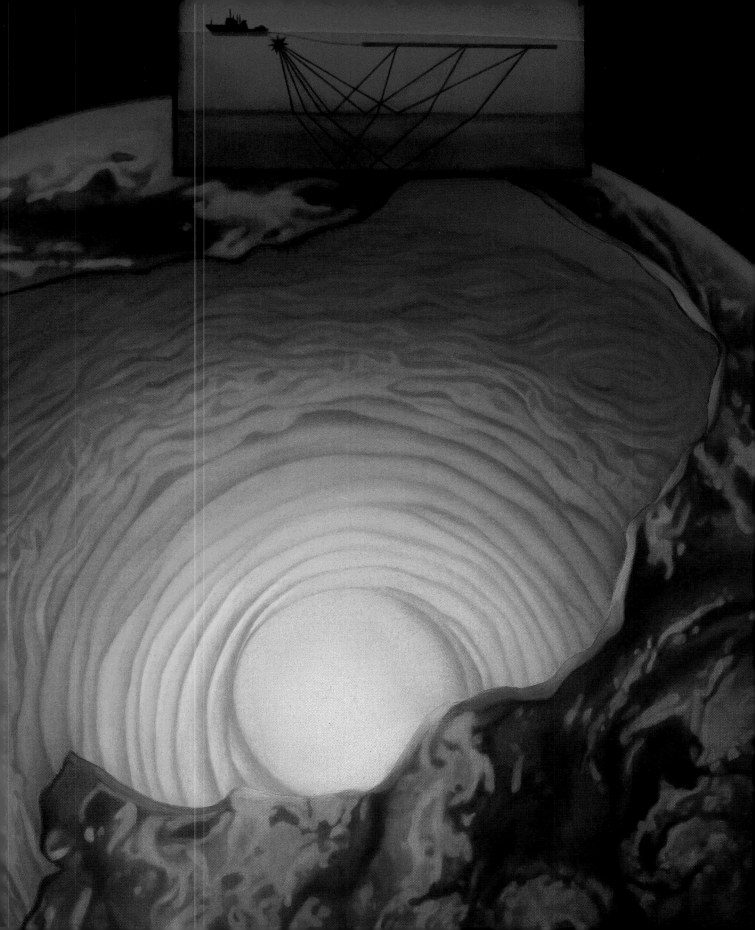

DRUM H. MATTHEWS is a Professor of Earth Sciences at the University of Cambridge, England, and a member of the British Institutions Reflection Profiling Syndicate.

(Overleaf) Illustration by Jane Meredith

Geologists, moving about the surface of the Earth, are able to map the distribution of different sorts of rocks. Dipping interfaces between them can be extrapolated down beneath the Earth's surface to infer the three-dimensional shape of rock bodies, and in some areas geologists can extend these observations by looking at cliff or mountain faces or by studying the results of drilling. (A dip, in geology, is the angle that a stratum or fault plane makes with the horizontal; a fault is a fracture in rock along which adjacent rock surfaces are differentially displaced). The deepest hole on Earth as of 1988 was the Soviet drill hole into the Kola Peninsula, which extended 12½ kilometers (one kilometer is about 0.62 mile) into crystalline rocks; most other holes are much shallower, and most are drilled into sedimentary rocks during searches for oil. In the lower crust and upper mantle, below the depth to which one may confidently extrapolate or drill, geologic structures have been left to the imagination of scientists. During the past ten years, however, new techniques of deep seismic reflection profiling, originally developed by the oil industry, have yielded factual information about such depths, although they cannot yet tell geologists all that they want to know.

Most rocks exposed at the surface are sediments, but in many places the underlying crystalline strata poke through. In some areas intrusive rocks can be seen; formed by melting crystalline rocks, these are pale granites and dark-colored gabbros. Molten rock (magma) is sometimes extruded at the surface as volcanic lava. Lavas and granites have not always appeared at the same place on the Earth's surface throughout geologic time, and many geologists see the problem of accounting for

Crust and mantle: lithosphere and asthenosphere

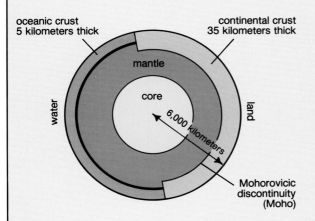

Figure 1. Cutaway drawing of the Earth's interior reveals, in concentric layers, the core, the mantle, the Mohorovicic Discontinuity (Moho, the boundary between the crust and the mantle), and a crust of varying thickness depending on whether it lies beneath deep oceans or under continents. Recent research has demonstrated that there are limitations to this concentrically layered model.

The crust and mantle of the Earth are best defined in terms of their seismic velocities; the crust is the outer part of the Earth in which seismic P waves travel with velocities less than 7.6 kilometers per second (4.7 miles per second). The boundary between the crust and mantle, the Moho, is at a depth between 30 and 80 kilometers (20 and 50 miles) beneath the continents. Lithosphere and asthenosphere are best defined in terms of stiffness or strength. The lithosphere is the cool, upper, rigid rock unit of the Earth, with a thickness strongly dependent on temperature. It lies about 100–200 kilometers (60–125 miles) under the continents and, therefore, includes the crust and uppermost mantle. The asthenosphere is the zone under the lithosphere where the rocks of the upper mantle approach their melting temperature and lose their strength. It is apparently identical with the low-velocity channel of Gutenberg, where S waves travel anomalously slowly. Deeper into the Earth the temperature continues to rise, but the effects of increasing pressure raise the melting point, and the rocks regain strength.

the movements of thermal energy within the Earth as central to their essential task of understanding the historical development of the planet since its formation an estimated 4.5 billion years ago.

Experiments in the laboratory have made clear the conditions of pressure, temperature, and stress under which sedimentary and intrusive rocks melt or are metamorphosed into crystalline basement rocks. These findings are used by geologists to infer conditions deep into the crust and upper mantle (Figure 1). However, below the depths to which surface observations can be extrapolated downward with confidence, observations can be made only by remote-sensing techniques. These can yield information on the physical properties of rocks, although they seldom provide decisive information on the questions that interest geologists most—the composition, mineral content, and age of formation of the rocks.

Of the remote-sensing techniques, the one that has yielded the most information during the 20th century is seismology, the study of the propagation of elastic waves through the Earth following an earthquake or an explosion. This article is concerned with one seismological technique, deep seismic reflection profiling. It is yielding unique new insights into geologic structures in the outer part of the Earth under the continents. First, however, it is necessary to understand some of the results of classical seismology, which has yielded most of the information about the deeper interior of the Earth.

Classical seismology

Seismographs were first deployed at the end of the 19th century, when instrumental seismology was born. The sources of the data recorded on these instruments were earthquakes. By 1914 tables of seismic-wave travel times provided knowledge of the distribution of seismic velocity within the Earth for P waves (primary) and S waves (secondary) (Figure 2). Revisions of these tables were made, most notably in 1929, and by World War II the general distribution of velocity with depth in the Earth was known. Well before that time an analysis of the data obtained comparatively close to the focus of an earthquake that occurred in 1909 in Hungary had led Croatian geophysicist Andrija Mohorovicic to the conclusion that there was a discontinuity in velocity at the base of the crust, where the velocity of P waves increased suddenly to about 8.2 kilometers per second. This feature has been found to be universal under both continents and oceans, and the Mohorovicic Discontinuity (Moho) is now considered to be the boundary between the crust and the mantle. The terms crust (P-wave velocity of 6 or 7 kilometers per second), mantle (P-wave velocity of 8.2 kilometers per second at the top and 13 kilometers per second at the bottom), and core came into general use about 1939.

The seismographs in use around the world until the 1960s were a motley collection whose instrumental responses varied from one to another. In the 1960s, however, much better seismological observations were needed so that nuclear explosions could be distinguished from naturally occurring earthquakes, a basic requirement for establishing an

a

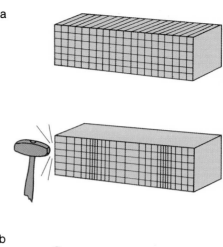

b

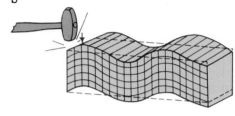

Figure 2. Two kinds of seismic waves can propagate within an elastic body like the Earth: P (primary) waves, in which the particles vibrate back and forth along the direction of propagation (a), and S (secondary) waves, in which the particles vibrate in a plane perpendicular to the direction of propagation (b). P waves travel about 1.7 times faster than S waves, depending on the elastic properties of the medium. S waves cannot pass through a fluid, whereas P waves can.

181

effective nuclear test-ban treaty. Consequently, the United States set up the World-wide Standardized Seismograph Network (WWSSN). With identical seismographs in use throughout the world, seismology took a great leap forward. It became possible to determine the direction of slip across fault surfaces within rocks, providing the essential key to the theory of plate tectonics. Moreover, it became clear that the concept of a concentrically layered Earth was no longer plausible.

Since that time much attention has been paid to the study of the small differences between the travel times of seismic waves predicted from the tables and the actual travel times observed. It is clear that the seismic velocities vary somewhat from place to place in the crust and mantle. However, the techniques of classical earthquake seismology do not have the resolution needed for mapping minor departures from the average velocity structure.

Explosion seismology

Classical seismologists study seismic waves generated by earthquakes and, more recently, by large chemical or nuclear explosions. An earthquake occurs when elastic energy accumulated during many years of gradual deformation of the crust is suddenly released and rocks slide past each other along a fault surface. Earthquakes can release large amounts of energy, and the source is rich in S waves. Seismic waves from a substantial earthquake or a nuclear explosion can be detected by suitable seismographs throughout the world. The time of an earthquake is unpredictable, however, and quakes generally occur only in relatively restricted "seismic zones" that are not distributed uniformly around the Earth. For observations out to distances of a few tens or hundreds of kilometers from the source, in order to study the velocities in the crust and upper mantle it is much more convenient to use relatively small chemical explosions, fired in the sea or in drill holes on land.

Figure 3 shows the ray paths by which seismic waves can reach a line of detectors suitably spaced along the ground surface away from an

Figure 3. Ray paths are shown in a model. Perpendicular to the front of the seismic wave as it propagates through a medium, ray paths represent the quickest routes for seismic energy to travel from shot to receiver through a structure. If seismic velocity increases downward in a layer, the rays entering the layer at a glancing angle will be bent by refraction and eventually turned and sent back to the surface. Such rays are the ones involved in "refraction" experiments.

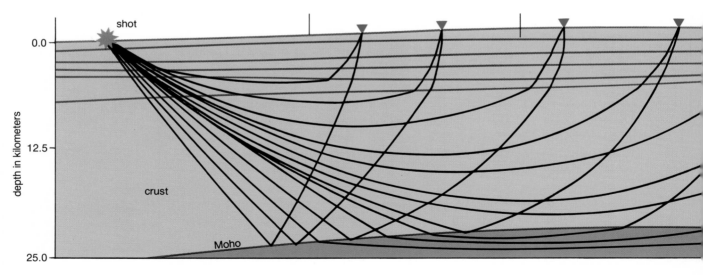

explosion fired in a drill hole. For the structure assumed in the model, in which the seismic velocity increases gradually downward in each layer and the velocity of the next layer down is discontinuously higher than in the previous layer, the first sound to arrive will have traveled most of the distance in the layer in which the ray was turned back to the surface. Arrival times at successive detectors (geophones) for which this sort of ray path is operative will enable the sound velocity in the layer to be determined. Sound that is reflected or refracted at shallow interfaces will reach the geophones later, appearing as impulses on the seismograms after the first arrival.

From the first-arrival times and, if one is lucky, from second or later arrivals, it is possible to build up a picture of the depth and the shape of layers and the velocity of seismic waves in them. This was the basis of the refraction method used by the oil industry in prospecting in the 1930s and 1950s, and it is still used by academic geologists to determine the velocity structure of the inaccessible bits of the crust beneath the deep oceans and on the continents.

A major advance—perhaps the most important observation by earth scientists in the 20th century—was made by British and U.S. geophysicists using the refraction method in the deep oceans during the ten years after 1945. They established that the Moho under the deep oceans is only five kilometers beneath the seafloor; that is, there are five kilometers of crustal rocks above the mantle. By contrast, the crust under the continents varies in thickness from about 30 to about 50 kilometers, though it is 80 kilometers thick under Tibet.

A glance at Figure 3, however, reveals the limitation of the refraction method. The rays must travel a long way through the overlying rocks before they sample the layer whose velocity and depth are being determined. If the overlying layers are not as uniform as they are in the model, some rays will be more delayed than others and the velocity and depth estimate will be wrong. Refraction seismology has the advantage of yielding velocity estimates but, as with classical seismology, it cannot

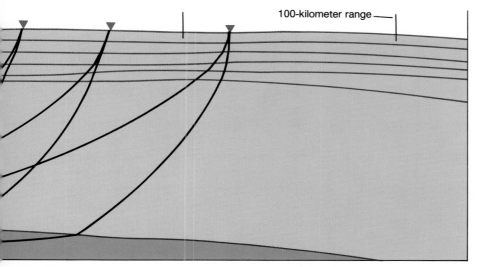

100-kilometer range

Figure 4. Among sound sources on land are explosives fired within a hole drilled into the ground (above) and a heavy truck that is lifted up on a base plate and vibrated hydraulically, transmitting a known signal into the ground (left). The signals from such sources are received on groups of geophones and then recorded on one channel of a multichannel tape in a recording truck (below).

resolve small structures such as those that serve as traps for oil. In the 1960s the oil industry began using another explosion seismological technique, normal-incidence reflection, as almost its sole method of exploration. Academic scientists were relatively slow to follow suit, constrained perhaps by lack of funds and by having different interests from those of the oil industry. By 1988, however, they were doing so, and the results were startling.

Normal-incidence reflection profiling

If one looks closely at the ray paths shown in Figure 3, it can be seen that they are of two sorts: rays that are refracted below interfaces and rays that are reflected from interfaces. For the rays that are reflected the distance between source and receiver is comparable to or greater than the depth to the reflector. It is not necessary, however, to go so far to receive reflected energy; indeed, the ideal would be to have the point at which the explosion originates (shot point) and the receiver at exactly the same place. In that way the reflected ray would be perpendicular to the surface of the reflector, just as it is when one sees one's eye in the mirror. Such rays travel the minimum possible distance through overlying strata and are least likely to be affected by velocity variations en route. Normal-incidence reflection profiling offers the best possible chance of detecting small geologic structures at depth; *i.e.*, it has the best possible resolving power.

184

Unfortunately, it is not possible to place a single geophone on the ground close to the top of the drill hole in which the explosive shot is fired (Figure 4) or to place a single hydrophone close to the sound source towed behind the ship when profiling at sea (Figure 5). Apart from the risk of blowing up the detector, there is the probability that waves traveling along the ground surface from the shot ("ground-roll") or through the sea, though moving comparatively slowly, will reach the detector first and blot out the reflections from deep interfaces. Moreover, there are many possible "multiple" ray paths that are reflected up and down between interfaces before reaching the surface; there are waves reflected through the sea from headlands or rocks on the seabed or from off-line geologic features (those that are out to the side of the line of the profile) underground; and there is the noise from vehicles or wind or waves at sea. Early seismic reflection crews working for the oil industry in the southern United States during the 1930s developed the

Figure 5. "Air guns" (above) generate underwater explosions by suddenly releasing compressed air into the sea. The research ship shown above left tows two arrays of such guns and also a long thin tube that contains hydrophones to detect the reflected sound.

(Both pages) photos, courtesy, PRAKLA-SEISMOS AG

185

technique of recording the signals from a number of geophone groups spread along the ground surface in order to combat and recognize these "noise" arrivals and to distinguish them from the "primary" reflections that they wanted to map across potentially oil-bearing structures.

The advent of magnetic tape recording in the 1950s made it possible to record several "channels" of information on different tracks of a wide tape and to manipulate the signals before display. In the 1960s digital recording on magnetic tape swiftly transformed the seismic reflection technique into the major tool used in the search for oil on land and under the shallow sea on the continental shelf. Digital processing of the data by large and fast computers, combined with electronic color displays, enabled the oil industry to understand the three-dimensional shape of buried rock bodies in sedimentary basins in a way that was undreamed of in 1960. It also enabled academic scientists to distinguish the weak reflections from structures deep in the crust and mantle in a way that was previously inconceivable.

This is not the place to write about the techniques of seismic reflection data processing. It will be enough to say that the objective is to combine the signals from individual geophone groups that are spaced out along a line on the land surface or hydrophones spaced out behind a ship so as to simulate the signal that would have been received by the ideal arrangement of a coincident shot point and receiver. A seismic record consists of a large number of these simulated "normal incidence" recordings (of geophone voltage plotted against time) displayed side by side (Figure 6). All the records illustrated in this article were processed in this way. During the processing, steps are taken to filter out unwanted signals, to determine velocities in the upper layers, to eliminate the rapidly varying time delays due to variations in soil and weathered rock layers near the surface, and to filter out events that do not appear to be real primary reflections. Finally, the gain is adjusted so that the weak echoes from

Figure 6. A seismic record consists of simulated "normal incidence" (coincident shot point and receiver) traces (recordings of hydrophone voltage plotted against time, one per shot), displayed side by side (a); to facilitate correlations from shot to shot the positive wiggles are shaded. Line drawings (b) are made of the correlations apparent in (a); the two reflections are from the seabed and from a faulted rock layer beneath it. Ray paths that would have been produced by the shots in (a) are shown in (c). If the rock layers are not flat, normal incidence reflections do not come from immediately beneath the shot. Additional computer processing can transform this time section into a depth section (a plot of surface, horizontal distance against vertical depth in the Earth) that places reflectors from dipping layers more nearly into their true spatial positions (d). A small portion of the seismic record shown in Figure 9 reveals many traces plotted close together so that deep reflections can be more easily correlated from trace to trace (e).

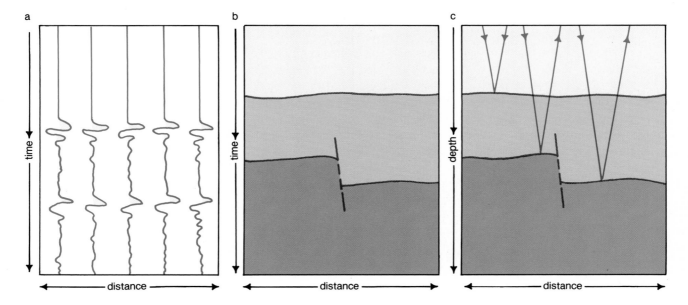

deep reflectors far from the source can be seen on the record as well as the strong echoes from shallow reflectors.

All these processes work on real data, but none of them works perfectly. The final result is only a fair approximation of the ideal one that would be obtained from the coincident shot point-receiver configuration. Much of the noise has been eliminated, but the record still contains unwanted "nongeologic" signals. The records are played out by the computer side by side, usually as wiggle-traces of geophone (or hydrophone) voltage. The traces are arranged on a long strip of paper, the distance from shot to shot scaled along the long axis of the strip and the echo time on the other axis. Such a chart is called a time section. If the processing has been done adequately, the eye can easily follow reflections, correlating wiggles from trace to trace, even if they are not clearly larger on a single trace than are the wiggles of the uncorrelated random noise.

It is easy for an enthusiastic geologist to regard such a time section as though it were in some sense a cliff section through the Earth. It is not. At best it is a plot of echo times and relative echo strengths from a line of impulse sources and coincident receivers placed along the earth (or sea) surface. The echo strength from an interface between two rock layers depends on the difference of their acoustic impedances. (Acoustic impedance is the product of density and seismic velocity; density in rocks varies only from two to three grams per cubic centimeter, while velocity increases from two to seven kilometers per second, and so most of the change in acoustic impedance is due to changes in seismic velocity.) Seismic velocity, determined from the echo time, is not well correlated with rock type. More important, the reflection does not necessarily come from beneath the shot point, where it appears on the record from an individual shot in the time section. If it is assumed that all the reflections come from the plane of the section and that none are from suitably inclined reflectors out of the plane of the section, and if the seismic

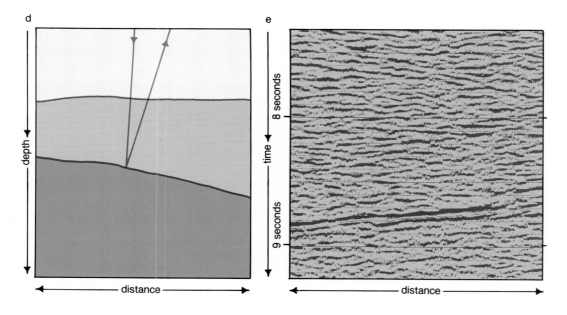

velocities are known at all points in the section (which they generally are not in deep seismic profiles), then, given a fast computer and a lot of storage, it is possible to convert the time section into a depth section in which reflectors appear in their proper places.

Deep seismic reflection profiling

Academic scientists have always been interested in the basement crystalline rocks in the Earth's lower crust and upper mantle, wishing to understand how the crust deforms under stress. Inferences can be made from the rocks exposed at the surface and from classical seismology, but the sudden improvement in seismic reflection techniques in the 1960s appeared to offer the chance of direct observation of rocks in the lower crust. For example, it might be possible to find out what happens to major geologic faults at great depths. Clearly they do not go all through the Earth, detaching a cap from the globe, but surface observations have no means of finally settling such questions.

In the mid-1970s Jack Oliver had recently moved from Lamont-Doherty Geological Observatory, part of Columbia University, New York City, where he had played a major role in the development of the theory of plate tectonics, to Cornell University, Ithaca, New York. He saw that the improvements in seismic reflection techniques might enable these techniques to be used effectively for looking much deeper into the Earth than the 10–12 kilometers achieved by the oil industry. By 1975 he had assembled funds and set up the Consortium for Continental Reflection Profiling, COCORP, a group of academic and industrial seismologists and geologists from all parts of the United States.

COCORP's first profiles, totaling 37 kilometers, were obtained in Hardeman County, Texas. Several strong, flat-lying reflectors were obtained down to an echo time of 4 seconds, and reflections were obtained from the depth range 11–15 seconds, one of which may have been from the Moho. Although these results were not dramatic when compared with subsequent records obtained by COCORP and by other groups worldwide, they were enough to demonstrate that the technique worked at Moho depths.

These experiments in the United States were not the first in the world. During the 1950s Gerhard Dohr had left recorders running during industry reflection surveys at 45 sites in West Germany and had plotted histograms of reflections that showed clear evidence of reflections from the lower crust and the Moho. Similar results were reported from the Soviet Union in 1962. By the early 1970s several reflection profiles had been obtained in West Germany. The reflections, particularly those near the Moho, were quickly interpreted as being from lamellations— thin (approximately 100 meters [330 feet]) rock layers with alternately high and low seismic velocities. In Canada researchers reported some 90 kilometers of deep-reflection profile obtained in southern Alberta during 1964. They too reported reflections from the lower part of the continental crust and from the Moho, which is at about 14 seconds in Alberta.

These highly successful experiments were not followed up, partly because of lack of funds and partly because of the barely adequate seismic prospecting techniques of the time. COCORP was formed and funded at exactly the right moment. By 1987 it had acquired more than 10,000 kilometers of profile across the continental United States.

By 1988 research groups were collecting deep (15-second echo time) reflection profiles in many countries; there were four independent groups in the United States and teams in Canada, the United Kingdom, France, West Germany, Sweden, Australia, and New Zealand, to name only the longer established. The group in the United Kingdom, BIRPS (British Institutions Reflection Profiling Syndicate), collected 12,000 kilometers of profile at sea over the wide continental shelf around Britain. This became, therefore, the best known part of the Earth's lithosphere, since 12,000 kilometers represents about one-third of the world's deep seismic profiling. BIRPS worked with seismic contracting vessels, using a tuned array of air guns as a source (Figure 6). Signals were recorded on a hydrophone streamer 3 to 4.2 kilometers in length with groups spaced every 50 meters; a typical record length is 15 seconds. BIRPS also recorded for longer times with shots that were necessarily more widely spaced. A particularly successful line was recorded to 30 seconds echo time and received reflections from structures 80 kilometers below the surface.

Remote sensing in the Earth sciences by geophysical techniques is particularly dependent on technological advances in electronics and engineering. When a new type of measurement becomes possible, results rush in, capsizing cherished theories. Misunderstandings and arguments are rife, and the old guard say that the new observations have raised more problems than they have solved. That is a fair description of the position in deep seismic profiling ten years after the technique was developed. The advancing edge of lively science is never neat and tidy. There are plenty of new data but few widely accepted interpretations. For the remainder of this article a few examples will be chosen to illustrate the state of play.

Thrust faulting

In 1976 and 1977 COCORP ran a profile across the Wind River Mountains in western Wyoming. The mountains trend northwest to southeast and are some 220 kilometers long and 70 kilometers wide, forming one range of the southern Rocky Mountains. Ancient crystalline rocks formed in the lower or middle crust are exposed in the core of the mountains, and on their southwest face these crystalline rocks can be seen to have been thrust over the flat-lying sedimentary rocks of the Green River Basin. Several holes drilled for oil through the toe of the thrust penetrated the crystalline rocks and reached into the underlying, much younger sediments. The thrust is a major geologic structure: the vertical displacement of the boundary between the sediments in the Green River Basin and the underlying crystalline basement rocks exposed in the mountains must exceed 13 kilometers. The Wind River Mountains are the largest of several Laramide basement uplifts in Wyoming, all of which are bounded by thrust faults.

Although it was well known that the Wind River thrust dipped at 30°–40° to the northeast at the places where it had been drilled, its attitude at depth was not known and was the subject of controversy. Either the thrust becomes steeper at depth, suggesting that all the Laramide uplifts are caused by vertical forces bringing up blocks of the crystalline basement, or the thrust maintains its relatively slight dip, in which case the stress that raised the basement must have been dominantly horizontal. The active plate margin of western North America, from which such stresses are presumed to originate, lay about 1,000 kilometers to the west of the Wind River Mountains at the time of the Laramide phase of uplift of the Rocky Mountains, about 80 million to 40 million years ago. Many Earth scientists were willing to assert that the lithosphere is not strong enough to transmit horizontal stress over such distances.

The COCORP profile obtained reflections from the Wind River thrust zone down to a depth of at least 24 (possibly 36) kilometers (Figure 7). The structure appears to be relatively planar, not steepening with depth. Thus, at the time of the Laramide uplifts of the southern Rockies, the lithosphere was able to transmit horizontal stress for 1,000 kilometers.

After COCORP ran the Wind River thrust line, other low-angle faults in crystalline rocks were found to be reflective. In sedimentary basins faults are largely inferred from the truncation of reflections from interfaces between flat-lying sedimentary rock units, but the faults themselves are seldom reflective. In crystalline rocks they are reflective, but no one knows why; mylonite zones (zones of extra-fine-grained rocks formed by intense shearing) and the presence of fluids trapped within the shear zones have been suggested as being able to change the acoustic impedance sufficiently to account for the reflections.

Composite sections, admittedly with more gaps than profile as yet, have been published across North America, the British Isles, and parts of

190

western Europe. They reveal that the continental crust down to the Moho is full of dipping reflectors, some of which can be correlated with thrust faults known and dated from surface geologic mapping. It is difficult to find areas of the land surface and upper continental crust that have not been moved at some time or other along dipping faults, away from the lower crust and upper mantle that originally underlay them. For example, a COCORP profile crosses the crystalline core of the Blue Ridge Mountains, the crystalline rocks of the Piedmont region, and the sediments of the Atlantic Coastal Plain. It revealed a gently dipping reflector that extends for 300 kilometers eastward under the crystalline rocks of the Blue Ridge and Piedmont before plunging down into the lower crust. At the west end this reflector comes to the surface in a thrust fault that brings the Blue Ridge crystallines over the ruckled old limestones (Cambro-Ordovician, about 500 million years old) and younger sediments of the Valley and Ridge region to the west. The profile is interpreted as meaning that all the ancient crystalline (Precambrian) rocks exposed in the Blue Ridge Mountains and the Piedmont were transported far to the west on a gently dipping thrust fault during the collision between proto-America and proto-Africa that first raised the Appalachians about 400 million years ago.

Sutures

Geologic ideas based on the theory of plate tectonics postulate that many mountain chains are caused by collisions between continents. The best evidence for intercontinental collisions is the juxtaposition of two quite distinct animal groupings that originally developed on different continents widely separated by deep ocean. In such a case the ocean floor has slid beneath a continent. Eventually the other continent comes along, riding passively on the oceanic plate, and a collision between the conti-

Figure 7. Deep seismic reflection profile (below) represents the upper portion of the thrust of the Wind River Mountains over the flat-lying sedimentary rocks of the Green River Basin in western Wyoming. The arrows define the position of events that represent reflections from the thrust plane. The profile reveals reflections from the flat-lying sediments of the Green River Basin (A), the uplift of sedimentary reflectors under the thrust fault (C), the position of the thrust against the base of the sediments (D), and a thrust reflection in the Precambrian crystalline rocks of the crust (E). Opposite page, a research team investigates the Wind River Mountains. Reflections in the thrust zone were obtained to a depth of at least 24 kilometers (15 miles).

(Below) courtesy of COCORP, Cornell University

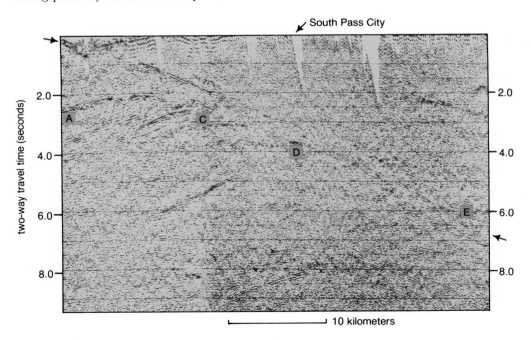

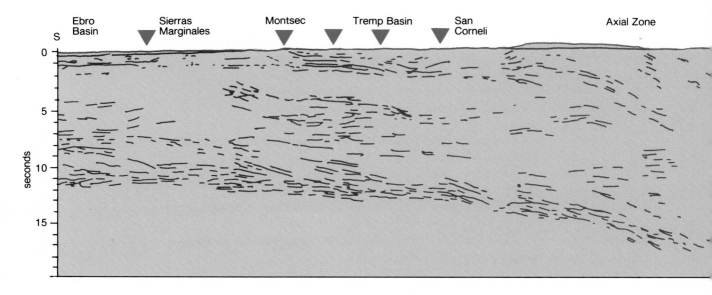

S

Ebro Basin   Sierras Marginales   Montsec   Tremp Basin   San Corneli   Axial Zone

seconds

0

5

10

15

Figure 8. Line drawing shows a deep seismic reflection profile across the Pyrenees Mountains from Spain to France. It reveals that the Moho (the base of the reflectors in the crust) is at a depth of about 10 seconds at the northern end of the mountains and about 12 seconds at the southern end. The reflectors at depths of about five seconds are not displaced by the North Pyrenean Fault, and so it is unlikely that the fault displaces the Moho.

Courtesy of the ECORS Group, Paris, France, and Madrid, Spain

nents ensues. The granitic crust of the continent is too buoyant, because of its relatively low density, to be thrust down into the mantle, and so the two continents collide and thicken by thrusting over each other.

If the process discussed above has been described correctly, one might hope to see something distinctive on deep seismic profiles that cross a suture zone where two different continental basements have been fused together. What one would expect to see depends on the age of the reflective structures imaged in the lower continental crust. If these were formed in the remote past, when the continents were formed, then one might expect to see quite different reflection patterns from two continents that were originally far apart prior to suturing. However, reflection profiling cannot, of itself, date reflectors. If the reflectors are due to fluids, mostly water, passing through the crust, or to basaltic lavas injected into the crust subsequent to suturing, then one would not expect any change at the suture except, perhaps, a dipping reflector marking the suture zone. Therefore, profiles crossing sutures have more significance than mere tests of ideas based on local geology. They also relate to the question of "exotic terranes" swept together in intercontinental collisions.

COCORP profiled three crossings in Georgia of the suture between proto-Africa and proto-North America. On all three crossings there is a broad (20-kilometer), thick band of dominantly south-dipping reflections that extend from the upper crust (not the surface) down through the lower crust until they terminate against the flat-lying reflections that are associated with the Moho. The dipping reflections are accepted as being in some way related to the suture, and this implies that the Moho reflectors have been emplaced after the continental collision. The question then arises as to whether there is any visible difference between the crust on either side of the suture.

The Grenville crust of North America, which underlies the major

192

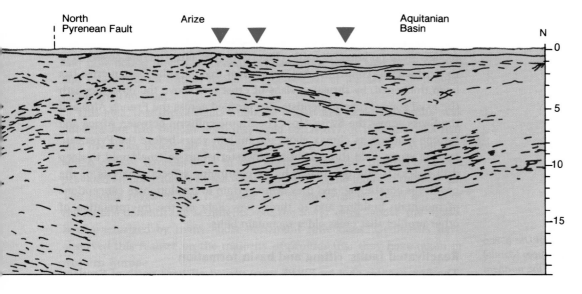

part of North America and the Appalachians, seems to provide few deep reflections or reflections from the Moho. South of the suture, reflections from the Moho are commoner, but the lower crust is reflective on only one out of the three profiles. Therefore, no convincing case can be made for a change in reflection character on either side of the suture.

Young mountains

Clearly, the younger the structures, the less likely they are to have been obscured by subsequent geologic events. In spite of the fact that all of the continental basement has had a long history of faulting and metamorphism, the best chance of understanding the deep structures that raise mountains comes from profiling across mountains that are still rising. This explains the interest in Tibet and the Himalayas, formed by the ongoing collision of India and Eurasia. The Himalayas, however, are difficult places into which to take the large vibrator trucks that are necessary for the experiments.

In 1985–86 French and Spanish scientists arranged to profile across the Pyrenees Mountains. Formed by movements between Spain and the rest of Europe about 40 million years ago, this mountain range has the geometry of a fan. In the north rocks have been thrust to the north over the foreland sediments of the Aquitaine basin in France. In the central area (the axial zone) the steeply dipping crystalline core is exposed. In the south the rocks are thrust to the south over the foreland sediments of the Ebro basin in Spain. The range is narrow from north to south; a north-south profile that was 250 kilometers long reached from Aquitaine to Ebro. Separating the Aquitaine and the crystalline axial zone, a major east-west fault, the North Pyrenean Fault Zone, had previously been thought to displace the Moho abruptly ten kilometers downward to the south. Four models for the deep structure of the Pyrenees were proposed,

Computer Viruses

by Eric J. Lerner

Programs that can spread rapidly
from machine to machine,
computer viruses can destroy
thousands of data files and
cripple central processors.
Defending against them may
alter radically the ways in which
computers are used.

ERIC J. LERNER *is president of Lerner*
Associates, Lawrenceville, New Jersey.

Illustrations by John Craig

It is November 1992, 9 PM on election night in the United States. Americans are watching the results of a bitter and closely fought election campaign in the midst of a grave economic crisis. Suddenly, CBS reports a computer difficulty that halts the vote tally. Within minutes all the other networks find that their computers are also unusable. By 9:15 all the election computers in the 26 states where polls have closed have also ceased to function, apparently trapped in an endless repetition of meaningless instructions. The election is thrown into chaos.

Election commission computers are far from the only ones afflicted. First in the eastern states but spreading within minutes across the rest of the country, tens, then hundreds, of thousands of computers succumb to the same mysterious malady. Utility companies lose control of the computers that govern power grids and nuclear reactors, leading to emergency shutdowns and blackouts in dozens of cities. Air traffic control computers shut down, halting air travel across the nation. Hundreds of near collisions and two fatal crashes occur as pilots and controllers work feverishly to land the aircraft caught in flight.

At the U.S. Air Force Space Command at Cheyenne Mountain, Colorado, the screens that monitor satellite sensors guarding against a surprise missile attack go blank. In a hurried telephone conference the president of the United States and the nation's top commanders argue about a response. Should the U.S.'s nuclear forces be put on red alert even though relations with the Soviets are the best that they have been in years?

Fortunately, before an alert can be issued, backup computers at Space Command headquarters are turned on, loaded with old but reliable programs, and the crippled computers are turned off. In seconds the screens jump to life, showing no signs of an impending attack.

In an emergency message broadcast over all the networks, military computer experts tell all computer users to turn off their machines, isolate them from outside communications, and reload them only with the oldest available backup disks and programs. The nation is informed that it has been the victim of a massive computer virus attack.

It then takes three weeks to determine who won the election. The destruction of programs and other data, as well as the damage caused by the blackouts, runs into billions of dollars. Months later the source of the computer infection is traced to programs introduced to the U.S. by a terrorist group in revenge for the assassination of an anti-American leader.

This scenario is, of course, fictional. As of today, however, there is nothing that would prevent it from happening. Since 1987 computer users have been increasingly afflicted with computer viruses—programs that instruct computers to copy them onto other programs, thus rapidly spreading the infection from machine to machine. Most viruses are malicious since they also instruct computers at a given signal or on a specified date to destroy data files or to go into repetitive loops of instructions that cripple their central processors.

While the possibility of viruses was beginning to be widely discussed in 1983, the first virus attacks occurred in 1987 and early 1988. During

200

a period of a few months, tens of thousands of computers at universities, government facilities, and major corporations were affected. While in some cases the viruses were relatively harmless pranks, causing computers to display Christmas trees or messages of peace, others destroyed valuable data, in a few cases wiping out student theses involving months or years of work. The programmers who wrote the virus programs, where known, were for the most part simply motivated by an urge to show off their cleverness. In at least one case in Israel, however, political sabotage was the clear aim.

There are no easy defenses against computer viruses. Nearly all computer systems, even those deemed the most secure, are vulnerable to attack. If, as seems likely, viruses become more common and more damaging, they may bring about radical changes in the way computers are used, for the only reasonably sure defense is the curtailment of free communication among computers.

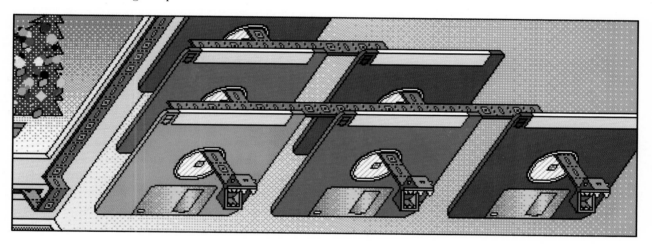

Origin of an epidemic

The epidemic of computer virus attacks began with two cases in November 1987. In the first a group of computer hackers, the Chaos Computer Club in Hamburg, West Germany, penetrated the U.S. National Aeronautics and Space Administration (NASA) Space Physics Analysis Network, a semipublic network used for exchanging technical results. The hackers introduced a virus that spread quickly through the network, causing disks to crash (become inoperable) and data to be erased.

During the same month students from Lehigh University, Bethlehem, Pennsylvania, found that many of the personal computer program disks they had borrowed from the University Computer Center were failing to "boot"—to begin operating when commanded to do so. After comparing their experiences, student programmers started to examine closely other disks in the center's loan library. They found that many had been tampered with and infected with a virus. The virus worked insidiously, initially doing nothing but copying itself onto disks that were being used by the infected program. After four copies were made, however, the virus then destroyed all the disks that were in the computer at that time.

Hundreds of students and faculty members lost theses and other valuable work before the virus was discovered and eradicated.

The next month, during the Christmas holiday season, an innocuous virus written by a West German student entered the main global communications network of the IBM Corp., a network linking approximately 250,000 computers. Within two hours the virus had spread to nearly every computer on the network, copying itself on every machine that had exchanged messages with its current host. When users read their computer mail, the virus drew a Christmas tree on their screens and then erased itself.

At nearly the same time a far more malicious attack was uncovered at the Hebrew University of Jerusalem. Experts detected the virus because an error in its own program was causing it to copy itself repeatedly onto disks that it had already infected. Students found that their programs were growing in size, apparently of their own accord. When this virus was tracked down, it became apparent that it had been introduced for a political purpose. It was programmed to destroy all stored data on May 13, 1988, the 40th anniversary of the last day of Palestine's political existence and the day before Israel's Independence Day. Hundreds of computers were infected before the Israelis were able to circulate a program to erase the virus.

In March 1988 a virus spread for the first time through commercially available software. The virus, fortunately an innocuous one, was carried in Freehand, an Aldus Corp. graphics package designed for use on Macintosh computers. The virus, which may have affected hundreds of thousands of users, displayed a "peace message" from Richard Brandow, the publisher of *MacMag,* a computer magazine. Staffers at *MacMag* had written the virus as an experiment to see how far it would travel. Eventually the virus reached the computer of software executive Marc Canter, whose company, Macromind Inc., was doing contract work for Aldus. The virus then infected a disk that Canter sent to the programmers at Aldus who wrote the Freehand program.

On Nov. 3, 1988, a virus designed as an experiment by a Cornell University graduate student, Robert T. Morris, Jr., spread like wildfire through Arpanet, the U.S. Department of Defense research network. As the virus tied up computer after computer in making thousands of copies of itself, more than 6,000 machines were knocked out. While the virus did no permanent damage, the loss of a day and a half of working time for Arpanet users probably represented a financial loss of nearly $10 million. Morris, the son of one of the nation's leading computer security experts, had not intended to produce the chaos that resulted. By an error he instructed the virus to multiply wildly rather than slowly and quietly as he had planned.

Other viruses have damaged files at the University of Delaware and have spread from there to the headquarters of hundreds of the nation's largest companies. Additional viruses have infected commercial programs. The entire industry is now beginning to recognize that no computer is safe.

202

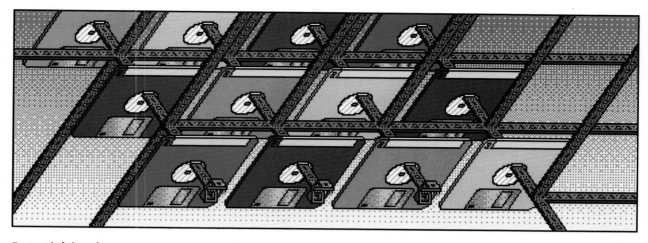

Potential for damage

Thus far, the damage done by computer viruses has been relatively limited. Even the Arpanet incident caused only about $10 million in damages, and other viruses have caused less than one million dollars in damages apiece. But the potential for much more serious consequences is there. Viruses can become far more widespread; they can affect far more critical computers; and they can do more subtle and long-lasting types of damage.

The simplest way to spread viruses is to increase the length of time during which they multiply themselves silently, without any apparent damage. For example, if the Lehigh University virus had copied itself 40 times rather than 4 times before erasing disks, it is entirely possible that, instead of hundreds of copies, tens of millions would have been made before the first copy erased a disk. By that time students using computer bulletin boards and other networks could have unknowingly spread the virus to a large fraction of the world's computers. Similarly, if a virus like the one at the Hebrew University of Jerusalem did nothing for a period of two years and then detonated on a given date, it might well spread as far and do as much or more damage as the hypothetical virus described at the beginning of this article.

Viruses may also affect computers that have functions far more vital than those of the mainly research and administrative machines infected so far. In a test of security at a major European airport, Fred Cohen, a computer expert who first studied viruses in 1983, was able to infect the air traffic control computer within only 17 minutes of launching a virus attack. Motivated by political revenge or blackmail, computer-trained terrorists could disable not only such airport computers but also those that control nuclear reactors or that coordinate the nuclear forces of a superpower. It is already clear that security measures guarding military and other sensitive computers are highly inadequate against virus attacks, because the measures are overwhelmingly aimed at keeping information from leaking out rather than at keeping viruses from coming in.

Finally, viruses do not have to be as obvious as those now in circulation. For purposes of industrial sabotage one company might infect a competitor's industrial-process-control computers with a virus that subtly shifts a control so that the resulting product is just slightly worse. It might be years before the competitor tracks the problem down, and by that time a market advantage might be irretrievably lost.

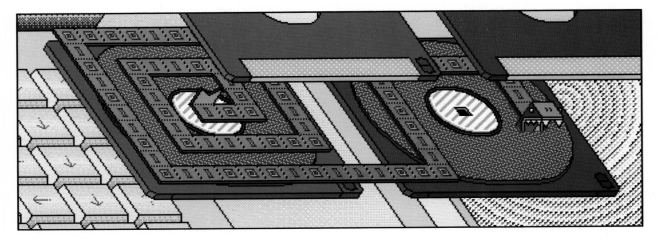

How viruses work

Viruses are so difficult to combat and therefore constitute such a grave threat mainly because there seems to be no limit to the different ways a virus can operate or to its ability to overcome security measures. The current crop of viruses is an elementary, "kindergarten variety," as virus expert Harold J. Highland, editor of *Computers & Security*, puts it. Future versions seem certain to be far worse.

However, since current viruses are so simple, they well illustrate how a virus works. The Lehigh virus is a good example. The virus was initially written into a key part of the operating system of a microcomputer, the heart of a personal computer system. An operating system is the program that runs the computer, calling up from disk storage other programs that a user wants to run. The virus code—its instructions—were placed in a section of the system called COMMAND. COM, a set of instructions that allows the computer to load some other program. This is a particularly vital section that is used whenever the computer is operating. The virus code directed the computer to read its instructions every time COMMAND. COM was used.

Whenever the computer accessed a disk with another program on it, the virus first checked to see if there was a COMMAND. COM on the disk. If there was, the virus told the computer to copy it onto that program, thus infecting it. A counter in the computer's memory kept track of how many copies had been made by a given virus. When four copies were completed, the virus erased the sector map of the disk, the portion that informs a user where all the data on the disk are stored. Without the sector map the disk is useless—effectively destroyed.

A computer virus thus works roughly like a biologic virus. A biologic virus takes over the DNA (deoxyribonucleic acid) instructions that run a cell, making the cell produce copies of the virus. When sufficient viruses

204

have been produced, the virus causes the destruction of the cell, releasing all the other viruses to spread further infection. Similarly, a computer virus takes over the brain of a computer—its central program—and instructs it to both copy the virus and, at a given time, perform some other virus-dictated task, such as displaying a message, destroying stored data, or altering the computer performance.

Unlike biologic viruses, however, computer viruses are products of human intelligence. This means that virtually any defense, once it is known to the attacker, can be easily overcome. The converse is not always the case. If a defender knows a particular virus, he or she can usually write a program to defend against it. It is far more difficult, however, to find out if a given program or disk has already been infected. What is more important is that the defender has to protect against not just one but a host of viruses, both known and unknown. This makes the defender's jobs inherently far more difficult than the attacker's.

Fighting the viruses

During recent months those responsible for computer security have been discovering how vulnerable computers are. In a recent test Highland used viruses to attack the computers of the Australian Strike Force, a high-security military unit. The computers had been equipped with antivirus protection programs. Two of four viruses used were detected, but the other two brought the entire system to a halt.

Many "virus filter" programs have been developed, but nearly all of them are far too simple to work effectively. Most either check for certain suspicious features in programs or issue a warning when a program does something potentially damaging, such as writing to a disk. The problem with the first method is that it is easy to write a virus that avoids the key features that would be checked by any existing filter. Warning programs, on the other hand, produce so many false alarms that they are useless. "You can get a dent in your finger if you have to press a key every time a spreadsheet program wants to write to a disk," commented Cohen.

Cohen proved mathematically that it is impossible to write a program that will detect an arbitrary virus. This means that absolute safety from viruses is impossible and a cure for existing infections very difficult.

There are, however, ways of making life harder for the virus attacker. The three basic approaches are what might be termed global checking, isolation, and limited functionality. In global checking an entire disk or program rather than just certain features is examined. One simple global check is to examine the boot sector maps and directories that describe where data are located on a disk. If a user copies all incoming disks onto those with a given format and sector map, all disks should then have the same map. A virus-altered disk can then be detected by changes in the map. Not all viruses, however, will produce such changes.

A more detailed check is to look at the source codes of incoming programs, examining them manually for peculiar features. With this approach a sufficiently skilled programmer can catch many viruses. The method is very time-consuming, however, and many source codes are

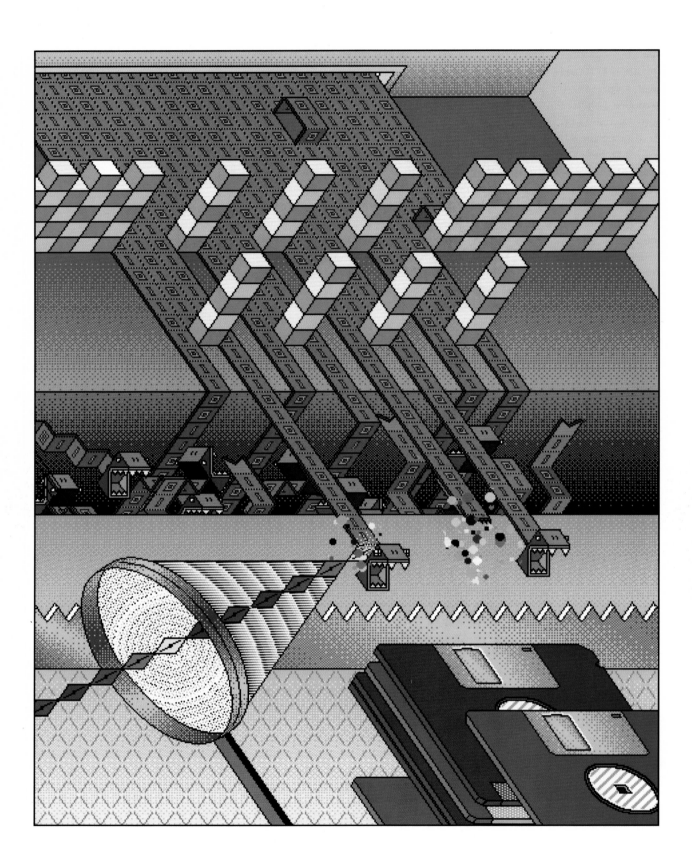

not available for inspection. A virus can avoid any checking routine by deliberately leaving a checked item unchanged or by disguising itself as a useful piece of program. One way around this problem is for the defender to encrypt the checking portion of the program so that the virus, or its programmer, cannot discover what is being checked.

Cohen devised a program that creates an encrypted "checksum" for each disk. The checksum is a number based on the data in each disk that will change if the disk is tampered with by a virus or by anything else. Since the checksum is itself encrypted, a virus must first break the code to find out how to modify the disk while leaving the checksum unchanged, or it must attack the part of the program that does the checksum itself. Thus, it becomes more difficult to make a successful virus.

The second main approach to combating viruses is to quarantine the infection, isolating it from uninfected programs and disks. At the simplest level disks can be "write protected." This physically prevents anyone from recording on the disks; consequently, no virus can be copied onto them. A further precaution is to encrypt programs as they are written

onto a disk and decrypt them as they are used. A virus that copied itself onto such a disk would then be "decrypted" into complete nonsense when the disk was used, thus exposing the existence of the infection without endangering the program.

These methods isolate the disks themselves from the infection. Better still is to prevent a virus from entering the system at all. To achieve this, sets of rules, often termed safe computing practices, are taught to employees of computer facilities. No outside programs are brought into the facility without prior testing in a separate test facility. Electronic mail would be read off-line by stand-alone machines that are not tied into the network from public computer bulletin boards.

While providing increased security, such procedures obviously cut down on the free access to new programs and rely on trusted employees to obey the rules and not deliberately violate them. If still-higher degrees of security are needed, information flow within a facility can be reduced, allowing programs to flow only from more reliable, more highly "cleared" personnel to less reliable ones. Such restrictions on information flow will not preclude the spread of a virus but will prevent its entrance to the most secure parts of the facility. Again, however, security is traded for increased restrictions on information flow. In an extreme case all critical programs for such a facility must be generated internally.

All of these methods rely to varying degrees on trusted employees. The only way to make sure a virus is not imported is to reduce the functionality of the computers used—that is, to eliminate the ability to create new programs. Thus, workstations for secretaries could operate only from word-processing or spreadsheet programs that had been wired in, allowing no programming. Similarly, diskless workstations for engineers attached directly to a central processor could allow users to call up programs but not to enter new ones of their own.

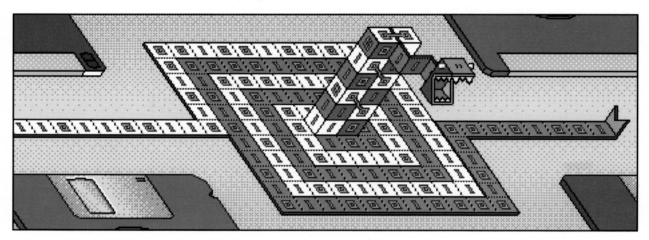

Offense versus defense

As of 1989 computer users were just starting to implement defenses, and viruses remained primitive. As viruses multiply and defenses become more widespread, it seems likely, as Cohen predicts, that a sort of biologic competition will arise, with new viruses and new defenses evolving in tandem. Viruses already can be written that change themselves in random or preprogrammed ways to foil defenses, and defenses also can automatically evolve in a similar fashion.

At present, attackers have a great advantage because of the unlimited variety of viruses possible and the comparatively small number of defenses available. Defenses that employ checking can be overcome by corruption or infection of the part of the program that does the checking. Isolation techniques can fail when users do not follow the rules. As more kinds of defense techniques come into existence, however, it will become more difficult to devise viruses that will get past all of them. Cohen speculated that eventually—in 20 years perhaps—virus defense will be as well understood as computer secrecy techniques are today.

Long before that time, however, viruses are likely to force some changes in the ways in which computers are used. In fact, by 1989 they were already doing so. First, the freewheeling exchange of programs

208

and messages over computer bulletin boards will obviously be sharply curtailed. Potentially this could slow advances in software. It is a waste of time to create one's own software package when a good one is available in the public domain, yet users will now wonder if that free program conceals a dangerous virus.

At the same time, as the virus threat reaches the most secret government-operated facilities, administrators there may be forced to cut back on secrecy. There is a paradoxical trade-off between ensuring secrecy and safeguarding the integrity of programs against viruses. If a facility prohibits information of programs from circulating downward from high- to low-security users for reasons of secrecy and also prevents programs from circulating upward to defend against viruses, nothing will be able to circulate at all. This could potentially cripple the work of programming groups that rely on collective effective efforts when undertaking large projects. Eventually such facilities may decide that it would be better to loosen secrecy restrictions and allow some downward flow of information in order to tighten defenses against viruses and still maintain some communications.

Another major shift may eventually be forced in the copyright laws protecting secret software codes. At present, the laws allow a company to copyright a program without revealing to anyone the source code. Because no one can check the code to make sure that it is uninfected, the spread of viruses is encouraged. By contrast, other copyrights and patents require public revelation.

It seems likely that the virus threat will produce significant pressure to reform the copyright laws, especially to withdraw protection from undisclosed programs. Market forces may help produce the same result as users decline to buy packages that they cannot examine themselves. In the long run, companies may give up their own secrecy in order to maintain access to security-conscious users. This may eventually lead to a restored exchange of programs. Sophisticated programmers, aided by a variety of antivirus procedures, will again be able to access programs freely while inspecting them to ensure freedom from infection.

The road to this future utopia, however, is likely to be rocky. The faster that computer users, especially those with the most vital functions, face up to the virus threat, the better it will be not only for them but for everyone.

Energy Technologies for the 21st Century

by Stephen Kuznetsov

New techniques for generating and storing energy seem certain to change the ways in which power will be supplied and used in the next century.

During the next 15 years, dramatic changes will take place in the ways that households in the United States obtain electric power. The cause of these changes will be the development of commercially feasible small power-generating systems for consumer use. When that development is complete, millions of consumers will have access to resources that will allow them to generate their own power efficiently and reliably.

This article examines five new power technologies that could be in mass production by the year 2001 and that would profoundly affect people's everyday lives. Three of the technologies generate DC (direct current) and AC (alternating current) electric power; a fourth conditions the electric power for practical use; and the fifth is one of the most efficient energy-storage inventions known to modern civilization.

The inventions and technologies described below are truly designed for a new age, as they are used for production rather than consumption of electric power. Furthermore, all the generators described here use renewable energy sources in performing their tasks. Their installation, use, and maintenance in a consumer environment represent a marked change from earlier times, when only power companies produced electric power.

Many incentives will encourage consumers to turn to self-generated electric power. In the past, governments have encouraged the use of solar, geothermal, and wind energy, and they seem likely to do so in the future. For example, since 1978 owners of home power-generating equipment have been guaranteed a fair selling price for the electricity they produce. Utilities are required to purchase from private producers any excess electricity, up to a limit of 80 megawatts, at the prevailing rate. By 2001 that rate could be $0.12 a kilowatt-hour or more, potentially making private power-generating systems an attractive investment.

STEPHEN KUZNETSOV is President and Technical Director of Power Silicon and Monolithic Technologies Corp., Chevy Chase, Maryland.

211

The energy-technology industry is undergoing explosive growth. Almost 4,000 new manufacturers have been springing up in the United States every year and, if current trends continue, that rate is likely to triple by 2001. New manufacturers differ from traditional energy-equipment firms because they concentrate on technologies that are suitable for small-scale applications. Traditional firms have concentrated on large-scale power generation exclusively.

One way to make home power generation practical is to make the technology less intimidating. Microprocessors provide the means to do this. With microprocessor-controlled systems one does not need to be an engineer to maintain a small generating unit. Instead, a microprocessor—perhaps aided by voice-recognition and speech-synthesis systems—can guide an owner through most maintenance and repair operations.

Home heat-generating equipment controlled by microprocessors has already become a part of many households. The equipment ranges from hot-water boilers to automatic fireplace lighters. In most installations, however, all equipment is controlled by a single, central processor—that is, the personal computer.

By 2001 the United States will almost certainly be in the midst of what is called the DIRAC (decentralized indirect-radiated automatic control) era. At that time each piece of energy-producing equipment—including rooftop generators, a basement storage unit, and hidden power modulators—will be controlled by its own microprocessor. Each piece of equipment will be able to react autonomously to conditions for peak

Prototype of a train powered by a linear induction motor is tested in Japan. Such trains have achieved speeds of 400 kilometers (250 miles) per hour.

© Takeshi Takahara—Photo Researchers

212

performance; therefore, no fiber-optic or hard-wire link will be required for modulators. Engineers have even speculated that by 2001 each wall socket in a home will be equipped with microprocessors that, following voice instructions and sensor information, will monitor all appliances and control the distribution of power in the room.

With the dramatic changes in energy technology will come a new language. In particular, five new terms may become familiar: LIMPET—linear induction machine programmed electric turbine; Supersea—superconducting self-excited armature; CAVET—closed-cycle advanced vapor electro-turbogenerator; FC—fuel cell; and PM—power modulator.

The LIMPET—an idea from the past

Roughly 15 years ago the linear induction motor (LIM), in which the motion between the rotor and the stator is linear rather than rotary, was introduced as a replacement for conventional electric motors in high-speed mass transit. LIM-powered trains built in the U.S. achieved record-breaking ground-transportation speeds of more than 400 kilometers (250 miles) per hour in 1974. However, scientists have predicted that homeowners and farmers will be the most common users of linear induction in the future.

The LIMPET is a relative of the LIM of the 1970s, although the mechanics behind the technique originally were conceived by Leonardo da Vinci in the 15th century. The device uses wind energy, a renewable energy source, to generate continuous AC electric power at 60 hertz in a way that differs dramatically from conventional wind-energy systems. Conventional systems use rotary-turbine motion and a rotary generator in one form or another and commonly employ one of two designs—either the generator is directly attached to the propeller, or it is connected to the blading through a long shaft, allowing the generator to be mounted on the ground. The latter design is that of a windmill, long a fixture in rural America. By 2001 those windmills will have been replaced with one or more LIMPETs, which will be mounted on the roof of a barn or a house (Figure 1).

The windmill is commonly used in rural areas to generate power by harnessing the energy of the wind. By the year 2001 energy researchers expect that many windmills will have been replaced with one or more LIMPETs (linear induction machine programmed electric turbines) mounted on the roof of a barn or a house.

Figure 1 (below right). A full-scale LIMPET is mounted on the roof of a house in Maryland. Its height of only 13 centimeters (5 inches) allows it to be unobtrusive, and its design eliminates the gyroscopic forces associated with large rotary turbines. Figure 2 (bottom). The LIMPET generates electricity by means of blades mounted on a conductive movable belt that surrounds an armature consisting of copper wires wound on a steel core. When wind strikes the blades, the belt moves, and 60-hertz electricity is produced.

Many features make the LIMPET an attractive investment. For example, its low height of 15 centimeters (6 inches) or less allows it to be unobtrusive and environmentally benign. Other advantages are its use of a renewable energy source and the elimination of the gyroscopic forces associated with large rotary turbines.

The principles governing the LIMPET are shown in Figure 2. It generates electricity by means of a bladed "venetian blind" system mounted on a conductive movable belt. The armature consists of an array of copper coils wound on a steel core. When wind strikes the blades, the belt moves, and 60-hertz electricity is generated in a manner analogous to the way electricity is generated in a rotary system. The belt generates electricity any time it moves at a speed between 0.3 and 8 meters (one and 25 feet) per second.

Current prototype LIMPETs have a power density of about 110 watts per kilogram (50 watts per pound). This means that a unit capable of producing 10,000 watts (10 kilowatts) will weigh 90 kilograms (200 pounds). Mounting such a unit on a roof is not a particularly easy task, but by the year 2001, lighter units, perhaps with aluminum belts and blades, are expected to be available. Those units will have lower power outputs, of approximately two kilowatts; however, many applications re-

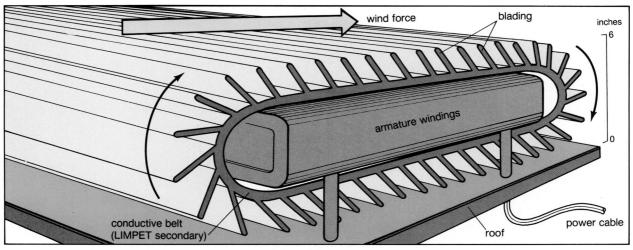

quire only that amount of power. If higher capacity is needed, two or more units can be used.

Energy storage

The LIMPET is just one of several power-generation technologies currently under investigation; two others, the CAVET and the fuel cell, are examined below. However, no matter what technology is used, one of the most significant problems in making the decentralized production of power practical is energy storage.

The element niobium—or, to be more precise, a wire made of a niobium-tin alloy—resolves the energy-storage problem. This wire has an extraordinary property—its electrical resistance drops to near zero at very low temperatures.

During the past 20 years, scientists at the United States National Laboratories have found that a supercooled electromagnetic coil made of that wire can be used to "store" a DC current for up to several days. That discovery lies at the heart of a technology dubbed Supersea. A cross section of such a superconducting armature is shown in Figure 3. Primarily it consists of a magnetic coil and a miniature refrigerator; there are no moving parts.

Figure 3. Cross section reveals the Supersea superconducting armature, which uses the property of a wire made of a niobium-tin alloy to "store" an electric current for several days. Supersea consists of an armature shield (0), armature conductors (1), stainless steel rotor damper shields (2), a copper ambient temperature damper (3), compression spacers (4), a vacuum (5), an 80 K heat radiation shield (6), a 4.2 K liquid helium containment vessel (7), rotor torque transfer banding (8), niobium-tin superconductor field winding (9), liquid helium cooling ducts (10), a field winding containment block (11), and rotor torque axial transfer coupling (12).

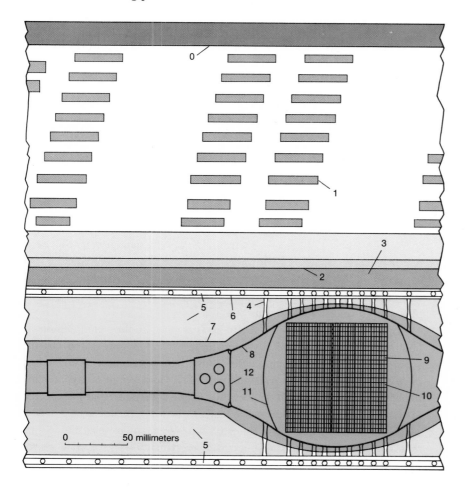

In 1989 several U.S. and Canadian companies were investigating the use of superconductive energy-storage coils for residences. Niobium-tin wire, which had been expensive and difficult to obtain, was being produced in larger quantities, though it still was appropriate only for winding miniature electromagnets. Such electromagnets are of limited utility; for instance, one measuring 0.6 × 0.9 meter (2 × 3 feet) would be capable of storing 4,000 kilojoules of energy. In practical terms, that is enough energy to power an appliance that draws 11 kilowatts, such as a large electric range, for one hour. A practical superconducting armature for a typical home is expected to weigh 115–135 kilograms (250–300 pounds). The price of niobium-tin wire is expected to have dropped dramatically by 2001 so that a unit could cost as little as $3,000–$5,000.

Supersea is an appropriate name for the technology since the unit provides a "sea of reserve energy" sitting (in the basement of the house) and ready to leap into action when needed. When the technology is mature, the owner of a large rooftop solar array will no longer have to use the energy only at midday. Instead, 95% of the energy generated at that time will be available at 6 PM. Supersea technology, therefore, will greatly increase the practicality of using climate-dependent solar and wind technologies.

There is one disadvantage to this technology—it is capable of storing energy only in the form of direct current (DC). The presence of AC causes the wire to lose its superconducting properties. Power modulators offer a solution to this problem. They can convert DC to 60-hertz AC in order to power all of the appliances in a home.

Power modulator

All of the power technologies now under investigation seem to share one common feature—they seem to operate best at some frequency other than 60 hertz. The task of translating frequencies produced by home-generating or storage equipment to 60 hertz will be handled by a power modulator. It will be able to handle three tasks: conversion from DC power to 60-hertz AC, inversion from low-frequency AC to 60-hertz AC, and cycloconversion from high-frequency AC to 60-hertz AC.

In contrast to the power electronics of 1989, which requires completely separate units to perform each of those steps, it is expected that by 2001 integrated power modulators capable of performing all three will have become available. Advances in semiconductor technology will play a large role in making this possible.

At present it is possible to obtain such power-handling components as field-effect transistors and thyristors in the form of integrated circuits (complexes of electronic components and their connections produced on or in a small slice of material—a substrate). However, it is not possible to obtain different types of devices on a single substrate. That is expected to change soon; manufacturers are learning how to produce arrays of 6 or 12 power-handling devices of different types on a single substrate. When that has been accomplished, a complete, versatile 20-kilowatt power modulator may be available on a single 10 × 15-centimeter (4 × 6-inch)

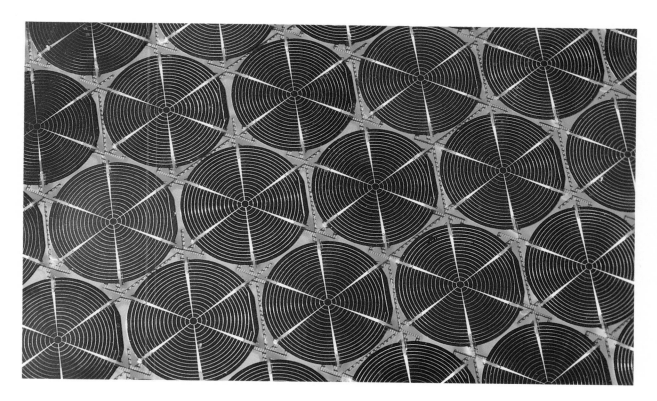

board. That board should sell for about $100–$150 and at first glance be almost indistinguishable from a plug-in computer board.

It is also speculated that by the year 2001 home power-modulator integrated circuits will use a substrate made of some material other than silicon or gallium arsenide. Potential advantages of using other substrates include faster power-modulating speeds and lighter appliances.

The CAVET

In the 1980s roof-mounted arrays of photovoltaic cells for collecting energy from the Sun became commonplace. By 2001, however, a major drawback of these installations may be discovered by their owners—the crystalline and amorphous silicon materials that make up those cells degrade somewhat under constant exposure to the Sun. Future repair, maintenance, or replacement costs can greatly offset any economic advantages offered by the cells.

However, a solar technology called CAVET may be less expensive in the long run for residential applications; by 1989 it was under development. In that technology a solar-thermal heat exchanger is coupled to a closed-cycle vapor turbine that directly drives a miniature alternator. CAVET offers the added advantage of producing high-frequency AC rather than DC. The system is shown in Figure 4.

The CAVET of 2001 is expected to be a heat exchanger, bladed turbine, and brushless alternator. Aside from the size of a rooftop heat exchanger, residential units capable of generating about 20 kilowatts will measure approximately 0.3 cubic meter (10 cubic feet).

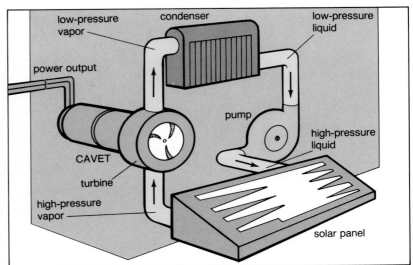

The CAVET's heat exchanger, which is similar to a photovoltaic solar-cell array, would be located on the roof of a house or other structure in order to collect solar energy. Its advantage over photovoltaic cells is that the exchanger is built from a corrosion-resistant metal, such as aluminum. The turbine and the alternator would be placed inside the attic.

Though the turbine would be designed to turn at a constant rate of 7,200 revolutions per minute (rpm), it is expected to be nearly silent. This is because by 2001 magnetic-levitation bearings could be standard in many home appliances, including the CAVET. Such bearings will allow the shafts to be supported by a cushion of magnetic lines of force.

The electrical portion of the system is a synchronous generator designed to produce 120-hertz AC. (A synchronous generator produces an alternating voltage when its armature or field is rotated by a motor, engine, or other means. The output frequently is synchronous, exactly proportional to the speed at which the generator is driven.) While designed to be synchronous at 7,200 rpm, the system can generate power at speeds as low as 6,500 rpm on days of reduced sunlight. The frequency of 120 hertz was chosen because it allows for generating equipment that is significantly lighter in weight than the 60-hertz equipment. A power modulator can be used to drop the frequency to 60 hertz.

The CAVET of the year 2001 is expected to have a power density of nine kilowatts per kilogram (four kilowatts per pound). By 1989 one experimental CAVET had achieved a power density of 11 kilowatts per kilogram (5 kilowatts per pound) but at a speed of 26,000 rpm. Its rotor had no mechanical contact with bearings or brushes; all linkages were magnetic.

A number of university research groups have built prototype CAVET systems. In one case the absence of a large roof area led to the use of sidewalk heat as the source for solar thermal energy. Consequently, the heat exchanger was cast in the concrete about ¾ inch below the top surface. Thus, with a little ingenuity, endless variations are possible.

Figure 4 (above). A prototype of the CAVET (closed-cycle advanced vapor electro-turbogenerator) operates at 26,000 revolutions per minute. The drawing at right shows a CAVET residential generating system (see text).

218

Advanced fuel cells

High-temperature solid-oxide fuel cell (SOFC) systems show great promise for the economical production of electricity and heat in a variety of commercial, residential, and industrial applications. Fulfilling this promise will clear the misconception that fuel cells are suitable only for space and military applications.

Relying on a readily available source of heat, such as natural gas, SOFC technology is based on the ability of a stable component, such as zirconia (zirconium oxide), to operate as a solid electrolyte at high temperatures. The operation of an SOFC is shown in Figure 5. The cell conducts oxygen ions from an air electrode (cathode) through a zirconia-based electrolyte to a fuel electrode (anode). At the anode the ions react with fuel gas and deliver electrons to an external circuit to produce electricity. The fuel cell operates at temperatures near $1,000°$ C ($1,830°$ F) and is a highly efficient source of both heat and electric power that does not require the presence of a turbine or rotating generator.

Advantages of fuel cells over battery- or solar-powered cells include the fact that they are air-cooled, requiring no cooling water; adaptable, allowing gaseous or liquid fuels to be used; and easy to install, as well as quiet and reliable, since there are no moving parts. Fuel cells are also modular, which allows for efficiency in both small and large units, and they can be located in populated areas, thus eliminating added transmission costs.

While these advantages are generally available for all types of fuel cells, the solid-oxide fuel cell has a number of additional advantages over other systems, making it a key contender for prominence in the future. For instance, operating at temperatures of $1,000°$ C, it shows promise of attaining higher overall system efficiency than other systems do. Furthermore, the solid-oxide fuel cell can produce exhaust heat of a higher temperature than the heat produced by other materials. At temperatures

Figure 5. A solid-oxide fuel cell conducts oxygen ions from the air electrode (cathode) through a zirconia-based electrolyte to the fuel electrode (anode). At the anode the ions react with fuel gas and deliver electrons to an external circuit to produce electricity. Fuel cells require no cooling water, accommodate either liquid or gaseous fuels, and are quiet and reliable because they have no moving parts.

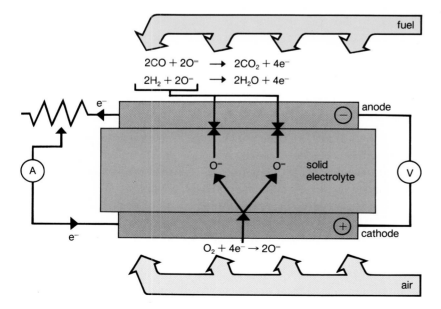

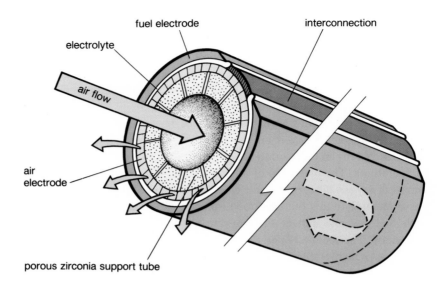

electrolyte · fuel electrode · interconnection · air flow · air electrode · porous zirconia support tube

of 600° C (1,100° F) to 1,000° C, the exhaust can be used to preheat incoming air and fuel, to generate steam that can be used to drive a turbine and produce yet more electric power, or to provide heating for a plant or factory.

Fuel processing and system design are simplified because the high temperature at which the SOFC operates makes catalysts unnecessary. Equally important is the fact that the use of a solid-state electrolyte eliminates material corrosion and electrolyte loss.

The technology is likely to be used in areas from Alaska to Arizona for underground, rooftop, or surface-mounted systems. With the added benefits of the ruggedness of the technology and the low cost of the materials, the SOFC systems, when fully commercialized, could serve in a wide range of power and heat applications.

A number of U.S. firms began investigating the commercial applications of solid-oxide technology for electric-power-generation systems. Whether widespread commercialization is possible will depend on the ability of robotic manufacturing plants to produce relatively small cells rapidly and at a low cost. The objective is the introduction of readily affordable residential products by the mid-1990s. Those could range from a small one-kilowatt energy system to a 200-kilowatt home plant.

The structure of a state-of-the-art solid-oxide electrolyte fuel cell developed by a U.S. Department of Energy contractor is shown in Figure 6. It features a porous zirconia 12-millimeter (0.5-inch)-outer-diameter support tube overlaid with a porous air electrode of modified lanthanum manganite (about one millimeter [0.04 inch] thick). A gas-tight electrolyte of yttria (yttrium oxide)-stabilized zirconia, about 50 micrometers thick, covers the air electrode except in an area about 9 millimeters (0.4 inch) wide along the entire active cell length. (One micrometer equals one one-millionth of a meter.) That strip of exposed-air electrode is covered by a thick (30 micrometers), dense layer of lanthanum chromite. That layer serves as the electric contacting area to an adjacent cell and

Figure 6. Solid-oxide electrolyte fuel cell developed by a U.S. Department of Energy contractor achieved a peak power level of about 0.2 watt per square centimeter (1.3 watts per square inch). A unit consisting of 24 interconnected cells obtained a peak power level of 384 watts and current levels of 80 amperes. For additional information see text.

is called the cell interconnection. The fuel electrode, a nickel-zirconia alloy, is about 150 micrometers thick and covers all the electrolyte surface except a gap about one millimeter wide along the interconnection in order to prevent short circuits of internal cells.

It is possible to obtain a peak power of about 0.2 watt per square centimeter (1.3 watts per square inch) with such state-of-the-art units as the one shown. The cells have been built and tested in single-, double-, and triple-cell configurations by the thousands. Testing has taken place at temperatures ranging from 700° C (1,290° F) to 1,000° C, at fuel efficiencies of 55 to 85%, and at air and pure-oxygen efficiencies of 5%. (Efficiency is the ratio of useful energy provided by a dynamic system to the energy supplied to it during a specific period of operation.) With air, peak power is 16.4 watts, while with pure oxygen, levels of more than 32 watts have been obtained.

Scientists have designed, built, and tested a 24-cell SOFC generator, and they have been able to obtain peak power levels of 384 watts and peak current levels of 80 amperes. The efficiency was 45%. The insulation package was capable of holding the average cell operating temperature above 1,000° C for currents of as much as 50 amperes or more; thus, the unit is thermally self-sustaining.

The U.S. government has been actively engaged in designing, building, and testing a five-kilowatt generator. It contains 324 fuel cells and includes design features of much larger generators. It is expected that during the next 15 years a standard fuel-cell generator will be developed that will contain 500–1,000 cells at a cost of approximately $5 per cell.

Small experimental units are being sold to a number of customers throughout the world. Many U.S. high-tech firms are pursuing the development of inexpensive larger units. These would be used for applications requiring 50–200 kilowatts. Natural gas is expected to be the fuel of choice for most residential and commercial customers.

Greater consumer awareness will lead to the widespread use of the fuel cell in the mid-1990s. A study by the Power Generation Committee of the Institute of Electrical and Electronics Engineers, New York City, estimated that 150,000–300,000 residential and small-scale commercial fuel-cell units, using both solid oxides and phosphoric acid, would be installed in homes and businesses by 2001.

Future prospects

This article has explored some promising power-generation technologies. The LIMPET and the CAVET use classic renewable energy sources and can be installed, operated, and maintained by the average homeowner. Coupled with a power modulator and a Supersea power-storage armature, either technology could completely fulfill its owner's electric-power requirements. Fuel cells fed by natural gas provide a reliable, efficient source of heat and may be used when higher-generating capacities are needed to provide power for individual residences, factories, or even entire communities. When used in larger-scale applications, they provide an attractive alternative to more costly and more dangerous technologies.

221

NEWS FLASH!

Scientist Speaks with Reporters

by Sharon Dunwoody

Tense relationships between scientists and journalists may not yet be a thing of the past, but there is good evidence that the level of cooperation between them is increasing. Moreover, scientists have learned that popularization of their work can bring rewards.

SHARON DUNWOODY *is an Associate Professor in the School of Journalism and Mass Communication, University of Wisconsin, Madison.*

Illustrations by Ron Villani; concepts by Charles Cegielski

When the U.S. space shuttle *Discovery* roared into orbit in September 1988, its tiled skin and its five occupants intact, journalists covering the event could barely contain their relief. "It's difficult to be objective," murmured NBC anchorman Tom Brokaw as he watched the spacecraft power past the 73-second point after launch, the moment when, more than two years earlier, exhaust leaking from a booster rocket had caused *Discovery*'s sister craft *Challenger* to explode, killing all seven aboard.

Indeed, media coverage of the launch and of *Discovery*'s return to Earth four days later reflected the jubilation that washed over both scientists and journalists on hand for the event. As science reporter John Noble Wilford noted in his page-one launch story in the September 30 issue of the *New York Times*, "Celebration was the mood of the day." Scientists and reporters alike were framing this technological event as a success story, and they were having a wonderful time to boot.

Over the years, however, few science stories have been written in such a heady atmosphere. Scientists and journalists frequently have disagreed on topic, content, or tone of stories. In fact, many of these major actors in the public dissemination of science have characterized their interrelationships not as consensual but as tension-filled and sometimes downright hostile. Scientists have muttered about being "burned" by journalists less interested in accuracy than in selling newspapers. Journalists, in turn, have professed dismay at the apparent indifference of scientists to the public's need to know about new developments in science and technology.

One way to explore the validity of such accusations is to take a larger look at the evolution of relationships between scientists and journalists. Whereas these relationships often have been uneasy, there appear to have been good reasons—both philosophical and pragmatic. Today the level of cooperation between scientists and journalists seems to be increasing, in part because scientists are learning that public visibility has distinct advantages. Moreover, there are even signs of a return to a 19th-century phenomenon, when popularizing was an accepted responsibility for scientists.

A century of science popularization

Most people think of science reporting as a form of science popularization done by journalists for newspapers, magazines, television, or radio—certainly a reasonable characterization of its present state. But a look into the past with the help of a skilled historian makes it clear that, while the mass media have long served as important vehicles for stories about science and technology, scientists themselves have done a good bit of the writing for them. In *How Superstition Won and Science Lost: Popularizing Science and Health in the United States* (1987), Ohio State University professor John C. Burnham describes a kind of two-tiered system of popularization in the mid- to late 19th century, with scientists earnestly trying to educate the public through lectures, textbooks, and magazine articles and journalists composing quite different accounts for newspapers.

224

The scientists were an eminent lot, experts in their fields. Burnham counts among them naturalist Louis Agassiz, geochemist F. W. Clarke, and geologist John C. Branner. Such men viewed popularization, quite literally, as part of their scientific work. According to Burnham, making science comprehensible to all was such an assumed responsibility for scientists that during the late 1800s nearly all of the officers of the American Association for the Advancement of Science (AAAS), a major scientific organization, had at some time contributed at least one article to *Popular Science Monthly.*

As these "men of science" worked to educate the masses in the pages of the leading popular science magazines, however, journalists tried to inform and entertain in the pages of newspapers. Improvements in printing had allowed newspapers to become truly mass media by the mid-19th century, and publishers competed fiercely for readers. For several reasons, the major weapon in this competition was the dramatic, emotional story, and science, like other elements of the prevailing culture, was enmeshed in many of those stories.

The reasons for the emphasis on dramatic prose were predominantly economic. Newspapers in the 19th century were distributed on the street, not delivered to homes. Circulation thus depended on persuading individuals heading to or from work to choose a particular product over its competitors. Dramatic stories on the front page could influence the decisions. Another economic reason was far more personal, at least to reporters. Rather than working for a set salary, as do most of today's reporters, 19th-century journalists were usually paid by the story. Surviving depended on convincing an editor that one's story was better, more important, or more exciting than those of other reporters. The result, not surprisingly, was that reporters exaggerated. During that early era, whether a story was accurate may have been far less important than whether it could grab an editor's attention.

In the early 20th century, scientists abandoned popularization efforts to the journalists. One reason was that specialization was taking its toll. Concentrating ever more deeply on ever smaller pieces of science meant that scientists could no longer afford to be conversant in many fields. And with the demise of generalists went both the ability to popularize and the interest in doing so. Second, at the turn of the century the scientific culture was working hard to professionalize. This effort included, among other things, putting intellectual distance between members of the profession and everyday folks. As scientists became more "learned," they developed their own training regimens, their own reward systems (which included rewards for publishing in professional journals but not in the mass outlets of the day), and their own definitions of what constituted good scientific conduct. In an effort to distinguish their members from "quacks," many professionalizing occupations—physicians, dentists, and scientists among them—declared advertising to be unethical behavior. Their definition of advertising was often broad enough to encompass anything in the mass media, even one's name in a newspaper story. By the end of World War II, few scientists (British geneticist J. B. S. Haldane and U.S. physicist George Gamow were among notable exceptions) willingly risked communicating with the public on a regular basis. The two-tiered system of the 19th century had become a one-tiered system in the 20th, and journalists were at the helm.

Battleground interviews

Nevertheless, to cover science and technology, journalists had to talk to scientists, who turned out to be among the most reluctant of sources. Many scientists in the 1950s and 1960s refused (some still do) to have any contact with journalists. Others agreed to interviews but only under stringent conditions. Even today, for example, one scientist at a major research institution will talk only to a journalist who agrees to three conditions: to let the scientist tape the interview, to allow a third party to witness the exchange, and to allow the scientist to check the story before publication.

Journalists' responses to such dictums often exacerbated the situation. To the journalist a request for prepublication review sounded like an

attempt at censorship and often was adamantly refused. Informed that a researcher had no intention of suffering the indignities of an interview, the journalist might retort that public funding of the scientist's work gave the researcher no choice but to offer a public account of the results.

Spending an hour or two locked in such combat was most unpleasant for both scientists and journalists, yet it described—and sometimes still characterizes—the world of science reporting. Why should such tensions exist? Why should these people be making life so difficult for each other?

No Nobel for public communication

The scientific community rewards few activities beyond research. Hence, it is no surprise that scientists who communicate with the public do not get a standing ovation from their colleagues. What is surprising is that scientists actually have been punished for popularizing. In an extreme case from several years ago, a researcher at a large medical center agreed to be interviewed about his work by a local newspaper reporter. The story ran as a feature in a Sunday issue. Several months later, when the re-

searcher applied for membership in a prestigious society that recognized individuals in his specialty, he was rejected because the society defined the use of his name in the newspaper story as "unethical advertising."

Punishment admittedly has rarely been so overt. A more subtle form was levied on a sociologist whose convention paper was picked up one year by a journalist and subsequently spread throughout the country via a wire service. Inundated with requests for information, the scientist had to hire a part-time secretary to handle them. Still, she was awash for days in interviews and correspondence, time she otherwise would have spent on research. Moreover, the gentle remonstrances of departmental colleagues made clear their disapproval of the whole incident. The message was obvious: good scientists avoid media attention.

One group of scientists has had to endure a steady stream of criticism from colleagues as a result of their roles as popularizers. They are the "visible scientists," so labeled by science communication researcher Rae Goodell of the Massachusetts Institute of Technology, who studied them in the 1970s. Goodell's subjects are familiar to many: astronomer Carl Sagan, chemist Linus Pauling, anthropologist Margaret Mead, and entomologist Paul Ehrlich, among others. They became regular, high-profile sources of information for journalists—media celebrities, in effect—and reaped not only fame but also vitriol from their own profession. Scientists have grumped that such stars are more than willing to talk about topics tangential to their own work and have complained that their popularity as sources gives them extraordinary power over the ways in which science is framed for the general public. Supporters of visible scientists, on the other hand, have argued that these articulate spokespersons are a breath of fresh air in an occupation full of obtuse communicators, and they have suggested that the criticism leveled at visible scientists may contain more than a hint of sour grapes.

The point, however, is that individuals who are likely to be punished for a particular behavior are not likely to engage in it. And some studies of scientists as sources of information suggest that the most vulnerable segment of the scientific community, young scientists, are the least likely to try public communicating. The reason is that it may be important to "make it" in the scientific culture before venturing into disputed terrain. Indeed, most of the scientists who have evolved into "visible" ones are seniors who have accumulated both rewards and power within the culture and who perhaps feel they can afford to take risks.

Educating versus informing

In a nutshell, scientists are intent on educating, while journalists are intent on informing. The words sound synonymous but they are not, and the difference is a major source of friction between scientists and journalists.

When scientists talk about educating the public, they have in mind two goals. Knowledge gain is certainly one of them; they want everyday folks to learn something about how science is done and about the patterns in nature that scientists cull from scientific endeavors. But scientists have an attitudinal goal as well. They also want nonscientists to like science, to

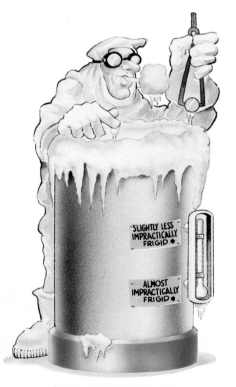

THE SCIENTIST'S TALE

228

perceive how much fun, how intellectually stimulating, and how satisfying science can be. Journalists, on the other hand, concentrate on neither knowledge gain nor attitude change. Their emphasis is on bringing people up to date, on telling them what is "new" about a particular area of science. Reporters argue that the very term newspaper incorporates that emphasis. The mass media's primary charge, they say, is to keep people aware of changes in their environment. Thus, a somnolent neighborhood will rate nary a word in the local newspaper, but let a house burn down and reporters are on the scene in minutes.

Aiming at different goals, an educator and an informer will compose very different stories. For example, assume that both have been given the task of telling the public something about the new high-temperature superconductors. The educator's tale would be a long one, filled with careful accounts of what these materials are, of physical principles underlying their actions, of the way scientists carried out their crucial experiments, and of theories-in-the-making erected to explain why certain combinations of elements superconduct at relatively high temperatures.

The informer would look for the latest development, perhaps a previously untried combination of elements for which a scientist is making a claim in the scientific literature, and would construct a much shorter story around it. Gone would be the pages of detailed explanations, replaced by single paragraphs offering skeletonized versions of the educator's points. Instead of answering the general question What do we now know about high-temperature superconductors? the informer would address a different question altogether: Has anything new taken place within the field of high-temperature superconductors in the recent past?

Why do scientists and journalists have such different expectations for media stories? Journalists' expectations are clearly grounded in their work habits. The act of producing a daily product for people on the go creates a kind of pragmatic straitjacket in which information must be packed. Folks who sit down for 20 minutes with their morning paper (the average time Americans spend with a newspaper) expect a fast walk through the events of their world. They course like greyhounds through the printed words, stopping only when something—a headline, a photo, a splash of color, a meaty sentence—attracts their attention. Once stopped, they likely will glance through only the first paragraph of the story—the verbal equivalent of dipping a toe in the water before a morning swim—before deciding either to read further or to move on to other stories. Journalists have learned to handle skimmers not by confronting them with lengthy exposition, no matter how exquisitely written, but by telling good, short tales.

Scientists' emphasis on education is also understandable. For one thing, the work of historians who study science popularization suggests that scientists have always considered popularization synonymous with education. In the 19th century, when scientists were active public communicators, they could play out those educative expectations themselves in the pages of magazines and books. Today, whereas scientists' expectations have not changed, the people who play the part of primary

THE JOURNALIST'S TALE

229

communicator have, and journalists simply do not frame stories with education in mind.

Another reason that scientists may misinterpret the purpose of science stories in the mass media centers on journalism's own traditional claim to a front-row seat in the social order—*i.e.,* that journalism performs a valuable role in giving people enough information about their world to help them make informed decisions. A persuasive argument over the decades, it has given journalism enough social and legal sanction in the United States to allow it intermittently to take on the major power brokers in society in the name of the public interest.

This philosophical description of journalistic work may not be accurate, however. Informed decisions require a knowledge base of some kind, but the nature of journalistic products makes them difficult entities to learn from. Journalistic stories are brief and event-oriented and thus are fragmented accounts of environmental change. Such accounts may provide little fodder for learning. In fact, a number of mass-communication scholars now argue that the primary role of the mass media is as an alerting mechanism, not as a teacher. Nevertheless, it is clear that scientists, like many individuals, assume mass media messages to have pronounced effects on knowledge and attitudes. And if one assumes major effects, then one worries about the accuracy, comprehensiveness, and tone of the message.

Whether the media have such effects is, of course, an empirical question but a difficult one to answer. Audiences are not passive sponges waiting to soak up information but instead actively select and process it. So even knowing, for example, how many viewers are watching an episode of "Nova," a weekly television series about science, reveals little about the impact of the program. Nielsen ratings suggest that 20% of all U.S. homes with television sets watch "Nova" for some length of time in the course of a month, but beyond the impressive body count, that statistic yields no information about who is learning what. Researchers are only now devising ways to isolate the impact of mass media science messages; scholars who have studied effects of more generic media messages warn that learning, if it does take place in the short term, will be modest at best.

Mutual strangers

One can create tension in any interaction by throwing together two individuals who know nothing about each other, which is often what happens when scientists and journalists get together. For decades, science journalists have been few in number, so the person most commonly sent to a scientist's office door has been a general reporter. Although likely to be a skilled interviewer, the journalist may have never encountered a scientist before and so is in for a surprise.

At times almost everything the scientist says could run counter to the journalist's experience. News sources usually are amenable to, and sometimes even enthusiastic about, being interviewed; scientists, on the other hand, may be reluctant and even belligerent. News sources usually accept

230

their role in an interview setting, settle back, and wait for questions; scientists are much less sanguine about being on the receiving end and often try to direct the questioning themselves. Most news sources never ask to critique a journalist's copy before publication; scientists sometimes do.

The journalist may be an unsettling experience for the scientist as well. This person probably will have little scientific training and no background in the subject at hand and will profess to have only hours to compose a story. The pace that the journalist sets for the interview will seem a mad gallop compared with the more leisurely tempo of the scientist's own writing and publishing. Making things worse will be the tendency of the scientist, a priori, to label the reporter a suspicious character and to treat him or her that way. In lieu of extensive experience with reporters, scientists sometimes erect a stereotype of the journalist as someone with a cavalier attitude toward the facts who is interested only in a good story and who would not hesitate to sensationalize if it improved the prose. As with all stereotypes, these inferences are simplistic and usually are grounded in a small sample—perhaps an encounter with one unpleasant character that is then generalized to the whole occupation.

As unscientific as such a generalization might be, those single instances can be memorable. As one example, an immunologist who was examining the ability of transplanted thymus tissue to help boost the immune systems of AIDS patients agreed to be interviewed for a story that a free-lance reporter wanted to market to gay publications. The scientist's reason was simple: research on the value of transplanted thymus tissue was in its very early stages, and he felt that the story would give him the opportunity to caution AIDS sufferers against too much optimism.

Whereas an appropriate story did find its way into the gay press, the reporter also sold the piece to a daily midwestern newspaper. The newspaper published it on the front page, and the message conveyed was much less cautious than the scientist had hoped. According to the newspaper

account, thymus transplants constituted a potential therapy for wrecked immune systems. Even worse, the newspaper story was picked up by a wire service and distributed around the U.S.

The immunologist was upset. Although technically correct, the story lent too much credence, he believed, to the prospects for thymus transplants. His research was just under way, and he literally had no idea whether these transplants would do any good. The stories, by mentioning his work without appropriate cautions, gave an impression completely at odds with his intention.

It took much cajoling before the immunologist ventured back into the public domain, and it is not difficult to understand why. Nevertheless, in spite of negative stereotypes of journalists and in spite of negative reinforcement from the scientific community, scientists today are becoming more willing participants in the public communication of science.

Evolving a shared culture

Journalists like to characterize their relationships with sources of information as mildly adversarial. According to this interpretation, sources have an agenda to push and it is up to the journalist to lay bare that motivation and ensure that the public has access to balanced—not biased—information. Scholars who study journalistic work, however, find little evidence for such a relationship. On a day-to-day basis, sources and journalists seem to cooperate much more than they conflict with each other.

Sociologists Jay Blumler and Michael Gurevitch of the University of Maryland, who have studied this cooperation, argue that news sources and journalists often do business within a "shared culture," a set of game rules that both sides understand and obey. A shared culture arises, say these scholars, when individuals find they can accomplish separate or joint goals by working together. The most obvious example occurs with politicians and journalists. Both need what the other has to offer: the journalist needs information, and the politician needs public visibility. In such circumstances, an adversarial relationship would handicap both sides. Therefore, journalists and politicians have evolved rules that govern their interactions and make them as efficient as possible. For example, they may share definitions of what constitutes "fair" coverage and even definitions of what is and is not news. When a governmental official gives her views on a particular issue, the rules of the game lead her to expect that the reporter will attempt to "balance" those views with the opinions of others. She will not be upset to find that her side of things has not been unconditionally accepted. Similarly, if the official agrees to speak with a reporter "off the record," she can assume that the journalist understands that rule and will not use her name in the story.

A shared culture does not make adversarial outcomes impossible. Even investigative reporting may be an acceptable part of the framework if such reporting explores problems that are defined as such by both journalists and sources. For example, a state government reporter uncovered a case of nepotism, a legislator employing a relative, and blew the whistle. At a later date the legislator wanted to publicize a major announcement

232

and offered it as a scoop to the same reporter who had exposed him in the past. Asked why, the politician replied that he did not resent the earlier story. Nepotism is against the rules, he said, and the reporter had only been doing his job when he uncovered and publicized it.

It has been rare to find such cooperative behavior between scientists and journalists—and for a fairly clear reason. While journalists have often needed scientists, scientists have rarely needed journalists. Today, however, a shared culture is indeed evolving. Although the evidence to date is anecdotal, it suggests that interest among scientists in communicating with the public is surging. For example, science writers, who traditionally have had difficulty convincing reluctant scientists to talk, now claim not only that most scientists seem willing and even eager to be interviewed but also that scientists increasingly are making the first overtures. This latter change is so disconcerting that many journalists have become wary of the scientist who calls with a "great story." One well-known science journalist remarked that her first question to such a person is "When is your grant up for renewal?" Other evidence comes from the increased popularity of "communication" sessions at scientific meetings. The AAAS, for example, now holds annual workshops on communicating science to the public, and each workshop plays to packed audiences. Finally, increased interest in public understanding of science is mirrored in the success of such organizations in the U.S. as the Scientists' Institute for Public Information (SIPI), a group devoted to improving the flow of scientific and technological information to the public. Its Media Resource Service, started in 1980, offers to journalists a bank of more than 20,000 experts in science, technology, and medicine who are willing to discuss specific issues for publication. Both scientists and journalists claim to find great value in the service.

But why should scientists be more interested now in popularization than they were in the past? At least two major reasons can be cited.

One is that mass media coverage of science and technology is not only more frequent these days but more "scientific" and thus more palatable to scientists. In the mid-1970s, when publishers realized that the growing number of well-educated individuals in the U.S. constituted a ready-made audience for science stories, they responded with a bundle of new and refurbished popular science magazines, among them *Omni, Science 80, Science Digest,* and *Discover.* Some have failed, some are thriving, and some new ones have since emerged, principally health-oriented magazines like *American Health* and *Hippocrates.* The 1980s also have witnessed a boomlet in science writing for newspapers. As of 1986, according to SIPI, nearly 70 newspapers had established science or medicine sections while another 80 had started science pages, and they had brought on board a number of science reporters to staff them.

The increased space for science coverage has been paralleled by increasing levels of education in science and science writing for journalists. In days past, few reporters asked for the science beat; they were often recruited from the ranks of general reporters and had to learn on the job. Today, although training for journalism remains a blessedly eclectic experience, individuals are often opting for science-writing careers as college students and are taking advantage of university courses in science and science reporting. The backgrounds of science writers working today run the gamut from high school diploma to Ph.D. or M.D., but increasing numbers of science journalists in the future will bring formal scientific training to their jobs.

The second reason behind the increasing enthusiasm of scientists for media coverage may be the more important. Scientists are cooperating with the media because they see distinct rewards for doing so. Those rewards may not yet come from the scientific culture, which at worse still seems to discourage popularization and at best is indifferent to it. Only a few professional bodies such as the AAAS and the American Institute of Physics have established awards for activities to enhance public understanding of science. Outside the formal professional boundaries, however, other rewards are apparently substantial enough to energize scientists.

First, scientists see a direct relationship between public visibility and their ability to accumulate research funds. Although no research has been done to establish this link, scientists cite a wealth of anecdotal evidence. For instance, a Canadian paleontologist who, with meager resources, unearthed some dinosaur skeletons in Alberta some years ago argues that media coverage of those excavations produced such an enthusiastic response from both the public and the Canadian government that he now has a fully staffed excavation program and a new dinosaur museum as well.

Second, scientists see the mass media as one means of communicating with the social and commercial infrastructure in which they live.

Whether it is a concern with issues, such as community reaction to experimental use of animals, or an interest in forging links with industry, scientists increasingly are willing to get their views into the public domain, where they can compete with the views of others and be read by relevant persons. Such motivation must have undergirded the comment of an engineer at a university who, when approached by the university's science writer about sending an account of the engineer's work to a major newspaper across the state, said "Good. I'd like to open up that market."

Finally, it is becoming increasingly clear to scientists that media coverage of their work alerts not only the public but also other scientists. The mass media, in other words, can set scientists' agendas as well as public agendas. For example, in the earlier account of the sociologist who was inundated with information requests after her research was publicized nationwide via the mass media, the plurality of requests came not from the general public but from other sociologists who had seen the media accounts and wanted a copy of her paper. The sociologist also notes that, among all her research articles, that particular paper was anthologized most frequently in compilations of sociological work. She interprets that as evidence for the value of public visibility as a validating tool for scientists: if it makes it into the mass media, it must be important.

Return of the scientist communicator
The increased interest of scientists in popularizing, then, makes some sense. Even without encouragement from the scientific culture, the rewards could be large for the individual who gets his or her message to the right people in society.

New Connections Mapped in Scientists' Brains

But what happened to education as a goal? Are all scientists who welcome journalists with open arms just trying to market themselves and their work? The answer, of course, is no. Research on the way the general public learns about science has convinced many scientists that the mass media are, in effect, major information arteries to a public who knows little about science and technology and their effects on society. To the extent that they can, increasing numbers of such scientists are grappling with the difficulties of communicating through these arteries. There is, in fact, such enthusiasm for this task that one can again see glimmers of that 19th-century "man of science" who regarded public understanding of his profession as a responsibility.

Much has changed since the 19th century, not least of which is the gender of many of the scientists who now regard themselves as legitimate popularizers. Nevertheless, increasing numbers of scientists today are venturing back into domains dominated by their predecessors some 100 years ago—the pages of general magazines and books and, in a 20th-century twist, television and radio.

Some are doing it on their own, relying on their visceral sense of how to communicate with the public. Others are opting for writing training in some of the more than 70 U.S. universities that offer science-reporting courses and programs. Sometimes their prose sags under the weight of pedagogic earnestness; sometimes it sings. Much of what they do is eminently readable and watchable, from evolutionary biologist Stephen Jay Gould's monthly essays in *Natural History* magazine, to such recent books as Douglas Hofstadter's *Gödel, Escher, Bach* and Freeman Dyson's *Disturbing the Universe*, to astrophysicist Philip Morrison's television series "The Ring of Truth," which aired on public television in 1987.

These scientists probably will not replace science writers. The differences in goals mean that scientist educators are not likely to be drawn to newspapers and broadcast news formats. Instead, these individuals are participating in a return to the two-tiered system of the past, when both informers and educators coexisted, each serving distinctly different public needs. What makes today's version different from its predecessor is that both journalists and scientists are now in a position to do it better.

FOR ADDITIONAL READING

John C. Burnham, *How Superstition Won and Science Lost: Popularizing Science and Health in the United States* (Rutgers University Press, 1987).

Sharon M. Friedman, Sharon Dunwoody, and Carol L. Rogers (eds.), *Scientists and Journalists: Reporting Science as News* (American Association for the Advancement of Science, 1989).

Barbara Gastel, *Presenting Science to the Public* (ISI Press, 1983).

Rae Goodell, *The Visible Scientists* (Little, Brown, 1977).

June Goodfield, *Reflections on Science and the Media* (American Association for the Advancement of Science, 1981).

Dorothy Nelkin, *Selling Science: How the Press Covers Science and Technology* (W. H. Freeman and Co., 1987).

Encyclopædia
Britannica
Science Update

Major Revisions from the 1989 *Macropædia*

The purpose of this section is to introduce to continuing *Yearbook of Science and the Future* subscribers selected *Macropædia* articles or portions of them that have been completely revised or written anew. It is intended to update the *Macropædia* in ways that cannot be accomplished fully by reviewing the year's events or by revising statistics annually, because the *Macropædia* texts themselves—written from a longer perspective than any yearly revision—supply authoritative interpretation and analysis as well as narrative and description.

Two articles have been chosen from the 1989 printing: ATOMS (in part) and INFORMATION PROCESSING AND INFORMATION SYSTEMS. Each is the work of distinguished scholars, and each represents the continuing dedication of the *Encyclopædia Britannica* to bringing such works to the general reader.

Atoms: Their Structure, Properties, and Component Particles

The atom is the smallest unit into which matter can be divided without the release of electrically charged particles. It also is the smallest unit of matter that has the characteristic properties of a chemical element. As such, the atom is the basic building block of chemistry.

Most of the atom is empty space. The rest consists of a positively charged nucleus of protons and neutrons surrounded by a cloud of negatively charged electrons. The nucleus is small and dense compared to the electrons, which are the lightest charged particles in nature. Electrons are attracted to any positive charge by their electric force; in an atom, electric forces bind the electrons to the nucleus.

It is easier to describe an atom mathematically than conceptually, and so physicists have developed several models to explain its various characteristics. In some respects, the electrons in an atom behave like particles orbiting the nucleus. In others, the electrons behave like waves frozen in position around the nucleus. Such wave patterns, called orbitals, describe the distribution of individual electrons. The behaviour of an atom is strongly influenced by these orbital properties, and its chemical properties are determined by orbital groupings known as shells.

This article opens with a broad overview of the fundamental properties of the atom and its constituent particles and forces. A more mathematical and technical discussion of its structure and nucleus is provided in subsequent sections. Included too is a historical survey of the most influential concepts about the atom that have been formulated through the centuries. For additional information pertaining to nuclear structure and elementary particles, see SUBATOMIC PARTICLES. For coverage of other related topics in the *Macropædia* and *Micropædia*, see the *Propædia*, sections 111, 112, 121, 122, 124, 125, and 128.

Components and properties of atoms

CONSTITUENT PARTICLES AND FORCES

Most matter consists of an agglomeration of molecules, which can be separated relatively easily. Molecules, in turn, are composed of atoms joined by chemical bonds that are more difficult to break. Each individual atom consists of smaller particles—namely, electrons and nuclei. These particles are electrically charged, and the electric forces on the charge are responsible for holding the atom together. Attempts to separate these smaller constituent particles require ever-increasing amounts of energy and result in the creation of new subatomic particles, many of which are charged.

As noted at the outset of this article, an atom consists largely of empty space. The nucleus is the positively charged centre of an atom and contains most of its mass. It is composed of protons, which have a positive charge, and neutrons, which have no charge. These constituent

Nucleons | protons and neutrons collectively are called nucleons. Protons, neutrons, and the electrons surrounding them are long-lived particles present in all ordinary, naturally occurring atoms. Other subatomic particles may be found in association with these three types of particles. They can be created only with the addition of enormous amounts of energy, however, and are very short-lived.

All atoms are roughly the same size, whether they have three or 90 electrons. Approximately 50,000,000 atoms of solid matter lined up in a row would measure one centimetre (0.4 inch). A convenient unit of length for measuring atomic sizes is the angstrom (Å), defined as 10^{-10} metre. The radius of an atom measures 1–2 Å.

Size of nuclei | Compared to the overall size of the atom, the nucleus is even more minute. It is in the same proportion to the atom as a marble is to a football field. In volume, the nucleus takes up only 10^{-14} of the space in the atom—i.e., one part in 100,000,000,000,000. A convenient unit of length for measuring nuclear sizes is the femtometre (fm), which equals 10^{-15} metre. The diameter of a nucleus depends on the number of particles it contains and ranges from about 4 fm for a light nucleus such as carbon to 15 fm for a heavy nucleus such as lead. In spite of the small size of the nucleus, virtually all the mass of the atom is concentrated there. The protons are massive, positively charged particles, whereas the neutrons have no charge and are nearly as massive as the protons. The fact that nuclei can have anywhere from one to about 250 nucleons accounts for their wide variation in mass. The lightest nucleus, that of hydrogen, is 1,836 times more massive than an electron, while heavy nuclei are nearly 500,000 times more massive.

Electrons | Although electrons exhibit complicated behaviour within an atom, they are characterized completely by a few parameters. The intrinsic properties of an electron are its charge, mass, an internal motion called spin, and magnetic moment. All electrons have identical properties. As the lightest charged particles in existence, they are absolutely stable because they cannot decay into smaller units. Their charge and mass, which are important determinants of atomic properties, are listed in Table 1. The spin of the electron provides it with a directional orientation. The electron has a magnetic moment along its spin axis. (Magnetic moment is a property of a particle, which, like a compass needle, causes its axis to align in a magnetic

field.) Electrons are subject not only to the electromagnetic force but also to the force of gravity and the so-called weak interaction, the force primarily manifested in the radioactive decay of nuclei.

Most properties of atoms—particularly those associated with chemical bonds, physical forces, and the properties of bulk matter—depend solely on the behaviour of the electrons surrounding the nucleus. The chemical properties of an atom depend on the arrangement of its electrons making up the cloud around the nucleus. The atoms of one element differ from those of other elements in the number of their electrons. Also, atoms form molecules by lending and sharing electrons. Some elements, such as alkali metals, have an electron that is loosely bound to the nucleus and thus easily removed in chemical reactions; other elements, such as the noble (or inert) gases, have very tightly bound electrons and little affinity for other electrons. Electrons that have been freed from their atoms can cause lightning, and freed electrons driven through wires make up ordinary electric currents.

The nucleus of an atom is characterized by the number of protons and neutrons in it. Besides a charge and mass, the nucleus also may have a spin and a magnetic moment of its own, depending on the internal arrangement of its protons and neutrons. The forces between nucleons include the three forces affecting electrons as well as the so-called strong force, which is much more powerful than any of the others. Because of the strong force, nuclear binding energies are 1,000,000 times the binding energies of electrons in atoms. The amounts of energy that can be released in a transformation of the nucleus are correspondingly larger than the chemical energies released by a transformation of the electron patterns in atoms. The protons and neutrons in the nucleus are governed by the laws of quantum mechanics (see below), which describe the complex internal structure of the nucleus.

Even the individual protons and neutrons that make up the nucleus have an internal structure of their own. The constituents of nucleons are called quarks. Unlike the particles composing the larger units of matter, the quark cannot be freed from the nucleon and studied in isolation. The strong force acting between quarks is so powerful that they can never be completely separated. Any attempt to probe the substructure of a nucleon releases particles of various types, but the particles produced contain quarks in fixed combinations, never single quarks. Particles containing quarks are collectively called hadrons. Hadrons are classified into two categories: baryons and mesons. Baryons, which are composed of three quarks, include protons and neutrons as their lightest examples. Mesons, which contain two quarks, are largely responsible for nuclear forces. Except for the nucleons, all such particles decay in a small fraction of a second after their creation. | Hadrons and quarks

There is one more broad category of subatomic particles, the leptons. Electrons and neutrinos are leptons. They have no detectable internal components and may be truly fundamental particles of nature. The neutrino is an uncharged particle with little or no mass that is created during the radioactive decay of nuclei. | Leptons

PROPERTIES OF ATOMS

Atomic number. The single most important characteristic of an atom is its atomic number, which is defined as the number of units of positive charge in the nucleus. A neutral atom has an equal number of protons and electrons, so that the positive and negative charges exactly balance. The atomic number determines the chemical properties of an atom, including the kinds of molecules that can be formed and their binding energies. Hence, the atomic number determines an atom's characteristics as an element. (An element is composed of atoms with the same atomic number.) Elements found in nature range from atomic number 1, hydrogen, to atomic number 92, uranium. In addition, artificial elements with atomic numbers beyond 100 have been produced.

Atomic mass number. The total number of nucleons (both protons and neutrons) in an atom is the atomic mass number, or mass number. Atoms with the same atomic number but different atomic masses are called

Table 1: Fundamental Atomic Constants		
	symbol	value
Avogadro's number	N_A	6.022×10^{23} mol^{-1}
Fundamental charge	e	1.602×10^{-19} C
Faraday	F	9.649×10^4 C mol^{-1}
Planck's constant	h	6.626×10^{-34} J $\cdot$ s
	$\hbar = h/2\pi$	1.055×10^{-34} J $\cdot$ s
Mass of electron	m_e	9.11×10^{-31} kg
Rest energy of electron	$m_e c^2$	8.2×10^{-14} J $= 5.11 \times 10^5$ eV
Mass of proton	m_p	1.673×10^{-27} kg
Rest energy of proton	$m_p c^2$	1.50×10^{-10} J $= 938.3$ MeV
Bohr radius	a_0	5.292×10^{-11} m $= 0.5292$ Å
Speed of light (in vacuum)	c	2.998×10^8 m s^{-1}

isotopes. Isotopes have identical chemical properties, yet they can have very different nuclear properties (see below *Isotopes*). The nuclear properties of an atom include possible radioactivity (the propensity to become radioactive in nuclear reactions), magnetic properties, and weight. The element potassium, for example, has two natural isotopes, ^{39}K and ^{40}K. They form exactly the same compounds, but ^{40}K is radioactive and decays into another element. In scientific notation, the isotope of potassium with 19 protons, 20 neutrons, and a total of 39 nucleons can be written either as $_{19}$K^{39} or as $^{39}_{19}$K.

Because isotopes have the same number of protons, all of the isotopes of a given element occupy the same place in the periodic table of elements. Most elements have stable isotopes. For example, hydrogen has three isotopes, each with one proton. The nucleus of ordinary hydrogen is an isolated proton, but the isotope deuterium has a neutron bound to the proton. Both of these isotopes are stable. The third hydrogen isotope, tritium, has two neutrons and is radioactive. Radioactive isotopes can be made for many elements; the more the number of neutrons deviates from the optimum number for that atomic mass, the shorter the life of the radioactive isotope.

Atomic weight. The term atomic weight, or atomic mass, refers to the mass of a fixed number of atoms of an element. The standard scientific unit for dealing with atoms in macroscopic quantities is the mole (mol), which is defined arbitrarily as the amount of a substance with as many atoms or other units as there are in 12 grams of the carbon isotope ^{12}C. The number of atoms in a mole is called Avogadro's number, the value of which is approximately 6×10^{23}. The atomic mass of an element expressed in daltons, or more commonly atomic mass units (amu's), is the number of grams in one mole of the element. The amu is convenient because atomic masses are nearly equal to atomic mass numbers and therefore are close to integer values.

Historically, the law for chemical combination according to molar weights was the primary evidence for the existence of atoms and molecules. For example, two grams of hydrogen combine with 16 grams of oxygen to form water. This represents two moles of hydrogen of atomic weight 1 combining with one mole of oxygen of atomic weight 16. Elements consisting of a mixture of several isotopes may not have an atomic mass close to an integer, because the mass will be the weighted average of the different isotopes. An example is chlorine, which has two common isotopes, ^{35}Cl and ^{37}Cl, and a weighted average mass of 35.5 amu.

Electric charge. The normal atom is electrically neutral, meaning that it carries a net electric charge of zero. Some atoms, however, have lost or gained electrons in chemical reactions or in collisions with other particles. Atoms with a net charge, either from the gain or loss of electrons, are called ions. If a neutral atom loses an electron, it becomes a positive ion; if it gains an electron, it becomes a negative ion.

The charge on any particle is a whole multiple of the electron's charge, either positive or negative. The quarks are an exception to this rule. They have charges of $+^2/_3e$ and $-^1/_3e$. However, they exist only in groups, and each group as a whole has an integral multiple of the electron's charge. The amount of charge in this fundamental unit is equal to 1.6×10^{-10} coulomb. This means that in a current of one ampere—roughly what a 100-watt light bulb uses in the ordinary 110-volt household circuit—about 6×10^{18} electrons pass through the wire every second.

Electron shells. The behaviour of electrons in atoms is quite subtle and is governed by the laws of quantum mechanics. According to these laws, electrons occupy various regions of the atom in frozen wave patterns called orbitals. The orbitals are most easily visualized as clouds surrounding the nucleus. The shape and size of the orbital, and the energy of the electron in it, are calculated by differential equations. The orbitals vary in shape from smooth and spherical for the electrons most tightly bound to the nucleus to rather diffuse and lumpy for the least bound electrons. The hydrogen atom has a single electron in a spherical cloud. The electron could go into other orbitals, but it would require additional energy in the atom to do

so. The quantum theory provides that the energy of an atom can only change in definite amounts called quanta. The different possible states an atom can be in, each with its own definite energy, are called energy levels. The light emitted from an atom has specific frequencies associated with the energy quanta. Energy at the atomic level is often expressed in electron volts (eV). There are 2.26×10^{25} eV in one kilowatt-hour. To remove an electron from an atom requires several electron volts, depending on the atom. Visible light has a quantum energy of about 2 eV.

Each electron in a multielectron atom has its own orbital, according to a law of quantum mechanics known as the Pauli principle (also called the Pauli exclusion principle or exclusion principle). Thus, in atoms with many electrons, many different kinds of orbitals are occupied. A group of orbitals with the same or nearly the same energy is called a shell. The pattern of filled and unfilled shells in each element is different; this variety gives the elements their distinctive characteristics.

Chemical behaviour. The chemical behaviour of atoms depends on the shells of the more loosely bound electrons. The Pauli principle is responsible for chemical valence, the principle of chemistry according to which atoms of one element bond to a definite number of atoms in other elements according to simple counting rules. If these shells are completely filled, the electrons are tightly bound and the atom does not readily share or lend its electrons to form chemical bonds. If there is only one electron in the last shell, it is weakly bound and the atom can be easily ionized. Examples of these situations are helium, which has a filled shell and is an inert gas, and lithium, which has one more electron in the next shell and is a highly reactive metal.

One kind of chemical bond is the ionic bond, in which a loosely bound electron from one atom transfers to a deeper shell in another atom. The two ions are held together by their electrical forces. Another kind of bond is the covalent bond. In this situation, the electron clouds of one atom are distorted by the presence of another atom. In the new cloud pattern, the outer electrons are more concentrated in the region between the two atoms. Thus, the atoms share their electrons. This allows atoms of the same element to form chemical bonds, which could not happen with ionic bonds. Chemical-bond energies typically measure several electron volts.

Nuclear properties. Like atoms, nuclei have a shell structure with the protons and neutrons in orbitals. Nuclei can exist in states of different energy, but ordinary stable nuclei are always in the most bound state. The scale of these energies is 1,000,000 times as large as atomic or chemical energies.

Nuclei can undergo transformations that affect their binding energies. If a transformation leads to more tightly bound nuclei, the excess energy will be released in some form. If one mole of atoms undergoes a nuclear transformation and releases 1,000,000 electron volts (1 MeV) of energy per nucleus, the total energy will be 10^{11} joules.

Some transformations can take place spontaneously, and such a process is called radioactivity. In one form of radioactivity, a neutron in the nucleus is converted to a proton or vice versa. If an electron is emitted at the same time, the process is known as beta radioactivity and the electron is called a beta ray. In another form of radioactivity, the nucleus disintegrates into one of lower mass number with the excess nucleons being ejected as a small nucleus. The small nucleus is commonly helium-4. This process is called alpha radioactivity, and the emitted helium-4 nuclei are called alpha rays. A third kind of ray observed in radioactivity is the gamma ray. Such rays are quanta of light of very high energy that are emitted when the nucleus makes a transition from one energy state to another of lower energy (see below *Radioactivity*).

Nuclear transformations also take place in nuclear reactions, which are the processes that occur when a nucleus is struck by some external particle. In a fusion reaction, two light nuclei come together and merge into a single heavier nucleus. Another important reaction is fission, the division of a nucleus into two roughly equal parts. Fission can be induced in the heaviest elements by reactions with free neutrons. Both fusion and fission can release energy by reforming the nuclei so that their atomic masses are closer to the middle range where nuclei have maximum binding energy.

Development of atomic theory

The concept of the atom that Western scientists accepted in broad outline from the 1600s until about 1900 originated with Greek philosophers in the 5th century BC. Their speculation about a hard, indivisible fundamental particle of nature was replaced slowly by a scientific theory supported by experiment and mathematical deduction. It was 2,000 years before modern physicists realized that the atom is indeed divisible and that it is not hard, solid, or immutable.

THE ATOMIC PHILOSOPHY OF THE EARLY GREEKS

Leucippus of Miletus (5th century BC) is thought to have originated the atomic philosophy. His famous disciple, Democritus of Abdera, developed and named the building blocks of matter *atomos,* meaning literally "indivisible," about 430 BC. Democritus believed that atoms were uniform, solid, hard, incompressible, and indestructible and that they moved in infinite numbers through empty space until stopped. Differences in atomic shape and size determined the various properties of matter. In Democritus' philosophy, atoms existed not only for matter but also for such qualities as perception and the human soul. For example, sourness was caused by needle-shaped atoms, while the colour white was composed of smooth-surfaced atoms. The atoms of the soul were considered to be particularly fine. Democritus developed his atomic philosophy as a middle ground between two opposing Greek theories about reality and the illusion of change. He argued that matter was subdivided into indivisible and immutable particles that created the appearance of change when they joined and separated from others.

The philosopher Epicurus of Samos (341–270 BC) used Democritus' ideas to try to quiet the fears of superstitious Greeks. According to Epicurus' materialistic philosophy, the entire universe was composed exclusively of atoms and void, and so even the gods were subject to natural laws.

Most of what is known about the atomic philosophy of the early Greeks comes from Aristotle's attacks on it and from a long poem, *De rerum natura* ("On the Nature of Things"), which the Latin poet and philosopher Titus Lucretius Carus (*c.* 95–55 BC) wrote to popularize its ideas. The Greek atomic theory is significant historically and philosophically, but it has no scientific value. It was not based on observations of nature, measurements, tests, or experiments. Instead, the Greeks used mathematics and reason almost exclusively when they wrote about physics. Like the later theologians of the Middle Ages, they wanted an all-encompassing theory to explain the universe, not merely a detailed experimental view of a tiny portion of it. Science constituted only one aspect of their broad philosophical system. Thus, Plato and Aristotle attacked Democritus' atomic theory on philosophical grounds rather than on scientific ones. Plato valued abstract ideas more than the physical world and rejected the notion that attributes such as goodness and beauty were "mechanical manifestations of material atoms." Where Democritus believed that matter could not move through space without a vacuum and that light was the rapid movement of particles through a void, Aristotle rejected the existence of vacuums because he could not conceive of bodies falling equally fast through a void. Aristotle's conception prevailed in medieval Christian Europe; its science was based on revelation and reason, and the Roman Catholic theologians rejected Democritus as materialistic and atheistic.

THE EMERGENCE OF EXPERIMENTAL SCIENCE

De rerum natura, which was rediscovered in the 15th century, helped fuel the 17th-century debate between orthodox Aristotelian views and the new experimental science. The poem was printed in 1649 and popularized by Pierre Gassendi, a French priest who tried to separate Epicurus'

atomism from its materialistic background by arguing that God created atoms.

Soon after Galileo Galilei expressed his belief that vacuums can exist (1638), scientists began studying the properties of air and partial vacuums to test the relative merits of Aristotelian orthodoxy and the atomic theory. The experimental evidence about air was only gradually separated from this philosophical controversy.

The Anglo-Irish chemist Robert Boyle began his systematic study of air in 1658 after he learned that Otto von Guericke, a German physicist and engineer, had invented an improved air pump four years earlier. In 1662 Boyle published the first physical law expressed in the form of an equation that describes the functional dependence of two variable quantities. This formulation became known as Boyle's law. From the beginning, Boyle wanted to analyze the elasticity of air quantitatively, not just qualitatively, and to separate the particular experimental problem about air's "spring" from the surrounding philosophical issues. Pouring mercury into the open end of a closed J-shaped tube, Boyle forced the air in the short side of the tube to contract under the pressure of the mercury on top. By doubling the height of the mercury column, he roughly doubled the pressure and halved the volume of air. By tripling the pressure, he cut the volume of air to a third, and so on.

Boyle's
law

This behaviour can be formulated mathematically in the relation $PV = P'V'$, where P and V are the pressure and volume under one set of conditions and P' and V' represent them under different conditions. Boyle's law says that pressure and volume are inversely related for a given quantity of gas. Although it is only approximately true for real gases, Boyle's law is an extremely useful idealization that played an important role in the development of atomic theory.

Soon after his air-pressure experiments, Boyle wrote that all matter is composed of solid particles arranged into molecules to give material its different properties. He explained that all things are "made of one Catholick Matter common to them all, and . . . differ but in the shape, size, motion or rest, and texture of the small parts they consist of."

In France Boyle's law is called Mariotte's law after the physicist Edme Mariotte, who discovered the empirical relationship independently in 1676. Mariotte realized that the law holds true only under constant temperatures; otherwise, the volume of gas expands when heated or contracts when cooled.

Forty years later, Isaac Newton expressed a typical 18th-century view of the atom that was similar to that of Democritus, Boyle, and Gassendi. In the last query in his book *Opticks* (1704), Newton stated:

> All these things being considered, it seems probable to me that God in the Beginning form'd Matter in solid, massy, hard, impenetrable, moveable Particles, of such Sizes and Figures, and with such other Properties, and in such Proportion to Space, as most conduced to the End for which he form'd them; and that these primitive Particles being Solids, are incomparably harder than any porous Bodies compounded of them; even so very hard, as never to wear or break in pieces; no ordinary Power being able to divide what God himself made one in the first Creation.

By the end of the 18th century chemists were just beginning to learn how chemicals combine. In 1794 Joseph-Louis Proust of France published his law of definite proportions (also known as Proust's law). He stated that the components of chemical compounds always combine in the same proportions by weight. For example, Proust found that no matter where he got his samples of the compound copper carbonate, they were composed by weight of five parts copper, four parts oxygen, and one part carbon.

Law of
definite
proportions

THE BEGINNINGS OF MODERN ATOMIC THEORY

Experimental foundation of atomic chemistry. The British chemist and physicist John Dalton extended Proust's work and converted the atomic philosophy of the Greeks into a scientific theory between 1803 and 1808. His book *New System of Chemical Philosophy* (part I, 1808; part II, 1810) was the first application of atomic

The specu-
lations of
Democritus

theory to chemistry. It provided a physical picture of how elements combine to form compounds and a phenomenological reason for believing that atoms exist. His work, together with that of Joseph-Louis Gay-Lussac of France and Amedeo Avogadro of Italy, provided the experimental foundation of atomic chemistry.

On the basis of the law of definite proportions, Dalton deduced the law of multiple proportions, which stated that when two elements form more than one compound by combining in more than one proportion by weight, the weight of one element in one of the compounds is in simple, integer ratios to its weights in the other compounds. For example, Dalton knew that oxygen and carbon can combine to form two different compounds and that carbon dioxide (CO_2) contains twice as much oxygen by weight as carbon monoxide (CO). In this case, the ratio of oxygen in one compound to the amount of oxygen in the other is the simple integer ratio 2:1. Although Dalton called his theory "modern" to differentiate it from Democritus' philosophy, he retained the Greek term atom to honour the ancients.

Dalton had begun his atomic studies by wondering why the different gases in the atmosphere do not separate, with the heaviest on the bottom and the lightest on the top. He decided that atoms are not infinite in variety as had been supposed and that they are limited to one of a kind for each element. Proposing that all the atoms of a given element have the same fixed mass, he concluded that elements react in definite proportions to form compounds because their constituent atoms react in definite proportion to produce compounds. He then tried to figure out the masses for well-known compounds. To do so, Dalton made a faulty but understandable assumption that the simplest hypothesis about atomic combinations was true. He maintained that the molecules of an element would always be single atoms. Thus, if two elements form only one compound, he believed that one atom of one element combined with one atom of another element. For example, describing the formation of water, he said that one atom of hydrogen and one of oxygen would combine to form HO instead of H_2O. Dalton's mistaken belief that atoms join together by attractive forces was accepted and formed the basis of most of 19th-century chemistry. As long as scientists worked with masses as ratios, a consistent chemistry could be developed because they did not need to know whether the atoms were separate or joined together as molecules.

Gay-Lussac soon took the relationship between chemical masses implied by Dalton's atomic theory and expanded it to volumetric relationships of gases. In 1809 he published two observations about gases that have come to be known as Gay-Lussac's law of combining gases. The first part of the law says that, when gases combine chemically, they do so in numerically simple volume ratios. Gay-Lussac illustrated this part of his law with three oxides of nitrogen. The compound NO has equal parts of nitrogen and oxygen by volume. Similarly, in the compound N_2O, the two parts by volume of nitrogen combine with one part of oxygen. He found corresponding volumes of nitrogen and oxygen in NO_2. Thus, Gay-Lussac's law relates volumes of the chemical constituents within a compound, unlike Dalton's law of multiple proportions, which relates only one constituent of a compound with the same constituent in other compounds.

The second part of Gay-Lussac's law states that if gases combine to form gases, the volumes of the products are also in simple numerical ratios to the volume of the original gases. This part of the law was illustrated by the combination of carbon monoxide and oxygen to form carbon dioxide. Gay-Lussac noted that the volume of the carbon dioxide is equal to the volume of carbon monoxide and is twice the volume of oxygen. He did not realize, however, that the reason that only half as much oxygen is needed is because the oxygen molecule splits in two to give a single atom to each molecule of carbon monoxide. In his "Mémoire sur la combinaison des substances gazeuses, les unes avec les autres" (1809; "Memoir on the Combination of Gaseous Substances with Each Other"), Gay-Lussac wrote:

Thus it appears evident to me that gases always combine in the simplest proportions when they act on one another; and we have seen in reality in all the preceding examples that the ratio of combination is 1 to 1, 1 to 2 or 1 to 3.... Gases... in whatever proportions they may combine, always give rise to compounds whose elements by volume are multiples of each other.... Not only, however, do gases combine in very simple proportions, as we have just seen, but the apparent contraction of volume which they experience on combination has also a simple relation to the volume of the gases, or at least to one of them.

Gay-Lussac's work raised the question of whether atoms differ from molecules and, if so, how many atoms and molecules are in a volume of gas. Amedeo Avogadro, building on Dalton's efforts, solved the puzzle, but his work unfortunately was ignored for 50 years.

In 1811 Avogadro proposed two hypotheses: (1) The atoms of elemental gases may be joined together in molecules rather than existing as separate atoms, as Dalton believed. (2) Equal volumes of gases contain equal numbers of molecules. These hypotheses explained why only half a volume of oxygen was necessary to combine with a volume of carbon monoxide to form carbon dioxide. Each oxygen molecule has two atoms, and each atom of oxygen joins one molecule of carbon monoxide.

Until the early 1860s, however, the allegiance of chemists to another concept espoused by the eminent Swedish chemist Jöns Jacob Berzelius blocked acceptance of Avogadro's ideas. (Berzelius was influential among chemists because he had determined the atomic weights of many elements extremely accurately.) Berzelius contended incorrectly that all atoms of a similar element repel each other because they have the same electric charge. He thought that only atoms with opposite charges could combine to form molecules.

Because early chemists did not know how many atoms were in a molecule, their chemical notation systems were in a state of chaos by the mid-19th century. Berzelius and his followers, for example, used the general formula MO for the chief metallic oxides, while others assigned the formula used today, M_2O. A single formula stood for different substances, depending on the chemist: H_2O_2 was water or hydrogen peroxide; C_2H_4 was marsh gas or ethylene. Proponents of the system used today based their chemical notation on an empirical law formulated in 1819 by the French scientists Pierre-Louis Dulong and Alexis-Thérèse Petit concerning the specific heat of elements. According to the so-called Dulong–Petit law, the specific heat of all elements is the same on a per atom basis. This law, however, was found to have many exceptions and was not fully understood until the development of quantum theory in the 20th century.

To resolve such problems of chemical notation, the Sicilian chemist Stanislao Cannizzaro revived Avogadro's ideas in 1858 and expounded them at the First International Chemical Congress, which met in Karlsruhe, Ger., in 1860. A noted German chemistry professor wrote later that, when he heard Avogadro's theory at the congress, "It was as though scales fell from my eyes, doubt vanished, and was replaced by a feeling of peaceful certainty." Within a few years, Avogadro's hypotheses were widely accepted in the world of chemistry.

Atomic weights and the periodic table. As more and more elements were discovered during the 19th century, scientists began to wonder how the physical properties of the elements were related to their atomic weights. During the 1860s several schemes were suggested. The Russian chemist Dmitry Ivanovich Mendeleyev based his system on the atomic weights of the elements as determined by Avogadro's theory of diatomic molecules. In his paper of 1869 introducing the periodic table, he credited Cannizzaro for using "unshakeable and indubitable" methods to determine atomic weights. "The elements, if arranged according to their atomic weights, show a distinct periodicity of their properties.... Elements exhibiting similarities in their chemical behavior have atomic weights which are approximately equal (as in the case of Pt, Ir, Os) or they possess atomic weights which increase in a uniform manner (as in the case of K, Rb, Cs)." Skipping hydrogen because it is anomalous, Mendeleyev arranged the 63 elements known to exist at the time into six groups according to valence. Valence, which is the combining power of an element, determines the proportions of the elements in a compound. For example, H_2O combines oxygen with a valence of 2 and hydrogen with a valence of 1. Recognizing that chemical qualities change gradually as atomic weight increases, Mendeleyev predicted a new element wherever there was a gap in atomic weights between adjacent elements. His system was thus a research tool and not merely a system of classification. Mendeleyev's periodic table raised an important question, however, for future atomic theory to answer: Where does the pattern of atomic weights come from?

Kinetic theory of gases. Whereas Avogadro's theory of diatomic molecules was ignored for 50 years, the kinetic theory of gases was rejected for more than a century. The kinetic theory relates the independent motion of molecules to the mechanical and thermal properties of gases—namely, their pressure, volume, temperature, viscosity, and heat conductivity. Three men—Daniel Bernoulli in 1738, John Herapath in 1820, and John James Waterston in 1845—independently developed the theory. The kinetic theory of gases, like the theory of diatomic molecules, was a simple physical idea that chemists ignored in favour of an elaborate explanation of the properties of gases.

Bernoulli, a Swiss mathematician and scientist, worked out the first quantitative mathematical treatment of the kinetic theory in 1738, picturing gases as consisting of an enormous number of particles in very fast, chaotic motion (see Figure 1). He derived Boyle's law by assuming that gas pressure is caused by the direct impact of particles on the walls of their container. He understood the difference between heat and temperature, realizing that heat makes gas particles move faster and that temperature merely measures the propensity of heat to flow from one body to another. In spite of its accuracy, Bernoulli's theory remained virtually unknown during the 18th century and early 19th century for several reasons. First, chemistry was more popular than physics among scientists of the day, and Bernoulli's theory involved mathematics. Second, Newton's reputation insured the success of his more comprehensible theory that gas atoms repel one another. Finally, Joseph Black, another noted British scientist, developed the caloric theory of heat, which proposed that heat was an invisible substance permeating matter. At the time, the fact that heat could be transmitted by light seemed a persuasive argument that heat and motion had nothing to do with each other.

Herapath, an amateur ignored by his contemporaries, published his version of the kinetic theory in 1821. He also derived an empirical relation akin to Boyle's law but

The contributions of Bernoulli, Herapath, and Waterston

From H.A. Boorse and L. Motz, *The World of the Atom* (1966)

Figure 1: As conceived by Daniel Bernoulli in *Hydrodynamica* (1738), gases consist of numerous particles in rapid, random motion. He assumed that the pressure of a gas is produced by the direct impact of the particles on the walls of the container (see text).

did not understand correctly the role of heat and temperature in determining the pressure of a gas.

Waterston's efforts met with a similar fate. A civil engineer and amateur physicist, he could not even get his work published by the scientific community, which had become increasingly professional throughout the 19th century. Nevertheless, Waterston made the first statement of the law of equipartition of energy, according to which all kinds of particles have equal amounts of thermal energy. He derived practically all the consequences of the fact that pressure exerted by a gas is related to the number of molecules per cubic centimetre, their mass, and their mean squared velocity. He derived the basic equation of kinetic theory, which reads $P = NMV^2$. Here P is the pressure of a volume of gas, N is the number of molecules per unit volume, M is the mass of the molecule, and V^2 is the average velocity squared of the molecules. Recognizing that the kinetic energy of a molecule is proportional to MV^2 and that the heat energy of a gas is proportional to the temperature, Waterston expressed the law as $PV/T = $ a constant.

During the late 1850s, a decade after Waterston had formulated his law, the scientific community was finally ready to accept a kinetic theory of gases. The studies of heat undertaken by the British physicist James Prescott Joule during the 1840s had shown that heat is a form of energy. This work, together with the law of the conservation of energy that he helped to establish, had persuaded scientists to discard the caloric theory by the mid-1850s. The caloric theory had required that a substance contain a definite amount of caloric (*i.e.,* a hypothetical weightless fluid) to be turned into heat; however, experiments showed that any amount of heat can be generated in a substance by putting enough energy into it. Thus, there was no point to hypothesizing such a special fluid as caloric.

At first, after the collapse of the caloric theory, physicists had nothing with which to replace it. Joule, however, discovered Herapath's kinetic theory and used it to calculate the velocity of hydrogen molecules in 1851. Then Rudolf Clausius, a German physicist, developed the kinetic theory mathematically in 1857, and the scientific world took notice. Clausius and two other prominent physicists, James Clerk Maxwell and Ludwig Eduard Boltzmann (who developed the kinetic theory of gases in the 1860s), introduced sophisticated mathematics into physics for the first time since Newton. In his 1860 paper "Illustrations of the Dynamical Theory of Gases," Maxwell used probability to produce his famous distribution curve for the velocities of gas molecules. Employing Newtonian laws of mechanics, Maxwell also provided a mathematical basis for Avogadro's theory. Maxwell, Clausius, and Boltzmann assumed that gas particles were in constant motion, that they were tiny compared to their space, and that their interactions were extremely brief. They then related the motion of the particles to pressure, volume, and temperature. Interestingly, none of the three committed himself on the nature of the particles.

STUDIES OF THE PROPERTIES OF ATOMS

Size of atoms. The first modern estimates of the size of atoms and the numbers of atoms in a given volume were made by the German chemist Joseph Loschmidt in 1865. Loschmidt used the results of kinetic theory and some rough estimates to do his calculation. The size of the atoms and the distance between them in the gaseous state are related both to the contraction of gas upon liquefaction and to the mean free path traveled by molecules in a gas. The mean free path, in turn, can be found from the thermal conductivity and diffusion rates in the gas. Loschmidt calculated the size of the atom and the spacing between atoms by finding a solution common to these relationships. His result for Avogadro's number is remarkably close to the present accepted value of 6.022 $\times 10^{23}$. The precise definition of Avogadro's number is the number of atoms in 12 grams of the carbon isotope ^{12}C. Loschmidt's result for the diameter of an atom was approximately 10^{-8} centimetres.

Much later, in 1908, the French physicist Jean Perrin used Brownian motion to determine Avogadro's number.

Loschmidt's determinations

Brownian motion, first observed in 1827 by the Scottish botanist Robert Brown, is the continuous movement of tiny particles suspended in water. Their movement is caused by the thermal motion of water molecules bumping into the particles. Perrin's argument for determining Avogadro's number makes an analogy between particles in the liquid and molecules in the atmosphere. The thinning of air at high altitudes depends on the balance between the gravitational force pulling the molecules down and their thermal motion forcing them up. The relationship between the weight of the particles and the height of the atmosphere would be the same for Brownian particles suspended in water. Perrin counted particles of gum mastic at different heights in his water sample and inferred the mass of atoms from the rate of decrease. He then divided the result into the molar weight of atoms to determine Avogadro's number. After Perrin, few scientists could disbelieve the existence of atoms.

Electric properties of atoms. While atomic theory was set back by the failure of scientists to accept simple physical ideas like the diatomic atom and the kinetic theory of gases, it was also delayed by the preoccupation of physicists with mechanics for almost 200 years, from Newton to the 20th century. Nevertheless, several 19th-century investigators, working in the relatively ignored fields of electricity, magnetism, and optics, provided important clues about the interior of the atom. The studies in electrodynamics made by the British physicist Michael Faraday and those of Maxwell indicated for the first time that something existed apart from palpable matter, and data obtained by Gustav Robert Kirchhoff of Germany about elemental spectral lines raised questions that would only be answered in the 20th century by quantum mechanics.

Until Faraday's electrolysis experiments, scientists had had no conception of the nature of the forces binding atoms together in a molecule. Faraday concluded that electrical forces existed inside the molecule after he had produced an electric current and a chemical reaction in a solution with the electrodes of a voltaic cell. No matter what solution or electrode material he used, a fixed quantity of current sent through an electrolyte always caused a specific amount of material to form on an electrode of the electrolytic cell. Faraday concluded that each ion of
Faraday's
discoveries a given chemical compound has exactly the same charge. Later, he discovered that the ionic charges are integral multiples of a single unit of charge, never fractions.

On the practical level, Faraday did for charge what Dalton had done for the chemical combination of atomic masses. That is to say, Faraday demonstrated that it takes a definite amount of charge to convert an ion of an element into an atom of the element and that the amount of charge depends on the element used. The unit of charge that releases a gram atomic weight of a simple ion is called the faraday in his honour. For example, one faraday of charge passing through water releases one gram of hydrogen and eight grams of oxygen. In this manner, Faraday gave scientists a rather precise value for the ratios of the masses of atoms to the electric charges of ions. The ratio of the mass of the hydrogen atom to the charge of the electron was found to be 1.035×10^{-8} kilogram per coulomb. Faraday did not know the size of his electrolytic unit of charge in units such as coulombs any more than Dalton knew the magnitude of his unit of atomic weight in grams. Nevertheless, scientists could determine the ratio of these units easily.

More significantly, Faraday's work was the first to imply the electrical nature of matter and the existence of subatomic particles and a fundamental unit of charge. Faraday wrote: "The atoms of matter are in some way endowed or associated with electrical powers, to which they owe their most striking qualities, and amongst them their mutual chemical affinity. Faraday did not, however, conclude that atoms cause electricity.

Light and spectral lines. In 1865 Maxwell unified the laws of electricity and magnetism in his publication "A Dynamical Theory of the Electromagnetic Field." In this paper, he concluded that light is an electromagnetic wave. His theory was confirmed by the German physicist Heinrich Hertz, who produced radio waves with sparks in

1887. With light understood as an electromagnetic wave, Maxwell's theory could be applied to the emission of light from atoms. The theory failed, however, to describe spectral lines and the fact that atoms do not lose all their energy when they radiate light. The problem was not with Maxwell's theory of light itself but rather with its description of the oscillating electron currents generating light. Only quantum mechanics could explain this behaviour (see below *The laws of quantum mechanics*).

By far the richest clues about the structure of the atom came from spectral lines. Mounting a particularly fine
Spectral
lines
and
atomic
structure prism on a telescope, the German physicist and optician Joseph von Fraunhofer had discovered between 1814 and 1824 hundreds of dark lines in the spectrum of the Sun. He labeled the most prominent of these lines with the letters *A* through *G*. Together, they are now called Fraunhofer lines. A generation later, Kirchhoff heated different elements to incandescence in order to study the different coloured vapours emitted. Observing the vapours through a spectroscope, he discovered that each element has a unique and characteristic pattern of spectral lines. Each element produces the same set of identifying lines, even when it is combined chemically with other elements. In 1859 Kirchhoff and the German chemist Robert Wilhelm Bunsen discovered two new elements—cesium and rubidium—by first observing their spectral lines.

Johann Jakob Balmer, a Swiss secondary school teacher with a penchant for numerology, studied hydrogen's spectral lines and found a constant relationship between the wavelengths of the element's four visible lines (see Figure 2). In 1885 he published a generalized mathematical formula for all of the lines of hydrogen. The Swedish physicist Johannes Rydberg extended Balmer's work in 1890 and found a general rule applicable to many elements. Soon more series were discovered elsewhere in the spectrum of hydrogen and in the spectra of other elements as well. Stated in terms of the frequency of the light rather than its wavelength, the formula may be expressed:

$$nu = R \left(1/n^2 - 1/m^2\right).$$

Here, *n* and *m* are integers and *R* is a constant. In the Balmer lines, *m* is equal to 2 and *n* takes on the values 3, 4, 5, and 6.

Adapted from W. Finkelnburg, *Structure of Matter* (1964); Springer-Verlag, Heidelberg

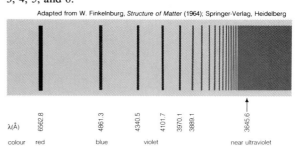

Figure 2: Spectrum of atomic hydrogen, showing the series of Balmer lines.

Discovery of electrons. During the 1880s and 1890s, scientists searched cathode rays for the carrier of the electrical properties in matter. Their work culminated in J.J. Thomson's discovery of the electron in 1897. The existence of the electron showed that the 2,000-year-old conception of the atom as a homogeneous particle was wrong and that in fact the atom has a complex structure.

Cathode-ray studies began in 1854 when Heinrich Geissler, a glassblower and technical assistant to the German physicist Julius Plücker, improved the vacuum tube. Plücker discovered cathode rays in 1858 by sealing two electrodes inside the tube, evacuating the air, and forcing electric current between the electrodes. He found a green glow on the wall of his glass tube and attributed it to rays emanating from the cathode. In 1869, with better vacuums, Plücker's pupil Johann W. Hittorf saw a shadow cast by an object placed in front of the cathode. The shadow proved that the cathode rays originated from the cathode. The British physicist and chemist Sir William Crookes investigated cathode rays in 1879 and found that they were bent by a magnetic field; the direction of deflection
Crookes's
study of
cathode
rays

suggested that they were negatively charged particles. As the luminescence did not depend on what gas had been in the vacuum or what metal the electrodes were made of, he surmised that the rays were a property of the electric current itself. As a result of Crookes's work, cathode rays were widely studied, and the tubes came to be called Crookes tubes.

Although Crookes believed that the particles were electrified charged particles, his work did not settle the issue of whether cathode rays were particles or radiation similar to light. By the late 1880s the controversy over the nature of cathode rays had divided the physics community into two camps. Most French and British physicists, influenced by Crookes, thought that cathode rays were electrically charged particles because they were affected by magnets. Most German physicists, on the other hand, believed that the rays were waves because they traveled in straight lines and were unaffected by gravity. A crucial test of the nature of the cathode rays was how they would be affected by electric fields. Heinrich Hertz, the aforementioned German physicist, reported that the cathode rays were not deflected when they passed between two oppositely charged plates in an 1892 experiment. The English physicist Thomson thought Hertz's vacuum might have been faulty and that residual gas might have reduced the effect of the electric field on the cathode rays.

Thomson repeated Hertz's experiment with a better vacuum in 1897. He directed the cathode rays between two parallel aluminum plates to the end of a tube where they were observed as luminescence on the glass. When the top aluminum plate was negative, the rays moved down; when the upper plate was positive, the rays moved up. The deflection was proportional to the difference in potential between the plates. With both magnetic and electric deflections observed, it was clear that cathode rays were negatively charged particles. Thomson's discovery established the particulate nature of electricity. Accordingly, he called his particles electrons.

From the magnitude of the electrical and magnetic deflections, Thomson could calculate the ratio of mass to charge for the electrons. This ratio was known for atoms from electrochemical studies. Measuring and comparing it to the number for an atom, he discovered that the mass of the electron was very small, merely 1/1,836th that of a hydrogen ion. When scientists realized that an electron was virtually 1,000 times lighter than the smallest atom, they understood how cathode rays could penetrate metal sheets and how electric current could flow through copper wires. In deriving the mass-to-charge ratio, Thomson had calculated the electron's velocity. It was 1/10th the speed of light, thus amounting to roughly 30,000 kilometres per second (18,000 miles per second). Thomson emphasized that "we have in the cathode rays matter in a new state, a state in which the subdivision of matter is carried very much further than in the ordinary gaseous state; a state in which all matter, that is, matter derived from different sources such as hydrogen, oxygen, etc., is of one and the same kind; this matter being the substance from which all the chemical elements are built up." Thus, the electron was the first subatomic particle identified, the smallest and the fastest bit of matter known at the time.

In 1910 and 1911 the American physicist Robert Andrews Millikan greatly improved a method employed by Thomson for measuring the electron charge directly. Millikan produced microscopic oil droplets and observed them falling in the space between two electrically charged plates. Some of the droplets became charged and could be suspended by a delicate adjustment of the electric field. Millikan knew the weight of the droplets from their rate of fall when the electric field was turned off. From the balance of the gravitational and electrical forces, he could determine the charge on the droplets. He could find charges only in integral multiples of a quantity that in contemporary units is 1.602×10^{-19} coulomb. Millikan's electron charge experiment was the first to detect and measure the effect of an individual subatomic particle. Besides confirming the particulate nature of electricity, his experiment also supported previous determinations of Avogadro's number. Avogadro's number times the unit

of charge gives Faraday's constant, the amount of charge required to electrolyze one mole of a chemical ion.

Identification of positive ions. In addition to electrons, positively charged particles also emanate from the anode in an energized Crookes tube. The German physicist Wilhelm Wien analyzed these positive rays in 1898 and found that the particles have a charge-to-mass ratio more than 1,000 times larger than that of the electron. Because the ratio of the particles is also comparable to the charge-to-mass ratio of the residual atoms in the discharge tubes, scientists suspected that the rays were actually ions from the gases in the tube.

In 1913 Thomson refined Wien's apparatus to separate different ions and measure their mass-to-charge ratio on photographic plates. He sorted out the many ions in various charge states produced in a discharge tube. When he conducted his atomic mass experiments with neon gas, he found that a beam of neon atoms subjected to electric and magnetic forces split into two parabolas instead of one on a photographic plate. Chemists had assumed the atomic weight of neon was 20.2, but the traces on Thomson's photographic plate suggested atomic weights of 20.0 and 22.0, with the former parabola much stronger than the latter. He concluded that neon consisted of two stable isotopes: primarily neon-20, with a small percentage of neon-22. Eventually, a third isotope, neon-21, was discovered in very small quantities. It is now known that 1,000 neon atoms will contain 909 of neon-20, 88 of neon-22, and 3 of neon-21. Dalton's assumptions that all atoms of an element have an identical mass and that the atomic weight of an element is its mass were thus disproved. Today, the atomic weight of an element is recognized as the weighted average of the masses of its isotopes.

Francis William Aston, an English physicist, improved Thomson's technique when he developed the mass spectrograph in 1919. This device spread out the beam of positive ions into a "mass spectrum" of lines similar to the way light is separated into a spectrum. Aston analyzed about 50 elements over the next six years and discovered that most have isotopes.

Discovery of radioactivity. Like Thomson's discovery of the electron, the discovery of radioactivity in uranium by the French physicist Henri Becquerel in 1896 forced scientists to radically change their ideas about atomic structure. Radioactivity demonstrated that the atom was neither indivisible nor immutable. Instead of serving merely as an inert matrix for electrons, the atom could change form and emit an enormous amount of energy. Furthermore, radioactivity itself became an important tool for revealing the interior of the atom.

The German physicist Wilhelm Conrad Röntgen had discovered X rays in 1895, and Becquerel thought they might be related to fluorescence and phosphorescence, processes in which substances absorb and emit energy as light. In the course of his investigations, Becquerel stored some photographic plates and uranium salts in a desk drawer. Expecting to find the plates only lightly fogged, he developed them and was surprised to find sharp images of the salts. He then began experiments that showed that uranium salts emit a penetrating radiation independent of external influences. Becquerel also demonstrated that the radiation could discharge electrified bodies. In this case, discharge means the removal of electric charge, and it is now understood that the radiation ionizing molecules of air allows the air to conduct an electric current. Early studies of radioactivity relied on measuring ionization power or on observing the effects of radiation on photographic plates.

In 1898 the French physicists Pierre and Marie Curie discovered the strongly radioactive elements polonium and radium, which occur naturally in uranium minerals. Marie coined the term radioactivity for the spontaneous emission of ionizing, penetrating rays by certain atoms (see below).

Experiments conducted by the British physicist Ernest Rutherford in 1899 showed that radioactive substances emit more than one kind of ray. It was determined that part of the radiation is 100 times more penetrating than the rest and can pass through aluminum foil 1/50th of a

Determining the properties of electrons

Millikan's electron charge experiment

Development of the mass spectrograph

Different forms of ionizing radiation

millimetre thick. Rutherford named the less penetrating emanations alpha rays and the more powerful ones beta rays, after the first two letters of the Greek alphabet. Investigators who, in 1899, found that beta rays were deflected by a magnetic field concluded that they are negatively charged particles similar to cathode rays. In 1903 Rutherford found that alpha rays were deflected slightly in the opposite direction, showing that they are massive, positively charged particles. Much later, Rutherford proved that alpha rays are nuclei of helium atoms by collecting the rays in an evacuated tube and detecting the buildup of helium gas over several days. A third kind of radiation was identified by the French chemist Paul Villard in 1900. Designated as the gamma ray, it is not deflected by magnets and is much more penetrating than alpha particles. Gamma rays were later shown to be a form of electromagnetic radiation, like light or X rays, but with much shorter wavelengths. Because of these shorter wavelengths, gamma rays have higher frequencies and are even more penetrating than X rays. In 1902, while studying the radioactivity of thorium, Rutherford and the English chemist Frederick Soddy discovered that radioactivity was associated with changes inside the atom that transformed thorium into a different element. They found that thorium continually generates a chemically different substance that is intensely radioactive. The radioactivity eventually makes the new element disappear. Watching the process, Rutherford and Soddy formulated the exponential decay law, which states that a fixed fraction of the element will decay in each unit of time. For example, half of the thorium product decays in four days, half the remaining sample in the next four days, and so on.

Until the 20th century, physicists had studied such subjects as mechanics, heat, and electromagnetism that they could understand by applying common sense or by extrapolating from everyday experiences. The discovery of the electron and radioactivity, however, showed that classical Newtonian mechanics could not explain phenomena at atomic and subatomic levels. As the primacy of classical mechanics crumbled during the early 20th century, quantum mechanics was developed to replace it. Since then, experiments and theories have led physicists into a world that is often extremely abstract and seemingly contradictory.

MODELS OF ATOMIC STRUCTURE

Thomson's discovery of the negatively charged electron had raised theoretical problems for physicists as early as 1897, because atoms as a whole are electrically neutral. Where was the neutralizing positive charge and what held it in place? Between 1903 and 1907 Thomson tried to solve the mystery by adapting an atomic model that had been first proposed by Lord Kelvin in 1902. According to this theoretical system, often referred to as the "plum pudding" model, the atom is a sphere of uniformly distributed positive charge about one angstrom in diameter. Electrons are embedded in a regular pattern like raisins in a plum pudding to neutralize the positive charge. The advantage of the Thomson atom was that it was inherently stable: if the electrons were displaced, they would attempt to return to their original positions. In another contemporary model, the atom resembled the solar system or the planet Saturn, with rings of electrons surrounding a concentrated positive charge. The Japanese physicist Hantaro Nagaoka, in particular, developed the "Saturnian" system in 1904. The atom, as postulated in this model, was inherently unstable because, by radiating continuously, the electron would gradually lose energy and spiral into the nucleus. No electron could thus remain in any particular orbit indefinitely.

Rutherford's nuclear model. Rutherford overturned Thomson's model in 1911 with his well-known gold foil experiment in which he demonstrated that the atom has a tiny, massive nucleus. Five years earlier Rutherford had noticed that alpha particles, beamed through a hole onto a photographic plate, would make a sharp-edged picture, while alpha particles beamed through a sheet of mica only 20 micrometres (or about 0.002 centimetre) thick would make an impression with blurry edges. For some parti-

cles, the blurring corresponded to a two-degree deflection. Remembering those results, Rutherford had his postdoctoral fellow, Hans Geiger, and an undergraduate student, Ernest Marsden, refine the experiment. The young physicists beamed alpha particles through gold foil and detected them as flashes of light or scintillations on a screen. The gold foil was only 0.00004 centimetre thick. Most of the alpha particles went straight through the foil, but some were deflected by the foil and hit a spot on a screen placed off to one side. Geiger and Marsden found that about one in 20,000 alpha particles had been deflected 45° or more. Rutherford asked why so many alpha particles passed through the gold foil while a few were deflected so greatly. "It was almost as incredible as if you fired a 15-inch shell at a piece of tissue paper, and it came back to hit you," Rutherford said later. "On consideration, I realized that this scattering backwards must be the result of a single collision, and when I made calculations I saw that it was impossible to get anything of that order of magnitude unless you took a system in which the greater part of the mass of the atom was concentrated in a minute nucleus. It was then that I had the idea of an atom with a minute massive centre carrying a charge."

Many physicists distrusted Rutherford's nuclear model because it was difficult to reconcile with the chemical behaviour of atoms. The model suggested that the charge on the nucleus was the most important characteristic of the atom, determining its structure. On the other hand, Mendeleyev's periodic table of the elements had been organized according to the atomic masses of the elements, implying that the mass was responsible for the structure and chemical behaviour of atoms.

Moseley's X-ray studies. Henry Gwyn Jeffreys Moseley, a young English physicist killed in World War I, confirmed that the positive charge on the nucleus revealed more about the fundamental structure of the atom than Mendeleyev's atomic mass. Moseley studied the spectral lines emitted by heavy elements in the X-ray region of the electromagnetic spectrum. He built on the work done by several other British physicists—Charles Glover Barkla, who had studied X rays produced by the impact of electrons on metal plates, and Sir William Bragg and his son Lawrence, who had developed a precise method of using crystals to reflect X rays and measure their wavelength by diffraction. Moseley used a crystal of potassium ferrocyanide as a diffraction grating to examine the spectra of X rays produced by different metals. He arranged his crystal so that he could control and vary the angle between the crystal face and the X-ray beam. The X rays from each element were reflected at a unique set of angles. By measuring the angle, Moseley was able to obtain the wavelength of the X ray hitting the crystal.

Moseley found that the X rays radiated by each element have a characteristic frequency that differs according to a regular pattern. The difference in frequency is not governed by Mendeleyev's change in mass, however, but rather by the change in charge on the nucleus. He called this the atomic number. In his first experiments, conducted in 1913, Moseley used the K series of X rays (X radiation associated with the K energy state of an atom) and studied the elements up to zinc. The following year he extended his work up to gold in the periodic table, using the L series of X rays (X radiation associated with the L atomic-energy state). Moseley was conducting his research at the same time that the Danish theorist Niels (phys.)Bohr was developing his quantum shell model of the atom (see below). The two conferred and shared data as their work progressed, and Moseley framed his equation in terms of Bohr's theory. Moseley presented formulas for the X-ray frequencies that were closely related to Bohr's formulas for the spectral lines in a hydrogen atom. Moseley showed that the frequency of a line in the X-ray spectrum is proportional to the square of the charge on the nucleus. The constant of proportionality depends on whether the X ray is in the K or L series. This is the same relationship that Bohr used in his formula applied to the Lyman and Balmer series of spectral lines. The regularity of the differences in X-ray frequencies allowed Moseley to order the elements by atomic number from aluminum to gold. He observed

Law of exponential decay

The so-called plum pudding model

Primacy of the positive charge on the nucleus

Collaboration with Niels Bohr

that, in some cases, the order by atomic weights was incorrect. For example, cobalt has a larger atomic mass than nickel, but Moseley found that it has atomic number 27, while nickel has 28. When Mendeleyev constructed the periodic table, he based his system on the atomic masses of the elements and had to put cobalt and nickel out of order to make the chemical properties fit better. In a few places where Moseley found more than one integer between elements, he predicted correctly that a new element would be discovered. Because there is just one element for each atomic number, scientists could be confident for the first time of the completeness of the periodic table; no unexpected new elements would be discovered.

Bohr's shell model. In 1913 Bohr proposed his quantized shell model of the atom to explain how electrons can have stable orbits around the nucleus. The motion of the electrons in the Rutherford model was unstable because, according to classical mechanics and electromagnetic theory, any charged particle moving on a curved path emits electromagnetic radiation; thus, the electrons would lose energy and spiral into the nucleus. To remedy the stability problem, Bohr modified the Rutherford model by requiring that the electrons move in orbits of fixed size and energy. The energy of an electron depends on the size of the orbit and is lower for smaller orbits. Radiation can occur only when the electron jumps from one orbit to another. The atom will be completely stable in the state with the smallest orbit, since there is no orbit of lower energy into which the electron can jump.

Electron orbits of fixed size and shape

Bohr's starting point was to realize that classical mechanics by itself could never explain the atom's stability. A stable atom has a certain size so that any equation describing it must contain some fundamental constant or combination of constants with a dimension of length. The classical fundamental constants—namely, the charges and the masses of the electron and the nucleus—cannot be combined to make a length. Bohr noticed, however, that the quantum constant formulated by the German physicist Max Planck (see below) has dimensions which, when combined with the mass and charge of the electron, produce a measure of length. Numerically, the measure is close to the known size of atoms. This encouraged Bohr to use Planck's constant in searching for a theory of the atom.

Planck's constant

Planck had introduced his constant in 1900 in a formula explaining the light radiation emitted from heated bodies. According to classical theory, comparable amounts of light energy should be produced at all frequencies. This is not only contrary to observation but also implies the absurd result that the total energy radiated by a heated body should be infinite. Planck postulated that energy can only be emitted or absorbed in discrete amounts, which he called quanta (the Latin word for "how much"). The energy quantum is related to the frequency of the light by a new fundamental constant, h. When a body is heated, its radiant energy in a particular frequency range is, according to classical theory, proportional to the temperature of the body. With Planck's hypothesis, however, the radiation can occur only in quantum amounts of energy. If the radiant energy is less than the quantum of energy, the amount of light in that frequency range will be reduced. Planck's formula correctly describes radiation from heated bodies. Planck's constant has the dimensions of action, which may be expressed as units of energy multiplied by time, units of momentum multiplied by length, or units of angular momentum. For example, Planck's constant can be written as $h = 6.6 \times 10^{-34}$ joule seconds or 6.6×10^{-34} kilogram-metre/second-metres.

Using Planck's constant, Bohr obtained an accurate formula for the energy levels of the hydrogen atom (see Figure 3). He postulated that the angular momentum of the electron is quantized—i.e., it can have only discrete values. He assumed that otherwise electrons obey the laws of classical mechanics by traveling around the nucleus in circular orbits. Because of the quantization, the electron orbits have fixed sizes and energies. The orbits are labeled by an integer, the quantum number n.

With his model, Bohr explained how electrons could jump from one orbit to another only by emitting or ab-

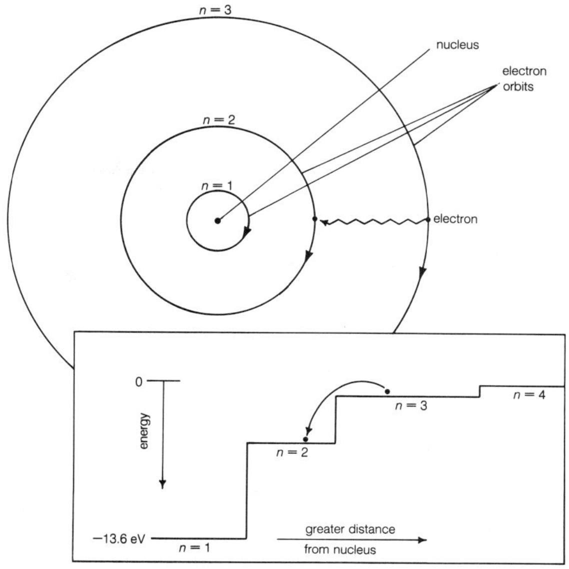

Figure 3: *The Bohr atom.*
The electron travels in circular orbits around the nucleus. The orbits have quantized sizes and energies. Energy is emitted from the atom when the electron jumps from one orbit to another closer to the nucleus. Shown here is the first Balmer transition, in which an electron jumps from orbit $n = 3$ to orbit $n = 2$, producing a photon of red light with an energy of 1.89 eV and a wavelength of 656×10^{-9} m.

sorbing energy in fixed quanta. For example, if an electron jumps one orbit closer to the nucleus, it must emit energy equal to the difference of the energies of the two orbits. Conversely, when the electron jumps to a larger orbit, it must absorb a quantum of light equal in energy to the difference in orbits.

Bohr's model accounts for the stability of atoms because the electron cannot lose more energy than it has in the smallest orbit, the one with $n = 1$. The model also explains the Balmer formula for the spectral lines of hydrogen. The frequency of the light is related to its energy by Einstein's formula $E = h\nu$. The light energy is calculated from the difference in energies between the two orbits. The Balmer formula can be expressed as the difference of two terms, each term giving the energy of an orbit. Bohr's model not only explains the form of the Balmer formula but also accurately gives the value of the constant of proportionality R.

The inherent stability of atoms

The usefulness of Bohr's theory extends beyond the hydrogen atom. Bohr himself noted that the formula also applies to the singly ionized helium atom, which, like hydrogen, has a single electron. The nucleus of the helium atom has twice the charge of the hydrogen nucleus, however. In Bohr's formula the charge of the electron is raised to the fourth power. Two of those powers stem from the charge on the nucleus; the other two come from the charge on the electron itself. Bohr modified his formula for the hydrogen atom to fit the helium atom by doubling the charge on the nucleus. Moseley applied Bohr's formula with an arbitrary atomic charge Z to explain the K- and L-series X-ray spectra of heavier atoms. The German physicists James Franck and Gustav Hertz confirmed the existence of quantum states in atoms in experiments reported in 1914. They made atoms absorb energy by bombarding them with electrons. The atoms would only absorb discrete amounts of energy from the electron beam. When the energy of an electron was below the threshold for producing an excited state, the atom would not absorb any energy.

Bohr's theory had major drawbacks, however. Except for the spectra of X rays in the K and L series, it could not explain properties of atoms having more than one electron. The binding energy of the helium atom, which has two electrons, was not understood until the development of quantum mechanics. Several features of the spectrum were inexplicable even in the hydrogen atom. High-resolution spectroscopy shows that the individual spectral lines

Limitations of Bohr's model

of hydrogen are divided into several closely spaced, fine lines. In a magnetic field the lines split even further. The German physicist Arnold Sommerfeld modified Bohr's theory by quantizing the shapes and orientations of orbits to introduce additional energy levels corresponding to the fine spectral lines. The quantization of the orientation of the angular-momentum vector was confirmed in an experiment in 1922 by other German physicists, Otto Stern and Walter Gerlach. They passed a beam of silver atoms through a nonhomogeneous magnetic field, one that is stronger on one side than on the other. The field deflected the atoms according to the orientation of their magnetic moments. (The magnetic moment of an object such as an atom or a compass needle is the measure of its interaction with a magnetic field. The moment points in some direction and is associated in classical physics with orbital currents and the angular momentum of charges.) In their experiment, Stern and Gerlach found only two deflections, not the continuous distribution of deflections that would have been seen if the magnetic moment had been oriented in any direction. Thus, it was determined that the magnetic moment and the angular momentum of an atom can have only two orientations. The discrete orientations of the orbits explain some of the magnetic field effects—namely, the so-called normal Zeeman effect, which is the splitting of a spectral line into three sublines. These sublines correspond to quantum jumps in which the angular momentum along the magnetic field is increased by one unit. decreased by one unit, or left unchanged.

An additional quantum number was needed to complete the description of electrons in an atom. In 1925 Samuel A. Goudsmit and George E. Uhlenbeck, two graduate students in physics at the University of Leiden, in The Netherlands, added a quantum number to account for the fact that some spectral lines are divided into more sublines than can be explained with the original quantum numbers. Goudsmit and Uhlenbeck postulated that an electron has an internal spinning motion and that the corresponding angular momentum is one-half of the orbital angular momentum quantum. An electron has a magnetic moment, and its energy depends on whether the spin is aligned with or against the magnetic field. Independently, the Austrian-born physicist Wolfgang Pauli also suggested adding a two-valued quantum number for electrons, but for different reasons. He needed this additional quantum number to formulate his exclusion principle, which serves as the atomic basis of the periodic table and the chemical behaviour of the elements. According to the exclusion principle, one electron at most can occupy an orbital, taking into account all the quantum numbers. Pauli was led to this principle by the observation that an alkali in a magnetic field has a number of orbitals in the shell equal to the number of electrons that must be added to make the next noble gas. These numbers are twice the number of orbits available if the angular momentum and its orientation are considered alone.

In spite of these modifications, Bohr's model seemed to be a dead end by the early 1920s. It did not explain most fine spectral lines or the anomalous Zeeman effect, which is a complicated type of spectral line splitting that sometimes involves up to 15 sublines. (Its name notwithstanding, the anomalous Zeeman effect is more common than the aforementioned normal Zeeman effect.) Efforts to generalize the model to multielectron atoms had proved futile, and physicists despaired of ever explaining them.

The laws of quantum mechanics. Within a few short years scientists developed a consistent theory of the atom that explained its fundamental structure and its interactions. Crucial to the development of the theory was new evidence indicating that light and matter have both wave and particle characteristics at the atomic and subatomic levels. Theoreticians had objected to the fact that Bohr had used an ad hoc hybrid of classical Newtonian dynamics for the orbits and some quantum postulates for limiting the motion. The new theory ignored the fact that electrons are particles and treated them as waves. By 1926, physicists had developed the laws of quantum mechanics, also called wave mechanics, to explain atomic and subatomic phenomena.

The duality between the wave and particle nature of light was highlighted by the American physicist Arthur H. Compton in an X-ray scattering experiment conducted in 1922. Compton showed that X rays scatter from electrons exactly like particles. The X rays have discrete amounts of momentum, which is a property of particles. When X rays are scattered, their momentum is partially transferred to the electrons. The recoil electron takes some energy from an X ray, and as a result the X ray frequency is shifted. Both the discrete amount of momentum and the frequency shift of the light scattering are completely at variance with classical electromagnetic theory.

Louis-Victor de Broglie, a French physicist, had proposed in his 1923 doctoral thesis that all matter and radiations have both particle- and wavelike characteristics. Until the emergence of the quantum theory, physicists had assumed that matter was distinct from energy and followed different laws: energy radiations were waves and matter was particulate. Planck's theory was the first to propose that radiation has characteristics of both waves and particles. Believing in the symmetry of nature, Broglie ended the wave-particle dichotomy by applying Einstein's mass-energy formula. Using the old-fashioned word corpuscles for particles, Broglie wrote, "For both matter and radiations, light in particular, it is necessary to introduce the corpuscle concept and the wave concept at the same time. In other words, the existence of corpuscles accompanied by waves has to be assumed in all cases." Broglie's conception was an inspired one, but it had no experimental or theoretical foundation. The Austrian physicist Erwin Schrödinger had to supply the theory.

Schrödinger's wave equation. In 1926 Schrödinger produced the mathematical wave equation that established quantum mechanics in widely applicable form. To understand how a wave equation is used, it is helpful to think of an analogy with the vibrations of a bell, violin string, or drumhead. These vibrations are governed by a wave equation, since the motion can propagate as a wave from one side of the object to the other. Certain vibrations in these objects are simple modes that are easily excited and have definite frequencies. For example, the motion of the lowest vibrational mode in a drumhead is in phase all over the drumhead with a pattern that is uniform around it; the highest amplitude of the vibratory motion is in the middle of the drumhead. In more complicated, higher frequency modes, the motion on different parts of the vibrating drumhead are out of phase, with inward motion on one part at the same time that there is outward motion on another.

Schrödinger postulated that the electrons in an atom should be treated like the waves on the drumhead. The different energy levels of atoms are identified with the simple vibrational modes of the wave equation. The equation is solved to find these modes, and then the energy of an electron is obtained from the frequency of the mode and Einstein's formula. Schrödinger's wave equation gives the same energies as Bohr's original formula but with a much more precise description of an electron in an atom. The lowest energy level of the hydrogen atom, called the ground state, is analogous to the motion in the lowest vibrational mode of the drumhead. In the atom the electron wave is uniform in all directions from the nucleus, is peaked at the centre of the atom, and has the same phase everywhere. Higher energy levels in the atom have waves that are peaked at greater distances from the nucleus. Like the vibrations in the drumhead, the waves have peaks and nodes that may form a complex shape. The different shapes of the wave pattern explain the quantum numbers of the energy levels, including the quantum numbers for angular momentum and its orientation.

The year before Schrödinger produced his wave theory, the German physicist Werner Heisenberg published a mathematically equivalent system using matrix algebra to describe energy levels and their transitions. Today, physicists use Schrödinger's system because it can be visualized more easily.

In 1929 the Norwegian physicist Egil Hylleraas applied the Schrödinger equation to the helium atom with two electrons. He obtained only an approximate solution, but his energy calculation was quite accurate. With Hylleraas' explanation of the two-electron atom, physicists realized that the Schrödinger equation could be a powerful mathematical tool for describing nature on the atomic level, even if exact solutions could not be obtained.

The existence of antiparticles. The English physicist P.A.M. Dirac introduced a new equation for the electron in 1928. The Schrödinger equation does not satisfy the principles of relativity, and so it can be used to describe only those phenomena in which the particles move much more slowly than the velocity of light. In order to satisfy the conditions of relativity, Dirac was forced to postulate not one but four distinct wave functions for the electron. Two of these correspond to the two spin orientations. The remaining components allowed additional states of the electron that had not yet been observed. Dirac interpreted them as antiparticles with a charge opposite to that of electrons. The discovery of the positron in 1932 by the American physicist Carl David Anderson proved the existence of antiparticles and was a triumph for Dirac's theory.

The discovery of the positron

After his discovery, subatomic particles could no longer be considered immutable. Given enough energy, electrons and positrons can be created from a few particles in a vacuum tube. They also can annihilate each other and disappear into some other form of energy. The history of subatomic physics from this point has been much the story of finding new kinds of particles that can be created in vacuums.

ADVANCES IN NUCLEAR AND SUBATOMIC PHYSICS

The 1920s witnessed further advances in nuclear physics with Rutherford's discovery of induced radioactivity. Bombardment of light nuclei by alpha particles produced new radioactive nuclei. In 1928 the Russian-born American physicist George Gamow explained the lifetimes in alpha radioactivity using the Schrödinger equation.

Discovery of neutrons. The constitution of the nucleus was poorly understood at the time because the only known particles were the electron and the proton. It had been established that nuclei are typically about twice as heavy as can be accounted for by protons alone and thus have to contain more than just such particles. A consistent theory was impossible until the English physicist James Chadwick discovered the neutron in 1932. He found that alpha particles reacted with beryllium nuclei, ejecting neutral particles with nearly the same mass as protons. Almost all nuclear phenomena can be understood in terms of a nucleus composed of neutrons and protons. Surprisingly, the neutrons and protons in the nucleus behave to a large extent as though they were in independent wave functions, just like the electrons in an atom. Each neutron or proton is described by a wave pattern with peaks and nodes and angular momentum quantum numbers. The theory of the nucleus based on these independent wave functions is called the shell model. It was introduced in 1948 by Maria Goeppert Mayer of the United States and J. Hans D. Jensen of West Germany, and it developed in succeeding decades into a comprehensive theory of the nucleus.

Shell model of the nucleus

The interactions of neutrons with nuclei had been studied during the mid-1930s by the Italian-born American physicist Enrico Fermi and others. Nuclei readily capture neutrons, which, unlike protons or alpha particles, are not repelled from the nucleus by a positive charge. When a neutron is captured, the new nucleus has one higher unit of atomic mass. If a nearby isotope of that atomic mass is more stable, the new nucleus will be radioactive, convert the neutron to a proton, and assume the more stable form.

Nuclear fission was discovered by the German chemists Otto Hahn and Fritz Strassmann in 1938. In fission, a uranium nucleus captures a neutron and gains enough energy to trigger the inherent instability of the nucleus, which splits into two lighter nuclei of roughly equal size. The fission process releases more neutrons, which can be used to produce further fissions (see below *Nuclear fission*). The first nuclear reactor, a device designed to permit controlled fission chain reactions, was constructed at the University of Chicago under Fermi's direction, and the first self-sustaining chain reaction was achieved in this reactor in 1942. In 1945 American scientists produced the first

atomic bomb, which used uncontrolled fission reactions in either uranium or the artificial element plutonium.

Quantum field theory. Dirac not only proposed the relativistic equation for the electron but also initiated the relativistic treatment of interactions between particles known as quantum field theory. An important aspect of quantum field theory is that interactions can extend only over a given distance if there is a particle to carry the force. The electromagnetic force, which operates over a long distance, is carried by a particle called the photon, the light quantum. In 1934 the Japanese physicist Yukawa Hideki proposed that there should be a particle that carries the nuclear force as well. Because the force is short range, the particle should be massive. Massive particles were indeed found in cosmic rays, but these did not have the correct interaction properties. They were later dubbed muons. Evidence for Yukawa's particle, known as the pion, was found in cosmic-ray tracks in 1947 by British physicist Cecil Frank Powell. The existence of the pion was confirmed when the particle was created in a particle accelerator in 1948.

Pions

Since then, the number of subatomic particles discovered has grown enormously. Most of them have been created and studied by means of accelerators that produce high-energy collisions between particles. The new particles, formed by the collision process, live only a short time before decaying into more stable particles. Particularly noteworthy among the many particles discovered since 1960 are those responsible for the interaction in beta radioactivity. In quantum field theory, beta radioactivity is a manifestation of an interaction called the weak force. The particle transmitting this force is known as the W boson, or simply W particle. W bosons were discovered in 1983; they were produced in collisions between protons accelerated to energies 200 times their rest energies.

Hadrons and quarks. Many of the newly discovered particles did not at first seem to have any specific role in subatomic physics. Particles of a class known as hadrons, which includes protons and neutrons, interact strongly with one another. They show patterns analogous to the patterns of energy levels in atoms. Just as the existence of energy levels in hydrogen is explained by the presence of the electron, the different hadrons are considered to be energy levels of a more fundamental particle inside them. The specific patterns of the hadrons have been explained by postulating a new fundamental constituent, the quark. Three quarks are thought to combine to form a proton, a neutron, or any of the massive hadrons known as baryons. A quark combines with an antiquark to form mesons such as the pion.

Quarks have never been observed, and physicists do not expect to find one. Presumably the forces between quarks are so strong that they cannot be separated from other quarks in a hadron. There are several indirect confirmations of the existence of quarks. In experiments conducted with high-energy electron accelerators in the 1960s, electrons that had been deflected by large angles in scattering from hadrons were observed. As in Rutherford's experiment, the large-angle deflection implies that there are very small objects inside the hadron surrounded by large electric fields. The small objects are presumed to be quarks. Physicists developed a quantum field theory known as quantum chromodynamics (QCD) during the mid-1970s to accommodate quarks and their peculiar properties. This theory explains qualitatively the confinement of quarks to hadrons. Physicists believe that the theory should explain all aspects of hadrons, but mathematical complications unfortunately prevent rigorous calculations.

Quantum chromodynamics

Atomic structure and interactions

ELECTRONS

As noted above, the electron was the first subatomic particle discovered. Its interactions determine atomic structure, the chemical behaviour of atoms in molecules, and the properties of larger aggregations of atoms such as bulk solids. There are four kinds of forces in nature, and the electron is subject to three of them—gravity, electromagnetism, and weak interaction. Only the electromagnetic force is significant in determining the properties of atoms and their chemistry. Within the framework of the equations used to describe the motion of the electron, the only two numerical properties that need to be specified are the electron's mass and its charge. These are given in Table I along with other basic atomic constants.

There are four levels of complexity in the equations used to describe the properties of electrons. At the simplest level, classical equations such as Newton's equation are applied. The motion of the electron beam in a television tube is adequately described by classical physics.

The equations of classical physics, however, become invalid when one attempts to describe the motion within distances smaller than the de Broglie wavelength of the electron. Atomic properties fall into this small-distance regime, and quantum equations must be used. The simplest quantum equation is the above-mentioned Schrödinger equation, which is valid when the velocity of the electron is small compared to the speed of light. The electron is described by a function that obeys a wave equation. The function may be visualized as a cloud; where the function is large, the cloud is dense and the electron's presence is strongly felt.

Atomic and chemical structure is well described by the Schrödinger wave functions when two additional nonclassical properties of the electron are included. The first property is spin, which is like an internal rotational motion of the electron. The magnitude of an electron's spin is fixed, but its orientation in space can vary. Spin appears in the Schrödinger equation as an attribute of the electron. There are, in fact, two separate wave functions associated with the probability that spin will be pointed in a particular direction or in the opposite direction. Other spin orientations are obtained by suitably combining the two functions to make intermediate directions. The other nonclassical property involved is the Pauli exclusion principle, which states in its general form that the wave function of identical particles must reverse sign when the coordinates of the particles are interchanged. As a consequence of the Pauli principle, two electrons cannot have the same wave function. This principle is extremely important in determining the structure of atoms, molecules, and bulk matter.

The third level of complexity in the description of the electron is Dirac's equation (see above), which is a quantum equation postulated to satisfy the requirements of Einstein's relativity. Any particle governed by the Dirac equation is called a fermion; the electron is the most familiar example. The mathematics of the Dirac equation require that its particles have two spin orientations and obey the generalized Pauli principle. Thus, all the properties needed for determining atomic structure are built automatically into the theory. Furthermore, the Dirac equation predicts that for each kind of fermion there is an oppositely charged antiparticle with the same mass. The electron's antiparticle is the positron. The electron can be made to disappear by combining with a positron. When the two particles annihilate each other, their rest energy is converted to gamma rays or some other form of energy. Electrons can also be created from other forms of energy, but always in association with positrons. According to the Dirac equation, charged fermions such as the electron have a magnetic moment pointing along the direction of spin. The magnetic moment of electrons is very close to the value predicted by the Dirac equation. The magnetism of permanent magnets arises from the combined effect of individual electrons having spins aligned in the same direction.

The most sophisticated level of complexity in describing electrons is the theory of quantum electrodynamics. Using the Dirac and other equations, this theory builds a wave function not only for observable electrons but also for particles and quanta that may be created from a vacuum. The predictions of quantum electrodynamics deviate only slightly from the Dirac equation. For example, the magnetic moment of electrons is predicted to deviate by 0.1 percent from the Dirac value due to vacuum modifications. These deviations have been measured accurately and agree perfectly with quantum electrodynamics as far as experiments can determine.

The electron as a fermion

Quantum electrodynamics

ELECTRONIC STRUCTURE OF ATOMS

Schrödinger's theory of atoms. The theory of the electronic structure of atoms is based for the most part on the Schrödinger equation, which in actuality is not a single equation. Each different physical system is described by its own equation, a partial differential equation that has as many variables as there are coordinates of interest in the application. For example, the Schrödinger equation for the hydrogen atom has three coordinates—the x, y, and z coordinates of the separation between the electron and the hydrogen nucleus. Similarly, there are six variables in the Schrödinger equation of the helium atom, since the positions of two electrons are required.

The Schrödinger equation has many solutions, each of which describes a possible state of the atom. Each state is specified by a function that depends on the coordinates of the particle(s) and by its associated energy. The function, called the wave function, is the mathematical representation of what is descriptively called the cloud. The wave function describes, among other things, the probability of an electron being at any given coordinate position. Electrons are more likely to be found in regions of the atom where the wave function is large. More precisely, the probability is proportional to the square of the wave function. At positions where the wave function goes through zero, the probability of finding electrons vanishes.

Normally, an atom is found in its ground state, *i.e.*, the state with the least energy or the most bound state. States with higher energy are called excited states. Atomic spectra are the light quanta emitted when an atom makes a transition from an excited state to one of lower energy.

The Schrödinger equation can only be solved exactly in special circumstances. Schrödinger himself found the solution for the hydrogen atom. It is important for physicists and chemists to understand the properties of the hydrogen atom obtained from the Schrödinger equation because these same properties appear in the behaviour of electrons in more complex atoms.

For atoms with more than one electron, no exact solutions of the Schrödinger equation are known. Nevertheless, it is possible to obtain very accurate numerical solutions using approximation methods. An approximation scheme introduced by the English physicist Douglas R. Hartree is the basis for most calculations and for the prevailing physical understanding of the wave mechanics of atoms. In this method it is assumed that the electrons move independently. The electrons are allowed to interact only through the average electric field made by combining the charge of the nucleus with the charge distribution of the other electrons. A Schrödinger equation for individual electrons moving in an average electric field must then be solved. Each electron has its own wave function, which is called an orbital.

A technical difficulty with this method is that the electric field is not known ahead of time because it depends on the charge distribution of the electrons. In turn, the charge distribution can be determined only from the wave functions, which require prior knowledge of the field. The difficulty is overcome by solving the Schrödinger equation in successive approximations. First, one makes a guess for the field, finds the wave functions, and then uses the derived charge distribution to make a better approximation for the field. This iterative process is continued until the final charge and electric field distribution agree with the input to the Schrödinger equation. The Hartree method (sometimes called the Hartree–Fok method to give credit to V. Fok, a Soviet physicist who generalized Hartree's scheme) is widely used to describe electrons in atoms, molecules, and solids.

The hydrogen atom. Bohr's model of the hydrogen atom is rudimentary but nevertheless remarkably accurate in its predicted energy levels. The derivation of the energy formula is as follows. Bohr begins with the classical equation relating the velocity of a charged particle in a circular orbit, v, to the radius of the orbit r and the electric force constants. The equation, obtained by balancing the centrifugal force and the electric force, is

$$mv^2/r = e^2/4\pi\varepsilon_0 r^2.$$

The Hartree method

Next, Bohr postulates that angular momentum is quantized in integer multiples of the reduced Planck's constant, $\hbar$. The angular momentum is then given by the formula

$$m_e v r = n\hbar,$$

where m_e is the mass of the electron, and n is an integer, which can have values 1, 2, 3, and so on. The two equations are combined to solve for the unknown quantities v and r. The resulting orbits have discrete radii, depending on n. The energies of the electrons in these orbits are given by Bohr's formula,

$$E_n = \frac{m_e e^4}{(4\pi\varepsilon_0)^2 \, 2\hbar^2} \frac{1}{n^2}.$$

When the Schrödinger equation is solved for the hydrogen atom, one finds that the possible energies of the electron are the same as those in Bohr's model (see Figure 4). The wave functions associated with these energies are, however, quite different from the circular orbits hypothesized by Bohr. The lowest orbital is a spherically symmetric function. It falls off with distance from the nucleus r according to

$$\exp(-r/a_0).$$

Here, a_0 is a length constant, which happens to coincide with the radius of the smallest Bohr orbit. Known as the Bohr radius, it is given by the formula

$$a_0 = \frac{4\pi\varepsilon_0 \hbar^2}{m_e e^2}.$$

The numerical value of a_0 is 0.53 angstrom; the meaning and values of the other quantities in this equation are given in Table 1. Since the wave function depends only on distance and not on angle, the electron cloud surrounding the nucleus has a spherical shape. Its radius is roughly one angstrom. The electron probability is highest at the nucleus and in its immediate vicinity. The probability falls off smoothly with distance from the nucleus, vanishing completely only at infinite distance. The wave function falls to inconsequentially small values at moderate distances, however. For example, the probability for the particle to be farther than $10a_0$ from the nucleus is only 1 in 30,000.

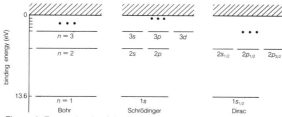

Figure 4: Energy levels of the hydrogen atom, according to Bohr's model and quantum mechanics using the Schrödinger equation and the Dirac equation.

Higher states of the hydrogen atom have more complex patterns in the wave function. All of the bound states of the hydrogen atom may be described by wave functions having the form

(polynomial in x, y, and z) $\exp(-r/n \, a_0)$,

where n is a positive integer called the principal quantum number. The energy of the state is given by Bohr's formula with the same integer value of n. Several different states may have the same energy, in which case they are said **Degenerate** to be degenerate. Shells are sets of degenerate states. The **states** number of distinct orbitals in a shell is its degeneracy or its multiplicity. For example, there are four orbitals with $n = 2$ at the energy E_2 in the Bohr formula, forming a shell. One of the orbitals in this shell, like the ground state, has a spherically symmetric wave function. Spherically symmetric orbitals are called s states; the nomenclature for orbitals of different symmetry is provided in Table 2. The excited s state differs from the ground state in that it is smaller at the centre, and it goes through zero at some intermediate distance from the nucleus. The ex-

cited s state has another peak beyond this point, and the overall probability extends farther out than in the ground state. The other $n = 2$ orbitals form a threefold shell that is designated the p shell. The polynomials in their wave functions are simply the monomials x, y, or z. The orbital having the monomial x has a vanishing probability on the plane with $x = 0$, which is therefore a nodal plane. Similarly, the other p states have nodal planes oriented in other directions but all going through the centre. The probability distributions of the electron for these orbitals are sketched in Figure 5. One could imagine a state with a nodal plane in some other direction as well. Such a state, however, could be made by adding the wave functions of the three original p orbitals, with some constant multiplying factors. According to the rules of quantum mechanics, this state would not be distinct from the original ones that produced it. The atom would have some probability of being in one of the three original states, depending on the multiplying factors.

Table 2: Spectroscopic Designation of Orbitals

angular momentum quantum number l	degeneracy	designation
0	1	s
1	3	p
2	5	d
3	7	f

States are distinguished from each other by numerical labels called quantum numbers. The principal quantum **Quantum** number n has already been mentioned. Three additional **numbers** quantum numbers are associated with the electron wave functions of the hydrogen atom. Two of these depend on the polynomial function of x, y, and z in the wave function. Conventionally, these two quantum numbers are labeled l, representing orbital angular momentum, and m, representing the orientation of the angular momentum with respect to some axis. The states of different l are often designated by letters, as given in Table 2. There are several general rules for determining the values of l and m allowed in a wave function. The orbital angular momentum takes on integer values starting from $l = 0$. Spherically symmetric wave functions have $l = 0$. Positive values of l apply to states whose wave function varies with angle. The more lobes there are in the angular pattern of the wave function, the higher is the value of l. The m quantum number, also called the magnetic quantum number, is restricted to a range of integers depending on l. The m quantum number ranges from -1 and increases in integer steps to $+1$. Distinct states exist for all values of m in this range. Thus, wave functions with a given orbital angular momentum l always have a degeneracy equal to $2l + 1$. The quantum number l and the associated degeneracy $2l + 1$ of the m states is a general feature of

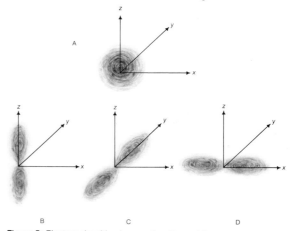

Figure 5: Electron densities in wave functions of the Schrödinger equation.
(A) The lowest s orbital, recognizable by its spherical symmetry and the absence of any nodes. (B, C, D) The three p orbitals.

wave functions obtained in physical systems with a force directed toward a centre. For example, the ground state of the hydrogen atom is spherically symmetric with $l = 0$ and only one distinct orientation. The p-wave states in the $n = 2$ shell have orbital angular momentum $l = 1$. By the rules of the orientational degeneracy, there are three distinct p states, labeled $m = -1$, 0, and +1. In higher shells one finds $l = 2$ states, which have two angular nodal surfaces and a degeneracy of 5.

The relationship between the principal quantum number n and the orbital angular momentum l has not been discussed up to this point. For each value of n, states of the hydrogen atom exist with l ranging from 0 to $n - 1$. The fact that all l states for a given n are degenerate is a special circumstance of the Schrödinger equation for the hydrogen atom. Each of the l's has a multiplet of m states, described in the previous paragraph.

The Schrödinger equation and Bohr's formula are quite accurate, but small deviations in energy can be observed in the hydrogen spectrum, and the actual multiplicity of states is twice that predicted by the Schrödinger equation. These flaws can be corrected by introducing the electron spin, with either the Schrödinger equation or the more precise Dirac equation. The electron spin behaves exactly like an angular momentum, but with a value $^1/_2$. There are two m states, with values $-^1/_2$ and $+^1/_2$, which provide the needed doubling in the multiplicity of states. The interaction of the spin changes the energies of the states, so they are no longer independent of l. The coupling of the spin to the orbital angular momentum is treated by defining a new angular momentum quantum number j. For a given l, j can have the value $l + ^1/_2$ or $l - ^1/_2$, depending on whether the orientations of the spin and orbital angular momentum are parallel or antiparallel. However, in an $l = 0$ state such as the ground state, only $j = ^1/_2$ is allowed. This method of combining spin and orbital angular momentum is known as spin-orbit coupling. In the Dirac equation the $n = 2$ states are shifted in energy by the spin-orbit coupling, with the $j = ^1/_2$ states slightly lower than the $j = ^3/_2$ state. The predicted splitting agrees very well with the observed fine structure in the spectrum.

Further refinements to the theory of the hydrogen atom have been made with quantum field theory. The theory predicts a very small energy difference between the two multiplets with $j = ^1/_2$. This tiny splitting has been observed, and its magnitude agrees with theory.

One final ingredient completes the description of the hydrogen atom—the interaction of its electron with the magnetic moment of its nucleus. The proton nucleus of ordinary hydrogen has a spin of $^1/_2$ and a magnetic moment. The energies of the atom depend on the relative orientation of the electron and proton's spin. This can be characterized by a new quantum number, the total spin F. It can have a value 0 or 1, depending on whether the two spins are parallel or antiparallel. The energy difference between these two states is very small, so that transitions are in the microwave region of the electromagnetic spectrum. The frequency of the radiation is 1.4×10^9 hertz, which is a well-known feature of the radiation from interstellar hydrogen gas observed in radio astronomy.

Multielectron atoms. The properties of multielectron atoms are governed to a large extent by simple principles that determine the electron wave function. Electrons are placed in orbitals similar to the wave functions of hydrogen, starting with the lowest energy $n = 1$ orbital. The Pauli principle requires that each electron go into a different orbital. (It should be remembered that the two spin orientations in a wave function count as different orbitals.) With this procedure, each element acquires a unique structure of electron orbitals that gives it its characteristic atomic and chemical properties. A simple example is the helium atom. Helium has two electrons, both of which go into the $n = 1$ orbitals according to the spin degeneracy rule. All $n = 1$ electrons are tightly bound, and so the helium atom is not readily ionized; neither does it form chemical bonds by sharing its electrons with other atoms. The next element, lithium, has three electrons; only two can go in the $n = 1$ orbitals, so the third must be placed in an $n = 2$ orbital. This shell is much higher in energy; thus, the last

Spin-orbit coupling

electron is loosely bound. The ionization energy, which is the energy required to remove an electron from an atom, shows clearly the effects of the electron shells. Figure 6, displaying the ionization energies of the elements, shows that helium is the highest of any element. There is a big jump from helium to lithium, which needs only 5 eV of energy to ionize.

Ionization energy

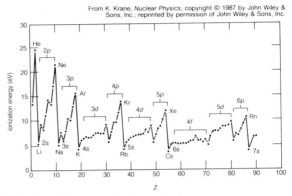

Figure 6: *Ionization energies of the elements.*
The shell of the least bound electron is designated by the principal quantum number n, followed by the letter for the angular momentum.

The shell behaviour of complex atoms is derived from the approximate solution of the Schrödinger equation, since exact solutions to the multielectron equation do not exist. The Hartree method (see above), treating each electron with its own wave function, gives an adequate approximation for most purposes. In Hartree's theoretical scheme, the Pauli principle is imposed by requiring all wave functions of the electrons to be distinct. An important part of the Hartree theory is the behaviour of the self-consistent force field governing the electrons. At small distances from the nucleus, the Hartree field is virtually the same as the field of the nucleus. The contribution from the electrons is small because they are spread out in all directions. At large distances the nucleus appears to be surrounded by a cloud of electrons screening its positive charge with their negative charges. The last electron, if it is far away, "sees" a field resembling that of a single positive charge. The electron wave functions in this potential are qualitatively very similar to the hydrogen wave functions, retaining strong shell effects. The range of the wave functions and their energies, however, depend on both the atomic number and the presence of electrons in other shells. The $n = 1$ electrons are closest to the nucleus and are exposed to nearly its full electric field. The highest shell electrons are farthest away on average and feel a field similar to that of a hydrogen atom.

The size of atoms does not vary much from element to element, growing only slightly from light to heavy elements. This is due to a compensation between two opposing tendencies. The outer electrons of heavy atoms are in higher shells, the probability distributions of which are farther from the nucleus. On the other hand, the size of each shell is dependent on nuclear charge; the higher charge in heavier nuclei pulls a given shell in closer.

Atomic spectroscopy and lasers. The energy levels of atoms are studied by measuring the wavelengths of light emitted by the atoms in excited states. Atoms become excited when they absorb energy. In a gas, excited atoms are produced with heat or electric currents. The light emitted is analyzed in a spectrograph, which disperses the light in different directions according to its wavelength or frequency. Transitions from higher to lower energy levels appear as bright lines in the spectrum (Figure 7). This technique is known as emission spectroscopy. If white light is passed through a gas of the element being studied, light will be absorbed for those frequencies that allow a transition of the atom from the ground state to an excited state. The absorption creates a dark line in the spectrum of the white light. This is called absorption spectroscopy. The characteristics of the lines can be measured with great accuracy using spectrographs together with other optical

Emission and absorption spectroscopy

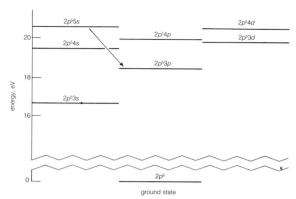

Figure 7: *Energy levels of the neon atom.*
The orbitals occupied by the six outer electrons are indicated on the levels. The transition responsible for the red light from common lasers (wavelength of 6330 Å) is shown by the arrow.

instruments called interferometers. Until lasers were developed, however, it was impossible to achieve the resolution desired because the frequency of the light emitted is affected by the motion of the atoms and collisions between them. The frequency shift from atomic motion, known as the Doppler effect, limits the resolution to about 1 part in 10,000. However, with intense light at a fixed frequency available from lasers, one can preferentially excite atoms moving at some particular velocity. Modern instrumentation makes it possible to observe structure in the lines to 1 part in 10,000,000. This accuracy allows the effects of nuclear spin, size, and shape to be measured directly with atomic lines.

The principle of the laser is based on the transitions between energy levels in an atom, or molecule. Normally, more atoms are in lower states than in upper states. Energy would be absorbed from a beam of radiation because most of the transitions would go from a lower level to an upper one. If the number of atoms in the upper and lower states is equal, there will be the same number of transitions in both directions. Therefore, the intensity of the atom's light beam would not change going through the medium. Conditions for the laser are obtained if more atoms are in the upper state than in the lower state; this is called a population inversion. As a result, a laser has more transitions going downward than upward, and a beam going through the medium is amplified. Passing the amplified beam back and forth between mirrors produces the very high intensity laser light.

Characteristic X rays. The inner shells of an atom are responsible for the characteristic X rays of an element. These are X rays of definite wavelengths emitted when atoms are bombarded with energetic electrons or other forms of radiation. The radiation knocks an inner electron out of its orbital, leaving a vacancy. An electron from a higher shell then jumps into the empty orbital, emitting a photon in the process. Because of the strong binding of inner shells in heavy atoms, such photons are produced with energies ranging from 100 to 100,000 eV in the X-ray region of the electromagnetic spectrum. The approximate energies of these transitions are given by the Bohr formula with a modified value of the nuclear charge. More accurate values for the energies can be calculated on the basis of the Hartree theory.

The ionization energy of atoms depends on the energy of the electron orbitals in the highest occupied shells. The variation of these energies with atomic number displays a periodic behaviour, as seen in Figure 6. Particularly noticeable is the increase in ionization energy as the p shells of the atom are filled. This is precisely what one expects to find: as the charge of the nucleus increases, the binding energy of the orbitals in a given shell increases. When a shell is filled, the next electron must go into a higher, less bound shell, producing a break in the ionization-energy plot. The fact that the behaviour is periodic shows that the inner cores of atoms act on the outer electrons in much the same way for different atomic numbers. The nuclear charge is screened by the inner electrons so that the outer

electrons are effectively governed by the field from a lower atomic number.

The electron affinity of atoms exhibits a similar periodicity. Electron affinity is the binding energy of the extra electron when an atom forms a negative ion. Such atoms as helium that have all their electrons in tightly bound filled shells do not attract additional electrons strongly enough to bind them. On the other hand, such atoms as fluorine that have a single vacancy in a tightly bound shell readily attract and capture an extra electron into that orbital. The systematics of the electron affinities are shown in Figure 8. Obviously, the behaviour of the loosely bound electrons and shell effects are crucial to an understanding of the chemical properties of elements. The basic period of eight in the periodic table is associated with the filling of the s and p orbitals of a given n shell (see Figure 9). For each spin orientation, there are one s orbital and three p orbitals, for a total degeneracy of eight. In the hydrogen atom, the s and p shells are degenerate, and in complex atoms they remain close in energy. Higher angular momentum shells, however, have considerably less binding than their s and p partners in the same n shell. As a result, they are filled out of sequence in the periodic table. For example, the $3d$ shell is filled after the $4s$ shell.

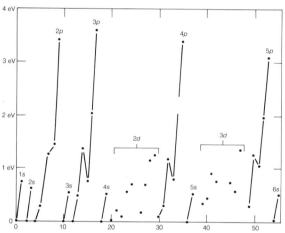

Figure 8: *Electron affinities of the elements.*
The shell of the most bound vacancy is indicated by its spectroscopic designation.

The diminished binding of the higher 1 shells can be understood simply with a classical picture of the electron's motion. The higher angular momentum shells correspond to orbits that are more nearly circular, whereas the s- and p-wave functions correspond to elliptical orbits in which the electron approaches the centre of the atom more closely. Because the centre has the strong attraction from the unscreened nucleus, these low 1 orbitals will have a greater binding. For a given energy, elongated orbits extend farther out than the circular orbits. This greater

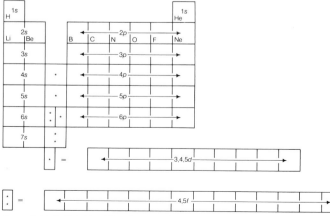

Figure 9: Periodic table of the elements showing the valence shells.

extension corresponds to the fact that in s and p orbits the electron probability is significant to larger distances. Most of chemistry has to do with these outer electrons. The $l = 3$ shell (f shell) is well shielded by other electrons, and the elements that differ only in the number of f-shell electrons have very similar chemical properties.

Exotic atoms. Atoms can be formed with other charged particles serving as the negatively charged electrons or the positively charged nucleus. Mu mesons, pi mesons, or antiprotons can be substituted for electrons, while a positron can replace the nucleus. These exotic atoms exhibit energy levels and transitions just like ordinary atoms. The transitions between high n orbits follow the Bohr formula, with an appropriate change in the mass m in that formula. The energy levels with low n are affected by the finite size of the particles and by other forces that may act besides the electric force. Physicists use these atoms to investigate the forces and the sizes of the particles involved.

Interatomic forces and chemical bonds. The forces between atoms are complex and varied. In close proximity, all atoms repel each other. At intermediate distances, the forces of chemical binding are prominent. Finally, at large distances, all atoms are attracted to each other by a much weaker force. These forces are all explained by the quantum theory of electrons in atoms. In the presence of other atoms, the electrons become rearranged. If the new arrangement has less energy, it is the preferred state of the atoms, and there is an attractive force to reach this state. Conversely, if the rearrangement increases the energy, the resulting force between the atoms is repulsive. The rearrangement of electrons may take place in different ways, and different names are given for the resulting chemical bonds (see below).

Repulsion between atoms

The universal repulsion between atoms at short distances is responsible for atoms taking up a definite amount of space and for the incompressibility of solid materials. This repulsion has two causes. First, as the atoms are pushed into each other, the shielding provided by the electrons around each nucleus is less effective and the electric force between the two nuclei repels them. A second repulsive influence arises from the Pauli principle. Not only is it forbidden to have two electrons with the same wave function but the wave functions must be different enough to construct an antisymmetric total wave function. When two atoms are close together, the electrons in the overlapping region spend part of their time in their original orbitals and part of their time in orbitals of higher energy in order to satisfy the Pauli principle.

In chemical bonds the rearrangement of electrons leaves atoms in a state of lower energy, stabilizing them at fixed distances from each other in definite geometric configurations. The amount of energy associated with chemical bonds ranges from 1 to 10 eV. A number of different kinds of bonds are recognized in chemistry. If the rearrangement causes a net shift of the electron's probability from one atom to the other, the bond is called heteropolar. An extreme example of this would be an ionic bond, in which an electron has moved from an orbital in one atom to that in the other. This electron transfer gives one atom a net positive charge and the other a net negative charge. The two resulting ions are then held together by the electric force of attraction between unlike charges. An example of ionic bonding occurs in alkali halide crystals such as sodium chloride (common table salt). The alkali metals are easily ionized, and the halogens have a strong affinity for additional electrons, as seen in Figures 6 and 8. The original concept of chemical binding was based on the attraction of opposite charges.

Strong chemical bonding of the homopolar, or covalent, type also occurs. In this case there is no net transfer of electrons from one atom to another. The rearrangement of the electron distribution is more subtle. In a covalent bond between two atoms, the electron density shifts from the outer surfaces of the atoms to the region between the two atomic centres. In general this does not happen, because the Pauli principle affects the wave functions by spreading the electrons apart. The Pauli principle, however, may be satisfied for a pair of electrons by giving them opposite spin orientations, in which case the spatial wave functions are combined to bring the two electrons closer together. A covalent bond can be formed between two atoms if there is an unpaired electron on each atom. In the bonded state the electrons will have their spins oppositely aligned. An atom can form a number of covalent bonds equal to the number of its unpaired electrons, which in turn depends on the shell degeneracy. For example, the nitrogen atom has five electrons distributed over four orbitals in the $n = 2$ s and p shells. Two electrons must occupy the same orbital as a pair, but the remaining three electrons can go unpaired in separate orbitals, giving nitrogen a valence of 3.

The geometry of chemical bonding, with definite angles between the bonds in triatomic and more complicated molecules, depends on the geometry of orbitals with lobes extending at various angles. If atoms bonded with pure p orbitals, the bonds would extend out at 90° angles from each other like the wave functions depicted in Figure 5. Actual chemical bonds, however, are made primarily by combining s and p orbitals together in the wave functions. This so-called hybridization produces wave functions with different geometries. In the carbon atom, for example, the hybridization yields four bonds directed toward the corners of a tetrahedron.

Hybridization

The ionic and covalent bonds are two extremes in a range of bonding behaviour. The bonding wave functions do not need to be localized on two neighbouring atoms. In so-called delocalized bonding the electron wave functions extend over several atoms.

All of these properties can be predicted quite well using the Hartree theory. The positions of the atomic centres are first roughly estimated. The Schrödinger equation is then solved for each electron, with the requirement that the total forces from all the atoms are consistent with the total charge density from the electrons and nuclei. After the wave functions of all the electrons are found, the energy of the molecule can be calculated. This is repeated for other positions of the atomic centres until the minimum energy is found. The resulting arrangement of atomic centres and electron wave functions provides the configuration of the stable molecule. Depending on the behaviour of the Hartree wave functions, one can find various kinds of chemical bonds. The Hartree theory is quite reliable in predicting the geometry of molecules and the character of the bonds, but it is less successful in predicting accurate bond energies.

Some forces between atoms at larger distances are too weak to form chemical bonds. These forces have two origins. One long-range force is associated with the electric fields that extend outside of any molecule with heteropolar electron distributions. An example is the water molecule, which has a net shift of electron charges from the hydrogen atoms to those of oxygen. The electric field attracts both positively and negatively charged ions, depending on the orientation of the water molecule. This explains why liquid water is such a good solvent for polar and ionicly bonded molecules. Another long-range force, called the van der Waals force, is a weak attraction between all atoms. It provides the cohesive force in nonpolar liquids such as liquid air or gasoline. These liquids have a low boiling point because the bond energies of the van der Waals force are very low (only a few tenths of an electron volt). The force arises from a subtle effect in quantum mechanics—namely, the existence of fluctuating electric fields outside an atom even though the electron wave function surrounds the nucleus and neutralizes its charge. The fluctuating fields are associated with the possible positions of the electron if it is frozen at some particular spot in its orbital.

Van der Waals force

Observing atoms. Individual atoms are far too small to be seen in any light microscope. The inherent limitation on such a microscope is the wavelength of light, which determines the minimum size of an image. In comparison, the distance between atoms in a solid is less than 1,000th of the wavelength of light. Therefore, the minimum size of any image would contain too many atoms for the eye to differentiate. There are, however, several direct methods for observing individual atoms and their arrangement in molecules and solids. In a transmission

Direct observation methods

electron microscope, electrons are transmitted through the material to be studied. Images are formed because the electrons are absorbed differently by different atoms. With this technique, one can just barely see the individual atoms of the heaviest elements when they are separated by several atomic lengths (see Figure 10). Another technique

Albert V. Crewe, Enrico Fermi Institute, University of Chicago

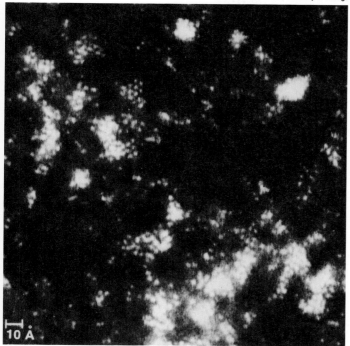

10 Å

Figure 10: Transmission electron micrograph of single uranium atoms and microcrystals obtained from a solution of uranyl acetate.

Diffraction techniques

involves the use of a field-ion microscope. In this case, a wire with a very fine tip is placed in a near-vacuum and given a positive electric charge. Individual atoms on the surface of the tip ionize residual gas molecules. The ions are then accelerated by the charge in straight lines away from the tip. They form spots on photographic plates at different positions corresponding to the location of atoms on the tip (see Figure 11). A third imaging technique is called scanning tunneling electron microscopy. Here, a wire with an extremely fine point is positioned within 10^{-9} metres of the surface to be studied. Electrons jump from the surface to the wire through individual atoms on the surface. The probe wire is moved back and forth over the surface in a raster pattern, and variations in the electron current indicate the positions of the atoms.

The positions of atoms in solids and molecules are commonly determined by wave diffraction. Diffraction refers to the highly directional patterns formed by waves when they travel through regularly ordered mediums. Diffraction techniques use a crystal or a large number of atoms in a regular arrangement. The pattern of the waves reflected from the crystal depends on the relative positions of the atoms in the crystal. The information contained in the wave pattern is far from complete, however, so there may be ambiguities in reconstructing the atomic arrangement. The most common technique of this kind is X-ray diffraction. X rays are similar to visible light, but they have much shorter wavelengths. Radiation of this type that can be used for diffraction has a wavelength of 10^{-10} metre or smaller, which is even smaller than atoms. As the X-ray waves are most affected by the electrons in atoms, this technique locates atoms primarily by their electron cloud. Another diffraction technique uses neutrons from a nuclear reactor. Neutrons, like all particles, have wave properties and can be diffracted from a crystal. Neutrons of a particular wavelength are beamed on a crystal, and diffraction sends them off in various directions. The geometric arrangement of the atoms being studied is inferred

from the diffraction pattern. Neutron waves interact most strongly with atomic nuclei, and so this technique complements X-ray diffraction by mapping the nuclear centres of atoms.

Bulk matter.   The behaviour of bulk matter depends on the relative magnitude of the binding forces between atoms or molecules and the thermal energy of motion. The thermal energy of motion at room temperature is about 0.025 eV. If the binding energy is less than about 10 times the thermal energy, the substance will be in a gaseous state under normal conditions. This typically applies to small molecules such as air molecules that interact only by the weak van der Waals force. With larger ratios of binding energies to thermal energies, the substance condenses into a liquid or a solid. Solids are classified into several types, depending on the kind of bonding between their atoms. Four main types of ordered solids are ionic crystals, molecular crystals, covalent crystals, and metals. Ionic crystals are held together entirely by the electrostatic forces between ions. Common table salt is an example. A molecular crystal is composed of distinct molecules held together by weaker forces such as the van der Waals force. In covalent crystals the chemical bonds extend from atom to atom over the entire crystal. Diamond, a form of carbon, is an example of a covalently bonded solid; as in simple organic compounds, each carbon atom has four bonds pointed to the corners of a tetrahedron. In metals the concept of chemical valence breaks down. The atoms are closely packed together, and the number of neighbours for a given atom is determined more by the geometry of touching spheres than by the number of valence electrons.

Classification of solids on the basis of bonding

The Hartree theory provides a common framework for describing the varying properties of these different kinds of solids. The electron orbitals are allowed to spread out over the entire solid. Effectively, one deals with an infinite number of electrons and orbitals, which can be handled with mathematical techniques developed by the Swiss-born U.S. physicist Felix Bloch and others. The orbitals display shell-like features even in a very large system. There are groups of orbitals with energies close together. Known as bands, they are separated by gaps in energy. The characteristics of any such solid depend very much on the extent to which the orbitals are filled in the highest band. This filling level is called the Fermi energy. If

Band structure of solids

By courtesy of the Department of Physics and Astronomy, Michigan State University

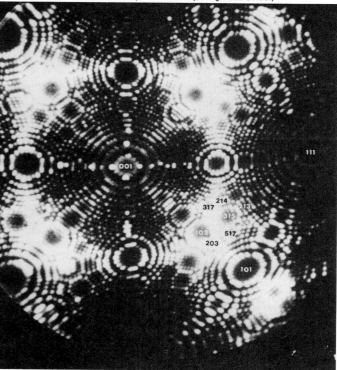

Figure 11: Field-ion micrograph of atoms on the surface of a platinum needle.

the orbitals are completely filled up to the band gap, the states of the electrons are essentially fixed and the material will be an insulator. On the other hand, if the band is only partially filled, electrons can jump from one state to another with only an infinitesimal change in energy. In this case, the electrons can move about, and the material is a conductor. The sharp distinction between insulators and conductors becomes blurred in materials called semiconductors, which have small energy gaps. In silicon, for instance, the energy gap is only 1.4 eV, and it is possible to make silicon conduct by exciting electrons to the higher band. In some materials there is no energy gap between the occupied and empty orbitals, but the number of orbitals at the Fermi energy is so small that conductivity is poor. Graphite, another form of carbon, has a band structure of this type.

THE NUCLEUS

Nucleons. The protons and neutrons that make up the atomic nucleus are the lightest members of the baryon family of subatomic particles. The proton has a mass of 1.673×10^{-27} kilogram, which is 1,836 times larger than the mass of the electron. The neutron has approximately the same mass as the proton—1.675×10^{-27} kilogram. Subatomic masses are commonly expressed in units of rest energy, which is related to mass by Einstein's formula $E = mc^2$. The proton's rest energy is 938.3 MeV and that of the neutron is 939.6 MeV. All baryons except the proton are unstable and can decay into lighter baryons. The neutron, having more rest energy than the proton, can decay into a proton with the emission of an electron and an anti-neutrino. Its lifetime outside the nucleus is 10 minutes. In the nucleus the binding energy is larger than the difference in rest energies between the neutron and the proton. The binding forces stabilize the nucleus against the decay of its neutrons.

Other properties of nucleons are their charge, spin, and magnetic moment. The charge on a proton is equal and opposite to the electron's charge. The neutron is uncharged. Like electrons and other elementary fermions, nucleons have a spin quantum number of $1/2$ and are described by a wave function that is doubled in multiplicity by two spin orientations. Nucleons and electrons also have a magnetic moment associated with their spin. However, the numerical value of a nucleon's magnetic moment, unlike an electron's, is quite different from that predicted by the Dirac equation; in fact, the proton's moment is 2.8 times the value predicted. Furthermore, the neutron has a somewhat smaller moment opposite to that of the proton, though according to the Dirac equation it should have none at all.

While electrons are point particles, nucleons have a finite extension. The distribution of the positive charge in a proton can be measured in electron scattering experiments. The charge is distributed in a smooth cloud extending to a distance of about 1×10^{-15} metre, or 1 femtometre, from the centre. The neutron is neutral overall, but electron scattering measurements show that it also has an internal structure with a slight positive charge in the core surrounded by a shell of negative charge.

Internuclear forces. The most important characteristic that distinguishes nucleons from electrons and other leptons has to do with the forces acting on them. Nucleons are subject to the three forces of nature affecting leptons: gravitation, electromagnetism, and the weak force. However, nucleons also exert a very powerful force on each other—namely, the nuclear, or strong, force. This force has an extremely short range so that its effects are not felt outside an atom. Indeed, even within an atom, the strong force is insignificant just a few fermis (one fermi = 10^{-15} metre) from the surface of the nucleus. By contrast, the effects of the electromagnetic and gravitational forces can be felt at all distances.

The character of the strong force is rather complicated and only partially understood. At very small distances between nucleons, less than one femtometre, the force is repulsive and tends to keep the nucleons apart. At intermediate distances, about one to two femtometres, the force is strongly attractive and can bind the nucleons by energy

Properties of protons and neutrons

Strong force

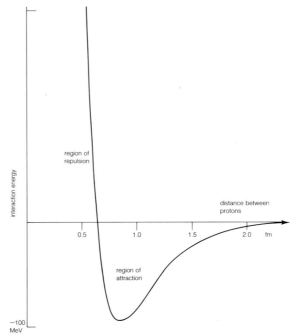

Figure 12: *Proton force.*
The interaction energy of two protons is shown as a function of the distance between them. At small separations, the energy is positive and the force is repulsive. At intermediate distances, the nuclear interaction is negative and the force is attractive. At distances larger than shown on the graph, the nuclear force becomes negligible and the repulsive electric force between the two charges is all that is left. The interaction depicted is for protons with antiparallel spins.

amounting to many millions of electron volts. Beyond a few femtometres, the strong force becomes inconsequential in comparison to the electromagnetic force. A graph of the behaviour of the strong force is shown in Figure 12.

The effects of the strong force are seen in the interactions of free nucleons and the binding energy of nuclei. Nucleon interactions can be studied by bombarding hydrogen with a beam of protons or neutrons. The beam particles passing within a certain distance of a proton from the hydrogen target will be deflected by the strong force. The strength of the interaction between beam and target nucleons is characterized by a quantity called the cross section, which has units of area. It is the apparent area of the target particle that intercepts the beam particle and results in an interaction or a deflection. The cross section of high-energy nucleons scattering or otherwise interacting with each other is about four square femtometres. If the particles are thought of as spheres that interact when they come into contact, the radius of the individual nucleon sphere would be about 0.7 femtometre. At low energies the cross sections become larger, partly because there is more time for the forces to act with slower moving particles. Quantum wave effects also become more important at low energy; they allow the influence of the force to be felt at larger distances and help increase the cross section.

Most of the existing detailed knowledge about nuclear forces comes from matching observed cross sections, including their dependence on energy and scattering angle, with quantum mechanical calculations based on models of the strong force. Yukawa's meson exchange picture (see above) explains the major features of the strong force beyond one femtometre. In quantum field theory, two particles may exert a force on each other at a distance only by exchanging a third particle. The particles exchanged in the strong force are mesons. The pion, the lightest of the mesons, is responsible for the longest range portion of the strong force. When the pion is exchanged, it can transfer a charge from one nucleon to another. In this process, called an exchange interaction, a proton is converted to a neutron and a neutron becomes a proton. At shorter distances, heavier mesons become important, and several pions may be exchanged at the same time. The main

The cross section

Exchange of mesons

attraction between nucleons in bound nuclei is caused by the exchange of multiple pions and higher mesons. The exchange of mesons also can change the internal structure of the nucleon, transforming it into some other baryon. Even when there is not enough energy to produce the excited baryon, its effects are felt in the strong force.

The strong force also depends on the spin orientation of the nucleons. This dependence adds to the complexity of the force. For example, the force between protons and neutrons is most attractive when the spins are pointing in the same direction. On the other hand, the Pauli principle does not allow two protons with parallel spins to be located close to each other, and the interaction with the opposite spin alignment is weaker. Part of the spin dependence is known as the tensor force. This force reorients the spin and exerts a torque on the nucleons. The tensor force helps explain a property of the deuteron, which is a neutron and proton bound together. Under the influence of ordinary forces, the wave function would be spherically symmetric. Due to the tensor force, however, the deuteron is elongated in shape. The elongation is measured as its quadrupole moment. Another significant part of the spin-dependent force is the spin-orbit force. This force acts when the nucleons are moving around each other and have orbital angular momentum. It tends to align the orbital angular momentum with the spin orientation.

Tensor and spin-orbit forces

An important consequence of the strong force is the binding of nuclei. The simplest example is the deuteron, with a binding energy of 2.2 MeV. The binding energy is the sum of an interaction energy and a kinetic energy of the particles. By itself, the interaction energy is much more than 2 MeV, but a large kinetic energy nearly cancels it. In heavier nuclei the interaction energy is higher because there are more neighbouring nucleons; consequently, the binding is greater. Protons also are attracted to each other by the strong force, but their interaction is not sufficient to bind them together. Thus, there is no isotope of helium consisting only of two protons.

Shape and size of nuclei. Most nuclei are spherical, and their size is determined by the number of nucleons present. The density of nucleons is roughly constant in the interior of a nucleus, and so the volume of the sphere is proportional to the atomic mass number. In this respect, the nucleus resembles a liquid drop, the volume of which is proportional to the amount of matter it contains. The density of nucleons in the interior of a nucleus is about 3×10^{17} kilograms per cubic metre; each nucleon takes up about six cubic femtometres of volume. The radii of nuclei found in nature range from two to eight femtometres.

The constant interior density of nuclei, called the saturation property, is quite different from the distribution of electrons in atoms. The density of electrons varies considerably with their distance from the centre of the atom; electrons are highly concentrated in the inner shells and more dispersed in the outer ones. The saturation of nuclear matter, on the other hand, arises from a delicate balance between the attractive and repulsive components of the nuclear force. Aspects of the interaction contributing to the saturation are: (1) the short-range repulsion that prevents the nucleons from occupying the same volume; (2) the charged pion exchange that is less effective at high density; (3) the tensor force; and (4) the interactions that make internal excitations of the nucleons.

Saturation property

The most precise information on nuclear sizes comes from electron-scattering measurements. Because of their quantum-wave properties, electrons scattering from nuclei exhibit diffraction, which is preferential scattering at specific angles. Detailed pictures of the size and shape of the nucleus can be inferred from these diffraction patterns. Figure 13 shows an example of inferred charge density on a slice through the centre of a nucleus of lead-208. The charge is roughly uniform inside a sphere and has a diffuse edge on the surface. The density falls from its inside value to zero over a distance of roughly two femtometres. One does not see the individual particles in the nucleus because their wave functions are diffuse clouds. There are, however, perceptible variations in density in the interior. These oscillations show that the wave functions of the nucleons inside a nucleus have a shell behaviour just like

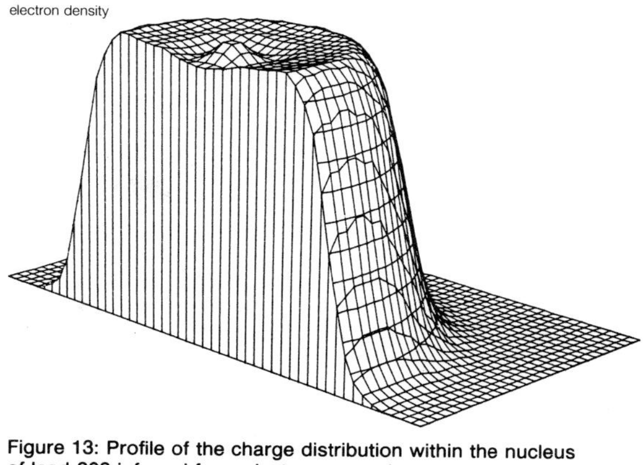

electron density

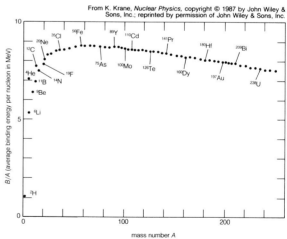

Figure 13: Profile of the charge distribution within the nucleus of lead-208 inferred from electron-scattering experiments.

the electrons in atoms. The peaks occur at positions where the proton wave functions are maximal, and the valleys occur where the wave functions pass through zero.

Mass and binding energy. The mass of a nucleus is typically about 1 percent less than the total mass of the nucleons composing it. This mass deficiency is related to the binding energy of nuclei by Einstein's formula $E = mc^2$. The binding energy determines which nuclei are stable and how much energy is released in a nuclear reaction. The picture of the nucleus as a charged liquid drop describes the overall trends of the binding energies. Each particle in the interior of a classical liquid is bound by the same amount. Very roughly, nuclear binding energies behave accordingly, with a typical binding energy of 8 MeV per nucleon. In detail, the trend of nuclear binding energies may be seen in Figure 14, which graphs the binding energy per nucleon as a function of the atomic mass number. The graph shows the near constancy of the binding energy from nuclei as light as helium-4 up to very heavy nuclei. By contrast, the binding energy of atoms varies greatly with atomic number because their inner shells are so tightly bound.

From K. Krane, *Nuclear Physics*, copyright © 1987 by John Wiley & Sons, Inc.; reprinted by permission of John Wiley & Sons, Inc.

Figure 14: Nuclear binding energies, shown as a function of atomic mass number.

Particles at the surface of a liquid have fewer neighbours to interact with, so there is surface tension and a deficiency of energy from the surface. In the same way, lighter nuclei have a relatively large surface-to-volume ratio and are not as strongly bound. This may be seen in Figure 14 in the behaviour of the curve for smaller atomic mass numbers.

Repulsion between the charges of protons reduces the binding energy of a nucleus. The negative contribution from this repulsion is called the Coulomb energy. The effect is largest for the highest atomic numbers, which are the most highly charged nuclei. The surface energy favouring large nuclei and the Coulomb energy favouring low atomic numbers oppose each other; consequently, the optimum mass number for a nucleus is in the middle

Coulomb energy

region, around mass 60 and the iron nucleus. Nuclear energy can be released by any process that transforms nuclei to others closer to the middle masses. Thus, nuclear energy can be released by fusing light nuclei or by splitting heavy nuclei in the fission process. Energy production in stars results primarily from the fusion of hydrogen to make helium. Hotter stars can fuse heavier elements, but all nuclear energy is exhausted when iron is attained as a fusion product. Terrestrial elements are believed to have been formed by this process of stellar nucleosynthesis. Elements heavier than iron may have been formed by very transient processes in supernova explosions. (For a more detailed discussion of stellar nucleosynthesis, see STARS AND STAR CLUSTERS.)

Nuclear binding energy also depends on the relative numbers of neutrons and protons in a nucleus. In light nuclei the most binding is obtained with an equal number of neutrons and protons, which optimizes the neutron-proton attraction. In heavier nuclei the Coulomb repulsion between protons gives more binding to nuclei with an excess of neutrons. The most stable heavy nuclei have 50 percent more neutrons than protons.

Nuclear spin and magnetic moment. Nuclei, like atoms or other particles, may have an internal angular momentum called spin. Because of the characteristics of the forces involved, the spin of a nucleus is zero if the nucleus has an even number of neutrons and protons. Nuclei with an odd number of nucleons always have a half-integer spin. In many cases the magnitude of the spin can be determined from the nuclear shell model (see below). A nucleus with a spin also has a magnetic moment aligned along the spin axis. The magnetic moment of a nucleus is very weak compared to that of an electron, but it can still produce an observable effect in atomic properties. The magnetic field from a nucleus disturbs the degeneracy of atomic levels and causes the atomic spectral lines to split. This splitting is called hyperfine structure, as distinguished from the fine-structure splitting caused by the magnetic moment of electrons.

Magnetic resonance An important application of nuclear magnetism is a method of analysis called magnetic resonance. In this technique, a material is placed in a strong magnetic field that tends to align the nuclear spins. Partially aligned spins will precess about the magnetic field direction, the way a gyroscope precesses when it is subjected to an outside torque. With the application of an extra time-varying magnetic field, the nuclei can be induced to precess in phase with each other. The resulting precessional motion of the spins causes the magnetization of the material to vary at a definite frequency, which is detected as a radio-frequency signal from the material. Magnetic resonance has several practical applications. Based on the fact that the precession rate is proportional to the field, it can be used to measure magnetic fields precisely. Notable is its use in a medical diagnostic procedure known as magnetic resonance imaging (MRI; see RADIATION: *Imaging techniques*). The nucleus most commonly employed in magnetic resonance is the proton in the hydrogen atom. Because the hydrogen nucleus has the largest magnetic moment for its spin, it provides the strongest resonance signals. Other nuclei used include those of phosphorus and fluorine.

Energy levels. Nuclei have energy levels just as atoms do. A typical excitation energy of a nuclear level is 1 MeV, which is 1,000,000 times larger than atomic energy levels. As in atomic transitions, a quantum of light may be emitted when the nucleus changes states. These quanta are the gamma rays that are often by-products of radioactivity.

Each energy level is characterized by its own values of spin, magnetic moment, and quadrupole moment. In addition, the quantum numbers of isotopic spin and parity are useful for describing nuclear levels. The isotopic spin quantum number characterizes the symmetry of the wave function when neutrons are interchanged with protons. Levels can exist in different nuclei with wave functions that are identical except for the interchange of neutrons and protons. Except for the Coulomb energy, these sets of wave functions have the same energies; the sets are called isospin multiplets (Figure 15). The parity quantum num-

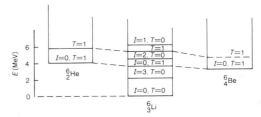

Figure 15: The energy levels of three nuclei with $A = 6$, relative to the ground state of ^{6}Li after subtraction of the calculated electrostatic energy. The isospin $T = 1$ levels exist in all three nuclei.

ber can take on only two values, even or odd, depending on whether the wave function reverses sign when the coordinates of the particles are reversed. The parity and spin quantum numbers are useful in understanding the rates of transitions between energy levels; selection rules govern changes in spin and parity for the favoured transitions.

To excite nuclei out of their ground states, energy must be provided from some external source. A common way to do this is with nuclear reactions. A nucleus is bombarded with energetic particles of one sort or another. The particles interact, giving up part of their energy to induce an excited state of the nucleus. Under special circumstances it is possible to excite a nucleus with the gamma ray produced by another nucleus. In a nuclear process known as the Mössbauer effect, the nucleus of some isotope absorbs a gamma ray that has been emitted by another nucleus of the same isotope. Because the transitions take place between the same two levels, the gamma ray has exactly the right energy to be absorbed. The effect is difficult to produce because part of the transition energy normally goes to nuclear recoil during emission and absorption and is unavailable to the gamma ray. Mössbauer effect

Among the many energy levels to which a nucleus can be excited, a few correspond to simple modes of motion for the nucleons. Deformed nuclei (see below) can be given energy in the form of rotational motion. Nuclei also can vibrate, and corresponding vibrational states may be found among the energy levels. Giant dipole resonance is an example of a nuclear vibration exhibited by all nuclei. In this mode of motion neutrons and protons in the nucleus oscillate back and forth, with the neutrons moving against the protons, as shown in Figure 16. Because there is a large oscillating electric field associated with this motion, gamma rays are absorbed and emitted readily. Another kind of vibration is called the quadrupole vibration. In this mode the nucleus oscillates in shape, changing between

From G.F. Bertsch and R.A. Broglia,
"Giant Resonances in Hot Nuclei," *Physics Today* (August 1986)

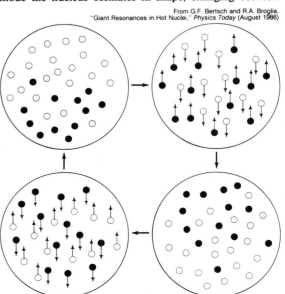

Figure 16: *Nuclear vibratory motion in the giant dipole resonance.*
Protons and neutrons, indicated by circles and solid dots, move in opposite directions.

prolate and oblate spheroids. This mode is easily excited by the inelastic scattering of particles from the nucleus. Its properties are deduced from the diffraction pattern observed in the scattering. In yet another kind of vibration, called the breathing mode, the nucleus expands and contracts. The frequency of the breathing mode depends on the compressibility of the nuclear medium and is used to establish its value.

Nuclear shell model. A comprehensive explanation of many nuclear properties is provided by a theory known as the shell model. It is based on the Hartree approximation to the Schrödinger equation. As noted earlier, this approximation assumes that all the particles have independent wave functions governed by a common force field. Of course, the forces in the nucleus are different from those in the atom as a whole. In the nuclear Hartree theory the forces are too strong to include directly, varying violently from repulsive to attractive. Instead, true interaction is replaced by smoother forces that are adjusted to reproduce the saturation property of nuclei.

The resulting force field pulls the nucleons in when they come to the surface, but it cancels out when nucleons are in the interior. The nucleons behave as though they were in a potential well with a flat bottom. The nuclear shells are the sets of wave functions that go with this flat-bottomed potential well. Some of the properties of these shells are similar to those of atomic shells, but there are also important differences. Provided the well is spherically symmetric, the shells have an angular momentum quantum number, as do the atomic shells. The lowest shell is the *s* shell, which can hold a neutron and proton of each spin orientation. Thus, the two protons and two neutrons of helium-4 fill the *s* shell and give this light nucleus its unusual stability. The energy levels of higher shells are shown in Figure 17. Differences from the atomic levels in hydrogen are readily apparent. First, there is no degeneracy between the *s* and *p* shells, so that the atomic periodicity of 8 does not occur in nuclear physics. Second, the spin-orbit force makes shells that have nucleon spin

Properties
of nuclear
shells

parallel to orbital angular momentum lower in energy than the shell with antiparallel spin. For example, in the *p* shell, there are two sub-shells, the $p_{3/2}$ and the $p_{1/2}$. The $p_{3/2}$, with orbital angular momentum 1 parallel to spin angular momentum $1/2$, is lower in energy than the $p_{1/2}$, which has an antiparallel spin and orbital angular momentum. Combining orbital and spin angular momentum in this way is called *j-j* coupling. The number of protons or neutrons that can go in a *j* shell is its multiplicity equal to $2j + 1$. From this filling rule and the shell ordering in Figure 17, one can determine the shell structure of a nucleus for any given proton and neutron number.

An important consequence of the *j-j* coupling is the energy gap between shells that occurs at proton or neutron numbers 28, 50, 82, and 126. These so-called magic numbers are the nuclear equivalent of the atomic numbers of the noble (or inert) gases 2, 10, 18, 36, 54, 86. Nuclei with magic numbers of protons and neutrons are unusually stable and have especially large gaps between their ground and excited states.

Magic
numbers

The ground state of nuclei with an odd number of neutrons or protons has a spin that is often given by a simple rule—namely, that the angular momentum of all the nucleons except the last are aligned to cancel. The last nucleon has the angular momentum of its shell, which gives the spin of the nucleus. For example, the nucleus of lithium-7 consists of three protons and four neutrons. According to the rule, the spin of lithium-7 is determined by the shell of the third proton. This is the $p_{3/2}$ shell, and indeed the spin of the nucleus is $3/2$. Another property that can be inferred from the shell model is the parity of the nucleus. It can be determined from the shell model simply by combining the parities of the individual shell wave functions for nucleons.

Nuclear excited states are described in the shell model either by changing the orbitals that nucleons occupy in a shell or by moving nucleons from a lower shell to a higher one. Wave functions constructed in this way accurately describe the excited-state properties of light nuclei and nuclei near magic numbers. Outside of these limited regions of nuclei, the shell model allows an enormous number of states. The numerical complexity of dealing with so many states, however, prevents precise calculations from being carried out. A simplified treatment of the wave function explaining many properties of nuclear vibrations is based on a generalization of the Hartree method to allow the potential field to vary in time. The nucleons move in the time-varying field, and the frequency of motion can be calculated by requiring the field generated by the nucleons to be consistent with the field in which they move.

Deformed nuclei. Not all nuclei are spherical in shape. In certain regions of the periodic table, many nuclei are spheroidal. Typically, these nuclei have a prolate distortion, meaning that they have an elongated shape like a lemon. For example, the nuclei near mass number 160 are prolate spheroids, with the longer axis about 30 percent larger than the other two axes. The existence of these deformations was first detected in atomic spectra: the quadrupole moment distorts the electric field around the nucleus, producing characteristic features in the hyperfine structure of the atomic spectrum. The energy levels of these nuclei also exhibit characteristic features. A body capable of rotation and governed by the laws of quantum mechanics has energy levels with spacings that increase uniformly with higher angular momentum. Deformed nuclei exhibit this type of spectrum (see Figure 18).

Elongation
of nuclei

Deformations can be explained by the Hartree theory of the nuclear wave function. The orbitals describing the individual nucleons are rarely spherically symmetric; many are, in fact, quite elongated. When a shell is filled, the various asymmetries in the different orbitals balance out so that the entire shell has a spherical mass distribution. If a shell is only partly filled, the overall shape deviates more or less from spherical symmetry, depending on which particular orbitals are occupied. In the case of an atom, the repulsion of the electrons tends to make the overall shape spherical: when one electron is in an orbital elongated in a certain direction, the energy is minimized if the other electrons are in orbitals elongated in other directions. The

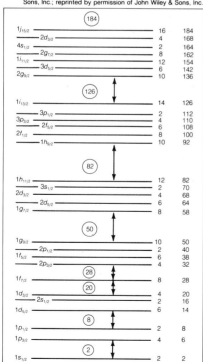

From K. Krane, *Nuclear Physics*, copyright © 1987 by John Wiley & Sons, Inc.; reprinted by permission of John Wiley & Sons, Inc.

Figure 17: Nuclear shells.
The spectroscopic designation includes the quantum number *j*, which is a half integer. The degeneracy of the shells and the cumulative number of particles contained are listed on the right. Especially stable nuclei are found at the magic numbers, shown in circles.

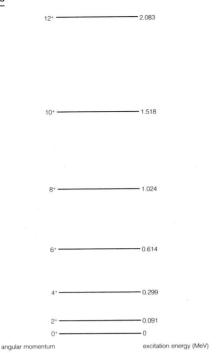

12⁺ ——————— 2.083

10⁺ ——————— 1.518

8⁺ ——————— 1.024

6⁺ ——————— 0.614

4⁺ ——————— 0.299

2⁺ ——————— 0.091
0⁺ ——————— 0

angular momentum   excitation energy (MeV)

Figure 18: Energy-level spectrum of the deformed nucleus erbium-164.

From K. Krane, *Nuclear Physics*, copyright © 1987 by John Wiley & Sons, Inc.; reprinted by permission of John Wiley & Sons, Inc.

overall density ends up being close to spherical, even when the individual orbitals are not. In a nucleus there is a net attraction between nucleons so that, if a proton's orbital is elongated in some particular direction, the neutron would tend to be in a similarly directed orbital. Many nucleons can act together and deform the entire nucleus. When the Hartree equations are solved for nuclei with partially filled shells, the resulting potential well is elongated and the nucleons occupy states elongated in the same direction.

Nuclear reactions. Nuclear reactions mediated by the strong force can occur when a nucleus is bombarded by some hadronic projectile, such as a proton, a pion, or an-other nucleus. For a reaction to occur, the projectile must come within a few femtometres of the nucleus, preventing positively charged particles from producing reactions at low energy. Since the nucleus is positively charged, a similarly charged projectile will not be able to come within range unless it has enough energy to overcome the force of the electric repulsion. For example, alpha particles will not come close enough to interact with an iron nucleus unless their energy exceeds about 10 MeV. For less highly charged nuclei, the numbers are smaller; a proton of 1 MeV can interact with a lithium nucleus. The first artificial nuclear reactions were induced by using a voltage source of 1,000,000 volts to accelerate protons to an energy of 1 MeV and bombard a lithium target. At high bombarding energies the electrostatic force is less important, and the cross section for producing a reaction is approximately equal to the area of a circle with the radius of the nucleus.

Neutrons can induce reactions at very low energies, even thermal energies, because they are not repelled by the positive charge of the nucleus. The cross section for reactions with thermal neutrons can be extremely large because the wave function of the neutron is spread out at low energy. Radioactive nuclei are commonly produced by bombarding nuclei with neutrons in nuclear reactors.

Reactions induced by hadronic projectiles may be divided into two main categories: direct reactions and more complex reactions. In direct reactions the projectile retains most of its energy and momentum. A small amount of energy is transferred to the target, producing transitions to particular excited states. These direct reactions occur when the projectile passes near the target nucleus without penetrating it. The angular distribution of scattered projectile particles shows diffraction behaviour depending on the properties of the energy level excited. An example of a direct reaction is the following:

$$p + {}^{40}\text{Ca} \longrightarrow d + {}^{39}\text{Ca}.$$

Here, a proton, p, passes by the calcium-40 nucleus, picking up a neutron to form a deuteron, d. The deuteron comes off in approximately the same direction as the motion of the incident proton but with diffractional variations in intensity at different angles. From the diffraction pattern, the orbital angular momentum of the neutron in the target may be inferred. Measurements such as these were important in establishing the validity of the shell model.

If the projectile goes into the target nucleus, it is likely

Hadronic reactions

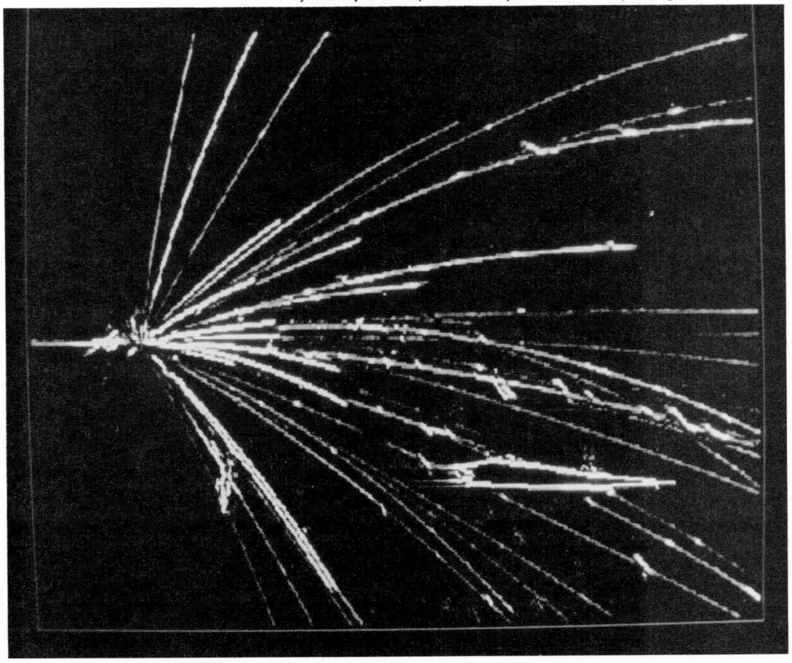

Figure 19: Particle tracks from the collision of an accelerated nucleus of a niobium atom with another niobium nucleus. The single line on the left is the track of the incoming projectile nucleus, and the other tracks are fragments from the collision.

to be absorbed completely, sharing its energy with the other nucleons in the nucleus. The resulting highly excited nucleus, called a compound nucleus, can decay in many different ways. The main constraints in determining the possible reactions are that the total number of neutrons and protons, the total charge, and the total energy must remain the same. These are the conservation laws for baryon number, charge, and energy. In principle, it is possible to change a neutron into a proton or vice versa in a hadronic reaction, but the probability is so small that this cannot be observed in the laboratory.

An example of a reaction following this more complex path is

$$a + {}^{14}N \longrightarrow {}^{17}O + p$$

This reaction was observed by Rutherford, who used alpha particles from a radioactive source. This provided enough energy to allow the alpha particle, a, to touch and fuse with the nitrogen-14 nucleus. There is a high probability that the resulting compound nucleus will decay by emitting a proton, but it can decay by other modes as well. The following example is a reaction that takes place when a hydrogen-containing medium is bombarded with low-energy neutrons, n:

$$n + {}^{1}H \longrightarrow {}^{2}H + \gamma$$

In this case, the energy released is equal to the binding energy of hydrogen-2, which is given off in the gamma ray, γ.

Many different kinds of reactions are possible in collisions induced by accelerated particles. Accelerators can give the projectiles enough energy to disrupt the nucleus completely and create new particles in the process. For example, a cyclotron can boost carbon nuclei to an energy

of 500 MeV, enough to dissociate all the nucleons in a target nucleus of oxygen. In practice, such a reaction would involve many different processes, and the end result would be the fusion and dissociation of the nuclei into fragments of various sizes (see Figure 19). The annihilation of a pion in a nucleus is another example of a hadronic reaction. In this process, the rest energy of the pion would be released, dissociating the nucleus and giving kinetic energy to nucleons or other fragments.

Nuclear reactions also can be induced by leptons such as electrons and neutrinos. The probability for an electron-induced reaction is smaller than for a hadronic reaction because of the difference in forces. The main process is inelastic scattering, in which the nucleus is excited to a higher energy level. If the inelastic scattering transfers a large amount of energy to the nucleus (*e.g.,* 20 MeV or larger), the nucleus becomes disrupted and ejects particles.

The weak interaction also causes reactions, but these are very difficult to observe. One part of the weak interaction changes a neutron into a proton or vice versa and brings about a corresponding conversion between an electron and a neutrino. The direction of the change is such as to conserve the total charge. An example of a neutrino-induced reaction is the reaction by which neutrinos were detected from a supernova in 1987. In this case, the neutrinos—or more precisely antineutrinos, $\bar{v}$—from the cosmic object interacted with protons of hydrogen atoms in a large tank of water. Positrons, e^+, were created according to the reaction

$$\bar{v} + p \longrightarrow n + e^+$$

The positrons were detected by the light they emitted as they traveled through the water.

(George F. Bertsch/ Sharon McGrayne)

Lepton-induced reactions

Information Processing and Information Systems

In popular usage, the term information refers to facts and opinions provided and received during the course of daily life: one obtains information directly from other living beings, from mass media, from electronic data banks, and from all sorts of observable phenomena in the surrounding environment. As a person uses such facts and opinions, he generates information of his own, some of which is communicated to others during discourse, by instructions, in letters and documents, and through other media. Information organized according to some logical relationships is referred to as a body of knowledge, to be acquired by systematic exposure or study. Application of knowledge (or skills) yields expertise, and additional analytical or experiential insights are said to constitute instances of wisdom. Use of the term information is not restricted exclusively to its communication via natural language. Information is also registered and communicated through art and by facial expressions and gestures or by such other physical responses as shivering. Moreover, every living entity is endowed with information in the form of a genetic code. These information phenomena

permeate the physical and mental world, and their variety is such that it has defied so far all attempts at a unified definition of information.

Interest in information phenomena has increased dramatically in the 20th century, and today they are the objects of study in a number of disciplines, including philosophy, physics, biology, linguistics, information and computer science, electronic and communications engineering, management science, and the social sciences. On the commercial side, the information service industry has become one of the newer industries throughout the world. Almost all other industries—manufacturing and service—are increasingly concerned with information and its handling. The different, though often overlapping, viewpoints and phenomena of these fields lead to different (and sometimes conflicting) concepts and "definitions" of information.

This article touches on such concepts, particularly as they relate to information processing and information systems. In treating the basic elements of information processing, it distinguishes between information in analog and digital form, and it describes their acquisition, recording, organization, retrieval, display, and dissemination. In treating information systems, the article discusses system analysis and design and provides a descriptive taxonomy of the main system types. Some attention is also given to the social impact of information systems and to the field of information science.

This article is divided into the following sections:

General considerations

BASIC CONCEPTS

Interest in how information is communicated and how its carriers convey meaning has occupied, since the time of pre-Socratic philosophers, the field of inquiry called semiotics, the study of signs and sign phenomena. Signs are the irreducible elements of communication and the carriers of meaning. The American philosopher, mathematician, and physicist Charles S. Peirce is credited with having pointed out the three dimensions of signs, which are concerned with, respectively, the body or medium of the sign, the object that the sign designates, and the interpretant or interpretation of the sign. Peirce recognized that the fundamental relations of information are essentially triadic; in contrast, all relations of the physical sciences are reducible to dyadic (binary) relations. Another American philosopher, Charles W. Morris, designated these three sign dimensions syntactic, semantic, and pragmatic, the names by which they are known today.

Information processes are executed by information processors. For a given information processor, whether physical or biologic, a token is an object, devoid of meaning, that the processor recognizes as being totally different from other tokens. A group of such unique tokens recognized by a processor constitutes its basic "alphabet"; for example, the dot, dash, and space constitute the basic token alphabet of a Morse-code processor. Objects that carry meaning are represented by patterns of tokens called symbols. The latter combine to form symbolic expressions that constitute inputs to or outputs from information processes and are stored in the processor memory (as data and programs).

Information processors are components of an information system, which can be defined as a class of constructs. An abstract model of an information system features four basic elements: processor, memory, receptor, and effector (Figure 1). The processor has several functions: these are (1) to carry out elementary information processes on symbolic expressions, (2) to store temporarily in the processor's short-term memory the input and output expressions on which these processes operate and which they generate, (3) to schedule execution of these processes, and (4) to change this sequence of operations arbitrarily in accordance with the contents of the short-term memory. The memory serves to store symbolic expressions, including those that represent composite information processes called programs. The two other components, the receptor and the effector, are input and output mechanisms whose functions are, respectively, to receive symbolic expressions or stimuli from the external environment for manipula-

tion by the processor and to emit the processed structures back to the environment. This abstract model of an information-processing system is representative of a broad variety of such systems, both natural and man-made.

The power of information processors is provided by their ability to carry out a small number of elementary information processes that operate on symbolic expressions. These processes are reading symbolic expressions (or generating representations of external stimuli by assigning them internal symbolic expressions in the processor memory), testing and comparing symbolic expressions by ascertaining whether tokens are part of the same symbol, creating and naming new, and modifying existing, symbolic expressions, copying and storing such expressions, and writing symbolic expressions (or transforming internal symbolic expressions into stimuli intended for the outside environment).

INFORMATION AS A RESOURCE AND COMMODITY

In the second half of the 20th century, information has acquired two major utilitarian connotations. On the one hand, it is considered an economic resource, somewhat on par with other resources such as labour, material, and capital. This view of information stems from the belief and evidence thereof that the possession, manipulation, and use of information can increase the cost-effectiveness of many physical and cognitive processes. The rise in information-processing activities in industrial manufacturing as well as in human problem solving has been remarkable. Analysis of one of the three traditional divisions of the economy, the service sector, shows a sharp increase in information-intensive activities since the beginning of the 20th century. By 1975 these activities accounted for half of the labour force of the United States (see Table), giving rise to the so-called information society.

As an individual and societal resource, information has some interesting characteristics that separate it from the traditional notions of economic resources. Unlike other resources, information is expansive with limits apparently imposed only by time and human cognitive capabilities.

Signs and their dimensions

Basic elements of information systems

A. Newell and H.A. Simon, *Human Problem Solving*, p. 20, © 1972, reprinted by permission of Prentice-Hall, Inc., Englewood Cliffs, N.J.

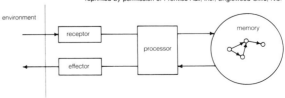

Figure 1: Structure of an information system.

Labour Distribution (%) in the United States, 1880–2000					
	1880	1920	1955	1975	2000 (est.)
Agriculture and extractive	50	28	14	4	2
Manufacturing, commerce, industry	36	53	37	29	22
Information, knowledge, education	2	9	29	50	66
Other services	12	10	20	17	10

Source: Graham T.T. Molitor, "The Coming of the Information Society," *Communications Tomorrow.*

Information as an expansive resource

Its expansiveness is attributable to three reasons: (1) it is naturally diffusive; (2) it reproduces rather than is consumed through use; and (3) it can only be shared, not exchanged in transactions. At the same time, information is compressible, both syntactically and semantically. Coupled with its ability to be substituted for other economic resources, its transportability at very high speeds, and its ability to impart advantages to the beholder of information, these characteristics are at the base of such societal industries as research, education, publishing, marketing, and even politics. Societal concern with the husbanding of information resources has extended from the traditional domain of libraries and archives to encompass organizational, institutional, and governmental information under the umbrella of information resource management.

Importance of the information service sector

The second perception of information is that it is an economic commodity, which helps to stimulate the worldwide growth of a new segment of national economies—the information service sector. Taking advantage of the properties of information and building on the perception of its individual and societal utility and value, this sector provides a broad range of information products and services: it reduces information to manageable quantities, protects information and intellectual property rights, replaces labour with automata, replicates rare expertise through computer software, and provides consultancy in many walks of life.

Elements of information processing

Humans receive information with their senses: sounds through hearing; images and text through sight; shape, temperature, and affection through touch; and odours through smell. To interpret the signals received from the senses, humans have developed and learned complex systems of languages consisting of "alphabets" of symbols and stimuli and the associated rules of usage. This has enabled them to recognize the objects they see, understand the messages they read or hear, and comprehend the signs received through the tactile and olfactory senses.

The carriers of information-conveying signs received by the senses are energy phenomena—audio waves, light waves, and chemical and electrochemical stimuli. In engineering parlance, humans are receptors of analog signals; and by a somewhat loose convention, the messages conveyed via these carriers are called analog-form information, or simply analog information. Until the development of the digital computer, cognitive information was stored and processed only in analog form, basically through the technologies of printing, photography, and telephony.

Information in binary form

Although humans are very adept at processing information stored in their memories, analog information stored external to the mind is not processed easily. Modern information technology greatly facilitates the manipulation of externally stored information as a result of its representation as digital signals—*i.e.,* as the presence or absence of energy (electricity, light, or magnetism). Information represented digitally in two-state, or binary, form is often referred to as digital information. Modern information systems are characterized by extensive transformations between different types of analog and digital information.

ACQUISITION AND RECORDING OF INFORMATION IN ANALOG FORM

The principal categories of information sources useful in modern information systems are text, video, and voice.

One of the first ways in which prehistoric humans communicated was by sound; sounds represented concepts such as pleasure, anger, and fear, as well as objects of the surrounding environment, including food and tools. Sounds assumed their meaning by convention—namely, by the use to which they were consistently put. Combining parts of sound allowed representation of more complex concepts, gradually leading to the development of speech and eventually to spoken "natural" languages.

Development of writing systems

For information to be communicated broadly, it needs to be stored external to human memory; accumulation of human experience, knowledge, and learning would be severely limited without such storage. Storage of information external to memory made necessary the development of writing systems.

Civilization can be traced to the time when humans began to associate abstract shape with concepts and with the sounds of speech that represented them. Early recorded representations were those of visually perceived objects and events, as, for example, the animals and activities depicted in Paleolithic cave drawings. The evolution of writing systems proceeded through the early development of pictographic languages, in which a symbol would represent an entire concept. Such symbols would go through many metamorphoses of shape in which the resemblance between each symbol and the object it stood for gradually disappeared, but its semantic meaning would become more precise. As the conceptual world of humankind became larger, the symbols, called ideographs, grew in number. Modern Chinese, a present-day result of this evolutionary direction of a pictographic writing system, has upward of 50,000 ideographs.

At some point in the evolution of written languages the method of representation shifted from the pictographic to the phonetic: speech sounds began to be represented by an alphabet of graphic symbols. Combinations of a relatively small set of such symbols could stand for more complex concepts as words, phrases, and sentences. The invention of the written phonetic alphabet is thought to have taken place in Sumer, a civilization in the southern part of the Tigris-Euphrates Valley, during the 4th millennium BC.

The pragmatic advantages of alphabetic writing systems over the pictographic became apparent twice in the present millennium: after the invention of the movable-type printing press in the 15th century and again with the development of information processing by electronic means since the mid-1940s.

Recording media and techniques

From the time early man learned to represent concepts symbolically, he used whatever materials were readily available in nature for recording them. The Sumerian cuneiform, a wedge-shaped alphabet, was impressed by a stylus into soft clay tablets, which were subsequently hardened by drying in the sun or the oven. The earliest Chinese writing, dating to the 2nd millennium BC, is preserved on animal bone and shell, while early Indian writing was done on palm leaves and birch bark. Applications of technology yielded other materials for writing. The Chinese had recorded their pictographs on silk, using brushes made from animal hair, long before they invented paper. The Egyptians first wrote on cotton, but they began using papyrus sheets and rolls made from the fibrous lining of the papyrus plant during the 4th millennium BC. The reed brush and a palette of ink were the implements with which they wrote hieroglyphic script. Writing on parchment, a material which was superior to papyrus and was made from the prepared skins of animals, became commonplace around 200 BC, some 300 years after its first recorded use, and the quill pen replaced the reed brush. By the 4th century AD, parchment came to be the principal writing material in Europe.

Paper was invented in China at the beginning of the 2nd century AD, and for some 600 years its use was confined to the Far East. In AD 751 Arab and Chinese armies clashed at the Battle of Talas, near Samarkand; among the Chinese taken captive were some papermakers from whom the Arabs learned the techniques. From the 7th century on, paper became the dominant writing material of the Islāmic world. Papermaking finally reached Spain and Sicily in the 12th century—1,000 years after its invention—and it took another three centuries before it was practiced in Germany.

With the invention of printing from movable type, typesetting became the standard method of creating copy. Typesetting was an entirely manual operation until the adoption of a typewriter-like keyboard in the 19th century. In fact, it was the typewriter that mechanized the process of recording original text. Although the typewriter was invented during the early 18th century in England, the first practical version, constructed by the American inventor Christopher Latham Sholes, did not appear until 1867. The mechanical typewriter finally found wide use after World War I. Today, its electronic variant, the computer video terminal, is used increasingly to record original text.

Development of photography

Recording of original non-textual (image) information was a manual process until the development of photography during the early decades of the 19th century; drawing and carving were the principal early means of recording graphics. Other techniques were developed alongside printing—for example, etching in stone and metal. The invention of film and the photographic process added a new dimension to information acquisition: for the first time, complex visual images of the real world could be captured accurately. Photography provided a method of storing information in less space and more accurately than was hitherto possible with narrative information.

During the 20th century, versatile electromagnetic media have opened up new possibilities for capturing original analog information. Magnetic audio tape is used to capture speech and music, and magnetic videotape provides a low-cost medium for recording analog voice and video signals directly and simultaneously. Such tape information can be transferred to an analog optical disc, a medium distinguished for its higher storage capacity and fidelity. Analog optical discs are employed in archival storage systems and other applications in which information is displayed without further processing.

Magnetic technology has other uses in the direct recording of analog information, including alphanumerics. Magnetic characters, bar codes, and special marks are printed on checks, labels, and forms for subsequent sensing by magnetic or optical readers and conversion to digital form. Banks, educational institutions, and the retail industry rely heavily on this technology. Nonetheless, paper and film continue to be the dominant media for direct storage of textual and visual information in analog form.

ACQUISITION AND RECORDING OF INFORMATION IN DIGITAL FORM

The versatility of modern information systems stems from their ability to represent information electronically as digital signals and to manipulate it automatically at exceedingly high speeds. Information is stored in binary devices, which are the basic components of digital technology. Because these devices exist only in one of two states, information is represented in them either as the absence or the presence of energy (electric pulse). The two states of binary devices are conveniently designated by the binary digits, or bits, zero (0) and one (1).

Coding systems

In this manner, alphabetic symbols of natural-language writing systems can be represented digitally as combinations of zeros (no pulse) and ones (pulse). Tables of equivalences of alphanumeric characters and strings of binary digits are called coding systems, the counterpart of writing systems. A combination of three binary digits can represent up to eight such characters; one comprising four digits, up to 16 characters; and so on. The choice of a particular coding system depends on the size of the character set to be represented. Among widely used systems are the Binary-Coded Decimal (BCD), a four-digit code representing decimal integers; the International Telegraph Code No. 2 (a modern version of the Baudot code, known as the International Telegraph Code No. 1), a five-digit combination representing the telegraph keyboard; the American Standard Code for Information Interchange (ASCII), a seven- or eight-bit code representing the English alphabet, numerals, and certain special characters of the standard computer keyboard; and the corresponding eight-bit Extended Binary Coded Decimal Interchange

Code (EBCDIC), used for computers produced by IBM (International Business Machines) and most compatible systems. The digital representation of a character by eight bits is called a byte.

The seven-bit ASCII code is capable of representing up to 128 alphanumeric and special characters—sufficient to accommodate the writing systems of many phonetic scripts, including Latin and Cyrillic. Some alphabetic scripts require more than seven bits; for example, the Arabic alphabet, also used in the Urdu and Persian languages, has 28 phonetic characters (as well as a number of vowels and diacritical marks), but each of these may have four shapes, depending on its position in the word.

For digital representation of nonalphabetic writing systems, even the eight-bit code accommodating 256 characters is inadequate. Some writing systems that use Chinese characters, for example, have more than 50,000 ideographs (the minimal standard font for the Hanzi system in Chinese and the kanji system in Japanese has about 7,000 ideographs). Digital representation of such scripts can be accomplished in three ways. One approach is to develop a phonetic character set; the Chinese Pinyin, the Korean Han'gŭl, and the Japanese kana phonetic schemes all have alphabetic sets similar in number to the Latin alphabet. As the use of phonetic alphabets in Oriental cultures is not yet widespread, this approach is not entirely satisfactory. A second technique is to decompose ideographs into a small number of elementary signs called strokes, the sum of which constitutes a shape-oriented, nonphonetic alphabet. Hanzi uses a five-stroke or an eight-stroke scheme to decompose ideographs, supplemented with coding of polysyllabic ideographs (words and phrases). This technique permits the use of the ASCII and EBCDIC codes. The third approach is to use more than eight bits to encode the large numbers of ideographs; for instance, two bytes can represent uniquely more than 65,000 ideographs.

Recording media. Punched cards and perforated paper tape were once widely used to store data in binary form. Today, they have been supplanted by media based on electromagnetic and electrooptic technologies except in a few special applications.

The earliest form of magnetic mass-memory storage was magnetic tape. This medium, developed in 1951, consists of a ribbon of plastic film coated with iron oxide. Data are recorded on the tape through selective changes in magnetization of its surface. Depending on the recording density, a reel of magnetic tape 2,400 feet long can hold more than 100,000,000 characters. Special-purpose, high-density (50,000 bits per inch) cassette tapes have a capacity of 5,000,000,000 characters; they can accommodate the storage needs of imaging applications. Tape-storage devices suffer from one shortcoming: relatively slow retrieval of data. Because data are recorded serially, it may at times be necessary to traverse the entire tape to locate the information sought.

Magnetic disks

Another type of magnetic storage medium, the magnetic disk, provides rapid, random access to data. This device, developed in 1962, consists of either an aluminum or plastic platen coated with a metallic material. Information is recorded on a disk by turning the charge of the reading/writing disk head on and off, which produces magnetic "dots" representing binary digits in circular tracks. A block of data on a given track can be accessed without having to pass over a large portion of its contents sequentially, as in the case of tape. Data retrieval time is thus reduced dramatically. Disk packs, collections of 10 or more disks connected by a spindle, are often used on larger computer systems. A single pack of this kind can store from 10,000,000 to several hundred million characters. Some of the largest computer systems use disk cartridges, which are more compact than disk packs. Because of their high storage capacity as well as ability to access data directly, magnetic disk systems have become the dominant medium for recording and storing computer data.

During the 1970s the so-called floppy disk—a small, flexible disk—was introduced for use in personal computers and other microcomputer systems. Compared to the storage capacity of the conventional "hard" disk, that of such a "soft" diskette is low—only about 1,000,000 characters.

Accessing data on the latter is also slower, but the retrieval time is adequate for most microcomputer applications.

Optical discs

An entirely different kind of recording and storage medium, the optical disc, became available during the early 1980s. The optical disc makes use of laser technology: digital data are recorded by burning a series of microscopic holes, or pits, with a laser beam into thin metallic film on the surface of a 4³/₄-inch (12-centimetre) plastic disc. In this way, information from magnetic tape is encoded on a master disc; subsequently, the master is replicated by a process called stamping. In the read mode, low-intensity laser light is reflected off the disc surface and is "read" by light-sensitive diodes. The radiant energy received by the diodes varies according to the presence of the pits, and this input is digitized by the diode circuits. The digital signals are then converted to analog information on a video screen or in printout form.

Optical discs fall into two classes: (1) prerecorded, exemplified by the compact disc-read only memory (CD-ROM), from which data can be read but not modified; and (2) writable/erasable, on which data can be both recorded and overwritten. The latter variety is the full functional equivalent of the magnetic disk. It employs magneto-optic technology: the erasable medium is magnetic. Information is recorded or erased by reversing the polarity of the material. Reading is accomplished optically.

Optical storage represents a considerable improvement over magnetic disks in terms of superior recording capability (it accommodates storage of voice, text, graphics, and video), of storage capacity (2,000,000,000 characters on a 12-inch disc), of ruggedness (the disc is sealed between two plastic surfaces), of portability, and of low cost—in fact, the lowest of per-bit storage of any digital storage media. In their present stage of development, optical discs still have some shortcomings, particularly a relatively slow rate of data access. Technological advances promise improvements, however. For example, the development of a flexible storage medium, a dye polymer coated onto a polyester substrate, is expected to result in the production of flexible optical discs with storage capacities far exceeding those of the rigid discs currently in use.

During the 1990s new types of portable digital media are likely to find extensive application in information systems. Among the most promising are the digital audio tape, which has a storage capacity of more than 1,000,000,000 characters; and the so-called softstrip card, a paper strip with information encoded as highly condensed optical binary patterns and with a storage capacity of 45,000 characters per 8 × 11-inch page.

Recording techniques. Digitally stored information is commonly referred to as data, and its analog counterpart is called source data. The capture of source data for electronic storage and digital processing is accomplished by manual and automatic techniques. Manual data entry is the transcription, by means of a keyboard, of alphanumeric information from document manuscripts or forms. Keyboarding data is straightforward for alphabetic writing systems but unwieldy for pictographic data. Chinese, Japanese, Korean, and other languages that employ ideographs thus require the use of phonetic or shape-oriented alphabets for entering data. Manual data entry, a slow and error-prone process, is facilitated to a degree by special computer programs that include editing software with which to insert formatting commands, verify spelling, and make text changes and document-formatting software with which to arrange and rearrange text and graphics flexibly on the output page.

It is estimated that U.S. business deals annually with 400,000,000,000 paper documents, two-thirds of which cannot be digitized by keyboard transcription because they contain drawings, signatures, or images or because such transcription would be highly uneconomical. Such documents are digitized by automatic image-processing techniques. Image processing is the primary means by which large volumes of data, such as that handled by government agencies, is recorded in digital form.

Image processing

Image processing involves the use of high-resolution scanning cameras. To generate a digital representation of a document page, such image scanners divide it into minute areas called picture elements (or pixels), and produce an array of binary digits, each representing the brightness of a pixel. The resulting stream of bits is enhanced and compressed by a device called an image controller and is stored on a high-density storage medium such as optical disc or microfilm. (A large storage capacity is required, since it takes 45,000 bytes to store a typical document page of 2,500 characters.) A 12-inch optical disc can hold about 40,000 such pages. Compared with manual data entry, image scanning is rapid—up to 60 pages per minute. Aside from its application in electronic document filing, image scanning is used for the digital conversion of document pages for transmission via telecommunications systems and their reconversion into analog images (facsimile transmission), as well as in satellite photography.

An image scanner digitizes an entire document page for storage and display as an image and does not recognize characters and words of text. The stored material therefore cannot be linguistically manipulated by text processing and other software techniques. When such manipulation is desired, analog text is digitized by a method called optical character recognition. An optical character reader (OCR) converts each optically scanned character into an electric signal and compares it with internally stored representations of an alphabet of characters, so as to select from it the one that matches the scanned character most closely or to reject it as unidentifiable. OCR machines range from inexpensive, hand-held readers capable of recognizing dozens of standard fonts to sophisticated devices that can be taught to interpret the shape, size, and pitch of symbols, including handwriting.

Optical character recognition

In some applications, optical character recognition and image scanning are used jointly. The U.S. Patent and Trademark Office converts the text of patents into digital form by means of the former and digitizes drawings by means of the latter. The resulting digital data is stored on optical discs.

The digital recording of sound is important because speech is the most natural carrier of communicable information. This process is now commonplace. In the entertainment industry, analog audio signals are captured with microphones and transformed by analog-to-digital converters to produce recordings for the consumer market. In the communications industry, this same technique makes it possible to carry speech as digital data over voice communications systems, with attendant technical and economic benefits. When perfected, direct voice-to-printer technologies are expected to have a tremendous impact on methods of information acquisition and recording.

(Vladimir Slamecka)

INVENTORY OF RECORDED INFORMATION

The development of recording media and techniques enabled society to begin building a store of human knowledge and experiences. The idea of collecting and organizing written records is thought to have originated more or less simultaneously in two regions, Sumer and Egypt, about 5,000 years ago. Early collections of Sumerian and Egyptian writings, recorded in cuneiform on clay tablets and in hieroglyphic script on papyrus, contained information about legal and economic transactions—laws and treatises, contracts, property records, taxes, and wills. In these and other early document collections (*e.g.,* those of China produced during the Shang dynasty in the 2nd millennium BC and Buddhist collections in India dating to the 5th century BC), it is difficult to separate the concepts of the archive and the library.

Development of document collections

From the Middle East the concept of document collections penetrated the Greco-Roman world. Roman kings institutionalized the population and property census as early as the 6th century BC. The great Library of Alexandria, established in the 3rd century BC, is best known as a large collection of papyri containing inventories of property, taxes, and other payments by citizens to their rulers and to each other. It is, in short, the ancient equivalent of today's administrative information systems.

The scholarly splendour of the Islāmic world from the 8th to 13th centuries AD can in large part be attributed to the maintenance of public and private book libraries. The

Bayt al-Ḥikmah ("House of Wisdom"), founded in AD 830 in Baghdad, contained a public library with a large collection of materials on a wide range of subjects, and the 10th-century library of Caliph al-Ḥakam in Córdoba, Spain, boasted more than 400,000 books.

Primary literature

The late but rapid development of European libraries from the 16th century on followed the invention of printing from movable type, which spurred the growth of the printing and publishing industries. Since the beginning of the 17th century, literature has become the principal medium for disseminating knowledge in science and education. The phrase primary literature is used to designate original information in various printed formats: newspapers, monographs, conference proceedings, learned and trade journals, reports, patents, bulletins, and newsletters. The scholarly journal, the classic medium of scientific communication, first appeared in 1665. Three hundred years later the number of periodical titles published in the world was estimated at more than 60,000, reflecting not only growth in the number of practitioners of science and expansion of its body of knowledge through specialization but also a maturing of the system of rewards that motivates, and sometimes pressures, scientists to publish. To render this bulk of primary literature more manageable in storage and more affordable, a portion of it is also issued on microfilm. Other media containing scientific information in analog form—audio and video recording—abound as well.

Secondary literature

The sheer quantity of printed information has for some time prevented any individual from fully absorbing even a minuscule fraction of it. Such devices as tables of contents, summaries, and indexes of various types, which aid in identifying and locating relevant information in primary literature, have been in use since the 16th century and led to the development of what is termed secondary literature during the 19th century. The purpose of secondary literature is to "filter" the primary information sources, usually by subject area, and provide the indicators to this literature in the form of reviews, abstracts, and indexes. Over the past 100 years there has evolved a system of disciplinary, national, and international abstracting and indexing services that acts as a gateway to several attributes of primary literature: authors, subjects, publishers, dates (and languages) of publication, and citations. The professional activity associated with these access-facilitating tools is called documentation.

The quantity of printed materials also makes it impossible, as well as undesirable, for any institution to acquire and house more than a small portion of it. The husbanding of recorded information has become a matter of public policy, as many countries have established national libraries and archives to direct the orderly acquisition of analog-form documents and records. Since these institutions alone are not able to keep up with the output of such documents and records, new forms of cooperative planning and sharing recorded materials are evolving—namely, public and private, national and regional library networks and consortia.

Bibliographic and numeric data bases

The emergence of digital technology in the mid-20th century has affected humankind's inventory of recorded information dramatically. During the early 1960s computers were used to digitize text for the first time; the purpose was to reduce the cost and time required to publish two American abstracting journals, the *Index Medicus* of the National Library of Medicine and the *Scientific and Technical Aerospace Reports* of the National Aeronautics and Space Administration (NASA). By the late 1960s such bodies of digitized alphanumeric information, known as bibliographic and numeric data bases, constituted a new type of information resource. This resource is husbanded outside the traditional repositories of information (libraries and archives) by data-base "vendors." Advances in computer storage, telecommunications, software for computer sharing, and automated techniques of text indexing and searching fueled the development of an on-line data-base service industry. Meanwhile, electronic applications to bibliographic control in libraries and archives have led to the development of computerized catalogs and of union catalogs in library networks. They also have resulted in the introduction of comprehensive automation programs in these institutions.

The vast inventory of recorded information can be useful only if it is systematically organized and if mechanisms exist for locating in it items relevant to human needs. The main approaches for achieving such organization are reviewed in the following section, as are the tools used to retrieve desired information.

(Yoke-Lan Wicks/ Vladimir Slamecka)

ORGANIZATION AND RETRIEVAL OF INFORMATION

In any collection, physical objects are related by order. The ordering may be random or by some characteristic called a key. Such characteristics may be intrinsic properties of the objects (*e.g.*, size, weight, shape, or colour), or they may be assigned from some agreed-upon set, such as object class or date of purchase. The values of the key are arranged in a sorting sequence that is dependent on the type of key involved: alphanumeric key values are usually sorted in alphabetic sequence, while other types may be sorted on the basis of similarity in class, such as books on a particular subject or flora of the same genus.

In most cases, order is imposed on a set of information objects for two reasons: to create their inventory and to facilitate locating specific objects in the set. There also exist other, secondary objectives for selecting a particular ordering, as, for example, conservation of space or economy of effort in fetching objects. Unless the objects in a collection are replicated, any ordering scheme is one-dimensional and invariably unable to meet all the functions of ordering with equal effectiveness. The main approach for overcoming some of the limitations of one-dimensional ordering of recorded information relies on extended description of its content and, for analog-form information, of some features of the physical items. This approach employs various tools of content analysis that subsequently facilitate accessing and searching recorded information.

Content analysis of analog-form records. The collections of libraries and archives, the primary repositories of analog-form information, constitute one-dimensional ordering of physical materials in print (documents), in image form (maps and photographs), or in audio-video format (recordings and video tapes). To break away from the confines of one-dimensional ordering, librarianship has developed an extensive set of attributes in terms of which it describes each item in the collection. The rules for assigning these attributes are called cataloging rules. Descriptive cataloging is the extraction of bibliographic elements (author names, title, publisher, date of publication, etc.) from each item; the assignment of subject categories or headings to such items is termed subject cataloging.

Descriptive and subject cataloging

Information on the same subject is located together in large libraries so as to minimize the physical effort of accessing such items and to make browsing possible. Consequently, librarianship has developed complex systems of classification by subject. The Dewey Decimal Classification, Universal Decimal Classification, and Library of Congress Classification are three widely used schemes for assigning every individual item a single classification number (which determines the location of the item on the shelves) and one or more subject headings (under which the item will appear in the library's subject catalog). The traditional card catalog is an alphabetic ordering of the items in a collection usually by three keys: author name, title, and subject matter.

Conceptually, the library catalog is a table or matrix in which each row describes a discrete physical item and each column provides values of the assigned key. When such a catalog is represented digitally in a computer, any attribute can serve as the ordering key. By sorting the catalog on different keys, it is possible to produce a variety of indexes as well as subject bibliographies. More importantly, any of the attributes of a computerized catalog becomes a search key (access point) to the collection, surpassing the utility of the card catalog.

The most useful access key to analog-form items is subject. The extensive lists of subject headings of library classification schemes provide, however, only a gross access tool to the content of the items. A technique called index-

Indexing and abstracting

ing provides a refinement over library subject headings. It consists of extracting from the item or assigning to it subject and other "descriptors"—words or phrases denoting significant concepts (topics, names) that occur in or characterize the content of the record. Indexing frequently accompanies abstracting, a technique for condensing the full text of a document into a short summary that contains its main ideas (but invariably incurs an information loss and often introduces a bias). Computer-printed, indexed abstracting journals provide a means of keeping informed of primary information sources.

Content analysis of digital-form information. Digitally stored data may represent alphanumeric, image, or audio information, each requiring different techniques for analyzing content. The objectives of content analysis of alphanumeric information are twofold. At the simple level the aim is to describe the record (document) in terms of some of its properties or characteristics so that the record can be located or assigned to a category of similar records. At a more complex level the objective is to represent the meaning or portent of the document so that its content can be "understood" and possibly further manipulated by machine in a cognitive sense.

The primary method for describing alphanumeric information is indexing. Although a document may be described in various ways (*e.g.*, indirectly by the citations of references contained in it), indexing typically provides pointers to the subject of documents. Whether carried out manually by humans or automatically by computers, indexing uses two main approaches: the assignment of subject descriptors from an unlimited vocabulary (free indexing), or their assignment from a list of authorized descriptors (controlled indexing). A collection of authorized descriptors is called an authority list or, if it also displays various relationships among descriptors such as hierarchy or synonymy, a thesaurus. The result of the indexing process is a computer file known as an inverted index, which is an alphabetic listing of descriptors and the addresses of their occurrence in the document body.

Full-text indexing, the use of every character string (word of a natural language) in the text as an index term, is an extreme case of free-text indexing: each word in the document (except function words such as articles and prepositions) becomes an access point to it. Used earlier for the generation of concordances in literary analysis and other computer applications in the humanities, full-text indexing placed great demands on computer storage because the resulting index is at least as large as the body of the text. With decreasing cost of mass storage, automatic full-text indexing capability has been incorporated routinely into state-of-the-art information-management software.

Free, controlled, and full-text indexing affect not only the economics of information services but also to some extent the specificity and exhaustiveness of computerized information retrieval. This fact notwithstanding, information technology forces indexing toward complete automation and, in some applications, toward extinction. When computer hardware is very fast, as is the case with array processors, the digital information store may be searched serially in its entirety for each query without ever creating an index. Full-text searching methods for the new type of computer architecture called parallel processing may also dispense with the index. (Parallel processing, designed for faster and more efficient performance, involves the simultaneous execution of many operations by a large number of integrated circuits in which millions of logic, memory, and input/output circuits work together.) In contrast, information stored on slow-access devices such as the optical disc will continue to depend on the index as a means of retrieving portions of the data base relevant to the query. The index, however, has to be computer-generated. In either case, digital technology reveals the granularity of human information store to a finer degree than ever before.

The analysis of digitally recorded natural-language information from the semantic viewpoint is a matter of considerable complexity, and it lies at the foundation of such potential applications as automatic question answering from a data base or retrieval by means of unrestricted natural-language queries (see below). The general approach

has been that of computational linguistics: to derive representations of the syntactic and semantic relations among the linguistic elements of sentences and larger parts of the document. Syntactic relations are described by parsing (decomposing) the grammar of sentences (Figure 2). For semantic representation, three related formalisms dominate. In a so-called semantic network, conceptual entities such as objects, actions, or events are represented as a graph of linked nodes (Figure 3). "Frames" represent, in a similar graph network, physical or abstract attributes of objects and in a sense define the objects. In "scripts," events and actions rather than objects are defined in terms of their attributes.

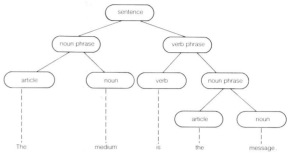

Figure 2: A parsing graph.

The content analysis of images is accomplished by two primary methods: image processing and pattern recognition. Image processing is a set of computational techniques for analyzing, enhancing, compressing, and reconstructing images. Pattern recognition is an information-reduction process: the assignment of visual or logical patterns to classes based on the features of these patterns and their relationships. The stages in pattern recognition involve measurement of the object to identify distinguishing attributes, extraction of features for the defining attributes, and assignment of the object to a class based on these features. Both image processing and pattern recognition have extensive applications in various areas, including astronomy, medicine, industrial robotics, and remote sensing by satellites.

C.S. Shapiro, "Natural Language Processing," from A. Ralston and E.D. Reilly, Jr. (eds.), *Encyclopedia of Computer Science and Engineering*, Van Nostrand Reinhold, 1983

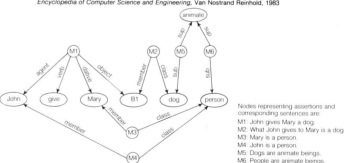

Nodes representing assertions and corresponding sentences are:
M1: John gives Mary a dog.
M2: What John gives to Mary is a dog.
M3: Mary is a person.
M4: John is a person.
M5: Dogs are animate beings.
M6: People are animate beings.

Figure 3: A semantic network representation.

The immediate objective of content analysis of digital speech is the conversion of discrete sound elements into their alphanumeric equivalents. Once so represented, speech can be subjected to the same techniques of content analysis as natural-language text—*i.e.*, indexing and linguistic analysis. Converting speech elements into their alphanumeric counterparts is an intriguing problem because the "shape" of speech sounds embodies a wide range of many acoustic characteristics and because the linguistic elements of speech are not clearly distinguishable from one another. The general technique used in speech processing is to classify the spectral representations of sound and to match the resulting digital spectrographs against prestored "templates" so as to identify the alphanumeric equivalent of the sound. (The obverse of this technique, the digital-to-analog conversion of such templates into sound, is a relatively straightforward approach to generating synthetic speech.)

Speech processing is complex as well as expensive in

terms of storage capacity and computational requirements. State-of-the-art speech recognition systems can identify limited vocabularies and parts of distinctly spoken speech and can be programmed to recognize tonal idiosyncracies of individual speakers. When more robust and reliable techniques become available and the process is made computationally tractable (as is expected with parallel computers), humans will be able to interact with computers via spoken commands and queries on a routine basis. In many situations this may make the keyboard obsolete as a data-entry device.

Storage structures for digital-form information. Digital information is stored in complex patterns that make it feasible to address and operate on even the smallest element of symbolic expression, as well as on larger strings such as words or sentences and on images and sound.

Data set

The sum of electronic representations, or data, in a modern information system is called its data set. Each data set typically consists of one or more data bases; the latter are cross-referenced sets of files, each comprising records consisting of fields. Data sets are organized in various types of data structures that facilitate the creation, accessing, and deletion of data and optimize the operating features of the storage media.

From the viewpoint of digital information storage, it is useful to distinguish between "structured" data, such as inventories of objects that can be represented by short symbol strings and numbers, and "unstructured" data, such as the natural-language text of documents or pictorial images. The principal objective of all storage structures is to facilitate the processing of data elements based on their relationships; the structures thus vary with the type of relationship they represent. The choice of a particular storage structure is governed by the relevance of the relationships it allows to be represented to the information-processing requirements of the task or system at hand.

In information systems whose store consists of unstructured data bases of natural-language records, the objective is to retrieve records (or portions thereof) based on the presence in the records of words or short phrases that constitute the query. Since there exists an index as a separate file that provides information about the locations of words and phrases in the data-base records, the relationships that are of interest (*e.g.,* word adjacency) can be calculated from the index. Consequently, the data-base text itself can be stored as a simple ordered sequential file of records. The majority of the computations use the index, and they access the text file only to pull out the records or those portions that satisfy the result of the computations. The sequential file structure is used with most commercial document-retrieval systems, including the ones containing digitized full text.

File structures

When relationships among data elements need to be represented as part of the records so as to make more efficient the desired operations on these records, two types of "chained" structures are commonly used: hierarchical and network. In the hierarchical file structure, records are arranged in a scheme resembling a family tree, with records related to one another from top to bottom (Figure 4A). In the network file structure, records are arranged in groupings known as sets; these can be connected in any number of ways (Figure 4B), giving rise to considerable flexibility. In both hierarchical and network structures, the relationships are shown by means of "pointers" (*i.e.,* identifiers such as addresses or keys) that become part of the records. Large numbers of pointers complicate the storage structure but facilitate navigating through it to locate related records and fields. The efficiency of information retrieval and processing in hierarchical and network storage structures depends on the skill of the system designer to identify a priori the multiplicity of relationships among records and fields so that they can be represented by pointers. When a query assumes relationships that are not represented explicitly, retrieval becomes considerably more difficult—a matter of writing special programs.

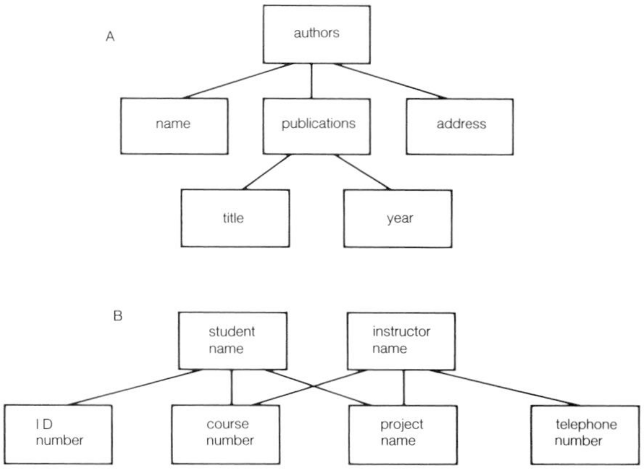

Another type of data-base storage structure, the relational structure, has become very popular since the 1970s. Its major advantage over the hierarchical and network structures is the ability to handle unanticipated data relationships without pointers. Relational storage structures are two-dimensional tables consisting of rows and columns, much like the conceptual library catalog mentioned above. The elegance of the relational model lies in its conceptual simplicity, availability of theoretical underpinnings (relational algebra), and the ability of its associated software to handle data relationships without the use of pointers. Like sequential files, relational data bases are supported by inverted indexes that improve their retrieval efficiency. The relational model is particularly suitable for data bases containing highly structured information.

The feasibility of storing large volumes of full text on an economic medium (the digital optical disc) has renewed interest in the study of storage structures that permit more powerful retrieval and processing techniques to operate on cognitive entities other than words, to facilitate more extensive semantic content and context analysis, and to organize text conceptually into logical units rather than those dictated by printing conventions.

Query languages. The uses of data bases are manifold. They provide a means of retrieving records or parts of records and performing various calculations before displaying the results. The interface by which such manipulations are specified is called the query language. Whereas early query languages were complex to a point that interacting with electronic data bases could only be done by specially trained individuals, recent interfaces allow "friendly" access to data-base information by casual users.

Types of query modes

The main types of popular query modes are the "menu," the "fill-in-the-blank" technique, and the structured query. Particularly suited for novices, the menu requires a person to choose from several alternatives displayed on the terminal video screen. The method is applicable for systems in which choices are arranged into hierarchies and is not suitable for key-word queries (though it may be combined with them). The fill-in-the-blank technique is one in which the user is prompted to enter key words as search statements. Employed in information-retrieval systems, it permits the user to expand or narrow down search statements by means of logical operators (conjunction and disjunction) and other tools. Effective use of these tools requires experience. To make the fill-in-the-blank technique more accessible to the casual user, it is often combined with friendly, menu-based interface software.

The structured query approach is effective with relational data bases. It has a formal, powerful syntax that is in fact a programming language, and it is able to accommodate logical operators. One implementation of this approach, the Structured Query Language (SQL), has the form

select [field Fa, Fb, . . . Fn] *from* [data base Da, Db, . . . Dn] *where* [field Fa = abc] *and* [field Fb = def]

Structured query languages support data-base searching as well as other operations by using commands such as "find," "delete," "print," "sum," and so forth. The sentencelike structure of an SQL query resembles natural language except that its syntax is limited and fixed. Instead of using an SQL statement, it is possible to represent queries

Figure 4: Examples of hierarchical (A) and network (B) file structures.

in tabular form. The technique, referred to as query-by-example (or QBE), displays an empty tabular form and expects the searcher to enter the search specifications into appropriate columns. The program then constructs an SQL-type query from the table and executes it.

The most flexible query language is of course natural language. The use of natural-language sentences in a constrained form to search data bases is allowed by some commercial data-base management software. These programs parse the syntax of the query; recognize its action words and their synonyms; identify the names of files, records, and fields; and perform the logical operations required. Experimental systems that accept such natural-language queries in spoken voice have been developed; however, the ability to employ unrestricted natural language to query unstructured information will require further advances in machine understanding of natural language, particularly in techniques of representing the semantic and pragmatic context of ideas. The prospect of an intelligent conversation between humans and a large store of digitally encoded knowledge is not imminent.

INFORMATION DISPLAY

For humans to perceive and understand information, it must be presented as print and image on paper; as print and image on film or on a video terminal; as sound via radio or telephony; as print, sound, and video in motion pictures, on television broadcasts, or at lectures and conferences; or in face-to-face encounters. Except for live encounters and audio information, such displays emanate increasingly from digitally stored data, with the output media being video, print, and sound.

Video. Possibly the most widely used video display device, at least in the industrialized world, is the television set. Designed primarily for video and sound, its image resolution is inadequate for alphanumeric data except in relatively small amounts. Use of the television set in text-oriented information systems has been limited to menu-oriented applications such as videotex, in which information is selected from hierarchically arranged menus (with the aid of a numeric keyboard attachment) and displayed in fixed frames. The television, computer, and communications technologies are, however, converging in a high-resolution digital television set capable of receiving alphanumeric, video, and audio signals.

Computer video terminals

The computer video terminal is today's ubiquitous interface that transforms computer-stored data into analog form for human viewing. The two basic apparatuses used are the cathode-ray tube (CRT) and the more recent flat-panel display. In CRT displays an electron gun emits beams of electrons on a phosphorus-coated surface; the beams are deflected, forming visible patterns representative of data. Flat-panel displays use one of four different media for visual representation of data: liquid crystal, light-emitting diodes, plasma panels, and electroluminescence. Advanced video display systems enable the user to scroll, page, zoom (change the scale of the details of the display image for enhancement), divide the screen into multiple colours and "windows" (viewing areas), and in some cases even activate commands by touching the screen instead of using the keyboard.

The information capacity of the terminal screen depends on its resolution, which ranges from low (character-addressable) to high (bit-addressable). High resolution is indispensable for the display of graphic and video data in state-of-the-art workstations, such as those used in engineering or information systems design.

Print. Modern society continues to be dominated by printed information. The convenience and portability of print on paper make it difficult to imagine the paperless world that some have predicted. The generation of paper print has changed considerably, however. Although manual typesetting is still practiced for artwork, in special situations, and in some developing countries, electronic means of composing pages for subsequent reproduction by photoduplication and other methods has become commonplace.

Since the 1960s, volume publishing has become an automated process using large computers and high-speed printers to transfer digitally stored data on paper. The appearance of microcomputer-based publishing systems has proved to be another significant advance. Economical enough to allow even small organizations to become in-house publishers, these so-called desktop publishing systems are able to format text and graphics interactively on a high-resolution video screen with the aid of page-description command languages. Once a page has been formatted, the entire image is transferred to an electronic printing or photocomposition device.

Microcomputer-based publishing systems

Printers. Computer printers are commonly divided into two general classes according to the way they produce images on paper: impact and nonimpact. In the first type, images are formed by the print mechanism making contact with the paper through an ink-coated ribbon. The mechanism consists either of print hammers shaped like characters or of a print head containing a row of pins that produce a pattern of dots in the form of characters or other images.

Most nonimpact printers form images from a matrix of dots, but they employ different techniques for transferring images to paper. One major type, the laser printer, uses a beam of laser light and a system of optical components to etch images on a photoconductor drum from which they are carried via electrostatic photocopying to paper. Light-emitting diode (LED) printers resemble laser printers in operation but direct light from energized diodes rather than a laser onto a photoconductive surface. Ion-deposition printers make use of technology similar to that of photocopiers for producing electrostatic images. Another type of nonimpact printer, the ink-jet printer, sprays electrically charged drops of ink onto the print surface. An entirely different technique is used by thermal printers, which apply heat to a ribbon coated with a wax-based pigment in order to transfer the pigment to the printer paper.

Microfilm and microfiche. Alphanumeric and image information can be transferred from digital computer storage directly to film by the COM (Computer-Output-on-Microfilm) process. Reel microfilm, the first microform introduced before World War II, and microfiche, a flat sheet of film containing multiple microimages reduced from the original by a factor of 12 to 48, have become popular methods of document storage and reproduction. Ultrafilm, which reduces the image 200 times or more, is the highest density medium for analog-form information storage. Though portable and durable, microforms require optical reading equipment; the latter ranges from inexpensive personal viewers to computer-assisted microfilm retrieval systems capable of storing millions of pages.

Voice. In synthetic speech generation, digitally prestored sound elements are converted to analog sound signals and combined to form words and sentences. Digital-to-analog converters are available as inexpensive boards for microcomputers or as software for larger machines. Human speech is the most natural form of communication, and so applications of this technology are appearing in situations where there are numerous requests for specific information (*e.g.,* time, travel, and entertainment), where there is a need for repetitive instruction, in electronic voice mail (the counterpart of electronic text mail), and in toys.

Speech synthesis

DISSEMINATION OF INFORMATION

The process of recording information by handwriting was obviously laborious and required the dedication of the likes of Egyptian scribes or monks in monasteries around the world. It was only after mechanical means of reproducing writing were invented that information records could be duplicated more efficiently and economically.

The first practical method of reproducing writing mechanically was block printing; it was developed in China during the T'ang dynasty (618–907). Ideographic text and illustrations were engraved in wooden blocks, inked, and copied on paper. Used to produce books as well as cards, charms, and calendars, block printing spread to Korea and Japan but apparently not to the Islāmic or European Christian civilizations. European woodcuts and metal engravings date only to the 14th century.

Printing from movable type was also invented in China (in the mid-11th century AD). There and in the book-making industry of Korea, where the method was applied more extensively during the 15th century, the ideographic type was made initially of baked clay and wood and later of metal. The large number of typefaces required for pictographic text composition continued to handicap printing in the Far East until the present time.

The invention of character-oriented printing from movable type (1440–50) is attributed to the German printer Johannes Gutenberg. Within 30 years of his invention, the movable-type printing press was in use throughout Europe. Character-type pieces were metallic and apparently cast from metallic molds; paper and vellum (calfskin parchment) were used to carry the impressions. Gutenberg's technique of assembling individual letters by hand was employed until 1886 when the German-born American printer Ottmar Mergenthaler developed the Linotype, a keyboard-driven device that cast lines of type automatically. Typesetting speed was further enhanced by the Monotype technique, in which a perforated paper ribbon, punched from a keyboard, was used to operate a typecasting machine. Mechanical methods of typesetting prevailed until the 1960s. Since that time they have been largely supplanted by the electronic and optical printing techniques described in the previous section.

Repro-
duction of
graphics Unlike the use of movable type for printing text, early graphics were reproduced from wood relief engravings in which the nonprinting portions of the image were cut away. Musical scores, on the other hand, were reproduced from etched stone plates. At the end of the 18th century the German printer Aloys Senefelder developed lithography, a planographic technique of transferring images from a specially prepared surface of stone. In offset lithography the image is transferred from zinc or aluminum plates instead of stone, and in photoengraving such plates are superimposed with film and then etched.

The first successful photographic process, the daguerreotype, was developed during the 1830s. The invention of photography, aside from providing a new medium for capturing still images and later video in analog form, was significant for two other reasons. First, recorded information (textual and graphic) could be easily reproduced from film and, second, the image could be enlarged or reduced. Document reproduction from film to film has been relatively unimportant because both printing and photocopying (see below) are cheaper. The ability to reduce images, however, has led to the development of the microform, the most economical method of disseminating analog-form information (see above).

Another technique of considerable commercial importance for the duplication of paper-based information is photocopying, or dry photography. Printing is most economical when large numbers of copies are required, but photocopying provides a fast and efficient means of duplicating records in small quantities for personal or local use. Of the several technologies that are in use, the most popular process, xerography, is based on electrostatics.

Methods and media of information dissemination continue to evolve. Today most forms of primary and secondary literature, from newspapers to scientific abstracting journals, are printed electronically. High-speed digital satellite communications facilitate electronic printing at remote sites; for example, the world's major newspapers transmit electronic page copies to different geographic locations for local printing and distribution. In business communications, documents and correspondence are generated via text-processing workstations and delivered electronically on an increasingly wider scale. Photocopying, facsimile transmission, and high-speed teleprinting are expected to be handled by a single device, a "universal" printer, in the near future.

Distri-
bution
of digital
informa-
tion by
electronic
publishing While the volume of information issued in the form of printed matter continues unabated, the electronic publishing industry has begun to disseminate information in digital form. The development of the microcomputer has provided the main impetus. Not only is such a system almost as versatile and efficient as larger computers in information retrieval, but it carries out this operation relatively economically. Certain types of information media lend themselves particularly well to distribution in digital form. These include catalogs, handbooks, indexes, data bases, and reference materials designed to be consulted rather than read in toto. Computer software also is well suited for distribution via electronic publishing.

The digital optical disc (see above) has given electronic publishing its strongest boost to date for issuing large bodies of archival information: legislation, court and hospital records, patents, full-text data bases of periodicals, and libraries of computer software. The optical disc provides the mass production technology for publication in machine-readable form. Because of it, the prospect of having a vast electronic library in every school and at many professional workstations may very well be realized by the end of the 20th century.

The marriage of computers and digital telecommunications is also changing the modes of informal communication in society. Throughout history, these modes have consisted of various types of face-to-face meetings (conferences, seminars, workshops, exhibitions, and the like) and personal communication by telephone and mail. While direct encounters continue, they are supplemented and in some instances replaced by increasingly popular means of informal communication: electronic mail, a method of forwarding and storing messages between computer users; electronic bulletin, a technique of broadcasting newsworthy textual messages via computer to persons having similar interests; and electronic teleconferencing, a method of linking remote users in real time by either voice or voice-and-image communications. These technologies for informal communication are forging together virtual societal networks—communities of geographically dispersed individuals who have common professional or social interests. Modes of
informal
communi-
cation

Information systems

The primary vehicles for the purposeful, orchestrated processing of information are information systems, constructs that collect, organize, store, process, and display information in all its forms (raw data, interpreted data, knowledge, and expertise) and formats (text, video, and voice). In principle, any record-keeping system—e.g., an address book or a train schedule—may be regarded as an information system. What sets modern information systems apart is their electronic dimension, which permits extremely fast, automated manipulation of digitally stored data and their transformation from and to analog representation.

The evolution of modern information systems may be characterized by six stages. The first three—introduction, expansion, and control of computerized functions—reflect a technological emphasis. The last three stages—functional integration, allocation of responsibility over information, and system maturity—manifest a user-oriented focus. In industrialized countries most major information systems are presently in the fourth stage, integrating information horizontally into data bases. Some are entering the fifth stage in which organizations begin to treat information as a corporate resource and designate units and individuals as responsible data owners. The mature stage, characterized by the development of organizational planning models based on the information resource, may be attained by some organization by the end of the present century. Developing countries, by contrast, appear to be in transition from the second to the third stage. Evolution
of elec-
tronic in-
formation
systems

IMPACT OF INFORMATION TECHNOLOGY

Electronic information systems are a phenomenon of the second half of the 20th century. Their evolution is closely tied with advances in the performance of four information technologies—namely, those involving digital processors, digital storage, communications, and software.

Since the invention of semiconductor devices known as transistors, improvement in the cost performance of digital processors has ranged from 15 to 25 percent annually, largely as a result of progress in integrated-circuit technology and its effects on the speed and reliability of digital devices. At one end, these advances produced the microcomputer; at the other end, they are leading to novel computer architectures that will enable machines to process data in a parallel fashion (see COMPUTERS: *Modern digital systems).* The information-processing efficiencies so attained are expected to be higher than in today's largest and fastest computers.

Advances in digital storage technology came in three steps: the serial magnetic tape, the direct-access magnetic disk, and the digital optical disc (see above). In terms of both affordability and versatility, the optical disc surpasses the microform as the most economical analog-form storage medium, and it permits the consolidation of the digital representations of text, image, video, and sound on a single medium.

Advances in computer software and their ramifications

The widespread deployment of digital technology also is a result of parallel advances in software, which allows this technology to be used by persons other than computer experts. Early programming languages, called assembly and procedure-oriented languages, required programmers to specify in minute detail how data would be processed. So-called higher level programming languages subsequently developed have permitted programmers to stipulate only the tasks to be done without concern over how the programs are to be executed. Competent usage of these and more recent programming languages is still limited to practitioners trained in the art of programming. What has opened computer use to the general public is its interactive applications in the office and other professional environments. These applications have been made possible by the development of easy-to-use software products for the creation, maintenance, manipulation, and querying of files and records. The data-base has become a central organizing framework for information systems, taking advantage of the concept of data independence that allows data sharing among diverse applications. Many of today's information systems are tantamount to data-base systems—organized collections of data maintained and used with the aid of data-base management system (DBMS) software.

Since the late 1970s microcomputers and "friendly" application software have placed the power of digital technology at the disposal of millions. One consequence of this development was not fully anticipated: that by coupling the computer to the telephone communications network, the video terminal would become, in the short span of a decade, a window and a link to the vast resources of the digital information world. To facilitate the linkage, the telephone network for voice communications has been adapted to carry digital information, first as modulated analog signals over a twisted-wire carrier or coaxial cable and then as digital signals over high-speed microwave and satellite transmission channels. Two key innovations, the

Impact of fibre optics and laser technology

optical fibre (threadlike fibre of either glass or plastic) and the laser, used together can transmit significantly more information over greater distances than can conventional metal wire. For example, a pulse of laser light of 2,000,-000,000 bits per second would transmit a 30-volume encyclopaedia across many kilometres in slightly more than one second. The optical fibre is replacing the coaxial cable in the integrated services digital network (ISDN), which is capable of carrying digital information in the form of voice, data, and video simultaneously. Common communication protocols (rules and procedures) permit computers of different manufacturers and sizes to communicate with each other in networks. Moreover, the networks themselves are interconnected by hardware devices and software called gateways that convert one protocol format to another.

Such technological advances are shaping the nature of modern information systems and presage the trends of their evolution. State-of-the-art information systems process and retrieve information ever faster; they are more robust in terms of the volume of data that they can process and in terms of reliability; and their performance is more cost-effective. Even more significant effects of technological developments lie along other dimensions, however.

First, the community of users of information systems is changing dramatically, from computer programmers and professional information workers to "end users" who interact with these systems directly and personally. This change, in turn, has had a major impact on the design of information systems.

Second, the transportability of electronic information, coupled with the development of high-capacity, high-speed telecommunications facilities that permit the transmission of large volumes of digital information (such as that generated in image-processing applications), is at the base of the present trend toward teleprocessing information systems in which the processors and the data repositories are geographically dispersed. This change is conducive to data sharing, whether within a single building (as local-area networks) or more globally (as wide-area networks). The central component of information systems, the data base, may be "distributed" over a number of processors in different geographic locations, yet queries can be processed simultaneously against the composite data base. Users of teleprocessing information systems interact and collaborate within as well as across organizational and political boundaries.

Use of teleprocessing information systems

Third, the functions of information systems are constantly expanding as all information formats converted to digital form are manipulable by increasingly sophisticated techniques and programs. Evolving techniques of natural-language processing and understanding, as well as of knowledge representation and manipulation, are joining the repertoire of more traditional methods of content analysis and manipulation. Jointly these developments contribute to the gradual but continuing transformation from data-processing to cognition-aiding systems.

ANALYSIS AND DESIGN OF INFORMATION SYSTEMS

The building of information systems falls within the domain of engineering. As is true with other engineering disciplines, the nature and tools of information systems engineering are evolving due to both technological developments and better perceptions of societal needs for information services. Early information systems were designed to be operated by information professionals, and they frequently did not attain their stated social purpose. Modern information systems are increasingly used by persons who have little or no previous hands-on experience with information technology but who possess a much better perception about what this technology should accomplish in their professional and personal environments. A correct understanding of the requirements, preferences, and "information styles" of these end users is crucial to the design and success of today's information systems.

Methodology of constructing information systems

The methodology involved in building an information system consists of a set of iterative activities that are cumulatively referred to as the system's life cycle (Figure 5). The principal objective of the systems analysis phase is the specification of what the system is to do. In the

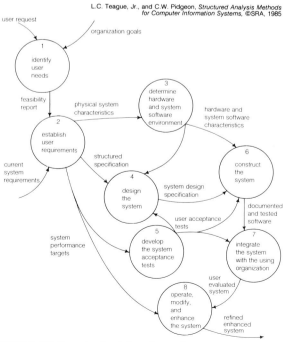

L.C. Teague, Jr., and C.W. Pidgeon, *Structured Analysis Methods for Computer Information Systems,* ©SRA, 1985

Figure 5: The life cycle of an information system.

systems design phase such specifications are converted to a hierarchy of increasingly detailed charts that define the data required and decompose the processes to be carried out on data to a level at which they can be expressed as instructions of a computer program. The systems development phase consists of writing and testing computer software and of developing data input and output forms and conventions. Systems implementation is the installation of a physical system and the activities it entails, such as the training of operators and users. Systems maintenance refers to the further evolution of the functions and structure of a system that results from changing requirements and technologies, experience with the system's use, and fine-tuning of its performance.

Many information systems are implemented with generic, "off-the-shelf" software rather than with custom-built programs; versatile data-base management software and its non-procedural programming languages fit the needs of small and large systems alike. The development of large systems that cannot use off-the-shelf software is an expensive, time-consuming, and complex undertaking. Some of the tools of computer-aided software engineering available to the systems analyst and designer verify the logic of systems design, automatically generate a program code from low-level specifications, and automatically produce software and system specifications. The eventual goal of information systems engineering is to develop software "factories" that use natural language and artificial intelligence techniques as part of an integrated set of tools to support the analysis and design of large information systems.

CATEGORIES OF INFORMATION SYSTEMS

A taxonomy of information systems is not easily developed because of their diversity and continuing evolution in structure and function. Earlier distinctions—manual versus automated, interactive versus off-line, real-time versus batch-processing—are no longer very useful. A more frequently made distinction is in terms of application: use in business offices, factories, hospitals, and so on. In the functional approach taken in this article, information systems may be divided into two categories: organizational systems and public information utilities. Information systems in formal organizations may be further distinguished according to their main purpose: support of managerial and administrative functions or support of operations and services. The former serve internal functions of the organizations, while the latter support the purposes for which these organizations exist.

Management-oriented information systems. The most important functions that top executives perform are setting policies, planning, and preparing budgets. At the strategic level, these decision-making functions are supported by executive information systems. The objective of these systems is to gather, analyze, and integrate internal (corporate) and external (public) data into dynamic profiles of key corporate indicators. Depending on the nature of the organization's business, such indicators may relate to the status of high-priority programs, health of the economy, inventory and cash levels, performance of financial markets, relevant efforts of competitors, utilization of manpower, legislative events, and so forth. The indicators are displayed as text, tables, graphics, or time series, and optional access is provided to more detailed data. The data emanate not only from within the organization's production and administrative departments but also from external information sources, such as public data bases. The structure of an executive information system contains a large mainframe computer that houses the data base and interfaces with facilities for importing internal data, accessing external data sources, and performing data analyses and modeling (Figure 6). The executive display device is a sophisticated high-resolution video terminal with which the manager interfaces by means of menus, a pointing device called a "mouse," and the keyboard.

In military organizations, the approximate equivalent of executive information systems is command-and-control systems. Their purpose is to maintain control over some domain and, if needed, initiate corrective action. Their

Executive systems

Command-and-control systems

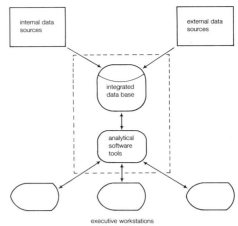

Figure 6: Structure of a typical executive information system.

key characteristic is the real-time nature of the monitoring and decision-making functions. A command-and-control system typically assumes that the environment exercises pressure on the domain of interest (say, a naval force); the system then monitors the environment (collects intelligence data), analyzes the data, compares it with the desired state of the domain, and suggests actions to be taken. Systems of this kind are used at both strategic and tactical levels.

Both executive and military command-and-control systems make use of computational aids for data classification, modeling, and simulation. These capabilities are characteristic of a decision-support system (DSS), a composite of computer techniques for supporting executive decision making in relatively unstructured problem situations. Decision-support software falls into one of two categories: (1) decision-aid programs, in which the decision maker assigns weighted values to every factor in the decision; and (2) decision-modeling programs, in which the user explores different strategies to arrive at the desired outcome.

Decision-support systems

Administration-oriented information systems. Administrative functions in formal organizations have as their objective the husbanding and optimization of corporate resources—namely, employees and their activities, inventories of materials and equipment, facilities, and finances. Administrative information systems support this objective. Commonly called management information systems (MIS), they focus primarily on resource administration and provide top management with reports of aggregate data. Executive information systems may be viewed as an evolution of administrative information systems in the direction of strategic tracking, modeling, and decision making.

Typically, administrative information systems consist of a number of modules, each supporting a particular function (Figure 7). The modules share a common data base whose contents may, however, be distributed over a number of machines and locations. Financial information systems have evolved from the initial applications of punched cards before World War II to integrated accounting and finance systems that cover general accounting, accounts receivable and payable, payroll, purchasing, inventory control, and financial statements such as balance sheets. Functionally close to payroll systems are personnel information systems, which support the administration of the organization's human resources. Job and salary histories, inventory of skills, performance reviews, and other types of personnel data are combined in the data base to assist personnel administration, explore potential effects of reorganization or new salary scales (or changes in benefits), and match job requirements with skills. Project management information systems concentrate on resource allocation and task completion of organized activities; they usually incorporate such scheduling methods as critical path method (CPM) or program evaluation and review technique (PERT).

Since the advent of microcomputers, information pro-

Financial and personnel information systems

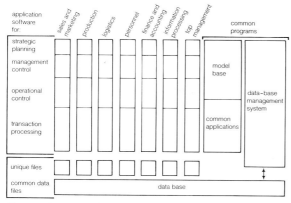

application software for:
sales and marketing / production / logistics / personnel / finance and accounting / information processing / top management

strategic planning

management control

operational control

transaction processing

common programs

model base

common applications

data-base management system

unique files

common data files

data base

Figure 7: Structure of an administrative information system.
G.B. Davis and M.H. Olson, *Management Information Systems*, McGraw-Hill, 1985

cessing in organizations has become heavily supported by office automation tools. These involve six basic applications: text processing, data base, spreadsheet, graphics, communications, and networking. Administrative systems in smaller organizations are usually built as extensions of office automation tools; in large organizations these tools form an interface to custom software. The current trend in office automation is toward integrating the first five applications into a software utility, either delivered to each microprocessor workstation from a "server" on the corporate computer network or integrated into other applications software.

Administrative information systems abound in organizations in both the private and public sectors throughout the industrialized world. In the retail industry, point-of-sale terminals are linked into distributed administrative information systems that contain financial and inventory modules at the department, store, geographic area, and corporate chain levels, with modeling facilities that help to determine marketing strategies and optimize profits. Administrative information systems are indispensable to government; the agencies of virtually all U.S. municipalities with over 10,000 inhabitants use such systems. The systems are generally centred around a generic data-base management system and are increasingly supported by software modules and programs that permit data modeling—*i.e.*, they acquire management orientation.

Service-oriented information systems. Such information systems provide support for the operations or services that organizations perform for society. The systems are vertically oriented to specific sectors and industries (*e.g.*, manufacturing, financial services, publishing, education, health, and entertainment). Rather than addressing management and administrative functions, they support activities and processes that are the reason for an organization's existence—in most cases, some kind of manufacturing activity or the rendering of services. Systems of this kind vary greatly, but they tend to fall into three main types: manufacturing, transaction, and expert systems.

The conceptual goal of modern factories is computer-integrated manufacturing (CIM). The phrase denotes data-driven automation that affects all components of the manufacturing enterprise: design and development engineering, manufacturing, marketing and sales, and field support and service. The development of the CIM concept has been gradual, from initial factory automation efforts aimed at saving labour costs to eventually addressing the gamut of activities of manufacturing organizations. The major components of the CIM concept are information systems for engineering design, for automation of production, and for the planning and control of these and other operations. Computer-aided design (CAD) systems were first applied in the electronics industry. Today they feature three-dimensional modeling techniques for drafting and manipulating solid objects on the screen and for deriving specifications for programs to drive numerical-control machines. Once a product is designed, its production process can be outlined using computer-aided process planning (CAPP) systems that help to select sequences

Computer-integrated manufacturing

of operations and machining conditions. Models of the manufacturing system can be simulated by computers before they are built. The basic manufacturing functions—machining, forming, joining, assembly, and inspection—are supported by computer-aided manufacturing (CAM) systems and automated materials-handling systems. Inventory control systems seek to maintain an optimal stock of parts and materials by tracking inventory movement, forecasting requirements, and initiating procurement orders.

The technological sophistication of manufacturing information systems is impressive, and it increasingly includes applications of artificial intelligence: robotics, computer vision, and expert systems (see COMPUTERS: *Artificial intelligence*). The core of the CIM concept is an integrated data base that supports the manufacturing enterprise and is linked with other administrative data bases.

In nonmanufacturing service organizations the prevalent type of information system supports transaction processing. Transactions are sets of discrete inputs, submitted by users at unpredictable intervals, which call for database searching, analysis, and modification. The processor evaluates the request and executes it immediately. Portions of the processing function may be carried out at the intelligent terminal that originated the request so as to distribute the computational load. Response time is an important characteristic of this type of real-time teleprocessing system. Large transaction-processing systems often incorporate private telecommunications networks.

Teleprocessing transaction systems constitute the foundation of service industries such as banking, insurance, securities, transportation, and libraries. They are replacing the trading floor of the world's major stock exchanges, linking the latter via on-line telecommunications into a global financial market. Again, the core of a transaction system is its integrated data base. The focus of the system is the recipient of services rather than the system operator. This orientation represents a departure from earlier transaction systems. For example, data bases in the insurance industry were structured around insurance policy types (so that a client with three different types of policy would be represented in the data base three times); the current trend is to structure the data base around a single client record. Similar reorientation is taking place in systems used in banking, securities, and social services.

A relatively new category of service-oriented information systems is the expert system, so called because its data base stores a description of decision-making skills of human experts in some domain of performance, such as medical image interpretation, taxation, brickwork design, configuration of computer system hardware, troubleshooting malfunctioning equipment, or beer brewing. The motivation for constructing expert systems is the desire to replicate the scarce, unstructured, poorly documented empirical knowledge of a few so that it can be readily used by others.

Expert systems have three components: (1) a software interface through which the user formulates queries by which the expert system solicits further information from the user and by which it explains to the user the reasoning process employed to arrive at an answer; (2) a data base (called the knowledge base) consisting of axioms (facts) and rules for making inferences from these facts; and (3) a computer program (dubbed the inference engine) that executes the inference-making process.

The knowledge base is a linked structure of rules that the human expert applies, often intuitively, in problem solving. The process of acquiring such knowledge typically has three phases: a functional analysis of the environment, users, and tasks performed by the expert; identification of concepts of the domain of expertise and their classification according to various relationships; and an interview, either by human or automated techniques, of the expert (or experts) in action. The results of these steps are translated into so-called production rules (of the form "IF condition *x* exists, THEN action *y* follows") and stored in the knowledge base. Chains of production rules form the basis for the automated deductive capabilities of expert systems and for their ability to explain their actions to users.

Expert systems are a commercial variety of a class of computer programs called knowledge-based systems, whose

Teleprocessing transaction systems

Components of expert systems

development forms one major goal of research in artificial intelligence (Figure 8). Knowledge in expert systems is highly unstructured (*i.e.*, the problem-solving process of the domain is not manifest), and it is stated explicitly in relationships or deductively inferred from the chaining of propositions. Since every condition that may be encountered must be described by a rule, expert systems cannot handle unanticipated events, but they can evolve with usage. Current expert systems are incapable of inductive inference; that is to say, they cannot generalize.

P. Harmon and D. King, *Expert Systems*, John Wiley and Sons, 1985

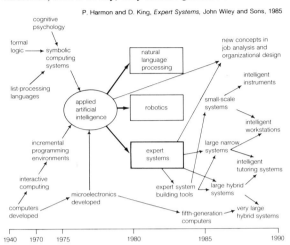

Figure 8: The domain and tools of artificial intelligence.

Public information utilities. Aside from the proliferation of organizational information systems, new types of teleprocessing systems became available for use by the public during the 1970s. With the proliferation of electronic data bases, the then new industry of "data-base vendors" began to make these resources available via on-line data-base search systems. Today, this industry operates for public access and uses hundreds of document data bases, some of them in full text; corporate and industry data and news; stock quotations; diverse statistics and time series; and catalogs of products and services.

On-line data-base search systems

In a growing number of countries, particularly in developing countries where the concepts of information resources and their management and use are relatively new, on-line data-base services are being coordinated in the form of planned "national" information systems, often in conjunction with public data networks and international telecommunications facilities. These efforts are accompanied by attempts to formulate national information policies for management and better exploitation of endogenous information resources and technologies.

In the United States, on-line data-base vendors constitute a kind of evolving electronic supermarket, a growing network of public information utilities. In addition to data bases, these services retail computer programs, acting as a giant multipurpose computational facility; software, ranging from products for business and scientific applications to computer games, may either be used on-line or be downloaded from the vendor (in the case of the latter, both programs and data—binary core images—are transferred from the vendor's computer to that of the user for execution). Recent services of public information utilities include transaction-processing systems: brokerage services to place on-line stock, bond, and options orders; home banking to pay bills and transfer funds; travel planning and reservations; and on-line catalog shopping. Some of these services combine on-line information retrieval (from, say, merchandise catalogs) and transaction processing (placing orders). Many include such functions as electronic mail and teleconferencing.

IMPACT OF COMPUTER-BASED INFORMATION SYSTEMS ON SOCIETY

Preoccupation with information and knowledge as an individual, organizational, and societal resource is stronger today than at any other time in history. The volume of

books printed in 16th-century Europe is estimated to have doubled approximately every seven years. Interestingly, the same growth rate has been calculated for global scientific and technical literature in the 20th century and for business documents in the United States in the 1980s. If these estimates are reasonably correct, the growth of recorded information is a historical phenomenon, not peculiar to modern times. The present, however, has several new dimensions relative to the information resource: modern information systems collect and generate information automatically; they provide rapid, high-resolution access to the corpora of information; and they manipulate information with previously unattainable versatility and efficiency.

The proliferation of automatic data-logging devices in scientific laboratories, hospitals, transportation, and many other areas has created a huge body of primary data for subsequent analysis. Machines even generate new information: original musical scores are now produced by computers, as are graphics and video materials. Electronic professional workstations can be programmed to carry out any of a variety of functions. Some of those that handle word processing not only automatically look for spelling and punctuation errors but check grammar, diction, and style as well; they are able to suggest alternative word usage and rephrase sentences to improve their readability. Machines produce modified versions of recorded information and translate documents into other languages.

Modern information systems also bring new efficiency to the organization, retrieval, and dissemination of recorded information. Since the commercial development of digital computers in the late 1950s, the control of and access to the world's printed information have been truly revolutionized; electronic access techniques reveal the granularity of humankind's information store in hitherto unattainable detail. A similar historic event is in the offing with respect to information dissemination. The invention of printing from movable type made documents affordable to virtually all levels of society and thereby decentralized the possession of documents by individuals. In like manner, modern information technology is beginning to decentralize for personal possession collections equivalent to the holdings of entire libraries and archives.

Possibly the most significant new dimension of modern information systems lies in their ability to manipulate information automatically. This capability is the result of representing symbolic information in digital form. Computer-based information systems are able to perform calculations, analyses, classifications, and correlations at levels of complexity and efficiency far exceeding human capabilities. They can simulate the performance of logical and mathematical models of physical processes and situations under diverse conditions. Information systems also have begun to mimic human cognitive processes: deductive inference in expert systems, contextual analysis in natural-language processing, and analogical and intuitive reasoning in information retrieval. Powerful information-transforming technologies now under development—data/text to graphics, speech to printed text, one natural language to another—will broaden the availability of information and enhance human problem-solving capabilities in ways not yet foreseen.

Automatic information manipulation

Whether in manufacturing or in management and administration, information systems applications are motivated by a desire to augment the mental information-processing functions of humans or to find adequate substitutes for them. Their effects have already been felt prominently in three domains: the economy, the governance of society, and the milieu of individual existence.

Effects on the economy. Information systems are a major tool for improving the cost-effectiveness of societal investments. In the realm of the economy, they may be expected to lead to higher productivity, particularly in the industrial and service sectors—in the former through automation of manufacturing and related processes, in the latter through computer-aided decision making, problem solving, administration, and support of clerical functions. Awareness that possession of information is tantamount to a competitive edge is stimulating intensified efforts at gathering technical and economic intelligence at the corporate and national levels. Similarly, concern is mounting over the safeguarding and husbanding of proprietary and strategic information within the confines of organizations as well as within national borders.

Changes in the distribution of labour

The growing number of information-processing applications is altering the distribution of labour in national economies. The deployment of information systems has resulted in the dislocation of labour, but it has not as yet had an appreciable long-term effect on unemployment because the implementation of such systems tends to engender a concomitant growth of other occupations, notably in the information service sector itself. Productivity increases induced by automation (particularly robotics) in industrially advanced countries, however, threaten to further lower the competitive potential of the labour-intensive economies of Third World nations, at least in the short run. It should be noted that most studies in this area have been controversial and that their findings remain inconclusive.

Effects on governance and management. That knowledge is power was understood by heads of state and military leaders long before the English essayist and statesman Francis Bacon (1561–1626) enunciated this maxim. In modern times the degrees of governmental control of information media serve as a testament to the power of information as well as a barometer of democracy.

Regardless of a country's political system, formal organizations tend to be better equipped than individuals to take advantage of information systems: their record-keeping practices are more mature and efficient; they have better facilities and skill to access and interpret information; and they possess larger financial resources to avail themselves of the powerful analytical tools that information systems provide. On the one hand, information systems harbour a potential for higher-quality governance and management but also entail possibilities for gross errors or for being misused. On the other, public information and communication utilities help to forge informal societal networks that counterbalance the power of formal organizations and increasingly divert their style of management in the direction of consultation with the well-informed.

An environment that encourages the use of information technology and systems fosters what might be termed high information maturity on the part of the populace, a prerequisite to participatory governance. Attempts to control information technology and resources may indicate budgetary exigencies but often signify a preference for autocratic forms of management.

Effects on the individual. Perhaps the most overt impact of modern information systems concerns the individual's standard and style of living. Information systems affect the scope and quality of health care, make social services more equitable, enhance personal comfort, provide a greater measure of safety and mobility, and extend the variety of leisure forms at one's disposal. More subtly but equally as important, they also affect the content and style of an individual's work and in so doing perturb the social and legal practices and conventions to which he is accustomed. At the same time, new kinds of information products and media necessitate a redefinition of the legal conventions regulating the ownership of products of the human intellect. Moreover, massive data-collecting systems bring into sharp focus the elusive borderline between the common good and personal privacy. Both the public and private sectors have recognized the need to safeguard stored data against accidental or illegal access. Unauthorized disclosure or misuse, including modification, of information of a confidential or personal nature (*e.g.,* data from income tax returns or family medical records) may result in serious damage or embarrassment at the least. In the United States, Canada, and many other countries, statutes have been enacted to impose legal requirements on government agencies to ensure the confidentiality of records in their possession. Other measures have been taken to promote data integrity and security, as, for example, the implementation of the Data Encryption Standard (DES), a cipher used in unclassified U.S. government applications for the protection of binary-coded data during transmission and storage in computer-based systems.

Concern over privacy and security

A more fundamental issue of paramount long-term significance for society has to do with the quality of the individual's spiritual existence in an increasingly knowledge-intensive environment. In such an environment, knowledge is the principal and perhaps most valuable currency. The growing volume and the rate of obsolescence of knowledge compel the individual to live in continuous presence of, and frequent interaction with, information resources and systems. Effective use of these resources and systems may be a modern definition of literacy, while the absence of such a skill may very well result in intellectual and possibly economic poverty. It has sometimes been suggested that automated machines, particularly "intelligent" systems, might eventually subjugate humankind. Yet, the real danger is not that such systems will take over but rather that humans, unwilling or incapable or not permitted to use them, may be relegated to an existence that falls short of the human potential.

Information science

The growing interest in information processing and the systems involved has given rise to an interdisciplinary field of study known as information science. This is an extremely broad field that draws on such disciplines as computer science, library science, communications, linguistics, and psychology.

THE EMERGENCE OF INFORMATION SCIENCE

The development of information science in the United States can be traced to events in the 1950s. One of these was the founding of the Center for Documentation and Communication as an adjunct to the library school at Western Reserve (now Case Western Reserve) University in Cleveland. The new centre led the way in the study of bibliographic information systems, particularly the computer-based variety. Efforts at the centre to define the territory of the new discipline through workshops and academic conferences led to the formation of several informal information study centres at other universities, including the University of California at Los Angeles (UCLA); American University, Washington, D.C.; University of Washington; and Georgia Institute of Technology.

The development of a discipline specializing in the study of information and information systems was given a major boost in 1958, when the U.S. National Defense Education Act directed the National Science Foundation to establish a service to "(1) provide . . . indexing, abstracting, translating, and other services leading to a more effective dissemination of scientific information, . . . and (2) undertake programs to develop new or improved methods, including mechanized systems, for making scientific information available." While the resulting Science Information Service focused on the handling of scientific and engineering bibliographies and texts, other areas received attention, including the study of communication processes in science and industry and the development of more efficient systems for organizing and storing scientific information.

The discipline of information science was formalized as a result of two conferences held at the Georgia Institute of Technology in 1961 and 1962. For the first time the interdisciplinary nature of the field was outlined, guidelines for research and study were established, and goals for a formal curriculum were defined. The 1961 conference offered the first comprehensive definition of information science as "the science that investigates the properties and behavior of information, the forces governing the flow of information, and the means of processing information for optimum accessibility and usability. The processes include the origination, dissemination, collection, organization, storage, retrieval, interpretation, and use of information. The field is derived from, and related to, mathematics, logic, linguistics, psychology, computer technology, operations research, the graphic arts, communications, library science, management, and other fields." This definition gave the new discipline great flexibility to grow with advances in related fields and also gave information scientists a mandate to search for the "grand, unifying relationships of human and human-machine communication."

Development of information science programs in the United States

Formal information science programs were quickly developed at colleges and universities throughout the United States. Some were established in separate departments or as independent programs, such as those at the Georgia Institute of Technology, Ohio State University, and Lehigh University, Bethlehem, Pa., while others, including those at the University of Chicago, Case Western Reserve University, and UCLA, were formed as integral parts of existing library science departments. Information science programs became entrenched in these and other schools during the mid- to late 1960s, and representatives from these schools used formal conferences and informal reports to convey their views and experiences in the new field to other academicians. In the years that followed, information science occasionally achieved departmental status; more often, however, it had elements of its subject matter integrated into the curricula of other departments. The general tendency has been for the theory- and technology-oriented subjects of information science to converge with computer science and engineering, while those pertaining to information management and services are taught as part of library science. Management information systems, on the other hand, have become a major concern of schools of business administration.

SUBJECTS OF RESEARCH

The initially applied activities of information science—automation of bibliographic control and nonnumeric, natural-language processing—provided the impetus for research in such areas as information description, coding, and organization. Operational information systems opened research opportunities in many other areas, including information economics, the study of information value and utility in different settings; and bibliometrics, the quantification of processes of written communication using mathematical methods to classify and evaluate scientific journals. Studies were also undertaken on models of the effectiveness of information storage and retrieval; modes of human–machine interaction; and the effect of form on the content and comprehension of information. Today, researchers in information science have three basic concerns: the search for an ever more general and useful definition and description of the nature of information; the study of the processes of information generation, transmission, transformation, storage, etc.; and the establishment of laws, theories, and other general principles that explain and predict information phenomena.

Interdisciplinary concerns

Because studies of information phenomena are extremely broad and diverse, more often than not they emanate from research communities whose domains of interest have allied foci: linguistics, the cognitive sciences, artificial intelligence, engineering, mathematics, the social and behavioral sciences, management, and of course computer science. Like the phenomena that it studies, information science is a composite, multidisciplinary field of inquiry whose structure continues to evolve.

PROFESSIONAL INFORMATION ASSOCIATIONS

There are hundreds of national, regional, and local professional associations concerned with information-related disciplines and topics. Some are large formal organizations that publish journals and newsletters and hold conventions; others are informal local groups of information professionals who meet to exchange ideas. Both are important sources of information for people working in this rapidly changing field, in which technological and institutional changes occur almost monthly.

Major national organizations

The largest U.S. organization of information processing professionals is the Association for Computing Machinery. Three important national organizations that are concerned with the general aspects of information and information science are the American Association for the Advancement of Science (Section T—Information, Computing and Communication), the American Library Association (Information Science and Automation Division), and the American Society for Information Science. Most information-related organizations are members of the American Federation of Information Processing Societies, which in turn is a member of the International Federation for Information Processing, in Geneva, Switz. The Association of Special Libraries and Information Bureaux is the main professional organization in Great Britain.

Other important associations are concerned with more limited or specific aspects of information science. Among these are the American Society of Indexers, Associated Information Managers, the Association of Information and Dissemination Centers, the Association for Systems Management, the Information Industry Association, and the Society for Management Information Systems.

BIBLIOGRAPHY

Concepts of information and information systems: A wide-ranging discussion by 39 scientists of the nature and goals of the information, computer, communication, and systems sciences appears in FRITZ MACHLUP and UNA MANSFIELD (eds.), *The Study of Information: Interdisciplinary Messages* (1983). A comprehensive, basic survey is offered in STEVEN L. MANDELL, *Computers and Information Processing: Concepts and Applications* (1987). Fundamental concepts of information representation and processes are dealt with, sometimes speculatively, in MARVIN MINSKY, *The Society of Mind* (1986); ROGER C. SCHANK, *Conceptual Information Processing* (1975); ALLEN NEWELL and HERBERT A. SIMON, *Human Problem Solving* (1972); and HERBERT A. SIMON, *The Sciences of the Artificial*, 2nd rev. ed. (1981). BÖRJE LANGEFORS, *Theoretical Analysis of Information Systems*, 4th ed. (1973), explores fundamental aspects of structure and design. The seminal publication А.И. МИХАЙЛОВ, А.И. ЧЕРНЫЙ, and Р.С. ГИЛЯРЕВСКИЙ, *Основы информатики*, 2nd rev. ed. (1968), available also in German translation as A.I. MICHAILOW, A.I. CERNYI, and R.S. GILJAREVSKIJ, *Grundlagen der wissenschaftlichen Dokumentation und Information*, 2 vol. (1970), offers an early Soviet viewpoint on the subject. For independent study of the subject, some reference sources can be of use. See DENNIS LONGLEY and MICHAEL SHAIN, *Dictionary of Information Technology*, 2nd ed. (1986), for a professional reader; and A.J. MEADOWS, M. GORDON, and A. SINGLETON, *Dictionary of Computing and New Information Technology*, 2nd ed. (1984), for a nonexpert. G.G. WILKINSON and A.R. WINTERFLOOD (eds.), *Fundamentals of Information Technology* (1987), is a survey of information processing methods.

Information processing: JENS RASMUSSEN, *Information Processing and Human-Machine Interaction: An Approach to Cognitive Engineering* (1986); and TERRY WINOGRAD and FERNANDO FLORES, *Understanding Computers and Cognition: A New Foundation for Design* (1986), address interface issues arising in computer processing. An in-depth exploration of natural-language processing, reasoning, vision, and learning is provided in EUGENE CHARNIAK and DREW MCDERMOTT, *Introduction to Artificial Intelligence* (1985). BARBARA J. GROSZ, KAREN SPARCK JONES, and BONNIE LYNN WEBBER (eds.), *Readings in Natural Language Processing* (1986), offers a compendium of contributions relating to information retrieval and artificial intelligence. GIO WIEDERHOLD, *File Organization for Database Design* (1987), treats digital information-storage structures systematically and quantitatively. A comprehensive discussion of text indexing and retrieval techniques is given in GERARD SALTON and MICHAEL J. MCGILL, *Introduction to Modern Information Retrieval* (1983); whereas C.J. VAN RIJSBERGEN, *Information Retrieval*, 2nd ed. (1979), offers a mathematical treatment. Standard earlier references on largely manual methods of content analysis of text include GERARD SALTON, *A Theory of Indexing* (1975); DAGOBERT SOERGEL, *Indexing Languages and Thesauri: Construction and Maintenance* (1974); B.C. VICKERY, *Classification and Indexing in Science*, 3rd ed. (1975); and HAROLD BORKO and CHARLES L. BERNIER, *Abstracting Concepts and Methods* (1975). Representative works on the processing of non-textual information include AZRIEL ROSENFELD and AVINASH C. KAK, *Digital Picture Processing*, 2nd ed., 2 vol. (1982); SATOSI WATANABE, *Pattern Recognition: Human and Mechanical* (1985); and STEVEN HARRINGTON, *Computer Graphics: A Programming Approach*, 2nd ed. (1987). THOMAS W. PARSONS, *Voice and Speech Processing* (1986), reviews appropriate techniques. An engrossing introduction to information processing for the artist is given in STEPHEN WILSON, *Using Computers to Create Art* (1986).

Organizational information systems: IVAN F. JACKSON, *Corporate Information Management* (1986), outlines pragmatic principles and problems of managing information in formal organizations; while PAUL A. STRASSMANN, *Information Payoff: The Transformation of Work in the Electronic Age* (1985), is concerned with justification of automation in such organizations. SITANSU S. MITTRA, *Decision Support Systems: Tools and Techniques* (1986), reviews tools of strategic decision making. Military decision making is the subject of A.M. WILLCOX, M.G. SLADE, and P.A. RAMSDALE, *Command, Control, & Communications (C3)* (1983). GORDON B. DAVIS and MARGRETHE H.

OLSON, *Management Information Systems: Conceptual Foundations, Structure, and Development*, 2nd ed. (1985), is a standard management-oriented text on information systems in business organizations. R.A. HIRSCHHEIM, *Office Automation: Social and Organizational Perspective* (1985), considers information systems in the office mainly from a cultural and anthropological point of view; a technological approach to the subject is found in WILLIAM M. NEWMAN, *Designing Integrated Systems for the Office Environment* (1987). ISAAC ASIMOV and KAREN A. FRENKEL, *Robots, Machines in Man's Image* (1985), is a popularly written introduction to the history, uses, and future of robots; scientific fundamentals of the developments are outlined in K.S. FU, R.C. GONZALEZ, and C.S.G. LEE, *Robotics: Control, Sensing, Vision, and Intelligence* (1987). Factory automation is studied in ULRICH REMBOLD, CHRISTIAN BLUME, and RUEDIGER DILLMANN, *Computer-Integrated Manufacturing Technology and Systems* (1985); and MARTIN J. HAIGH, *An Introduction to Computer-Aided Design and Manufacture* (1985). PAUL HARMON and DAVID KING, *Expert Systems: Artificial Intelligence in Business* (1985), provides a readable treatment of the subject.

Public information utilities: A broad view of the state-of-the-art library networking in the United States appears in SUSAN K. MARTIN, *Library Networks, 1986–87: Libraries in Partnership* (1986). B.C. VICKERY, RICHARD G. HESELTINE, and CAROLYN S. BROWN, *Information System Dynamics: The Impact of Interactive Information Networks on the UK Library and Information System* (1982), studies the British situation. ANTONE F. ALBER, *Videotex/Teletext: Principles and Practices* (1985), examines commercial aspects of information technology. J.S. QUATERMAN and J.C. HOSKINS, "Notable Computer Networks," *Communications of the ACM*, 29:932–971 (October 1986), reviews the multiplicity of global telecommunications networks and their services. STARR ROXANNE HILTZ and MURRAY TUROFF, *The Network Nation: Human Communication via Computer* (1978), deals with the early use of computer networking for informal communication in science. ROBERT JOHANSEN, *Teleconferencing and Beyond: Communications in the Office of the Future* (1984), explores the potential of electronic communication in business. Development of integrated services digital networks is outlined in ROBERT K. HELDMAN, *Telecommunications Management Planning: ISDN Networks, Products, and Services* (1987).

Impact of information systems: Seminal studies of the "information era" include FRITZ MACHLUP, *Knowledge, Its Creation, Distribution, and Economic Significance*, 3 vol. (1980–84); MARC URI PORAT, *The Information Economy*, 9 vol. (1977); DANIEL BELL, *The Coming of Post-Industrial Society: Venture in Social Forecasting* (1973, reprinted 1976); and JAMES R. BENIGER, *The Control Revolution: Technological and Economic Origins of the Information Society* (1986). The French view of the social effects of computers in telecommunications is presented in SIMON NORA and ALAIN MINC, *The Computerization of Society: A Report to the President of France* (1980; originally published in French, 1978); and Japanese research on the subject is summarized in Y. ITO and K. OGAWA, "Recent Trends in Johoka Shakai and Yohoka Policy Studies," *Keio Communication Review*, vol. 5 (1984). The importance of preserving individual freedoms in the information age is argued eloquently in ITHIEL DE SOLA POOL, *Technologies of Freedom* (1983). A number of future scenarios are examined in CLEMENT BEZOLD and ROBERT OLSON, *The Information Millennium: Alternative Futures* (1986), which draws on popular intuitive accounts of the early 1980s. DONALD MICHIE and RORY JOHNSTON, *The Knowledge Machine: Artificial Intelligence and the Future of Man* (1985), speculates on the impact of advanced computers on everyday life. Changes in the nature of work processes brought about by information technology are discussed in TOM FORESTER, *High-Tech Society: The Story of the Information Technology Revolution* (1987). ARTHUR R. MILLER and MICHAEL H. DAVIS, *Intellectual Property: Patents, Trademarks, and Copyright in a Nutshell* (1983), elaborates on issues of property rights in information; and CEES J. HAMELINK, *Cultural Autonomy in Global Communications: Planning National Information Policy* (1983), addresses transborder information flows. SIDNEY KARIN and NORRIS PARKER SMITH, *The Supercomputer Era* (1987), provides a readable survey of developments in computer capacity and examines its role in science and business.

Information science: PRANAS ZUNDE, *On Empirical Foundations of Information Science* (1981), explores fundamental philosophical and methodological aspects of information science. Interdisciplinary theoretical concepts integral to information theory are examined in LAURENCE B. HEILPRIN (ed.), *Toward Foundations of Information Science* (1985). The connection of information science to librarianship is discussed in JESSE H. SHERA, *Introduction to Library Science: Basic Elements of Library Service* (1976); B.C. VICKERY and A. VICKERY, *Information Science: Theory and Practice* (1984); *Encyclopedia of Library and Information Science*, edited by ALLEN KENT et al., 35 vol. (1968–83), continued with supplemental volumes (irregular); DOROTHY B. LILLEY and ROSE MARIE BADOUGH, *Library and Information Science* (1982); and CHARLES H. DAVIS and JAMES E. RUSH, *Guide to Information Science* (1979).

Bibliographic sources: Useful series of printed reviews in information science include *Annual Review of Information Science and Technology; Advances in Information Systems Science* (irregular); *Advances in Computers* (irregular); *Advances in Robotics* (irregular); *Computer Integrated Manufacturing Review* (quarterly); *Computing Reviews* (monthly), a major abstracting journal, with an accompanying annual *ACM Guide to Computing Literature; Computer Literature Index* (quarterly), a major indexing source in the field; *Computer Abstracts* (monthly), a significant abstracting journal; and *Computer Book Review* (monthly), surveying new publications in a broad range of subjects on computing. Useful secondary sources that list publications dealing with information science and systems include *Information Science Abstracts* (monthly); and *Library & Information Science Abstracts* (monthly), containing abstracts of literature of librarianship and archives, documentation, publishing, dissemination of information, and mass communications.

(Vladimir Slamecka)

Science

Year in

Review

Contents

The Year in Science: An Overview

by James Trefil

At any time, there are great unanswered questions in science. Sometimes they are answered all at once by some unexpected discovery or theoretical insight. Sometimes they remain unsolved for decades, like an albatross around the neck of science. More often, though, they yield to a slow "nickel and dime" assault, in which the problem eventually gives way as new information and new theoretical tools are developed and applied. It is always difficult, of course, to discern that crucial moment when just enough progress has been made so that the solution to the problem becomes nothing more than a matter of time. I suspect that the past year may be remembered as one in which two very old and very difficult problems finally began to unravel. I refer to the problem of the "greenhouse" effect and the problem of the way that the evolution of life has proceeded—the so-called punctuated equilibrium versus gradualism debate.

The greenhouse effect. The greenhouse effect was very much in the news during the summer of 1988. I spent the summer, as is my custom, at my wife's family home in Montana. Each day the pall of smoke moving eastward from the fires in Yellowstone National Park reminded us of the fact that we were living through one of the worst droughts and heat waves in history. Those who spent the summer in eastern cities have their own memories of this time; "horrible" was the usual adjective I heard.

Whenever there is an unusual bout of weather, people try to explain it as part of a long-term change in the climate. In the 1940s and 1950s, for example, a wave of cold winters filled the newspapers with stories about the return of the Ice Ages. Indeed, the unusually cold winter of 1976–77 prompted a minirevival of such articles. In the same way, the hot, dry summer of 1988 triggered stories about the impending global warming due to the greenhouse effect. This time around, however, the weather came at the end of a decade-long scientific debate about whether this effect is real, and it therefore had a special significance.

One can understand what the greenhouse effect is and why there should be an argument about it by noting that the Earth is constantly absorbing energy from the Sun. Over the long haul all of this

JAMES TREFIL is Clarence Robinson Professor of Physics at George Mason University, Fairfax, Virginia.

energy must be radiated back into space. If it is not, the Earth will heat up. Since warm bodies radiate more energy than cold ones, the warmer the planet gets, the more it radiates until eventually an equilibrium is reached and the energy outflow equals the energy input. Every planet in the solar system has come to this sort of long-term balance with its environment.

Most of the energy from the Sun comes to the Earth in the form of visible light. About a quarter of it is reflected back into space immediately by clouds, but the rest is absorbed in the atmosphere or on the surface. The heated absorber then gives off the energy in the form of infrared radiation. This radiation moves out through the atmosphere into space, balancing the energy budget of the planet. On the way out some of the infrared radiation is absorbed by various gases in the atmosphere. This trapped radiation warms the surface of the planet, raising its temperature until a long-term energy balance is established. If it were not for this absorption process in the atmosphere, the average temperature at the surface of the Earth would be about −40° C (−40° F).

The raising of the Earth's temperature by the absorption of outgoing infrared radiation in the atmosphere is called the greenhouse effect. In a greenhouse, or even in an automobile with the windows rolled up, the glass plays the role of the atmosphere. Visible light from the Sun comes through it and is absorbed on the inside, while the infrared radiation trying to get out is blocked. As a result, the inside of such a structure can be warm even on a very cold winter day.

The question that has been debated by scientists is whether human beings, by adding absorbing gases to the atmosphere, are raising the temperature of the Earth. Many human activities generate gases that absorb infrared radiation. Whenever a fossil fuel—coal, gasoline, or natural gas—is burned, carbon dioxide is added to the atmosphere. Other activities produce other "greenhouse gases" that absorb infrared radiation. Adding these gases to the atmosphere obviously will increase the normal greenhouse effect. It remains to be seen what the effects of these additions will be.

There are two points on which every scientist in the debate agrees:

1. Carbon dioxide is a gas that absorbs infrared radiation.

2. The levels of carbon dioxide and other gases in the atmosphere are increasing because of human activities. Atmospheric levels of carbon dioxide are about 25% higher now than they were before the Industrial Revolution.

Beyond these two fundamental points, however, there is spirited debate on almost every other aspect of the greenhouse effect.

The debate arises from a simple fact: the Earth is a very complicated system, and it is not at all obvious what the final outcome of adding carbon dioxide to the atmosphere will be. For example, it is possible that an initial increase in temperature would cause more water to evaporate. This would increase the cloud cover, which would cause more sunlight to be reflected back into space. This is one example among many of a common phenomenon in the Earth sciences—the "counterintuitive" outcome. In this case intuition tells us that adding carbon dioxide to the atmosphere will cause more infrared radiation to be absorbed and therefore raise the temperature. Because of the possible cloud effects, however, there is a possibility that the temperature might actually be lowered. It is the question of whether such counterintuitive effects might be important that has generated much of the debate about the greenhouse effect.

Predictions of the changes that might result from adding carbon dioxide to the atmosphere are normally made by using mammoth computer codes known as general circulation models (GCM). The problem is that the Earth's atmosphere is so complex that it is not at all unusual for a single long-range prediction to require weeks and even months of time on the biggest supercomputers. This means that some compromises must be made in the calculations. For example, one state-of-the-art GCM divides the surface of the Earth up into squares about 500 kilometers (310 miles) on a side and treats the weather in each square as a single unit. Is this an ad-

equate way to study clouds, which are seldom more than a few kilometers on a side? No one knows, but it is not difficult to see how arguments could develop in the face of such uncertainties.

The theoretical uncertainties about what will happen in a greenhouse future are mirrored in arguments about what is actually happening now. Was the summer of 1988 the beginning of a warming trend, or was it just a normal fluctuation in temperature? In principle, one would think that the answer to a question like this could come from temperature records, but it is not that simple. There are no long-term temperature records for much of the Earth (the ocean surfaces or tropical forests, for example), and those that do exist can be interpreted in many ways.

One small example (among many) of the kind of difficulties encountered arises because many official weather stations are located at major airports. When many of these airports were built, they were out in the country. O'Hare Airport in Chicago, for example, is designated ORD by the airlines because it was once located in an area of apple orchards. Today, it is in the middle of a built-up urban area, and all that cement and asphalt produces slightly warmer temperatures than the countryside did. Therefore, if the thermometers at O'Hare record a one-degree rise in average temperature over a 20-year period, should that be attributed to the greenhouse effect or to the urbanization of the surroundings? Similar arguments have arisen in regard to other sorts of temperature data.

Given that there is such an argument among the experts, what is the average citizen supposed to think? If there is really a threat to the environment, then political action must be taken to meet it. However, this seems to be a case where the people charged with determining whether a crisis is at hand cannot get their act together. What is to be done?

The difficulty faced by the citizen in deciding what to do in this sort of situation is not something that is unique to the greenhouse effect; it is a general property of all public debates that involve undecided issues in science. In fact, the news media in the U.S. seem to have a difficult time reporting scientific debates. From my point of view there are two reasons for this weakness. One is the newsperson's need for sensational stories; the other is an apparent need to provide a sort of formulaic evenhandedness in news coverage of science.

It is a truism among newswatchers that the person who shouts that the sky is falling will get a lot of attention, while the person who maintains that it probably will not tends to be ignored. Editors want stories that will attract the reader's (or viewer's) attention, and this, in turn, puts pressure on reporters to play up the sensational aspects of what they are

Data from 30 years of continuous measurements of carbon dioxide at Mauna Loa in Hawaii reveal the increasing concentration of this gas in the atmosphere.

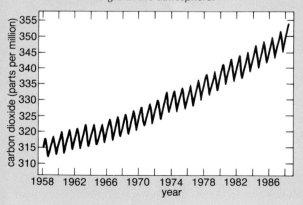

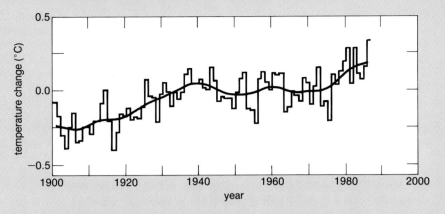

Global-mean air temperatures at the Earth's surface, compiled by an Anglo-American research team, show a gradual warming trend since 1900 and a more pronounced rise since 1980.

reporting. However, issues being debated by scientists tend to be fuzzy and not well-defined. This is why scientists like to wrap their pronouncements in a cocoon of "maybes" and "mights." If these protective layers are removed, as they often are in science reporting, the public gets no notion of the real uncertainties that exist. If these qualifiers are kept, on the other hand, the story tends to sink into a morass of uninteresting details.

Reporters who are careful about being precise in their attributions, therefore, tend to look for people who will make unequivocal statements. In the case of the greenhouse effect, this means that the public debate will be carried out largely by those who have already made up their minds and that little of the uncertain feelings of the "scientist on the street" is expressed.

The invisibility of the middle ground is enhanced by the common method of presenting both sides of a debate. Thus, a story will quote Professor X, who says that something will happen, and go on to quote Professor Y, who says that it will not. After writing such a story, a reporter would have fulfilled his or her obligation to present both sides of the issue, but the readers really are not much better off. They have moved no closer to an understanding of what the debate is all about nor to a sense of why working scientists, starting from the same data, are reaching different conclusions.

Both of these problems were manifest in the debate over the greenhouse effect in 1988. Some scientists consider the past four summers as the beginning of the long-awaited climate warming, while others argue that this period has been a statistical fluke. The fact that many of the original predictions made in the 1970s by primitive ancestors of the modern GCMs greatly overestimated the increases in temperatures that were supposed to have taken place by 1988 has not helped matters either.

Amid all the controversy the question as to whether the global warming has started remains. My sense

is that, while there is still a full spectrum of views among scientists, there has been a general shift to the point of view that says that the current warming may well mark the beginning of the greenhouse effect. An example of new information that has fueled this shift is a new compilation of global temperatures by an Anglo-American research group that suggests that the warming of the last few years may well be part of a long-term trend. I have to emphasize, however, that it would take only a couple of cool, wet summers to destroy this newly forming consensus.

Nevertheless, however the argument about whether the greenhouse effect has already started plays itself out, it is only prudent to start thinking seriously about changes that might be caused by the warming. That is why I find a new line of inquiry about the greenhouse effect so interesting. Instead of asking whether the warming became detectable in 1988, scientists are starting to ask what will happen to the Earth if and when the warming actually occurs.

At a landmark conference in Washington, D.C., scientists from a wide variety of fields came together in October 1988 to discuss this question and to see if their pooled expertise could produce some answers. Freed from the need to discuss the details of worldwide temperature data, ecologists, paleontologists, biologists, and meteorologists could focus their attention on what would happen if the average temperature of the Earth were to increase by several degrees Celsius, as predicted by the greenhouse models. Their general conclusions, which should stand the test of time, were quite interesting.

The first thing one should keep in mind is that while the warming predicted for the greenhouse effect is large, it is not unprecedented in the history of the Earth. For example, the temperature changes that accompanied the retreat of the glaciers 10,000 years ago were as large or larger. What would be unprecedented about the greenhouse warming, should it occur, is its speed. The predictions call for the temperature to rise by a few degrees per century rather than by a few tenths of a degree per century, as it did after the last Ice Age. Except for periods following major catastrophes, such as the impacts of large meteorites, the Earth has never been subjected to such a rapid change. Therefore, when scientists approach the problem of what will happen to the biosphere if the temperature rises, they do not have a previous model to help them track the details of the way changes will occur. Instead, they try to calculate the end state of the change, without paying attention to how the system will get from here to there.

The general results of these calculations can be summed up simply: in response to a warming, the main climate zones on the Earth will move northward. As a rule of thumb, each degree Celsius of climate warming corresponds to a 100–160-kilometer (60–100-mile) change in latitude. Thus, a greenhouse warming of 5° C would have the rough effect of moving the temperatures of Los Angeles up to San Francisco and those in Washington, D.C., up to Boston.

To take just one example of what kinds of changes might occur, one might consider the Boundary Waters Wilderness Area, a large tract of evergreen forest, interlaced with rivers and lakes, located on the border between Minnesota and Canada. If the greenhouse warming occurs, the trees now living there will migrate northward, and the area will become a hardwood forest dominated by maples. This sort of change, taking place over a century or less, is typical of the consequences scientists expect from greenhouse warming. The movement of climate zones will probably be most damaging in the polar regions, where the present zones have nowhere to go.

At present, the GCM do not do well in predicting the details of the expected changes in climate. Therefore, such questions as Will Midwestern droughts become regular features of a greenhouse world? simply cannot be answered at this time. Nevertheless, it is clear that if a global warming occurs, there will be changes everywhere. What is now productive farmland will require irrigation, and what is now tundra may become forest. Anticipating and planning for these changes will become a major task for governments.

Some forward-looking scholars have already begun to think about dealing with the greenhouse effect as a practical matter. Most of the policies they talk about have the enormous advantage of making sense, whether a greenhouse warming is imminent or not. For example, carbon dioxide is added to the atmosphere by the burning of fossil fuels. One way to reduce the changes due to the greenhouse effect, then, is to use fuel more efficiently—to do the same job with less burning. A well-insulated house or a fuel-efficient automobile can reduce the amount of carbon dioxide added to the atmosphere without reducing the level of comfort or the ability to get around. What is also important is that they save money. Conserving energy, a concept introduced in the U.S. by the oil shortages of the 1970s, is one of the most important ways for a person to minimize the impact of the greenhouse effect.

Another policy option that is being put forward is the massive planting of trees. As trees grow, they remove carbon dioxide from the air and incorporate the carbon into their wood and leaves. As long as they live, that carbon stays locked up and cannot contribute to the greenhouse effect. Estimates of the size of the forest needed to compensate for the burning of fossil fuels range from the size of Pennsylvania to the size of the U.S. west of the Mississippi River. Nonetheless, as large as this project may seem, it should be remembered that planting even a small area with trees is a good thing to do, whether it will reverse the greenhouse effect or not.

Thus, provided the weather does not change soon, the unusually hot and dry summer of 1988 will be remembered as the phenomenon that triggered much serious thought among scientists and citizens about the greenhouse effect: how to deal with its consequences and how to minimize them.

Trilobite ribs and the rate of evolution. The second great scientific question on which significant progress was made during the past year concerned the theory of evolution. First, it is important to distinguish between the theory of evolution and the fact of evolution. That life on Earth has changed and evolved over geologic time is not seriously contested. This is the fact of evolution. What is contested are various statements about how this change took place. These statements are the theories of evolution, and any (or all) of them can be wrong without changing the fact that evolution took place.

When Charles Darwin first proposed a theory of evolution in the 19th century, he developed a point of view that is now called gradualism. According to Darwin, change in living systems occurs as an accumulation of small steps, driven by natural selection. The basic mechanism was simple to understand. For example, in a population of giraffes there will always be a few with longer necks. If the longer necks allow those individuals to reach leaves high up on trees, it increases the likelihood that they will survive long enough to have lots of offspring. This means that the next generation will have more long-necked individuals than the current one. Working slowly over long periods of time, Darwin might have argued, such a process could easily produce the present-day giraffe.

Darwin worked out his theory before the birth of the modern science of genetics and more than a century before the structure and role of DNA (deoxyribonucleic acid) in inheritance was understood. What modern genetics accomplished, in essence, was to provide an explanation of how it is that members of a population can differ from each other and how those differences can be transmitted from one generation to the next.

It is a measure of Darwin's genius that his theory reigned supreme for more than a century from its first publication, despite the fact that during that century there was a profound upheaval in almost every other branch of science. In 1972, however, two U.S. paleontologists, Niles Eldredge and Stephen Jay Gould, published a theory that, while not anti-Darwinian, suggested that evolution actually took place quite differently from the way Darwin thought it did.

They called their theory "punctuated equilibrium." The basic idea was that large changes do not result from the slow accumulation of small ones but happen suddenly, in bursts. The evolutionary record, according to them, was actually characterized by long periods when no significant changes occurred ("stasis") broken by short bursts of rapid change ("punctuations").

One might wonder why there is a debate over a subject like this—is it not possible to just look at the evolutionary record and see which theory is right? In a word the answer to this question is no. Past life on Earth is known only through fossils that are preserved in rocks. In order for a living organism to become a fossil, it must die, be buried, and, over geologic time, have its molecules replaced by minerals carried in the groundwater that flows past it. The end product is a replica in stone of the original organism.

However, there are many ways that an organism can miss being preserved in the fossil record. Bones can be chewed up or decompose before they are buried. Geologic processes can bury the fossils deep underground, away from human discovery. In fact, scientists estimate that only about one species in 10,000 has been revealed through its fossils.

But even if a particular type of plant or animal is known, the ability to see how it evolved is limited by the fact that so few individuals are known as fossils. It is not at all unusual, for example, for a species to be identified from a single fossil or to be represented by a few fossils of individuals separated by thousands or even millions of years in time. It is this spotty and erratic nature of fossil preservation that makes resolving the gradualist-punctuationist issue so difficult.

The diagrams on this page illustrate this point. Suppose that it is believed that species A evolves into species B over a period of time. A typical fossil record is shown on the left; there would be a few

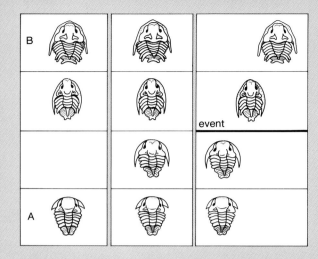

fossils of species A and then, later, a few more of species B. A question arises, however: did the transition from A to B take place smoothly, as shown in the center, or suddenly, as shown on the right? The honest answer, given the available data, is that it is not possible to make a clean distinction between the two competing theories.

In December 1987 a paper was published in the prestigious journal *Nature* that triggered renewed debate on the gradual versus punctuation issue but with an important difference. In an extraordinary display of sheer perseverance, a British paleontologist, Peter Sheldon, collected and analyzed a set of more than 3,000 fossils that seemed to allow a full view of the process by which one species changes into another.

The fossils Sheldon collected were of extinct marine animals called trilobites, distant cousins of today's horseshoe crab. These creatures dominated life in the ocean about 300 million years ago and created one of the richest collections in the fossil record. On a remote mountainside in Wales Sheldon found places where streams had cut into layers of limestone, exposing rich deposits of fossils. For more than ten years he collected and catalogued them, thinking about what to do with the accumulating boxes. Finally, in a burst of activity that involved working 14-hour days, 7 days a week, for more than a year, he analyzed the fossils and presented the results to the scientific community.

To understand Sheldon's work one must know a few things about trilobites. Like modern crabs, they grew by shedding old shells and growing new ones. Most of the fossils are of discarded shells. These shells have ribs on them (presumably to make them stronger), and the number of ribs is one of the markers that scientists use to distinguish one species of trilobite from another. What Sheldon did was to count the ribs in the tail portions of the shells of

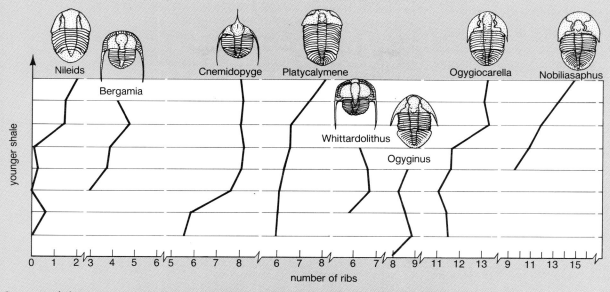

Summary of changes in average number of ribs for eight lineages of trilobites shows that there was a gradual increase over a period of about three million years.

Adapted from "Parallel gradualistic evolution of Ordovician trilobites," Peter R. Sheldon, reprinted by permission of *Nature*, vol. 330, no. 6148, pp. 561–563, Dec. 10, 1987 © Macmillan Magazines Ltd.

about 3,500 fossils—about 45,000 ribs altogether. For each of the species he then tabulated the number of ribs as time progressed. Because of this tremendous effort there is now a record that, for one animal at one time in the past, can be seen in great detail.

From the point of view of the gradualist-punctuationist debate, the most important thing about Sheldon's results is that they show a smooth transition between trilobites that had been classified as different species before his work. In this case, at least, there seems to be no evidence for the kind of sudden change proposed by the punctuation theory.

The debate will not end there, however. Punctuationists have already pointed out that the number of ribs on a trilobite may not be the best way to characterize a species, since this number may be an accidental result of genetic change rather than a characteristic related to natural selection. They have also argued that Sheldon's work simply shows that the different "species" were not different after all. I have to admit that I find this last argument less than compelling. It smacks of moving the foul lines after the batter has hit the ball.

Regardless of how the debate eventually turns out, Sheldon's work symbolizes a new era. Instead of arguments based on mixtures of philosophy and a few fossils, there is now the possibility of arguments based on extensive, well-documented data sets. As a physicist I can only applaud my colleagues' new attention to the type of information that is needed to resolve the fundamental questions they raise. I hope that Sheldon's work will lead to a reexamination of other voluminous data sets that have been collected in the past and to a resolve to make the extraordinary effort required to collect new sets in the future.

For the record my own guess is that the answer to the gradualist-punctuationist debate will turn out to be "all of the above." I suspect it will be found that some evolutionary changes (perhaps those involving Sheldon's trilobites) were gradual and others sudden. The world is just too complex to expect simple answers.

Ribs are clearly revealed in two of the trilobite fossils studied by Peter Sheldon, one from the genus Platycalymene (left) and one from the genus Cnemidopyge (right).

Photos, Peter R. Sheldon, University of Wales, Cardiff

Anthropology

Anthropology during the past year continued to emphasize that it is the study of humans in all places at all times. Its worldwide growth steadily increased, as reflected by the opening of Bangladesh's first anthropology department, at Jahangirnagar University. The diversity of the discipline was illustrated by meetings of the 12th International Congress of Anthropological and Ethnological Sciences in Zagreb, Yugos., where 2,500 participants from around the world met in nearly 200 panels. A special event of the meetings included a trip to the Neanderthal rock shelter of Krapina. Conference paper topics ranged from the latest discoveries of tools used millions of years ago to an analysis of the stress of different occupations in today's technological world. A major session focused on the writings of ethnographers (cultural anthropologists) and analysis of the ways in which the act of writing affects the presentation of another culture.

National and regional meetings. Although the congress meets only once every five years, national organizations of anthropologists meet yearly. For example, Michael Banton, president of the Royal Anthropological Institute of Great Britain and Ireland, addressed the society on the topic of race relations. The general meeting covered subjects from prehistory to human evolution. A more specialized segment of British anthropologists, the Association of Social Anthropologists, focused during the year on the topic of Youth, Maturation, and Aging. A majority of papers discussed problems of old age, with research divided equally between European societies and traditional ones in Africa and Asia.

West German ethnologists and anthropologists met with their Austrian counterparts during the year to discuss museum technology and ethnic peoples of Africa and Asia. A relatively new topic for their discussion was applied anthropology, suggesting a European trend toward more interest in this area.

Applied problems made up a major portion of the Australian Anthropological Society meetings in August. Sessions were held on Aborigine land tenure, health care, and general governmental policy. One session was devoted to anthropology and computers, another to visual anthropology—the use of film to record ethnographic detail. Traditional fields of anthropology, such as kinship and cosmology, continued to be of interest.

The November meetings of the American Anthropological Association revealed how vast and diverse anthropology had become in North America. Twenty constituent societies of the association—with such special interests as nutrition, filmmaking, black studies, agriculture, medicine, and education—organized meetings within the broader program so that some 20 concurrent sessions were held each morning and afternoon on November 16–20. An evening plenary session was titled "Sovereignty Issues for American Indian Tribes"; at another evening session Mary Douglas, a British social anthropologist, offered an analogy about a travel experience to explain the relations among cognition, memory, and uncertainty. Use of analogy highlighted the discipline's current interest in how anthropologists present the results of their research.

U.S. anthropologists were also organized into regional societies, often focusing on regional events. For example, in March the Central States Anthropological Society, meeting with the American Ethnological Society, heard a speaker analyze the archaeological content of Cahokia Mounds in Illinois in relation to ethnographic collections. The research report coincided with the opening of a multimillion-dollar museum at the Cahokia Mounds State Historic Park; the site is unique in North America because its density and specialization of population suggest that it was an urban center 1,000 years ago.

Other U.S. societies were organized by topic, some becoming quite specialized. As an example, national societies of ethnobiology held their first international congress July 19–24 in Belém, Brazil, and concluded their meeting by forming an international society that will meet next in China in 1990. At the 1988 sessions, resolutions called for the preservation of indigenous cultures as well as of endangered species, and the congress issued warnings about the dangers of deforestation and certain types of development projects.

Religion and ritual. Ethnobiology was exemplified by *Passage of Darkness* (1988) by ethnographer Wade Davis. The book describes the Haitian zombie, a well-known stereotype that until recently was virtually ignored by social scientists. Davis's research began with an examination of the poison that produces a drastic—although temporary—reduction in metabolism, giving the appearance of death, but the work led him to examine how belief in zombies influences power relations throughout society up to the national level.

In further research on ritual and religious beliefs, Raymond DeMallie and Douglas Parks edited *Sioux Indian Religion: Tradition and Innovation* (1987). For their part of the book they reexamined the concept of wakan, a central feature of the religion of the Dakota (Sioux) Indians. Well-versed in the Lakota (Western Dakota) language, the two authors revealed how the omnipotent animating force of all life (wakan) patterns the universe. The concept was a unifying force because it readily incorporated other religious traditions, including Christianity, to give meaning to peoples under diverse social conditions, ranging from bison hunting to segregated, depen-

Wade Davis

Haitian prepares poison that places a person in a deathlike "zombie" state. Ethnographer Wade Davis examined the influence of belief in zombies on power relations in Haitian society.

dent life on reservations. Joining in this analysis of religion were a number of Lakota people who were trained in anthropology or religious studies. These scholars analyzed other major components of religious life, such as the Sun Dance, the sacred Buffalo Calf Pipe, and healing rituals of the *yuwipi*, the Dakota term for shaman.

While the incorporation of indigenous people in ethnographic research occurred in the earliest work of anthropologists, who trained informants to record folklore and other texts, the DeMallie and Parks collection represents a stage where native people are fully equal colleagues. Indeed, native anthropologists now frequently study their own culture independently of others. For example, in *The Invention of Africa: Gnosis, Philosophy, and the Order of Knowledge* (1988), V. Y. Mudimbe undertook an analysis of Western ethnography about Africa to show how societies there were "invented" by Western scientists to fit their preconceptions.

Presentation of data. The analysis of how ethnographers present their data is a major focus of anthropology. Clifford Geertz summarized much of this effort in *Works and Lives: The Anthropologist as Author* (1988), while he also analyzed some classic ethnographies that serve as guidelines for research in cultural anthropology. By contrasting the works of such ethnographers as Claude Lévi-Strauss, E. E. Evans-Pritchard, Bronislaw Malinowski, and Ruth Benedict (French, British, Polish, and U.S., respectively), he suggested the ways in which nationality influences perception. More importantly, he related the ethnographer's personality and life experience to his or her perception of what Geertz describes as the "Other" and analyzed how these factors affect reflection and description of that Other.

Geertz concluded that the experience of colonialism was a major factor influencing French and British perceptions of the Other. Even though anthropologists from those countries sympathized with their subjects more than did other colonizers, they did regard their informants as "subjects" and presented them as such in written analysis. U.S. anthropologists did not escape a similar bias, even without colonies. In the case of Benedict, who analyzed North American Indians in the 1930s and Japanese in the World War II era, her influence on anthropology derived essentially from her expository style. Her fieldwork with Indians was cursory or based on documents, and her Japanese research was conducted from Washington, D.C. Neither of her analyses offered much theory, yet they were as influential as any others in anthropology. Geertz attributes this popularity to an assured, resolute literary style that "definitely expressed definite views."

Much of the ethnography before World War II could rely heavily on the simple fact of what Geertz concisely describes as "Being There." Fieldwork in an exotic community made one an authority because no one else could speak with experience on the lives of Others. In today's world, however, developers, Peace Corps volunteers, reporters, and others have invaded the exotic world to such an extent that exotic domains no longer exist; moreover, representatives of the Other Community have now studied in the West and have become historians or anthropologists who can speak for themselves. Mudimbe, for example, not only speaks for what the Other (in his case, African) is but analyzes the ethnography of Africa written by Westerners to show how and why they so inaccurately described it or, in his words, "invented" it.

The political considerations that concerned anthropologists often were reflected in their ethnography. Experimentation to involve the Other more fully in ethnography included teamwork with an anthropological Other or development of writing styles that allowed informants greater latitude in speaking for themselves. Even the term informant was being criticized. Some ethnographers were substituting "consultant" to connote greater involvement.

Analysis of style is illustrated by James Clifford and George Marcus, eds., in *Writing Culture: The Poetics and Politics of Ethnography* (1986). The subject is further treated by Marcus and Michael Fischer in *Anthropology as Cultural Critique: An Experimental Moment in the Human Sciences* (1986). This latter work is particularly useful in recalling that ethnography intends not only to reveal the Other with scientific objectivity but also to examine the Self, or one's own culture. Anthropology, when looking at the exotic, sees itself; other cultures act as a mirror. Marcus and Fischer recognize that anthropologists now frequently study Western culture directly, but they contend that study of the Other will be the most useful way to achieve a cultural critique of Western life-styles.

In May the Museum of the American Indian/Heye Foundation returned 11 wampum belts to hereditary chiefs of the Iroquois confederacy in Canada. It was feared that the return of the belts might intensify friction between elected and hereditary chiefs, but instead the occasion appeared to lessen some of their conflict.

In other matters of ethics, the organization Cultural Survival, staffed by anthropologists promoting the rights of small communities of indigenous peoples, helped draft a bill for the U.S. Congress, the "International Cultural Survival Bill of 1988." It would require that U.S. foreign-assistance programs promote the rights of tribal people and ensure that no projects adversely affect their rights or livelihood. Social and economic development through small-scale projects instead of major ones such as large dams and highways would likely be emphasized. These smaller projects have been found to promote development more effectively and also do less damage to the rights of indigenous peoples.

—Ernest L. Schusky

Archaeology

The year 1988 was another exciting one for archaeology. Elaborate finds were made in North America, South America, and the Mediterranean region. Improved communications and collaboration between U.S. and Soviet, as well as U.S., Australian, and Chinese, archaeologists resulted in rapid advances in Siberian/Alaskan and interior Asian prehistory. Improved economic conditions, rapid growth, and relatively peaceful internal politics spurred interest in regional prehistories and indigenous populations in parts of South America and Africa.

Problems remained, however, with the largest and most troubling being looting, vandalism, and destruction of sites and records of the past. This problem was especially acute in the Americas, where the dominant cultures had little or no obvious relationship to the cultures reflected in archaeological remains. No definitive solution was in sight, although several countries had enacted strong antiquities laws or appealed to pride in national heritage as a means of controlling the burgeoning antiquities trade.

In several U.S. states the problem was being approached through a mixture of federal, state, and local laws combined with public education programs. For example, professionals in Texas, Missouri, Colorado, Utah, and Nevada, among others, encouraged active participation in all aspects of archaeological research by avocational (nonprofessional) groups. Arizona and Utah, in particular, instituted highly successful annual "Archaeology Weeks," week-long periods of free lectures, exhibits, school outreach programs, and press releases focusing on each state's cultural heritage and the need to care for that heritage properly.

Colorado, Utah, Nevada, and other states developed certification programs. Using classroom and field instruction, these aimed to introduce interested laypersons to the broad history, techniques, potentials—and the tedium and romance—of archaeological research. The Utah Avocational Archaeologist Certification Program, for example, was proving highly successful in attracting participants from various chapters of the statewide amateur group. It consisted of three levels, each with three or four courses, that led participants through the history and philosophy of archaeology as a scholarly field, through Utah and regional prehistory, and also through map reading, surveying, site reporting, note taking, and excavation techniques. The program was taught by academic, state, and federally employed archaeologists throughout Utah and took about 18 months to complete. Those completing each level received a certificate and recognition from the state preservation office, the Utah Professional Archaeological Council, and the amateur society. After completion of the third level, participants would become eligible to work on contract and research projects. As of early 1989, over 100 avocational archaeologists had completed the program through level two.

Avocational archaeologists were also being recognized on a national level. The 1988 winner of the Don E. Crabtree Award for Avocational Archaeology was Julian Dodge Hayden, a construction contractor from Arizona whose work in archaeology spanned nearly 60 years. This award, along with others at state and regional levels, increased communication and appreciation between avocational and professional archaeologists throughout the U.S.

The National Geographic Society turns 100. The encouraging trend toward greater communication was both the result and the cause of the rapidly growing interest in archaeology and the past that

An excavation in northern Peru uncovered a rich tomb of a pre-Inca warrior priest (far left). Found in the tomb was a miniature gold and turquoise warrior, about the size of a man's thumb (left). It is among the finest pieces of jewelry from pre-Columbian America.

had become apparent during the last several years. Much of the credit must be given to the National Geographic Society. Not only had the society funded a remarkable number of research projects during its century of existence, it had also been at the forefront of disseminating information in and sparking interest about the past.

Evidence of widespread public interest in archaeology—and the society's role in creating that interest—could be seen in the October 1988 centennial edition of *National Geographic,* the society's magazine. This issue was dedicated to what is currently known about the peopling of the Earth and featured some of the more spectacular research findings of the past year, among them a remarkably rich tomb of a pre-Inca warrior priest in northern Peru. Also included were a cogent discussion of the evolution of modern humans, as seen through a diverse array of archaeological and paleoanthropological research; a report on a recent find in central Washington State of a cache of some of the largest Clovis spearpoints ever discovered; and an interesting discussion of art in the Lascaux cave, France, and its implications for understanding Paleolithic society. What may be the earliest carved human representation ever found decorated the cover, and there was a thoughtful discussion of its origins, manufacture, and implications for understanding Paleolithic culture.

Prehistoric settlements on Cape Cod. Recent discoveries at Indian Neck, on outer Cape Cod, Massachusetts, revealed evidence for settled communities and relatively large indigenous populations several hundred years prior to the European colonization of North America. For example, a large ossuary, or mass burial, of at least 56 men, women, and children was found during excavation of a septic tank on the Cape. As reported by Francis McManamon and James Bradley of the U.S. National Park Service, the find presents solid evidence for permanent prehistoric coastal settlements in an area that was previously thought to have been used only sporadically.

Radiocarbon dates of the bones indicate that the burial is about 900–1,000 years old. The organization of the bones in the burial suggests that ritualistic behavior was involved. The people apparently died at different times, possibly over a span of a dozen years, prior to interment in the ossuary. The lowest remains, those interred first, were cremated and placed in the pit while still hot enough to singe those piled on them. This differential treatment implies differences in social status between those of higher rank, who were presumably cremated, and those of somewhat lower rank, who were not. All ages and both sexes were represented, suggesting that the ossuary held the remains of everyone in a community who died during a certain period.

Ethnohistoric and historic evidence suggests that such a pattern of burial was the hallmark of a sedentary way of life. A model for such a pattern comes from the Huron, a sedentary group in Ontario, whose lifeways were documented by early settlers and fur traders in the region. Primary Huron villages were built near large ossuaries that received remains not only from the village but also from surrounding settlements up to about 20 km (12 mi) away. The ossuaries served as foci of rituals designed to integrate village and regional social structures and to reassert ties with villages that budded out of a central ancestral village as its population grew. Ceremonies were held every 8, 10, or 12 years so that outlying villagers could add the remains of their dead to the ancestral ossuary.

Ossuaries have been found along the coasts of Maryland and North Carolina. They appear to have served similar unifying functions for sedentary villagers, who, like their New England counterparts, lived on the riches of the coastal environment. Evidence of this natural bounty can be seen in numerous shell middens along the coasts. National Park Service archaeologists have recorded several sites of this kind around Cape Cod, Martha's Vineyard, and Nantucket. Shells from these sites—some dated to the Late Woodland, the same period as the Indian Neck ossuary—provide evidence in their growth rings indicating the season when they were collected. Analysis of the rings showed that the vast majority dating to Late Woodland times were collected during winter and early spring, seasons when it had been thought that there was little or no human occupation of the coastal regions. Shells from sites dated to Early and Middle Woodland times were collected throughout the year.

Changes in collection seasons between the earlier periods and Late Woodland times are attributed to the advent of horticulture in the region. This had been deduced independently from evidence found at other sites in New England. The presence of domesticated plants and horticulture is usually thought to be a requisite for sedentary life.

The combination of an ethnohistoric analogue and changes in shell-collecting strategies indicating some reliance on horticulture strongly suggests that the Indian Neck ossuary represents people who lived in relatively large numbers in settled villages. This conclusion is supported by records of early European settlers that describe large numbers of encampments around Cape Cod and Wellfleet Harbor. The sedentary pattern seems to have been established in the region about 1,000 years ago.

Dating the Shroud of Turin. One of the most newsworthy events related to archaeology during the past year was the radiocarbon dating of the Shroud of Turin. The shroud had been the focus of intense debate since it came to public notice in the 1350s. Photographs and other representations of it came under intensive scientific scrutiny in the 1970s, culminating in multidisciplinary analyses of the shroud itself for a short time in 1978. Scientists who worked on the relic at that time performed almost every possible analysis on the fabric and image but were not allowed to remove samples for radiocarbon dating, which most experts considered to be crucial as a test of the cloth's authenticity. It was thought that if the linen dated to about 2,000 years ago, its association with the crucified Christ would at least be credible.

During the past year church authorities in Turin gave permission for radiocarbon dating of the shroud, using accelerator mass spectrometer techniques that require very small samples. Only two square centimeters of linen were needed to obtain dates from three independent laboratories located in Arizona; Oxford, England; and Zürich, Switz. Special double-blind tests were conducted on the samples so that none of the laboratories knew which samples, of the several they were given, actually belonged to the shroud. Results were released on Oct. 13, 1988, by Anastasio Cardinal Ballestrero, the archbishop of Turin, and his science adviser, Luigi Gonella. Actual radiocarbon dates were not made public, but the archbishop declared that the cloth was dated, with 95% certainty, to the period between AD 1260 and 1390. Thus, the cloth was medieval, but he stressed that the Roman Catholic Church has never claimed the shroud was anything more than a representation of Christ's burial cloth. It remains, however, a fascinating puzzle, since no one has been able to discover how the image was transferred, in a perfect negative, onto the surface of the fabric.

The Neolithic at 'Ain Ghazal. Results of research at a major Neolithic site near Amman, Jordan, were reported by Alan Simmons of the Desert Research Institute in Reno, Nev., Gary Rollefson of San Diego (Calif.) State University, and Zeidan Kafafi of Yarmouk University, Irbid, Jordan. 'Ain Ghazal was a large population center between about 7200 and 5000 BC, the period when plant and animal domestication spread through the region. The site has provided important information about events and adaptations in the middle and late Neolithic, particularly art and ritual and the rise of pastoralism.

Discovered at the major Neolithic site of 'Ain Ghazal in Jordan were a clay fertility figurine (right), resembling earlier Paleolithic "Venus" figures, and two clay cattle figures (far right) "ritually killed" with flint bladelets.

'Ain Ghazal became a major center during the period called Pre-Pottery Neolithic B (PPNB), between about 7200 and 6000 BC. At least five building sequences belonging to this phase have been identified, including residences and public administrative and ceremonial buildings. Evidence of ritual and art during this time consists of numerous clay statues and figurines, including two caches of near-life-size plaster statues—some of the earliest such art forms recorded—buried under the floors of abandoned buildings. Smaller human and animal figurines, including probable fertility objects similar to earlier Paleolithic "Venus" figures, were also found throughout the site. Cattle representations comprised the majority of the animal figures, suggesting domestication and the possible cult status of these animals. Burial practices, including an apparently ceremonial reopening of graves to remove the skulls, were also considered to be evidence of ritualistic behavior.

Diet during PPNB times was remarkably varied, including a wide range of wild and domesticated plants, as well as a number of different wild animals. Goats were an important species, although it is not clear whether these animals were as yet domesticated. The dietary evidence shows that even after a number of plants, and possibly goats, were domesticated, residents of 'Ain Ghazal continued to rely heavily on hunting and gathering. A dramatic shift in diet occurred in the next periods, Pre-Pottery Neolithic C (PPNC) and the Yarmoukian, dated to between around 6000 and 5000 BC. The number of species used for food declined severely, particularly the number of animals. Sheep or goats, now domesticated, were the predominant species, supplemented by a substantial number of pigs and cattle. This trend is visible during the PPNC, and by Yarmoukian times domesticated and wild plant remains are rare. This suggests that pastoralism was becoming the dominant economy. Declining population and a shift to seasonal occupation of 'Ain Ghazal appears to mark the Yarmoukian period. The site was abandoned at the end of this period as nomadic pastoralism became predominant.

Why did these changes occur? The authors suggest that the residents of 'Ain Ghazal exploited their local, once rich, environment to the extent that it deteriorated beyond habitability. This pattern can be seen at other sites, but most major centers in the region were reinhabited, albeit at a much reduced level, after a period of time. 'Ain Ghazal was not reoccupied until the advent of modern farming techniques.

A model for the shift from agriculture to pastoralism was presented by Ilse Köhler-Rollefson of San Diego (Calif.) State University. She proposed that nonirrigation agriculture and animal husbandry were initially complementary strategies. Once a critical population was reached, and local environmental degradation began, the site's location at the margins of predictable rainfall created stress for both strategies. The management of goat herds at 'Ain Ghazal required more and more land, with the result that agriculture and herding became mutually incompatible. Both activities were needed to maintain the relatively large population, but the only way to continue them was to move the goat herds farther and farther away. This was the first step in developing nomadic pastoralism. As the environment continued to decline, and rainfall remained unpredictable, nonirrigation agriculture became less viable. More resources were put into pastoralism until eventually, about 5000 BC, the entire population was oriented around it. Nomadic pastoralism remained an essential lifeway in the region until the recent past, when modern technology allowed large-scale farming to reemerge as the dominant strategy.

—James D. Wilde

See also Feature Article: POLLEN: NATURE'S FINGERPRINTS OF PLANTS.

Architecture and civil engineering

Architecture. Architectural trends neither start and stop within neat yearly packages nor evolve in a void. Architecture, as well as other art forms, evolves in response to a vast array of social issues and technological advances. Rarely can one building signify a breakthrough in the way that a new discovery in a scientific field such as chemistry can. Each year significant buildings are built that reinforce current stylistic trends. Other buildings explore new ways to mold space or exploit ever evolving technological advances as their basis for experimentation with form. Eventually the test of time will prune away many of the experimental changes in style, yet the seeds of meaningful and lasting change are also being sown. During their birth and early evolution, it is impossible to predict with certainty which new forms will endure. There remain, however, structures whose impact is discernible and lasting.

Australia celebrated its bicentennial in 1988. Appropriately, the occasion was marked by the dedication of a new Parliament House. Its bold design, by the firm of Mitchell/Giurgola & Thorp, was the winner of an international competition. A pair of great tapering curved walls, each 460 m (1,509 ft) long and rising to a height of 27 m (88 ft) at their center, sweep through the complex. These twin converging arcs funnel visitors in a formal progression through a ceremonial forecourt with its pool to a Great Veranda that frames the Great (reception) Hall. Slicing through the circular site, the walls unify the entire complex of buildings and gardens while delineating

Parliament House in Canberra, Australia, was completed in 1988. Designed by Mitchell/ Giurgola & Thorp, it cost almost $800 million and was the most ambitious construction project in the nation's history.

areas within the lower side hollows of the paired convex curves. The House of Representatives and Senate chamber buildings sit on opposite sides, and the approaching walls then open up to display the Ministerial Area beyond. In the center the polished granite-covered walls reach their apex. Three meters (ten feet) thick at this point, they support the base of a four-legged stainless steel frame that carries a flag the size of a badminton court above the roof of the Members Hall below. Costing close to $800 million, the building was the most ambitious construction project in Australia's history.

Asia was enriched by the addition of one of the world's most significant office towers. Rising 369 m (1,209 ft) over Hong Kong, the Bank of China is the fifth tallest building in the world. Designed by I. M. Pei & Partners, it contains more than 90,000 sq m (one million square feet) of space and is taller than any building in Europe. In plan the building is a 52-m (170-ft) square. This square is divided by its diagonals into four quadrants, each triangle forming the base of a prism. As the building ascends, the prisms drop off at 13-story intervals—the first at the 25th floor, another at the 38th, and a third at the 51st level, leaving only one soaring to the top. A central column descends to the 25th level, where it transfers its load to the top of the tetrahedron-shaped framing system; this, in turn, transfers the load to four massive corner columns. By moving all the vertical loads to the four perimeter columns, the designers imparted great stability to the structure, and the use of composite (concrete-filled hollow beams and concrete-encased steel columns) permitted a structural weight of only 112 kg per sq m (23 lb per sq ft).

In Ottawa Moshe Safdie's new National Gallery of Canada was completed. A cohesive arrangement of spaces and volumes, it accommodates a variety of galleries and ceremonial public spaces. The stepped glass cages of its Great Hall rise with subdued re-

spect for the nearby Victorian, polygonal Library of Parliament. Acting as a modern echo of its venerable neighbor, the Gallery's silhouette and form are at peace with a predecessor that has long been one of the symbols of Canada. Penetrating daylight is a dominating theme in the Gallery. Multistory atrium passageways connect the three major public spaces. Toplighted art galleries surround small-scale atrium courts. Daylight is carried down through slots in the floor of the second-story art galleries to the first-level exhibits.

The Tegel Harbor Housing in West Berlin, designed by Moore Ruble Yudell, is an outstanding

"Tent City" near downtown Boston, consisting of buildings ranging in height from 4 to 12 stories, was designed to provide affordable housing for people with a variety of incomes.

292

example of low-key postmodernism, with its facades displaying a nostalgic borrowing of pseudoclassical symbolism. The project is notable for its delicate and sensitive molding of space.

One of the best examples of socially responsible housing is Goody, Clancy & Associates' "Tent City." Built in response to fears of gentrification, it contains mixed economic levels of affordable housing. Architecturally it serves as a bridge between affluent Copley Place and the sprawl of Boston's South End. The project incorporates 12-story structures with 4-story stacked duplex units. Open spaces are woven into a site plan that accommodates itself to the historic street patterns, even providing storefronts along part of the perimeter.

An increasing number of distinguished historic buildings were restored. In response to an awakening appreciation of their inherent values, venerable structures, which in the recent past might have been torn down, were refurbished and revitalized to serve today's needs. For example, Union Station in Washington, D.C., designed by Daniel Burnham at the turn of the century as the world's largest railroad terminal, was restored to its former glory. The original exquisite details were respected and returned to their former splendor. The U.S. Congress, in a rare concern for architecture, passed the "Union Station Act" to provide funding. A number of architectural firms, led by Harry Weese & Associates, were responsible for the work. Its more than 55,-700 sq m (600,000 sq ft) of floor area contain a multitude of spaces, the largest being the Main Hall located beneath a 29-m (96-ft)-high coffered barrel-vault ceiling.

In London the 1911 Michelin (Tire Co.) House was restored and expanded by Conran Roche and YRM. Stained-glass windows and tile work were carefully refurbished and rebuilt to provide a unique ambience for the building's restaurant, store, and upper-level offices.

Mario Botta, in the belief that "the best way to respect the past is to be authentically modern," continued to influence architectural thinking with his André Malraux Cultural Center in Chambéry, France. Entry to this movie and theater complex is carefully orchestrated. Visitors must first traverse the courtyard of an old army barracks and then cross through part of the barracks itself in order to enter the new complex via a glass-enclosed link. The bold geometric shapes of the center respond dramatically to their functions, while the slotted texture provided by the narrow windows evokes the emotional impact of forts of the Middle Ages.

Much architectural interest and public concern was focused on a variety of buildings whose forms and interrelation of shapes seem to have no visible historic roots. This development caused concern as

Carol Highsmith

Union Station in Washington, D.C., originally built to be the world's largest railroad terminal, has been restored to its former glory by several architectural firms, led by Harry Weese & Associates.

both architects and the public grasped at ways to understand and evaluate these structures. "Deconstructivist" architecture, whether a passing fad or the start of a major movement, will unquestionably affect the built environment for some time to come, as the museums and other public buildings erected under its sway will remain to influence or mock architecture for years to come.

U.S. architects, such as Frank Gehry and Michael Graves, attracted attention with their use of geometric forms, as did Ton Alberts in The Netherlands with his use of plastic shapes. New materials augmented by sophisticated engineering methods enabled architects to circumvent or free themselves from the limitations of spatial forms dependent upon traditional structural logic. A variety of different geometric forms can now be made to abut or intersect one another, creating spatial relationships that please and excite some while jarring others who are more comfortable with the traditional relationships between form and function.

Architectural constructions, called "follies," that sometimes provide unconventional forms while simultaneously enclosing space for a wide variety of activities, attracted attention and publicity. Particularly popular in France, follies shape and delineate space, occasionally exploiting the inherent capabilities of the material from which they are constructed.

293

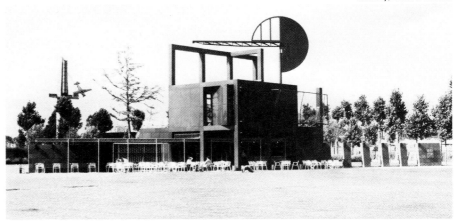

"Follies," designed by Bernard Tschumi for the Parc de La Villette in Paris, enclose space within unconventional forms for a wide variety of activities.

Among the most acclaimed of these structures were those designed by Bernard Tschumi for the Parc de La Villette in Paris, which exploit the confrontation between function and the transformation of an ideal cube.

The American Institute of Architects awarded its gold medal, after a hiatus of two years, to Joseph Esherick, whose work includes the recently opened Monterey Bay (California) Aquarium. The International Pritzker Prize, also awarded for an entire body of work, was shared for the first time. The two recipients, Gordon Bunshaft of the U.S. and Oscar Niemeyer of Brazil, were outstanding modernists.

Civil engineering. Great engineering has always produced "architecture," the Gothic cathedrals proving the inseparability of the two. The gymnastics pavilion built for the 1988 summer Olympic Games in Seoul, South Korea, continued that tradition. It was the world's first cable dome. Designed by the engineering firm of David H. Geiger and Associates, it took the use of cable construction to a new dimension. Previous buildings for the Olympics, such as Frei Otto's stadium in Munich, West Germany, used cable roof systems of various kinds. Cables are the most economical way to span long distances, as can be readily recognized by their exclusive use for long-span bridges. Until recently their major architectural drawback was the nature of the space beneath their sagging vertical curve. Building on a concept called tersegrity, originated by Buckminster Fuller, the gymnastics pavilion was roofed with a rising domelike structure created with a tensile cable pattern interwoven with vertical compression struts.

The Norwegians were completing the construction of a $1.5 billion drilling rig in the North Sea capable of withstanding the impact of waves 30 m (100 ft) high. The 360-m (1,180-ft)-tall platform, designed and built by Norwegian Contractors A/S, Stavanger, will be the largest concrete offshore platform in the world. It is supported on four tapered shafts, each

resembling a giant industrial chimney. They rise from a base constructed of 24 82-m (270-ft)-high concrete cylinders. The completed structure will be towed 200 km (125 mi) to its drilling location and then lowered to the ocean floor. The 82,000 tons of steel bars used to reinforce the concrete are more than ten times the weight of the Eiffel Tower's entire iron framing.

The Canadian Pacific Railroad completed construction of the longest railroad tunnel in North America. The 14.7-km (9.1-mi) bore speeds traffic through the Canadian Rocky Mountains. Reaching a height of 289 m (946 ft), 311 South Wacker Drive in Chicago became the world's tallest concrete-framed building. The all-concrete system utilized concrete able to withstand pressures of 12,000 psi.

Work neared completion on Japan's 9.7-km (6-mi)-long link of bridges across the Inland Sea

Cyclists ride on Japan's Minami Bisan-seto Bridge just before it was opened to train and vehicle traffic in April 1988. Its span of 1,118 m (3,667 ft) is the longest in Japan and fifth longest in the world.

294

between the islands of Honshu and Shikoku. The project includes three suspension bridges, each spanning more than 915 m (3,000 ft); several viaducts; a continuous-span curved truss; and a pair of 425-m (1,400-ft) cable-stayed bridges. The Minami Bisanseto Bridge's span of 1,118 m (3,667 ft) is the longest in Japan and the fifth longest in the world. It was designed to carry both vehicles and trains above Bisan Strait while providing a 66-m (217-ft) clearance for shipping.

The Sunshine Skyway Bridge across Florida's Tampa Bay, with a clear span of 366 m (1,200 ft), became the world's longest cable-stayed bridge. It opened to traffic amid growing concern that over half of the world's more than 200 cable-stayed bridges were in serious structural trouble because of problems of vibration and corrosion.

The Civil Engineering Society bestowed its 1988 Outstanding Civil Engineering Award to Boston's Southwest Corridor Project, a $750 million achievement that relocated rapid transit and railroad services and revitalized the neighborhoods along its 7.6-km (4.7-mi) path. It was the first time that U.S. federal highway funds were used for a mass transit project and was the largest public construction project in the history of Massachusetts. The Great Salt Lake West Desert Pumping Project in Utah and the Sunshine Skyway Bridge in Florida received Awards of Merit.

—David Guise

Astronomy

During the past year a new coating technique led to improved X-ray telescopes. Chiron, believed to be an asteroid, displayed activity more appropriate for a comet. The Great Red Spot of Jupiter was modeled both mathematically and physically. Supernova 1987A continued to supply clues to the supernova process. An eclipsing millisecond pulsar was discovered. More dwarf galaxies were detected, and the elusive Einstein's ring was found. New clues to the structure of galaxies were announced. Galaxies were discovered at distances comparable to the most distant quasars.

Instrumentation. The first high-resolution images of the entire corona of the Sun taken in soft X-rays (those having comparatively long wavelengths and poor penetrating power) were announced by Arthur Walker, Jr., and Joakim Lindbloom (Stanford University), Troy Barbee, Jr. (Lawrence Livermore Laboratory, Livermore, Calif.), and Richard Hoover (Space Science Laboratory, Huntsville, Ala.). The improved resolution, better than 1.5 seconds of arc, was obtained by means of direct-incidence reflecting optics. (The X-rays strike the optical surface directly.) Previously, imaging X-ray telescopes in this

spectral region had to use grazing-incidence optics (in which the X-rays strike the surface at a small glancing angle) because when X-rays strike surfaces directly, they normally are not reflected but instead penetrate the surfaces and are absorbed. The grazing-incidence mirrors are difficult to make and generally give only moderate resolution with small effective collecting areas.

The direct-incidence telescopes employ a recently developed technique in which alternating layers of a high-atomic-number material and a low-atomic-number material are deposited on the surfaces of the mirrors. By applying tens to hundreds of such layer pairs, reflectivity can be enhanced to as high as 50%. The reflection remains high over a limited range of wavelengths, however, and so a mirror with this type of coating forms an image in essentially one wavelength (or essentially one color if the image were to be formed in visible light). The telescope used by Walker and his colleagues had a diameter of 6.4 cm (2.5 in) and formed an image in the band of wavelengths from 171 to 175 angstroms. (One angstrom equals one ten-billionth of a meter.) It was used in a sounding rocket to obtain the solar pictures.

Larger multilayer telescopes are likely to be constructed in the future to obtain the resolution of 0.1 second of arc required for studying the detailed physical processes taking place in the solar corona. In addition, the application of this technique to instruments for space satellites will permit the imaging of such X-ray sources as supernova remnants, the hot interstellar medium in galaxies, and the regions surrounding compact X-ray sources.

Solar system. Chiron, an unusual asteroid discovered in 1977, revealed its true character during the past year. Chiron had been considered odd because it orbits the Sun between Saturn and Uranus (most known asteroids orbit between Mars and Jupiter), has a relatively large diameter for an asteroid, and reflects light more poorly than most asteroids. David Tholen (University of Hawaii), William Hartmann (Planetary Science Institute, Tucson, Ariz.), and Dale Cruikshank (Ames Research Center, Moffett Field, Calif.) observed Chiron to be twice its usual brightness in 1988, indicating that it had expelled gas and dust that reflected additional sunlight and thus made it brighter. They concluded, therefore, that Chiron is a comet, not an asteroid. In 1995, as it does every 51 years, Chiron will reach the nearest point to the Sun in its orbit at roughly 8.5 astronomical units. (One astronomical unit equals 150 million km [93 million mi].) Increased cometary action can be anticipated as it receives more radiant energy from the Sun. It apparently is a comet that was captured into its present orbit and certainly will be ejected from it in the future. It is possible that in several thousand years, if Chiron swings inward toward the Sun, the Earth's inhabitants will be treated to a proper—maybe even spectacular—cometary display.

The Great Red Spot on Jupiter has been observed continuously for more than 300 years. At one time it was thought to be a circulation pattern induced in Jupiter's atmosphere by a feature on the surface of the planet. Theoretical studies and results from the Voyager probes, however, clearly indicated that Jupiter does not have a solid surface beneath its thick clouds. It is liquid throughout except for a possible solid inner core. The Voyager observations showed the spot to be a huge vortex with a diameter twice the size of the Earth spinning counterclockwise in Jupiter's atmosphere. Strong winds blow to the west north of the spot and to the east south of it. Severe turbulence is generated between these winds.

Astronomers have questioned how the Red Spot could exist so long in the turbulent atmospheric flow if nothing is there to anchor it. Philip Marcus (University of California at Berkeley) developed a computer model that simulated what appears to be happening in Jupiter's atmosphere. He modeled a zone as it would be seen from Jupiter's south pole in which winds blow counterclockwise at the northern border and clockwise at the southern border. As the simulated winds increased in velocity, small vortices emerged in the shear region between the contrary winds, spinning counterclockwise themselves. The vortices merged to form larger ones. Finally a large elliptical vortex formed, driven by the counterclockwise spin between the winds blowing at its northern and southern limits. Marcus persuaded Joël Sommeria, Steven Meyers, and Harry Swinney at the University of Texas to construct a mechanical model. They built a circular tub one meter (3.3 feet) across with an inner ring of inlets and an outer ring of outlets. When the tub is rotated to simulate Jupiter's rotation and water is pumped through the inlets and outlets, water toward the outer wall of the tub flows counterclockwise and water toward the center flows clockwise. Just as in the computer simulation, small vortices develop between the oppositely flowing water, combining into larger ones until finally a large, elliptical vortex is established. The next problem in explaining the Great Red Spot will concern the precise mechanism by which the intense winds arise that give Jupiter its banded appearance.

In recent years some astronomers have suggested that the Sun may have been several seconds of arc larger (corresponding to a linear change of some 2,000 km) in the later 1600s and early 1700s than it appears to be today. This was refuted, however, by a reexamination during the past year of observations of the May 3, 1715, eclipse (in the Gregorian calendar) that crossed England. The work was done by Leslie Morrison (Royal Greenwich Observatory, East Sussex, England), F. Richard Stephenson (University of

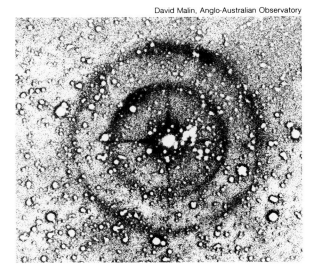

David Malin, Anglo-Australian Observatory

Two rings of light surrounding Supernova 1987A, photographed on July 15, 1988, are caused by light from the original explosion reflected by two sheets of interstellar dust in the Large Magellanic Cloud.

Durham, England), and John Parkinson (University College London). Edmond Halley, of comet fame, had solicited naked-eye observations of the eclipse by citizens throughout England, which he then collected for analysis. Halley was able to define the northern and southern limits of the eclipse shadow by reports from Darrington, Yorkshire, in the north and Cranbrook, Kent, in the south, both of which lay just at the shadow limits. By assuming the modern value for the size of the Sun's apparent diameter and correcting for irregularities in the Moon's limb, the present investigators calculated the limits of the shadow path as they would be seen in England had the eclipse occurred in this epoch. The calculated path limits agree almost perfectly with the observations recorded by Halley, demonstrating that the apparent size of the Sun was not significantly different in Halley's day from what it is now.

Stars. By 1989 Supernova 1987A had faded to obscurity as far as naked-eye observations were concerned, but it was still supplying information about the supernova process. The gamma rays and X-rays expected from the decay of radioactive cobalt created in the supernova explosion were detected as the ejected material expanded and became more transparent. In October 1988 the Mir space station of the U.S.S.R. and the Ginga satellite of Japan detected the X-rays. Roughly one month later balloon-launched instruments and the Solar Maximum Mission satellite of the U.S. National Aeronautics and Space Administration (NASA) detected the gamma rays.

The detections are a striking conformation of the theory of the supernova process as it is now understood. In addition, light echoes from the supernova were found. Alin Crotts (University of Texas) was the first to discover two rings of light around the supernova location, which are caused by light from the original outburst reflected by two sheets of interstellar dust in the Large Magellanic Cloud, located about 470 and 1,300 light-years in front of the supernova location. The rings are continually expanding as the ever enlarging sphere of light from the supernova reaches more distant parts of the two sheets of interstellar dust.

An apparently ordinary star that is quite similar to the Sun and designated as HD 114762 was discovered to have a companion that has a mass at least ten times that of Jupiter and an orbit about the size of that of Mercury. David Latham, Robert Stefanik, Richard McCrosky, and Robert Davis (Smithsonian Astrophysical Observatory, Cambridge, Mass.) and Tsevi Mazeh (Tel Aviv [Israel] University) found that HD 114762 has a variation in its Doppler shift corresponding to about 500 m per second with a period of 84 days. (The Doppler shift is the amount of the change in the observed frequency of a wave due to the relative motion of the source and the observer.) This indicates that the star is oscillating because of the gravitational pull of an unseen, orbiting companion. Before this discovery, the star was thought to have a known and constant Doppler shift. Consequently, it was under consideration to be used as a standard in a search for stars with variable Doppler shifts, which could be systems containing planetlike bodies. HD 114762 is the first star with a planetlike companion for which a complete orbit has been observed.

While conducting a survey to discover millisecond pulsars (stars that emit pulsating radiation at millisecond intervals) with the Arecibo radio telescope in Puerto Rico, Andrew Fruchter, Daniel Stinebring and Joseph Taylor (Princeton University) discovered the Pulser PSR 1957 +20 with a spin rate of 622 times per second. That in itself is interesting, but this object also is eclipsed by an orbiting, invisible companion. The eclipses occur every 9.17 hours and last about 50 minutes. An analysis of the data indicates that the companion has a tight, nearly circular orbit with a diameter only 2.4 times that of the Sun. Since the pulsar itself has a small orbital velocity, only about five kilometers (three miles) per second, the companion must have a small mass, estimated to be about 23 Jupiter masses; this is too small for it to be shining by the thermonuclear process that powers the Sun. In addition, the radio pulses from PSR 1957 +20 are delayed just before and after an eclipse. This delay is presumably caused by ionized gas surrounding the companion. The opaque part of the companion, by which the radio pulses are completely blocked, is calculated to be three-quarters the

size of the Sun, or 1,044,000 km (648,742 mi) in diameter, so large that in such a close system, the more massive pulsar is capable of stripping matter from the companion. Millisecond pulsars are believed to form in binary systems in which the pulsar is caused to spin faster by accreting matter from its companion. This appears to be the case for PSR 1957 +20, which should destroy its companion in less than a billion years.

Extragalactic astronomy. The evidence that our Galaxy contains a black hole at its center is becoming overwhelming. It now appears that both our neighbor, the Andromeda galaxy, and its companion galaxy, M32, also have black holes at their centers. Alan Dressler (Mount Wilson and Las Campanas Observatories, Carnegie Institution of Washington, Pasadena, Calif.) observed both systems on a night of exceptional observing conditions. When Douglas Richstone (University of Michigan) compared Dressler's excellent data with computer simulations of star motions near the center of a galaxy, he found that the data implied that the Andromeda galaxy should contain a black hole of about 50 million solar masses and M32 a black hole of approximately 5 million solar masses. According to Dressler's data, the stars in the innermost regions of the two galaxies move so rapidly that there must be huge unseen masses at the galactic centers, gravitationally binding the stars to the central locations. Andromeda not only is larger and more massive than our Galaxy but also appears to have a larger black hole at its center than our black hole of ten million solar masses.

Dwarf galaxies, those with masses that are hundreds to thousands of times smaller than our Galaxy, are thought to be the most numerous of all galaxies. Recent work by Chris Impey (University of Arizona), Greg Bothun (University of Michigan), and David Malin (Anglo-Australian Observatory, Epping, New South Wales, Australia) not only confirmed that idea but indicated that the dwarfs may be much more common than previously thought. The team of observers searched the Virgo cluster of galaxies for faint galaxies overlooked in previous studies of the cluster because they were either too diffuse or too faint. Using a photographic technique that amplified small differences in contrast on photographic images, they looked for faint objects with angular diameters greater than 30 seconds of arc. They found 137 galaxies with low surface brightness, of which 27 had not been found before. One of those was a spiral galaxy lying beyond the Virgo cluster, but the other 26 were dwarf elliptical galaxies most likely belonging to the Virgo cluster. Samples of the galaxies were observed both with a CCD (charge coupled detector) in order to refine the knowledge of their apparent structure and at radio wavelengths to measure their hydrogen gas content. The investigators concluded that there may be large populations of galaxies with extremely low surface brightness. If the number of faint dwarfs is eventually shown to be large enough, these dwarfs could contribute as much mass to the universe as the larger galaxies like our own.

Stuart Vogel (Rensselaer Polytechnic Institute) and Shrinivas Kulkarni and Nicholas Scoville (California Institute of Technology) observed the Whirlpool galaxy, M51, with the Owens Valley Radio Observatory facilities in California. M51 is a classical spiral galaxy about 31 million light-years away. The observations were designed to detect molecular gas in the galaxy and to develop a detailed map of both the positions and velocities of the gas. Clouds of molecular gas, predominantly hydrogen, were found concentrated in the spiral arms of M51. The arms are also the location of the highest density of interstellar dust and young stars.

The concentration of the molecular clouds in the arms is not surprising in itself since the clouds are known to be regions where star births can occur. What is significant, however, is the discovery that the gas in the galaxy is rotating about the galactic center more rapidly than are the spiral arms. This conforms to the density-wave theory of spiral arms, in which the arms are regions of high density that exist as waves in the basic galactic structure. Thus, when the clouds catch up with the arms, they undergo a severe change in velocity, becoming redirected inward along the arms by the gravitational fields of the arms. In addition, newly formed massive stars, recognized by their ability to ionize nearby hydrogen, appear somewhat to the sides of the arms opposite to the direction in which the gas enters the arms. The most probable explanation for these stars is that the molecular clouds suffer a gravitational shock as they enter the arms, thus triggering star formation. The stars themselves appear some 30 million years afterward, by which time they are on the opposite sides of the arms. While the precise mechanism is not yet known, the investigators suggest that the gravitational fields of the arms cause the incoming clouds to be pulled closer together. This in turn induces more frequent collisions between the clouds, causing some to collapse into stars as their density is enhanced by the collisions.

In 1936 Albert Einstein predicted the possibility of gravitational lensing, in which light from a distant star directly behind a foreground star would be imaged into a ring of light. He dismissed it, however, as something that had no chance to be observed because of the extremely precise alignment that would be required. Jacqueline Hewitt (Haystack Observatory, Westford, Mass.), Edwin Turner (Princeton University), Donald Schneider (Institute for Advanced Study, Princeton), Bernard Burke and Glen Langston (Massachusetts Institute of Technology), and Charles Lawrence (California Institute of Technology), while conducting a survey of radio sources with the Very Large Array near Socorro, N.M., found the source MG1131 +0456 to be a tiny oval-shaped ring roughly two seconds of arc across with two elongated bright spots at either end of the oval. The question arose as to whether this unusual object was an example of gravitational lensing. The most likely answer is yes. The investigators subsequently identified a faint optical object that appeared to be a distant large elliptical galaxy, which could be the gravitational lens. While Einstein had carried out his calculation under the assumption of point sources, the alignment requirement for forming a ring is not nearly so severe when the imaging mass is an extended object, such as a galaxy. Calculations indicated that the source being imaged was a radio galaxy with the elliptical galaxy located in front of one of its lobes, imaging that lobe into the elliptical ring. The core of the radio galaxy was imaged into the two bright spots. The second lobe of the radio galaxy could be seen faintly outside the ring.

For many years the objects with the largest known

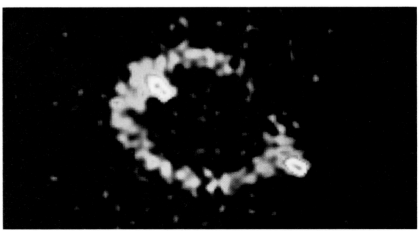

The oval-shaped MG1131 +0456 might be an example of an Einstein ring in which light from a distant star directly behind a foreground star is imaged into a ring of light. This phenomenon, predicted by Albert Einstein, is called gravitational lensing.

Courtesy of Jacqueline N. Hewitt, Edwin L. Turner, and Bernard F. Burke

National Optical Astronomy Observatories; Kenneth Chambers, George Miley, and Wil van Breugel; Johns Hopkins University, Space Telescope Science Institute, University of California, Berkeley

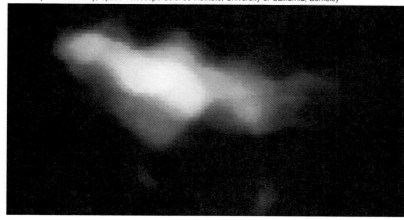

Glowing hydrogen gas was produced by the radio source 4C41.17. With a redshift of 3.8, this galaxy is the most distant yet discovered, some 6 billion to 15 billion light-years from the Earth. Until 1988 only quasars had been found at that distance.

redshifts (displacements of their spectra toward longer wavelengths) and, therefore, the greatest distances from the Earth have been quasars. Galaxies had not been found with redshifts much greater than one. In 1988, however, that changed as attention was turned to galaxies that were strong sources of radio waves. Simon Lilley (University of Hawaii) searched for and found the optical counterpart to the radio source designated as 0902 +34. Its optical image clearly showed it to be an extended object that did not have the point-source characteristics of a distant quasar. The spectrum of this object, obtained with the 3.6-m Canada-France-Hawaii Telescope and the 3.8-m United Kingdom Infrared Telescope on Mauna Kea in Hawaii, revealed lines of hydrogen and carbon with a tremendous redshift of 3.4.

Almost as soon as this startling result was announced, Kenneth Chambers (Johns Hopkins University, Baltimore, Md.), George Miley (Leiden [Neth.] University), and Wil van Breugel (University of California at Berkeley) presented an even more distant galaxy with a redshift of 3.8. The team had conducted a survey that searched for distant radio galaxies. They began by identifying radio sources in catalogs that had radio emission that decreased sharply with increasing frequency. Experience has shown that sources with this characteristic tend to be the most energetic sources and should be detectable at the greatest distances. Next, in order to obtain good positions for them, they observed the faint sources so identified by utilizing the excellent resolution of the Very Large Array. They then used the 2-m optical telescope at Kitt Peak National Observatory, Tucson, Ariz., to search for optical counterparts. They followed up those that were identified by obtaining spectra with the 4-m telescope at Kitt Peak. Each step in the process took one year. In all, they found eight galaxies with redshifts in excess of two. One of them, radio source 4C41.17, which had an optical image roughly 8 seconds of arc across,

displayed a redshift of 3.8. Depending upon the value of the Hubble constant (the rate at which the velocity of recession of the galaxies increases with distance) that is used, this huge, energetic galaxy is at a distance of 6 billion to 15 billion light-years, well within the realm of distant quasars.

—W. M. Protheroe

Chemistry

Research in chemistry during the past year ranged from investigations of the newfound catalytic abilities of RNA molecules and antibodies to development of reduced-cholesterol eggs and low-calorie fat substitutes to speculation about the presence in interstellar space of large quantities of soccer-ball-shaped clusters of carbon atoms. Excitement over the recently discovered superconducting ceramics remained high as investigators synthesized new classes of the mixed metal oxides, including one type that once more raised the record temperature for superconductive behavior.

Inorganic chemistry

During 1988 inorganic chemists synthesized and characterized several new high-temperature superconductors, prepared a benzene-related compound whose ring contains atoms of aluminum and nitrogen rather than of carbon, discovered a new chemical method for making the promising semiconductor gallium arsenide, and worked to improve biomedical knowledge of the mechanisms by which various metal complexes exert their pharmaceutical effects in the body.

Chemistry of high-temperature superconductors. During 1986 and 1987 early reports of the discovery of so-called high-temperature superconductors created an explosion of scientific activity and interest

299

worldwide (see *1989 Yearbook of Science and the Future* Year in Review: CHEMISTRY: *Inorganic chemistry*). In early 1987 the highest temperature at which a material becomes superconducting (its transition temperature, or T_c) was roughly 95 K, achieved by the compound $YBa_2Cu_3O_{7-x}$ ($x \lesssim 0.1$). (To convert kelvins, K, to degrees Celsius, subtract 273; thus, 95 K = $-178°$ C, or $-289°$ F.) Subsequently, after a year of intensive, highly competitive research by large groups of scientists in many different laboratories, the record T_c was raised to 125 K ($-148°$ C or $-235°$ F). Although this higher temperature, as well as the newly discovered superconductors, offered reason enough for optimism, achieving superconductivity at room temperature (about 298 K [25° C, or 77° F]) still seemed far down the road.

Inorganic chemistry has afforded the basis for this development of high-temperature superconductors, which are mixed metal oxides largely prepared and characterized by solid-state inorganic chemists. During the past year there was good progress in syntheses and characterization, but as has been so often the case in science, theory lagged behind experiment, and there arose no satisfactory understanding of the mechanism of superconductivity in these mixed metal oxides. This situation, however, did not deter inorganic chemists from using well-established empirical guidelines based on the chemistry of the elements derived from their positions in the periodic table and their known oxidation states. With $YBa_2Cu_3O_{7-x}$ as a starting point, researchers prepared and tested many mixed metal oxide compounds for superconductivity. Initially they found that the elements yttrium (Y) and barium (Ba) could be replaced by analogous M(III) and M(II) metals (metals with oxidation states of +3 and +2, respectively) but that the element copper (Cu) seemed necessary for superconductivity.

With the discovery of barium-potassium-bismuth oxide (Ba-K-Bi-O) superconductors in 1988, it was realized that copper is not essential. What appeared to be needed was a metal of variable oxidation state; *e.g.*, Cu(I, II, or III) or Bi(III, IV, or V). Although other transition metals have variable oxidation states, by the end of 1988 only copper and bismuth were reported to form superconductors in these systems. Among new superconductors reported were $(MO)_mM'_2Ca_{n-1}Cu_nO_{2n+2}$, in which M' may be barium or strontium (Sr) and in which M may be thallium (Tl), bismuth, or a mixture of bismuth and lead (Pb), of bismuth and thallium, or of thallium and lead; $(TlO)_2Ba_2Ca_{n-1}Cu_nO_{2n+2}$, where $n = 1, 2,$ or 3; and $(BaK)(Bi,Pb)O_3$. Of all the new mixed-metal-oxide superconductors prepared in the past year, $Tl_2Ca_2Ba_2Cu_3O_{10}$ held the distinction of superconductivity at the highest T_c, 125 K. The newest series of superconductors reported can be represented by the formula $Pb_2Sr_2(Ca,M)Cu_3O_{8+y}$, in which M can be different rare earth metals.

In the absence of a theoretical understanding of superconductivity in mixed metal oxides, experimental inorganic chemists were developing qualitative empirical guidelines on the basis of experimental observations. One guideline is that oxide superconductors always contain mixed-valent cations, such as Cu(I, II, III) and Bi(III, IV, V). Another is that high-temperature superconductivity occurs only in oxides in which there is very high covalency. Yet another is that electropositive cations such as Y(III) and Ba(II) seem to be needed, perhaps because they increase the covalency of the Cu—O bond, because they stabilize the high oxidation states Cu(III) and Bi(V), or for both reasons. These guidelines, knowledge of the periodic relationships of the elements, consideration of the charge and size of metal ions, and good intuition held promise for yet higher T_c values and

Structures a, b, and c are benzene;
d, e, and f are borazine;
and g, h, and i are alumazine (not yet prepared).

for the discovery of new types of superconducting mixed metal oxides.

Main-group chemistry. The main-group elements in the periodic table include both metals and nonmetals other than transition metals and inner transition metals (lanthanides and actinides). For decades little research was done on the chemistry of main-group elements, particularly in the U.S., but within the past 20 years there has been a marked change, with the development of new important chemistry (see *1985 Yearbook of Science and the Future* Year in Review: CHEMISTRY: *Inorganic chemistry*).

Benzene, C_6H_6, is a well-known organic compound that owes its high stability and planar structure to its aromaticity. Aromatic compounds are cyclic compounds having a particular combination of single and double bonds that permit delocalization (spreading) of the electron cloud above and below the plane of the ring. Thus, benzene can be represented as either (1a) or (1b), but chemists know that neither structure is correct because all carbon-carbon bond distances are identical. This suggests that the real structure is an average of (1a) and (1b), which the chemist represents as (1c). Electrons, being negatively charged, repel each other. They resist confinement together and tend to spread out over space, which is the reason electron delocalization helps stabilize aromatic compounds.

Boranes are compounds of boron (B) and hydrogen (H) and are akin to hydrocarbons, which are compounds of carbon (C) and hydrogen. Borane chemistry began in 1912 with the classic investigations of Alfred Stock in Germany that led to the synthesis of diborane (B_2H_6) with its mysterious bonding that challenged chemists for years. The ensuing research culminated in the awarding of the 1976 Nobel Prize for Chemistry to William Lipscomb of Harvard University "for his studies of boranes which have illuminated problems of chemical bonding." In 1926 Stock and E. Pohland reported the preparation of borazine by the reaction $3B_2H_6 + 6NH_3 \rightarrow 2B_3N_3H_6 + 12H_2$, which is run at 180° C (356° F).

Borazine fascinates chemists because it is isoelectronic with (has the same number of electrons as) benzene and because it has the same planar hexagonal-ring structure as well as similar physical properties. Consequently, borazine is often called inorganic benzene and is represented as having aromaticity analogous to benzene (see 1d–1f). The weight of chemical evidence, however, suggests that borazine has little aromatic character. Its delocalized electron cloud above and below the flat ring is "lumpy," with more electron density localized on nitrogen (N), which is more electronegative than boron. This partial electron localization makes the boron-nitrogen bonds weaker than benzene's carbon-carbon bonds and gives borazine less aromatic stabilization.

A look at the periodic table suggests that aluminum, which is just below boron, may likewise form a benzene-borazine analogue; *i.e.*, alumazine ($Al_3N_3H_6$). Inorganic chemists have long been intrigued by the possibility of making this compound (1g–1i), which as of early 1989 had yet to be prepared. A derivative of alumazine, however, was recently reported by Philip Power and Krista Waggoner of the University of California at Davis. They produced the compound in high yield by means of a two-stage reaction between trimethylaluminum, $[Al(CH_3)_3]_2$, and 2,6-isopropylaniline (see 2). Its molecular structure is that of a central, planar, six-membered ring having alternating aluminum and nitrogen atoms, the basic structure expected of alumazine.

The alumazine derivative prepared is a member of a group of compounds called polyiminoalanes, which are aluminum-nitrogen compounds with different alkyl and aromatic groups. The polyiminoalanes adopt a variety of structures, and the compounds have the general formula $(RAlNR')_n$ in which R and

301

R′ are alkyl or aryl groups attached to Al and to N, respectively. These alanes are saturated compounds, having only single bonds to Al and to N and having values of four or greater for n. Compounds having n values of less than four (three for alumazine) imply the presence of aluminum-nitrogen multiple bonding. Existence of multiple bonding in the alumazine derivative reported by Power and Waggoner is supported by its shorter aluminum-nitrogen bond length of 1.78 Å, compared with bond lengths of 1.89–1.98 Å for the single-bonded polyiminoalane compounds. (One angstrom, Å, is a hundred-thousandth of a centimeter.) The preliminary chemistry of this derivative suggests that, like borazine, it falls short of being completely aromatic. Since nitrogen is more electronegative than aluminum, it was believed there is more electron density on nitrogen than on aluminum.

Another exciting development in main-group-element research was the synthesis of an arsinogallane that is readily converted chemically to gallium arsenide (GaAs). Gallium arsenide is a III-V semiconductor (so called from the positions of the two elements in the periodic table) that shows high promise in modern electronics technology. The standard procedure for preparing thin films of GaAs is cumbersome and depends on a highly toxic starting material, arsine (AsH_3). More specifically, the manufacture of GaAs devices is based on a chem-ical-vapor-deposition process involving reaction of trimethylgallium with arsine at elevated temperature: $(CH_3)_3Ga + AsH_3 \rightarrow GaAs + 3CH_4$.

Many research groups have been searching for alternative precursors and routes to GaAs. During the past year Klaus Theopold and co-workers at Cornell University, Ithaca, N.Y., reported the synthesis and characterization of the first monomeric arsinogallane and its chemical conversion into the semiconductor GaAs (see 3).

An X-ray structural determination of (3c) shows it is monomeric with a short gallium-arsenic bond length of 2.43 Å. Addition of tert-butanol to a pentane solution of (3c) results in formation of strong silicon-oxygen bonds in $(CH_3)_3COSi(CH_3)_3$, which then drives the reaction toward removal of the —$OSi(CH_3)_3$ groups from As and reaction of the $C_5(CH_3)_5$ groups with hydrogen to remove these groups from Ga. Thus, a finely divided amorphous powder of GaAs separates from solution; when heated at 500° C (930° F) for two days, the powder affords crystalline GaAs. Little is known about the mechanism of the reaction that forms GaAs, but as inorganic chemists learn more about mixed-metal main-group organometallics, it should become possible to design a new generation of precursors for III-V semiconductors.

Metal complexes as pharmaceuticals. Perhaps the earliest use of a metal to treat disease was the ap-

3

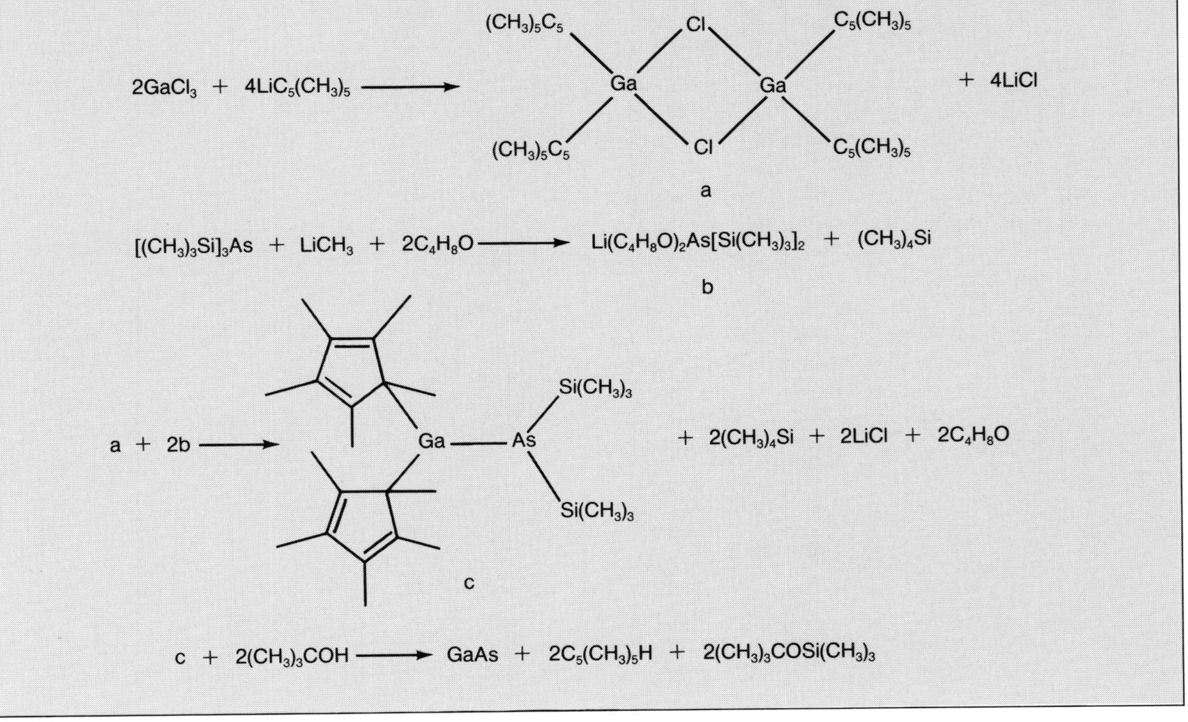

$2GaCl_3 + 4LiC_5(CH_3)_5 \longrightarrow$ a $+ 4LiCl$

$[(CH_3)_3Si]_3As + LiCH_3 + 2C_4H_8O \longrightarrow Li(C_4H_8O)_2As[Si(CH_3)_3]_2 + (CH_3)_4Si$

b

a + 2b $\longrightarrow$ c $+ 2(CH_3)_4Si + 2LiCl + 2C_4H_8O$

c + $2(CH_3)_3COH \longrightarrow GaAs + 2C_5(CH_3)_5H + 2(CH_3)_3COSi(CH_3)_3$

plication of mercury to alleviate syphilis. Because mercury is toxic, this practice resulted in the death of many patients. In modern times several metal complexes have become important pharmaceuticals, and in the last two decades extremely important advances have been made, largely by bioinorganic chemists. A few examples are discussed below.

The metal complex best known for its use as a pharmaceutical is cis-[Pt(NH₃)₂Cl₂], referred to as cisplatin or cis-DDP and presently a leading anticancer drug. Although cisplatin was first prepared more than a century ago and its anticancer properties have been recognized for two decades, sophisticated research has continued in an attempt to understand at the molecular level how and why the drug works as an antitumor agent (see *1981* and *1988 Yearbook of Science and the Future* Year in Review: CHEMISTRY: *Inorganic chemistry*).

Experts seem to agree on the importance of platinum-DNA interactions for the anticancer effect of cisplatin. This interaction is thought to inhibit DNA replication (necessary for cell division) but not transcriptional activity (RNA synthesis) or translational activity (protein synthesis). In spite of the elegant research done on these systems, investigators have yet to understand how the platinum-DNA complex affects cancerous cells. One recent approach toward an understanding has involved preparing DNA helixes with platinum bound at unique structurally determined sites and then testing and comparing their physical and biologic properties. In 1988 this work was under way in the laboratory of Stephen Lippard at the Massachusetts Institute of Technology in order to determine the extent and nature of DNA helix axis bending induced by cisplatin intrastrand crosslinking as well as the toxicity of specific lesions introduced in the DNA by the addition of platinum. Such work should help scientists understand how platinum complexes disrupt DNA and how cells repair the damage. It also may aid the design of platinum drugs that are more potent than cisplatin and have fewer side effects.

Platinum is a noble metal—*i.e.*, it is not very reactive chemically—but its complexes do react, cisplatin being a case in point. Thus, it is interesting that another noble metal, gold, forms complexes that are important antiarthritic drugs. As early as 1929 J. Forestier, a French physician, reported that gold complexes had greater efficacy on rheumatoid arthritis than on the tuberculosis for which they were being prescribed. Subsequent testing showed that gold complexes in some cases induced remission of the diseased state. Because their early use was marred by serious toxicity and occasional deaths, gold complexes were temporarily replaced by cortisone for treating arthritis. Disenchantment with cortisone's side effects and improved control over dosages of

gold complexes led to a resurgence of gold therapy in the early 1970s.

Myochrysine (AuSTm) and Solganal (AuSTg), used clinically in the U.S., are oligomers of gold(I) (*see* 4). They are large, somewhat ill-defined, complicated molecules, which have compounded the difficulty of studies at the molecular level on how gold complexes work against arthritis. Introduction of a second-generation drug, Auranofin (Et₃PAuSAtg), and of Et₃PAuSTg (*see* 4), both of which are less complicated, has made it easier to investigate the activity of gold in the body.

One laboratory engaged in gold therapeutic chemistry in 1988 was that of C. Frank Shaw III of the University of Wisconsin at Milwaukee, where research was being conducted on the protein chemistry of antiarthritic gold(I) complexes. Gold is a member of the copper triad (copper, silver, and gold) in the periodic table, and the chemistry of gold is well known to involve compounds in oxidation states of one and three, Au(I) and Au(III), respectively. In an oxidation state of one, gold is very polarizable and forms stable complexes with polarizable ligand atoms such as phosphorus (P; in PR₃) or sulfur (S; in SR⁻). (A substance is said to be polarizable, or "soft," if its electron cloud is readily distorted. Soft metals combine readily with soft ligands.) Since most natural proteins are known to contain thiol groups (RSH), it seems reasonable that gold may replace hydrogen in some of these groups. Investigations on three proteins, serum albumin, hemoglobin, and metallothionein, provided evidence for the occurrence of such a mechanism in the body.

4

Myochrysine

Solganal

Auranofin

Et₃PAuSTg

Ac = —COCH₃   Et = —C₂H₅

5

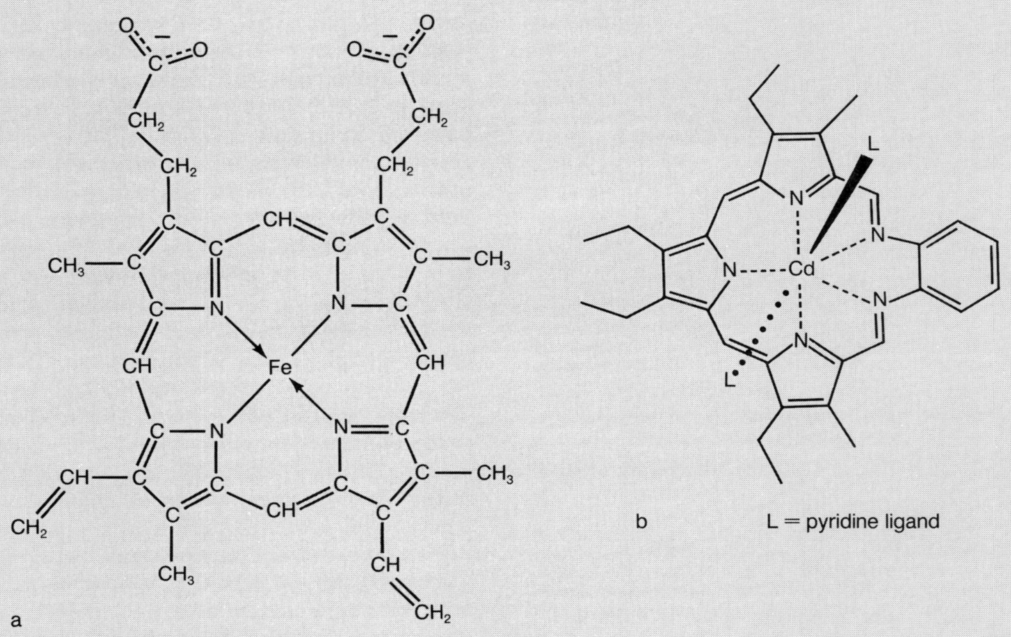

a

b   L = pyridine ligand

Although information on the nature of bonding of the gold complex was a good beginning, many questions remained as to details of the biologic reactions caused by the drug that gives it its antiarthritic properties.

During the past year members of another type of metal complex underwent clinical trials for the treatment of cancer, particularly for tumors that lie close to body surfaces or that can be reached with fiber-optic devices. These are metalloporphyrins, known to be effective photosensitizers for the production of singlet oxygen ($^1O_2$), an energetic, electronically excited state of oxygen. Certain porphyrins and metalloporphyrins are known to accumulate selectively in tumors, which when then irradiated with particular wavelengths of visible light are destroyed by the $^1O_2$ produced. This process is known as photodynamic therapy (PDT).

One serious difficulty with the use of PDT described above is that heme (5a), a natural iron-containing metalloporphyrin that forms part of the hemoglobin molecule, absorbs light in the same wavelength region as does the metalloporphyrin agent; thus, the irradiation necessary in PDT also damages hemoglobin in blood. David Dolphin and co-workers of the University of British Columbia were tackling this problem by attempting to make metalloporphyrins that absorb light at wavelengths longer than those absorbed by hemoglobin. They were doing this by varying the metal atom and making changes in the macrocyclic porphin ligand, the large ring-shaped structure surrounding the metal atom.

Porphins always have four nitrogen atoms in a cyclic structure that can coordinate to a metal atom, but recently Jonathan Sessler and co-workers at the University of Texas reported making an analogous compound (5b) having five nitrogen atoms coordinating to an atom of cadmium. Because this macrocyclic ligand and its metal complexes absorb light at wavelengths longer than those absorbed by hemoglobin, they may prove to be just what the doctor ordered for this tumor-destroying application of PDT.

—Fred Basolo

Organic chemistry

During the past year chemists synthesized receptor molecules capable of selectively and strongly binding small molecules of biologic interest. Insight was obtained into the natural rules that govern the self-assembly of small molecular units into larger structures. Methods for the highly selective cleavage of DNA were devised, while the development of antibodies as enzymes and the discovery of RNA enzymes highlighted current research. Chemists involved in organic syntheses benefited from the ability to use enzymes in organic solvents and reported making molecules with highly unusual structures.

Host-guest chemistry. Major advances have been made during the past two decades in understanding

view: *Inorganic chemistry*, above; MATERIALS SCIENCES: *Ceramics*; and PHYSICS: *Condensed-matter physics*.)

Diamonds and diamondlike films. The ability to form reproducible thin carbon films having a diamond structure has important technological applications because of diamond's strength and hardness, its extremely low electrical conductivity, and its excellent heat conductivity. These properties result from the strong, rigid, symmetrical tetrahedral bonding between carbon atoms, which produces an extremely elastic lattice having low phonon amplitudes; in other words, the thermal motions of the atoms have limited amplitudes, giving diamond the lowest specific heat of all elements as well as high heat-transfer rates. Diamondlike carbon films have been deposited by various plasma-deposition, chemical-vapor-deposition, and ion-beam techniques, but progress in this field has been hampered by lack of reproducibility and by imbedded impurities resulting from the use of only moderate vacuum conditions and of non-mass-selected hydrocarbon discharges as a source of carbon.

Physical chemist J. Wayne Rabalais and graduate student Srinandan Kasi of the University of Houston, Texas, used low-energy beams of positively charged carbon ions (C^+) to deposit pure carbon films in a diamondlike structure that is chemically bonded to the surface of the substrate (single-crystal nickel or silicon or polycrystalline tungsten, tantalum, or gold). When mass-selected C^+ beams at energies of 20–200 eV struck atomically clean surfaces, the

Researchers from Case Western Reserve University grew diamond film (shown in the scanning electron micrograph below) from a vapor of small hydrocarbons and atomic hydrogen at ambient pressure and a temperature of 900° C.

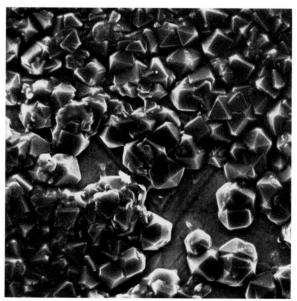

John C. Angus, Cliff C. Hayman, and Larry Staikoff, Case Western Reserve University

first atomic layer of carbon grew as a carbide structure chemically bonded to the surface. As deposition continued over the next several atomic layers, the film evolved a diamondlike structure, but the growth mechanism was unknown. Such strongly adhering, pure carbon films have significant applications, especially as insulators and doped semiconductors.

Chemical engineers John C. Angus and Cliff C. Hayman of Case Western Reserve University, Cleveland, Ohio, grew diamonds at ambient pressure on a substrate held at about 900° C (1,650° F) from a vapor containing active small hydrocarbons and atomic hydrogen. These diamonds possessed the hardness and thermal conductivity of natural diamonds. They also prepared diamondlike hydrocarbons by allowing 50–200-eV hydrocarbon ions formed in a plasma (a hot ionized gas) to hit a substrate. The films had a hardness approaching that of diamond, contained 20–30% hydrogen by numbers of atoms, could be deposited on large areas at rates as high as 80 micrometers (μm; about 0.00316 in) per hour, and were only slightly permeable to organic solvents and inorganic acids. When annealed at 400° C (750° F), the films became more diamondlike in their electrical conductivity. Vapor-grown diamondlike materials may find applications in abrasives, tool coatings, bearing surfaces, electronics, optics, and corrosion protection. (See also *1989 Yearbook of Science and the Future* Year in Review: PHYSICS: *Condensed-matter physics*.)

Foods. Studies have associated high levels of cholesterol in the blood with atherosclerosis, a dangerous condition in which fatty deposits clog arteries and cause certain types of heart disease. Furthermore, sodium has been implicated in high blood pressure (hypertension), which afflicts millions of people worldwide. In October 1988 Rosemary Farm of Santa Maria, Calif., began marketing fresh eggs that are 55% lower in cholesterol and 23% lower in sodium than regular eggs. Paul May, general manager of Rosemary Farm, said that the eggs, which look and taste exactly like regular eggs and which were selling for about 30% more in stores along the central California coast, owe their properties to a special chicken feed, composed of secret ingredients.

Low-cholesterol powdered eggs with 70–75% of the cholesterol removed were developed by food scientist Glenn Froning of the University of Nebraska at Lincoln. His extraction process involves blending dried eggs with carbon dioxide gas (CO_2) and exposing the mixture to high pressures and temperatures, whereupon the CO_2 binds itself to cholesterol and fat molecules and is drained off as a liquid. The residual yellow powder cooks better and tastes more authentic than yoke-substitute, low-cholesterol products currently available. Michael Foods Co., Minneapolis, Minn., was perfecting the new product and intended to sell it first to fast-food outlets, makers of

Simplesse, a new low-calorie, low-cholesterol fat substitute, is made from egg-white and milk proteins. A proprietary process shapes the proteins into microscopic spheres that collectively mimic the taste and feel associated with fats.

convenience foods, hospitals, and school cafeterias before offering it to shoppers.

After seven years of work James Cox, executive vice-president of research and development at Bon Dente Co., Lynden, Wash., announced the production of Egglite, a whole-egg analogue that has one-third the calories of a hen's egg and no cholesterol and that looks and cooks like a regular shelled egg. It consists of conventional egg white, yolk matter formulated from vegetable fats and chicken extracts, and a thin membrane (derived from vegetable gums, poultry, meat, and seaweed) that supports the yolk. The entire assemblage is packaged in an egg-size plastic cup. Egglite, for which clearance from the U.S. Food and Drug Administration (FDA) was pending at the end of 1988, can be hard-boiled in its plastic container or fried, scrambled, poached, cooked over easy, or used in baking.

For decades several companies have worked to develop low-calorie, low-cholesterol fat substitutes to fill a market niche that could be worth billions of dollars annually. In 1987 Proctor & Gamble Co., Cincinnati, Ohio, announced a no-calorie, no-cholesterol sucrose polyester (SPE) "fake" fat, named olestra (see *1989 Yearbook of Science and the Future* Year in Review: CHEMISTRY: *Applied chemistry*). Submitted to the FDA in June 1987, olestra was still awaiting approval a year and a half later. In

early 1988 Robert Shapiro, chairman of NutraSweet Co., a division of Monsanto Co., Saint Louis, Mo., announced that it would market a low-calorie, low-cholesterol fat substitute, thus beating a number of expected similar products to market. Tradenamed Simplesse and first discovered in 1979, the new fat substitute is made from milk and egg-white proteins by a proprietary combination of heating and shearing called microparticulation, which results in minuscule spherical particles 0.1–0.2 μm (0.0000039–0.0000078 in) in diameter. Particles of this size and shape roll over one another and produce on the tongue the rich taste and texture associated with fats.

Unlike P&G's olestra, Simplesse cannot be used for frying or baking, and its most immediate applications will be in reducing the calorie count and fat and cholesterol content of such processed foods as ice cream, yogurt, butter, cheese spreads, dips, sour cream, salad dressings, and mayonnaise. Simplesse contains 1.3 cal per g (about 0.035 oz), compared with 9 cal per g for fat; it would reduce a 115-g (4-oz) serving of chocolate ice cream from 283 to 130 cal and a tablespoon of mayonnaise from 99 to 30 cal.

A controversy arose between NutraSweet and the FDA over the need for FDA approval of Simplesse. Unlike olestra, Simplesse is a natural substance that is physically, but not chemically, changed during processing; thus, NutraSweet claimed, it does not need FDA approval for sale to the public. Shapiro said that products made with Simplesse could be available within 12–18 months because the fat substitute should fit within the FDA's list of substances "generally recognized as safe," but FDA commissioner Frank Young criticized him for not consulting the agency.

During the 1960s and 1970s amphetamines were used as appetite suppressants, but their addictiveness proved troublesome. Recently Michael DiNovi and co-workers at Monell Chemical Senses Center, Philadelphia, synthesized what may prove to be a suitable appetite suppressant. The fructose analogue 2,5-anhydro-D-mannitol was synthesized from glucosamine, which in turn was derived from crab and lobster shells. The compound exerts its appetite suppressant effects on the liver, unlike traditional suppressants, which act on the brain. In animal testing it did not prevent rats from getting hungry but made them satisfied with less food. DiNovi's ultimate aim was to describe a mechanism for appetite control, and he was synthesizing derivatives of the new compound to learn which part of its molecular structure is responsible for appetite suppression.

Herbicides and pesticides. Over the past few years three new groups of herbicides were discovered by three different companies by means of traditional screening methods: sulfonylureas such as Du Pont's Oust (sulfometuron methyl) or Glean (chlorosulfuron), imidazolinones such as American Cyanamid's Scepter (imazaquine), and triazolo pyrimidines or sulfonanilides such as Dow's 1,2,4-triazolo-(1,5-a)-2,4-dimethyl-3-(N-sulfonyl-(2-nitro-6-methylaniline))-1,5-pyrimidine. Although structurally different, all three groups of compounds inhibit the same enzyme, acetolactate synthase (ALS), whose gene has a DNA sequence very similar to that of another enzyme, pyruvate oxidase. During the past year John Schloss, Lawrence Ciskanik, and Drew Van Dyk of the Du Pont Central Research & Development Department, Wilmington, Del., concluded that the herbicide binding site on ALS is equivalent to the quinone binding site on pyruvate oxidase. They found a striking parallel between the diverse group of molecular structures that inhibit ALS and the equally diverse compounds that inhibit plant photosynthesis by binding to a quinone site. Because the quinone site binds with a variety of compounds, it should provide a wide-ranging screening test for potential herbicides.

To satisfy the U.S. Environmental Protection Agency and environmental groups concerned with the use of live genetically engineered bacteria as biopesticides, chemical engineer Andrew Barnes, vice-president for operations and corporate development of Mycogen Corp., San Diego, Calif., developed a novel alternative—that of using dead bacteria as delivery systems for environmentally safe toxins. Barnes's process, called MCap, treats genetically en-

Genetically engineered Pseudomonas bacteria, killed and treated to strengthen their cell walls, serve as a novel delivery system, called MCap, for the crystals of insecticidal protein (large gray inclusions) that they made while living.

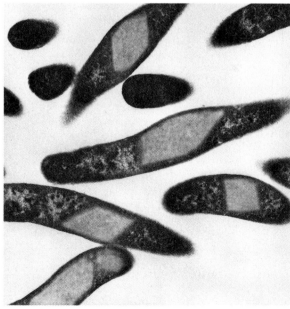

Mycogen Corporation; photo, Jewel Payne

gineered bacteria with glutaraldehyde, iodine, and heat, which kill and embalm them into tiny capsules containing the biotoxin that the bacteria synthesized while living. Since the capsule protects the fragile biotoxin until an insect eats it, the "toxins remain active two to five times longer than those that are not encapsulated," according to Barnes. Other embalming materials were under investigation by research entomologist George Tompkins of the U.S. Department of Agriculture's Insect Pathology Laboratory, Beltsville, Md. Russell Travers, director of biocontrol research at Novo Laboratories, Danbury, Conn., expressed skepticism about the process, doubting that the benefits would outweigh the costs.

Fuel oil. In northwestern England three agencies, the Greater Manchester County Council, the University of Manchester Institute of Science and Technology, and the University of Salford Industrial Centre, developed a patented process for quickly converting household rubbish, which is largely cellulose from foodstuffs and paper, into nonpolluting fuel oil, a transformation that nature requires millions of years to accomplish. Waste material mixed with a metal catalyst such as nickel and a liquid (usually a light oil) is pumped in suspension into a high-pressure reactor vessel (autoclave) maintained at 350° C (660° F). In as little as ten minutes the resulting oil is removed along with the only significant by-products—carbon dioxide and water. An experimental plant running continuously for several hours produced oil almost as good as the best natural crude oil at a rate of 450 liters (119 gal) per ton of feedstock. Because it contains no sulfur or nitrogen, the oil does not contribute to acid rain when burned. It can also be decomposed by heating (cracked) to yield lower-molecular-weight products such as gasoline.

Polymers and coatings. Johnson & Johnson, New Brunswick, N.J., developed Acuvue, a disposable soft contact lens that can be worn continuously for as long as a week before being replaced by a new sterile lens. The process used the same materials as regular soft lenses but employed a new technique called stabilized soft molding. The lens material is worked in a swollen, hydrated state, rather than dry, so that the final lens shape as worn in the eye is consistently predetermined, thus solving the problem of unpredictable changes on absorption of water that occurs with regular soft lenses. The process involves a polymerization mixture containing hydrophilic monomers (hydroxyethyl methacrylate [HEMA] with N-vinylpyrrolidine or methacrylic acid), a crosslinking agent (diesters or triesters such as ethylene glycol or dimethacrylate), and an organic diluent (mixtures of acetic acid with propylene glycol or succinic acid with glycerol) that is replaced by water when the lens has been shaped by pressing into a mold. J&J test-marketed the product in

Undesirable deposit buildup on an extended-wear contact lens after a month's wear (left) is compared with the buildup on an Acuvue disposable lens after one week (right), the time the latter lens is worn before being discarded.

Florida, California, and the U.K. In 1988 the lenses cost about $300–$400 for a year's supply, plus optician's fees.

The Defence Science Centre, New Delhi, India, developed a new type of silicone resin, containing siloxane bonds with methyl groups attached to the silicon atoms, as an acid- and moisture-resistant coating. Soluble in such common hydrocarbon solvents as benzene, petroleum, ether, or xylene, the resin, in a 10–15% solution, produces a protective coating on ferrous and nonferrous surfaces that is stable at temperatures as high as 230° C (446° F). High-tension insulator surfaces and printed circuit boards can be waterproofed with the resin, which can be removed by treatment with nonpolar solvents.

To meet more stringent air-quality standards, the Swedish firm Nobel Chematur developed a microsphere system that outperforms the activated carbon commonly used to remove such noxious chemicals as aromatic and chlorinated solvents, alcohols, and ketones from industrially polluted air before it is released into the atmosphere. The system, trade-named Polyad FB, employed the company's novel polymer-based Bonopore adsorbent, consisting of highly porous plastic microspheres that are both hydrophobic (lacking affinity for water) and polar. A gram of microspheres, each of which measures 0.5 mm (0.02 in) in diameter, has a total surface area of about 800 sq m (8,600 sq ft) and can withstand a high degree of mechanical stress without rupturing. In addition to their cleanliness, ease of handling, and imperviousness to high moisture content of the air, unlike activated carbon, they do not catalytically degrade or polymerize unstable solvents during recovery. Heating the beads releases the adsorbed solvents, which are condensed and collected in storage tanks. In 1988 the system was in use in Göteborg, Sweden, and was to be employed in other countries, including the U.S.

Hydrogen from water. Hydrogen, a nonpolluting fuel that produces only water when burned, has been the subject of much research in recent years (see *1984 Yearbook of Science and the Future* Year in Review: CHEMISTRY: *Applied chemistry*) and may well become the fuel of the future. The classical method for producing hydrogen from water, electrolysis, is uneconomical; more than 4.3 kw-hr of electricity are needed to produce one cubic meter (35.3 cu ft) of hydrogen at atmospheric pressure. After years of work, researchers at the Dornier System GmbH, Friedrichshafen, West Germany, developed and successfully tested a high-temperature procedure for electrolyzing water that is more energy efficient than conventional electrolysis. Steam heated to about 1,000° C (1,830° F) is directed past a solid electrolyte and split into its components (hydrogen and oxygen) by an electrical charge. Although heating water to produce steam requires energy, the new procedure, called Hot Elly, saves energy by using the heat of a high-temperature reactor. Only ceramic materials can resist the high heat, and the pipes for separating the products were manufactured by transforming zirconium oxide mixed with yttrium oxide, by a spray-drying process, to a fine-grained powder, which was then molded to form the final parts.

Two golden anniversaries. The year 1988 marked the 50th anniversary of two important products of applied chemistry that are taken for granted today. In 1938 Du Pont chemist Roy J. Plunkett serendipitously discovered Teflon (polytetrafluoroethylene), the slipperiest substance known and one of the most resistant to chemical attack. That same year Charles M. A. Stine, Du Pont's vice-president in charge of research, made the first public announcement of nylon—specifically what is now called nylon-6,6, or poly(hexamethylene adipamide)—the first completely man-made fiber, which ushered in the so-called materials revolution.

—George B. Kauffman

See also Feature Article: ORGANOMETALLICS: WORKHORSES OF CHEMISTRY.

Defense research

A new generation of tactical aircraft built around electronics technology began taking shape during the past year in all three U.S. military services. The three aircraft development programs, known as the Air Force's Advanced Tactical Fighter (ATF), the Navy's Advanced Tactical Aircraft (ATA), and the Army's Light Helicopter, Experimental (LHX), represented an opportunity to employ the latest advances (including "stealth" techniques to reduce optical and radar visibility) in order to maintain effective fighting forces well into the 21st century.

Military research efforts under way during the past decade began emerging from the laboratories and became available to aircraft developers for the first time. These included the following:

● very high-speed integrated circuit (VHSIC) and microwave and millimeter wave integrated circuit (MIMIC) electronic components to be used in the powerful airborne computers and radars of the future

● optical fibers for high-speed data transmission and fly-by-light flight control to replace current mechanical and electrical systems

● new passive infrared sensors that, unlike radars, do not emit electromagnetic energy and thus are able to detect enemy forces without risking detection of the aircraft

● "fail soft" distributed system architecture (so called because aircraft subsystems would continue working in a slightly degraded mode even if a few components failed) built around powerful microprocessors

● "fused sensors" that accept several different kinds of information and presort it to create more readily understandable displays for the flight crew

● powerful software packages (including the artificial intelligence technique known as "expert systems") written with the new Ada programming language that the U.S. Department of Defense made mandatory for all its new weapons programs.

This infusion of new technology, in turn, led to an unprecedentedly high proportion of the total costs of all three new aircraft devoted to electronics—as much as 40% by some estimates. This represented a departure from the way that aircraft were developed in the past, when designers started with the latest, most powerful engines, added the best aerodynamic design available to them, and then, almost as an afterthought, inserted the electronics into whatever space was left over. The result was a multitude of separate electronic receivers, transmitters, and countermeasures, each dealing with a particular segment of the electromagnetic spectrum and each vying for aircraft weight and power as well as the pilot's attention. Now, by building the aircraft around integrated aviation electronics, or avionics, the designers have been able to tailor each plane to its actual mission—with resulting improved performance and opportunities for economies of scale.

The basic avionics building block considered the best choice for all three new aircraft—ATA, ATF, and LHX—was the Standard Electronics Module (SEM), originally developed more than 20 years ago at the Naval Avionics Facility, Indianapolis, Ind. A number of different formats evolved over the years, and the 1990s generation aircraft were expected to use what is known as SEM-E, a printed circuit card on which the electronic components are mounted. Standardizing all the electronics functions on these cards eliminates the need for costly logistic support—a particularly valuable asset for aircraft operating at sea on board carriers or at forward bases that cannot stock large numbers of spare parts. Furthermore, this elimination of intermediate-level maintenance increases the availability of each aircraft to conduct its mission.

These SEMs, or "common modules," are made by the complementary metal oxide semiconductor (CMOS) process, in which each transistor or other element on the chip measures less than 1.5 microns (millionths of a meter) in feature size. (By way of comparison, a human hair is approximately 100 microns in diameter.) Although this is at the leading edge of electronics technology, it is considered sufficiently mature for use in the ATF-ATA-LHX generation of aircraft. Furthermore, as more advanced semiconductor-processing techniques become available, the transistors can be made even smaller

Artist's drawing reveals the U.S. Army's Light Helicopter, Experimental (LHX). It is one of the new generation of tactical aircraft that will utilize advanced electronics technology. In 1988 the U.S. Congress cut back funding for the craft.

than a micron without redesigning the modules.

First, however, a way had to be found to connect these chips into systems that could continue to operate if a few of them failed—either through normal wear or in combat. This was accomplished through an Air Force program designated Pave Pillar. It essentially defined the integrated digital architecture, such as the common modules for signal processing, so that the appropriate sensors could be attached. The idea spread to the other services, and under a memorandum of agreement signed by all three in March 1987, a Joint Integrated Avionics Working Group was established in the Department of Defense to coordinate their individual efforts. The Air Force became the lead service because its ATF was the furthest along in development at that point. As of early 1989, however, it appeared that roll-out ceremonies for the Navy's ATA would occur in late 1990, a few months before the first flights of two competing ATF designs early the following year. The Army's LHX, meanwhile, encountered cost problems, resulting in funding cuts by Congress.

In addition to being a likely user of common modules, LHX was once considered the best opportunity for application of an all-fiber-optic flight-control system, known as the Advanced Digital Optical Control System, and the Army began sponsoring a development program for it in 1981. The goal was to produce a new generation of helicopters to replace the more than 7,000 remaining in the Army's inventory since the Vietnam war. These helicopters were becoming obsolete, the Army contended, but Congress refused to approve the more than $60 billion that would be needed to produce the new LHXs.

Although the Army appeared to have dropped out of this new generation of tactical aircraft, standardization of the electronic components promised to accomplish for the Air Force and Navy what U.S. Secretary of Defense Robert McNamara had failed to achieve during the 1960s, when he unsuccessfully tried to force the TFX (Tactical Fighter, Experimental) on both services. Neither was totally satisfied with its resulting model of the F-111 airframe, and they twice went their separate ways with a new generation of fighter aircraft of their own, first the Navy's F-14 and the Air Force's F-15 and later the Air Force's F-16 and the Navy's F/A-18, despite demands from Congress that they get together on one aircraft.

Standardization at the airframe level had always been a problem because of the different environments in which the three services operated their aircraft. Even the avionics modules would have to be modified for special requirements, such as the Navy's need for protection against the corrosive effects of salt water, but commonality at the electronic module level was determined to be technically feasible and

should be acceptable to the users of the aircraft and to those who had to pay for them.

Congress approved the procurement of 750 ATF aircraft at a cost of $35 million each (in 1985 dollars before the impact of inflation is taken into account), and the Air Force planned to award a contract for full-scale engineering development in early 1991. In preparation for that selection, two companies began developing flying prototype aircraft under parallel $691 million Air Force contracts awarded in October 1986: Lockheed Corp. with its YF-22A and Northrop Corp. with its YF-23A. Lockheed teamed with Boeing Co. and General Dynamics Corp., and Northrop joined with McDonnell Douglas Corp. The Air Force hoped to begin supplying the Tactical Air Command with one of the new fighters in the mid-1990s.

The Navy, which designated its ATA the A-12, selected a team consisting of General Dynamics and McDonnell Douglas to develop it. The Navy disclosed little information about the aircraft's stealth features, although it was expected to use radar-absorbing composite materials and conformal surfaces to reduce visibility.

The two-person A-12 (pilot and bombardier/navigator) was to replace the carrier-based A-6 Intruder, which was introduced into the fleet in 1960 as a long-range, all-weather, deep-penetration strike aircraft. It was estimated that the 450 A-12 aircraft to be procured would cost $35 billion–$40 billion, or about $80 million per aircraft.

The A-12 was also being evaluated by the Air Force for its attack missions, and the Navy was considering purchasing as many as 619 ATF aircraft for its future fighter needs. Thus, standardization at the subsystem level was becoming increasingly attractive for easing the burden on logistics systems of both services.

Still to be determined was the degree to which the new aircraft could use fiber optics. Because optical fibers do not radiate any signals detectable by radar and are immune to electromagnetic interference and the electromagnetic pulse effects caused by nuclear blasts, the military program managers were particularly interested in them for any aircraft requiring stealth capabilities.

Advanced optical fibers had become available commercially in recent years from such companies as AT&T and Corning, which were installing them in commercial telephone systems. However, the fibers would have to be modified to meet military requirements; in particular, their tensile strength would have to be increased, and they would have to withstand greater temperature extremes. With potential data rates of 100 million bits per second or even more, these advanced fibers were becoming increasingly attractive. The fibers would also reduce weight—and costs—drastically below those of conventional

The first U.S. Air Force B-2 advanced technology (Stealth) bomber is rolled out in Palmdale, Calif., on Nov. 22, 1988. It is designed to fly at both high and low altitudes and to be virtually invisible to enemy radar.

copper cables. By 1989 the Air Force had tentatively selected fiber optics for the ATF, and the Navy was showing interest.

Weight was a critical consideration for the designers. The ATF, for example, was projected as a 22,700-kg (50,000-lb) aircraft. At a flyaway cost of $35 million each, each kilogram on each aircraft is worth $1,500. With a planned procurement of 750 aircraft, a reduction of one kilogram on each would cut total costs by more than $1.1 million. Thus, integrating the avionics so that they totaled less than 0.75 kg (1½ lb) per common module would contribute significantly to holding down the overall cost of each plane.

The Department of the Navy led the services in the operational use of fiber optics in airborne applications, beginning in 1983 with the first production deliveries of an aircraft, the Marine Corps' AV-8B Harrier, which was equipped with a short (10-m [33-ft]) fiber-optic data link between a digital map set in the navigation system and a cockpit panel. That link had a modest data rate of 125,000 bits per second, but it proved to the Navy's satisfaction that maintenance personnel could successfully work with this new technology under operational conditions.

By 1989 the Navy had begun considering a much more ambitious application of fiber optics in its experimental Naval Air Ship Study Program to develop a new generation of airships (much more advanced than the blimps used for advertising purposes at sports events) for over-the-horizon detection of anti-ship missiles. Under a joint development effort by Westinghouse Electric Corp. and the British firm Airship Industries, optical fibers were being considered for both the data bus to transmit targeting data from the radar to the central processors and for a fly-by-light flight-control system.

Also likely to be incorporated in the next generation of tactical aircraft were gallium arsenide (GaAs) chips from the Defense Department's MIMIC development program. These chips had a theoretical improvement in speed over conventional silicon chips of at least fivefold. The proposed application for them was in the new aircraft's multifunction radar systems. These radars would probably use designs based on an experimental program conducted by Westinghouse for the Air Force, known as the Ultra-Reliable Radar, in which an active-aperture radar was built with a phased-array antenna put together with GaAs modules. That experimental radar also used a modern airborne computer built of VHSIC components and designated the Common Signal Processor. Should the Air Force and Navy both choose this computer for their new aircraft, it would be one more example of cost-saving commonality.

The one area where new technology would not be required for these tactical aircraft of the future was their engines. The ATA program, for example, would use engines derived from the General Electric F404 engine that was used to power the F/A-18 Hornet. This decision was made before the selection of the airframe contractor team and involved upgrading the current F404-400 model from its present 8,000 kg (17,600 lb) of thrust to an enhanced performance engine capable of 10,400 kg (23,000 lb) of thrust. Each A-12 aircraft would have two engines. The modified engine was also expected to be used in future models of the F/A-18 to improve the plane's takeoff, climb, ground attack, and supersonic performance as well as to ease the logistics requirements on board a carrier housing both A-12s and F/A-18s. The F404-400 model was also used by the Canadian, Australian, and Spanish air forces, and other models of the engine powered the U.S. A-6F Intruder, Sweden's JAS 39 Gripen, Singapore's A-4 Skyhawk, and such experimental aircraft as the Grumman X-29 and Rockwell-MBB X-31.

In an attempt to maintain competition and assure continuous production of the engines, the Navy required an alternate source for them, the Pratt & Whitney Aircraft Division of United Technologies Corp. This was known as a "leader/follower" arrangement in which each producer received about 40–60% of the year's engine procurement on the basis of cost and other considerations.

—John Rhea

See also Feature Article: THE NATIONAL AEROSPACE PLANE.

Earth sciences

The severe drought in North America during the summer of 1988, the possible warming of the Earth's atmosphere because of the "greenhouse effect," the hypothesis that life might have originated at deep-sea hydrothermal vents, and the devastating earthquake in Soviet Armenia were among the many subjects pursued by Earth scientists during the past year. Researchers from the different disciplines cooperated in studying such phenomena as the drought and the greenhouse effect.

Atmospheric sciences

During the past year public interest in atmospheric science heightened as a result of claims that the "greenhouse effect" and depletion of ozone in the stratosphere could be causing major changes in global climate. There was also continued concern about the general problem of air pollution. Several field programs were conducted in order to increase understanding of the Earth's weather. The development of new observational measurement systems and the acquisition of powerful computer systems to simulate weather and climate continued.

Observational field programs and weather forecasting. A field test for the Experiment on Rapidly Intensifying Cyclones over the Atlantic (ERICA) program was performed during January 1988. Designed to investigate the frequent explosive deepening of winter storms in the northwestern Atlantic Ocean, the intensive field phase of ERICA was planned for Dec. 1, 1988, to Feb. 28, 1989. On Jan. 25, 1988, two U.S. National Oceanic and Atmospheric Admin-

Loran-C dropwindsonde system, deployed by small parachutes from an airplane, accurately measures wind, temperature, and moisture from the flight level to the Earth's surface.

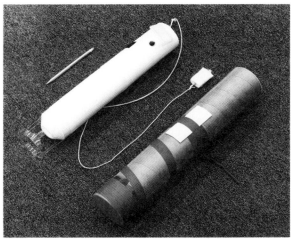

National Center for Atmospheric Research

istration (NOAA) P-3 aircraft and three U.S. Air Force WC-130 airplanes monitored a storm from Cape Cod, Massachusetts, across the Gulf of Maine to Nova Scotia and Newfoundland. Among the important results of the flights was the successful testing of the National Center for Atmospheric Research (NCAR) loran-C dropwindsonde system. The measurement platform deployed by small parachutes from the P-3 aircraft permits very accurate wind, temperature, and moisture measurements to be made from the flight level to the surface. ERICA, initiated and funded by the U.S. Office of Naval Research, by 1989 had developed into a cooperative research study among a number of universities and governmental organizations from the U.S. and Canada.

In response to an increased awareness of the importance of wind shear on the safety of takeoffs and landings of aircraft, the Federal Aviation Administration (FAA) was spending $20 million from 1989 to 1992 to install a surface-based detection system at 108 airports in the U.S. Dangerous wind shear, which often occurs in the vicinity of thunderstorms, can result in loss of lift to airplanes near the ground as a strong head wind changes rapidly to a tail wind. Referred to as microbursts or downbursts, wind shear has been implicated in at least 500 deaths in the U.S. since the mid-1960s. Although an improvement over the previous system, the new system will measure only surface winds, and those findings will be used to estimate winds higher up. In July 1988 a Doppler radar system, which also monitors wind above the ground, performed well in a test by NCAR researchers at Stapleton Airport, Denver, Colo. The FAA was expected to order 47 such systems, the first of which were to be ready by 1991.

During the spring of 1988, scientists from China and the U.S. conducted a two-month cruise aboard the Chinese research vessel *Xi-ang-yanghong #14* in order to investigate ocean and atmospheric conditions in the western Pacific. Part of the two nations' joint Ocean Heat Transport and Climate Study, these measurements were designed to improve the understanding of ocean-atmospheric influences on seasonal weather patterns. This was the fourth cruise in this study, and four more were planned for the near future. Near-surface ocean and weather conditions in the western Pacific are closely related to anomalous weather patterns observed at long distances from this region, including changes in weather caused by El Niño. El Niño, the name of unusually warm ocean-surface temperatures off the northwestern coast of South America that occur at intervals of several years, has been linked to abnormal weather patterns in such diverse locations as the U.S. and Australia.

China placed into orbit its first experimental weather satellite, called Wind and Cloud No. 1, in September 1988. The polar-orbiting spacecraft,

Cuban fishing vessel sits on a beach at Cancún, Mexico, where it was blown in September 1988 by Hurricane Gilbert. With gusts of more than 320 kilometers per hour (200 miles per hour), Gilbert was the most intense Atlantic Ocean hurricane ever recorded.

launched from Taiyuan (T'ai-yüan) in north-central China, was designed to obtain measurements that include cloud patterns, temperatures of the ocean surface, and ice and snow cover. China planned to launch several more satellites in the 1990s.

U.S. National Aeronautics and Space Administration (NASA) scientist David Des Marais, using a new analysis procedure, found that 30 million to 35 million tons of carbon are emitted annually into the atmosphere from volcanic vents in the oceans. This represented more than 90% of the carbon emanating from the mantle of the Earth.

In September 1988 Hurricane Gilbert developed into the most intense Atlantic Ocean hurricane ever recorded. Winds in gusts reached more than 320 km/h (200 mph), with a minimum sea-level pressure of 885 millibars. Despite improvements in the ability of meteorologists to monitor such storms and of computers to predict their path and intensity, warnings of a landfall on the Gulf coast of Texas were in error, as the storm struck the northeastern coast of Mexico.

The devastating impact on agriculture of locust swarms in Africa was the topic of a July 1988 workshop in Tunis, Tunisia. The secretary-general of the World Meteorological Organization (WMO), G. O. P. Obasi of Nigeria, urged the use of meteorologic data and their effective dissemination to WMO member countries in order to assist local agricultural authorities with a quick assessment of locust threats. During the summer of 1988, the worst locust plague in 30 years affected The Sudan. Serious crop losses across northern Africa from the locusts were a potential threat. Locust swarms travel up to 325 km (202 mi) in a day, depending on wind patterns. It was expected that it would take a decade to control the current infestation.

In late 1987 a massive ice sheet separated from the Antarctic ice cap. Measuring more than 160×40 km (100×25 mi) and about 230 m (755 ft) thick, the ice ran aground on an underwater protuberance just off the Antarctic coast in April 1988.

Air pollution. During July 1988 a NOAA aircraft flew four flights from Newport News, Va., and four flights from Bermuda in order to monitor air pollution moving off the middle Atlantic coast of the U.S. The aircraft rendezvoused with the NOAA research ship *Mt. Mitchell*. Part of the National Acid Precipitation Assessment Program, the project was designed to determine the fate of human-generated sulfur, nitrogen, and other trace gases and aerosols over the western Atlantic.

The deposition of pesticides and other toxic organic compounds directly from the atmosphere into the Great Lakes was to be measured as part of the Great Lakes Atmospheric Deposition (GLAD) program. Scientists in the U.S. and Canada were concerned that this pollution could be having a harmful effect on water quality and aquatic life in these large freshwater basins. Major urban and industrial areas, such as Chicago, Detroit, Toronto, and Cleveland, Ohio, border this largest reservoir of fresh water in the world.

During 1988 the WMO and the International Atomic Energy Agency (IAEA) successfully tested the use of the WMO Global Telecommunication System (GTS) for rapidly disseminating notification of nuclear accidents. Of the 25 countries participating, most national meteorologic centers received test messages from the IAEA Headquarters within 20 minutes of its initial distribution. The test was a direct response to the slow transmittal of information associated with the Chernobyl reactor accident in April 1986.

Earth sciences

In September 1987 cesium-137 was illegally extracted from a medical device stolen from an abandoned radiotherapy clinic in Goiânia, Brazil. More than 2,000 sq m (21,520 sq ft) within the city limits were contaminated through personal contact and air movement, and 20 individuals were seriously exposed to beta and gamma radiation. Four died. During the year the economic impact of the accident continued to be assessed. More than 130,000 man-hours were required for the cleanup, which included removal of soil down to a depth of approximately 50 cm (20 in).

Climate change. Concern over climate change received considerable attention during the past year. Claims were made that the four warmest years of the 20th century, averaged throughout the world, occurred during the 1980s. The drought in a large part of the agricultural region of the U.S. during the summer of 1988 heightened public perception of a change in weather. The global warming during 1987, the most recent complete year for which records are available, was attributed to an increase of average tropical air temperatures by 0.4° C (0.7° F). In both hemispheres cooler than average conditions occurred poleward of the tropics.

Several researchers concluded that the warm years in the past decade were the initial evidence for greenhouse gas warming. On the basis of computer modeling of the Earth's atmosphere, it was thought that an increase of carbon dioxide and methane due to industrial and vehicular activity and deforestation may prevent long-wave radiation from the Sun from being returned to space. According to the models, the resulting change in climate will be a global warming, particularly at polar latitudes, and an expansion of desert areas northward. Levels of carbon dioxide in the atmosphere have increased 25% since the mid-1800s, reaching a current average global concentration of more than 350 parts per million.

Such models, however, ignore or incompletely represent the effect on climate of an increase of human-generated aerosols and their influence on global cloud cover. Similarly, the response of the vegetation to increased carbon dioxide concentrations is only partially understood.

Despite the claims of several researchers, most scientists have not found evidence of a general global warming. In fact, contradictory evidence was reported by Patrick Michaels, a climatologist at the University of Virginia. For example, the area of polar-sea ice in both hemispheres has been stable or has increased in recent decades. There has also been a dramatic expansion of cold water from the Arctic Ocean into the North Atlantic during the last decade. In Antarctica in August 1987, the South Pole and Vostok stations experienced the coldest month ever recorded.

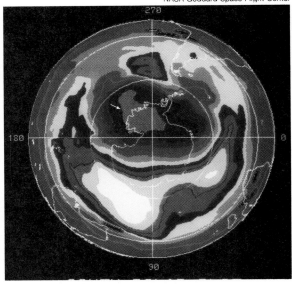

Plot of ozone distribution over the Southern Hemisphere on Oct. 2, 1988, reveals that the region of lowest ozone (arrow) covered less area than in 1987 and was displaced away from the South Pole toward the eastern Pacific Ocean.

The status of regions over Antarctica with anomalously low concentrations of ozone in the stratosphere, referred to by the media as the "ozone hole," continued to receive scrutiny during the early Southern Hemisphere spring of 1988. Man-made chlorofluorocarbons have been implicated in this depletion of ozone. Concern about the levels of ozone over the Arctic region also mounted. Ozone acts as an absorber of short-wavelength ultraviolet radiation from the Sun, thereby protecting living organisms on the Earth from potential harmful effects of these high-energy electromagnetic waves. The absorption of this solar energy also creates the stratosphere, in which temperature is nearly constant, and even warms, with height. The stratosphere limits the height to which storm systems in the lower atmosphere extend. Researchers have estimated that a global 45% reduction in stratospheric ozone could decrease the temperature in the stratosphere by at least 20° C (36° F). Such cooling could result in much deeper and, therefore, more severe thunderstorm activity in the tropics and during midlatitude summers. Hurricane and winter storm intensity could also increase as the storms penetrate higher into the Earth's atmosphere.

Observations of ozone during the early Antarctic spring of 1988, however, found that the stratospheric ozone depletion was more than three times less severe in 1988 than in 1987. The reduction in ozone was about 10–15%. As contrasted with the previous five years, this limited depletion could be a result of enhanced mixing of stratospheric air over Antarctica

320

with air from more temperate latitudes. Scientists planned to continue their observations in Antarctica and over the Arctic in the spring of 1989 in order to monitor ozone levels.

Lee Thomas, the administrator of the Environmental Protection Agency, urged that a complete phaseout of the use of chlorofluorocarbons be mandated in order to protect the ozone layer. This conclusion went beyond the international protocol signed by 45 nations to take effect in January 1989, in which a 50% cutback in the use of chlorofluorocarbons is required. Thomas stated that "regretfully, our new analysis [of ozone depletion] predicts an even worse scenario than anticipated."

With the heightened public and scientific concern and attention regarding human-caused climate change, the new president of the United States, George Bush, proposed an international conference to discuss the seriousness of the problem. Procedures for mitigating potentially damaging agricultural, economic, and political effects may be needed if these human-generated climate changes are determined to be real.

—Roger A. Pielke

Geologic sciences

Geology and geochemistry. During the past year geologists attended to their traditional task of inferring the history of the Earth by applying the general principles of physical and biologic science with particular creativity and ingenuity. Among the major subjects of research were the greenhouse effect, mass extinctions, and the severe earthquake in Soviet Armenia.

Greenhouse effect. The possibility of a causal connection between the unusually hot, dry summer of 1988 and an increasing emission of pollutants from the burning of fossil fuels raised a subject of interest not only to the general public and climatologists (see *Atmospheric sciences,* above) but to paleoclimatologists and geologists as well. Svante Arrhenius suggested nearly a century ago that increases in the concentration of carbon dioxide in the atmosphere would result in global warming. Carbon dioxide, while transparent to the Sun's ultraviolet radiation, absorbs infrared radiation emitted by the relatively warm surface of the Earth, preventing it from being reflected back into space and consequently warming the atmosphere—the "greenhouse effect."

The intimate relationship between the activity of living organisms and the composition of the Earth's atmosphere has led to dramatic evolutionary changes in both through geologic time. A principal participant in this interaction has been carbon dioxide. Inorganic processes too may affect the concentration of carbon dioxide in the atmosphere. For example,

the concentration of carbon dioxide in volcanic gases is high enough to contribute to appreciable increases in the concentration of carbon dioxide in the atmosphere during episodes of intense and widespread volcanism. The concentration of carbon dioxide in the atmosphere might have been reduced, on the other hand, during periods of coal formation, when vast quantities of carbon were removed from circulation by burial.

It has been suggested that changes in the concentration of atmospheric carbon dioxide may have been a principal factor in the pronounced climatic changes during the geologic past. With the release of buried carbon by the burning of fossil fuels, the concentration of carbon dioxide in the atmosphere has appreciably increased since the middle of the 19th century. R. Revelle and H. E. Suess, writing in 1957, called the increase in atmospheric carbon dioxide resulting from the activity of humans "a large-scale geophysical experiment." It may indeed be regarded as an experiment, however inadvertent.

Because the warming and cooling of the Earth's atmosphere is an immensely complex process involving many factors other than changes in the concentration of carbon dioxide in the atmosphere—including, for example, changes in the amount of radiation emitted by the Sun—predictions based on changes in a single variable are necessarily suspect. While warming as great as that predicted by some climatologists would certainly be widely regarded as striking verification of the theory of global warming by the greenhouse effect, the experiment should not be regarded as completed. The complexity of the factors involved in climatic change and the difficulty of distinguishing among their effects led John Maddox, writing in the July 21, 1988, issue of *Nature,* to caution against jumping to the conclusion that recent weather conditions are to be attributed to the release of carbon dioxide into the atmosphere through industrial pollution.

Compared with such other features of the Earth's surface as mountains, oceans, and even rivers, lakes are, geologically speaking, short-lived. Climate, not surprisingly, is a principal determinate in the origin and persistence of lakes. The influence of the greenhouse effect on the Great Lakes inevitably arose during the Colloquium on Great Lakes Water Levels: Shoreline Dilemmas, held in Chicago in March and sponsored by the National Research Council. The average annual precipitation in the Great Lakes region has been higher in the years since 1965 than it was in the period between 1900 and 1965, resulting in the recent record-high water levels. Frank H. Quinn of the U.S. National Oceanic and Atmospheric Administration reported, however, that the continued accumulation of carbon dioxide and other pollutants in the atmosphere may reverse the trend toward

Rig drills deep into the Jemez Mountains in New Mexico as geologists try to discover how geothermal systems are formed in volcanic fields.

higher water levels in the lakes. He calculated that a rise in temperature of 4° C (7° F) during the next century would lower the water level in Lakes Michigan and Huron from 1 to 2 m (3 to 7 ft) and in Lake Erie from 0.6 to 1.2 m (2 to 4 ft).

Mass extinctions. In view of the intense interest in cataclysmic extinction generated in 1980 by the suggestion of Luis Alvarez and his colleagues that an asteroid had struck the Earth some 65 million years ago, leading to the extinction of the dinosaurs and many other animals and plants, it is not surprising that climatic change, either by itself or in conjunction with an asteroid impact, has been hypothesized as a causal factor in such extinctions. Thomas J.

Crowley of the Applied Research Corp., College Station, Texas, and Gerald R. North of Texas A&M University suggested that climatic change, long supposed by geologists to be gradual, may under certain combinations of slowly changing boundary conditions be quite sudden, geologically speaking. In support of the hypothesis of a causal connection, the authors noted evidence of the coincidence of appreciable climatic change and episodes of extinction.

Evidence of abrupt change in the geologic past has indeed been accumulating. It was demonstrated over a decade ago that in the higher latitudes of the North Atlantic and Antarctic, the warming of the seas at the end of the ice age occurred, geologically speaking, very rapidly, perhaps over a period of only 2,000 years. W. S. Broecker of the Lamont-Doherty Geological Observatory, Palisades, N.Y., and his co-workers reported that they have gathered evidence that the warming trend was also abrupt in lower latitudes. They studied a core of sediments from the bottom of the South China Sea and noted an abrupt change in the character of sediments from about 13,000 years ago, a date that correlated closely with the recorded warming of the sea in higher latitudes. The authors suggested that the change in the nature of the sediments might have occurred as the continental ice melted and the adjacent continental shelf, exposed above sea level during the height of glaciation, was flooded. When this occurred, much of the suspended load of rivers that had previously been deposited in the deeper regions of the sea would have been deposited on the shelf.

Suggested agents of cataclysmic extinction have not been limited to the impact of meteorites and sudden climatic changes. Robert A. Duncan and Doug G. Pyle of Oregon State University suggested that the rapid and extensive eruption of flood basalts in what is now western India at the end of the Cretaceous Period, 65 million years ago, lends support to the view that a volcanic catastrophe, either by itself or in conjunction with the impact of a meteorite, was responsible for the widespread extinction of plants and animals that occurred at that time.

K. G. Cox of the University of Oxford responded to Duncan and Pyle by maintaining that if volcanic catastrophes are to be invoked in the explanation of mass extinctions, then not only must a temporal correlation between a period of intense volcanic activity and an episode of extinction be demonstrated but the length of the interval between the individual eruptive events that constitute a volcanic catastrophe must also be known. If the quiescent periods between individual eruptive events were long, then there might have been sufficient time for the recovery of the affected plants and animals. If, on the other hand, the intervals were short, then extinction might indeed have occurred, but it probably did so in a stepwise fashion rather than all at once, as would be expected if the impact of a meteorite were the sole agent of extinction.

Heated discussions of the periodicity of extinction continued during the year. David M. Raup and John J. Sepkoski of the University of Chicago defended their conclusion that during the past 250 million years major episodes of extinction have recurred every 26 million years, while Stephen M. Stigler and Melissa J. Wagner, also of the University of Chicago, contended that the apparent periodicity may be a statistical artifact. Stigler and Wagner insisted that they were not claiming that there is no periodicity of extinction but were simply stating that the paleontological data and the statistical procedures employed were inadequate for the task of demonstrating it.

Geology and biologic processes. Despite the prevalence of the extinction of species throughout history, life has managed to persist on Earth for a very long time. An ingenious indirect method led geochemists to conclude that life must have existed on Earth as long as 3,860,000,000 years ago. It has been known for half a century that of the two stable isotopes of carbon, carbon-12 and carbon-13, which make up the bulk of available carbon on Earth, plants have a strong tendency to select the lighter isotope, carbon-12, in the formation of biologic compounds during photosynthesis. During the past year Manfred Schidlowski of the Max Planck Institute, Mainz, West Germany, described the way this intriguing fact has been used to determine how long life has existed on Earth. If, on the assumption of uniformity that lies at the foundation of all historical inferences, it is assumed that plants have always discriminated against the heavier isotope, then the presence in sediments of carbon compounds rich in carbon-12 may be taken as evidence of the existence of life at the time the sediments were deposited. Such compounds were found in sedimentary rocks from western Greenland that appear to have been deposited some 3.8 billion years ago. It should be noted that this inference involving the two stable isotopes of carbon is entirely different from the one that permits the dating of recent geologic events on the basis of the disintegration of the rare radioactive isotope of carbon, carbon-14.

Although the great abundance and diversity of life depend primarily upon photosynthesis, a process that utilizes the Sun's energy, some bacteria are able to manufacture living material by using energy derived from chemical reactions. With the increased understanding of the Earth's dynamics and with advances in the technology of deep-sea exploration, it has become evident that chemoautotrophic bacteria, which are able to derive energy from the oxidation of sulfur compounds in total darkness, stand at the base of the food chain of some very rich animal communities that occur along hydrothermal vents at ocean depths of thousands of meters. These vents are found along oceanic ridges, which, according to the "new tectonics," mark lines where crustal plates are being formed and separated. Continued study of these communities promises not only to increase specific knowledge of previously unknown kinds of animals but also to enhance general knowledge of ecology and evolution (see *Oceanography*, below).

Recent work has demonstrated how biologic inferences may increase the understanding of processes as far removed from biology proper as seismology and earthquake prediction. It is known on the basis of historical accounts and geologic evidence that three major earthquakes—in 1480, 1785, and 1857—occurred along the San Andreas fault near Los Angeles. Gordon C. Jacoby and Paul R. Sheppard of the Lamont-Doherty Geological Observatory and Kerry E. Sieh of the California Institute of Technology, in order to further document another earthquake in the same region, used the fact that trees growing in close proximity to major fault movement may suffer trauma sufficient to be reflected in their annual growth rings. They examined the growth rings of nine trees distributed along a distance of 12 km (7.5 mi) and all growing within 20 m (66 ft) of the fault. All of those trees show evidence of suppressed growth in the form of abnormally narrow annual growth rings that can be dated as having begun in the winter of 1812–13 and persisted for a number of years. The authors concluded that the poorly documented San Juan Capistrano earthquake, which occurred on Dec. 8, 1812, was the source of the trauma that led to the suppression of growth in the studied trees. The authors cautioned that the irregular pattern of recurrence of major earthquakes along this segment of the San Andreas fault, which is confirmed by the tree rings, increases the uncertainty of forecasting such earthquakes.

Other developments. The price of oil rose gradually during the past year and more rapidly in the spring of 1989. Domestic exploration in the U.S. continued at record-low levels, however, and, consequently, there was low employment in the petroleum industry as well as declining enrollments in college and university geology programs. The discussion among academic geologists about how to respond to the dwindling demand for employment opportunities in petroleum geology continued.

Meanwhile, a controversial plan could dramatically change geologic education in the United Kingdom. At the request of the University Grants Committee, Ronald Oxburgh of the University of Cambridge recommended that university geology departments be placed in one of three categories, depending on the degree to which their activities were devoted to research, and that resources be allocated on the basis of this classification. Many academic geologists objected that such marked distinctions among departments on the basis of their commitment to research could simply not be made, pointing to, among other things, what they considered to be an important creative link between teaching and research. The University Grants Committee proposed a plan of its own, which, like the Oxburgh report, recommended a concentration of resources in departments that emphasized basic research, but it differed from that report in recognizing a spectrum of departments whose functions differed with respect to teaching and research. The most controversial effect of the implementation of the plan would be a phasing out of nearly a quarter of the Earth-science programs in the 34 universities in the United Kingdom where they were now being offered.

In addition to playing an increasingly significant role in the day-to-day practice of geology, women received special recognition in 1988. The Association for Women Geoscientists was, for example, granted status as an associated society of the Geological Society of America, and the National Science Foundation chose four women to receive substantial grants under the 1988 Visiting Professorships for Women program.

—David B. Kitts

Geophysics. The past year in geophysics was dominated by the earthquake that struck Soviet Armenia in December. Noteworthy research developments included several controversial new geophysical measurements of gravity, progress in seismic monitoring of nuclear explosions, and new insights into the structure and dynamics of the deep Earth.

Armenian earthquake. A devastating earthquake with a magnitude of 6.9 on the Richter scale struck the north-central Armenian S.S.R. on Dec. 7, 1988. The main shock was followed four minutes later by a magnitude-5.8 aftershock. The city of Spitak and several dozen villages in the area near the epicenter of the earthquake were almost completely destroyed, and the larger cities of Leninakan and Kirovakan suffered localized severe damage. Essentially all of the damage was caused by strong ground shaking; there was little evidence of landsliding or other ground failure. Preliminary reports suggested that levels of ground acceleration within 100 km (one kilometer equals 0.62 mi) of the epicenter were generally typical for a large crustal earthquake.

Engineering design and construction practice evidently played large roles in damage patterns, especially in Leninakan, where block after block of similar large apartment buildings collapsed. In mid-January 1989, after most of the rescue work had been completed, the Soviet government reported the official casualty and damage tolls: 25,000 dead, tens of thousands injured, and more than $15 billion in property damage.

Within hours of the shock seismologists determined its size and location from their analyses of seismic waves recorded far from the earthquake (called teleseismic waves). Using several different techniques, the seismologists estimated magnitudes that ranged from 6.3 to 6.9, a typical variation for large crustal earthquakes. The National Earthquake Information Center officially reported a magnitude of 6.9, determined from the amplitudes of teleseismic waves that travel along the Earth's surface. Seismologists at the California Institute of Technology, using a seismogram modeling technique, reported a magnitude of 6.8.

In an unprecedented demonstration of openness and cooperation, foreigners were allowed into the epicentral region immediately after the earthquake; thus, Soviet rescue, medical, engineering, and scientific personnel were joined by colleagues from all

Soviet leader Mikhail Gorbachev (at left in hat) talks in Leninakan with victims of the earthquake that struck the city and surrounding areas of Armenia in December 1988. Measured at 6.9 on the Richter scale, the powerful earthquake left 25,000 dead, tens of thousands injured, and more than $15 billion in property damage.

over the world. Sponsored by the Soviet and U.S. national science academies, a team of geologists and seismologists from the U.S. Geological Survey joined Soviet and French geoscientists in Armenia shortly after the December 7 shock. The geologists' objective was to observe and measure geologic manifestations of the earthquake at the Earth's surface—the length and orientation of faulting and the amount and direction of fault slip (the actual relative displacement along a fault plane of two points that were formerly adjacent on either side of the fault). The seismologists' goal was to deploy portable seismograph recorders near the main shock epicenter to record aftershocks.

Geologists found the fault trace (the intersection of the fault surface with the surface of the Earth) south and west of Spitak. It intersected a road two kilometers south of the city and extended eight kilometers to the west-northwest. Detailed inspection of rocks on each side of the trace showed these average relationships: the fault surface dipped 50°–60° to the north-northeast, and rocks in the northern block were displaced 1–1.5 m (3–5 ft) southward over rocks in the southern block. This type of deformation reflected north-south compression and crustal shortening between the converging Eurasian and Arabian tectonic plates, part of a larger convergent belt extending from the Alps to the Himalayas. The Armenian earthquake generally fit Earth scientists' prevailing ideas about the complex tectonics of the region rather well. However, the fault itself had not been recognized prior to the shock, and the eight-kilometer length of the fault trace was considered anomalously short for a magnitude-6.9 earthquake.

Seismologists deployed several dozen portable seismographs within a 100-km radius of the epicenter of the main shock and monitored aftershock activity for several months. The strategy that they followed in Armenia had evolved over two decades of earthquake investigations in the U.S., Europe, and Japan. Although seismologists can measure the magnitude and location of a large earthquake from teleseismic records, they need high-quality local records to study the details of faulting and the generation and propagation of damaging seismic waves. Unfortunately, the precise times and locations of large earthquakes are unpredictable; given limited instrumentation, there are never enough good local seismograms of large shocks, and sometimes there are none. Large earthquakes are always followed by aftershocks, however, and researchers have discovered that much can be learned about main-shock faulting and ground motion by studying aftershocks. Thus, deployment of portable seismographs during aftershock sequences provides a practical strategy for earthquake research.

In the past seismologists strove to measure only the arrival times and durations of seismic waves.

Such observations at a network of local stations allow the computation of earthquake origin times and locations and also produce rough estimates of earthquake size. Modern microprocessor-controlled seismographs, however, can digitize and record the complete ground-motion signal. Digital seismograms lend themselves to a myriad of powerful computer reduction and analysis techniques. Among other things, they provide precise estimates of the amplitude and frequency content of ground shaking, which are used by engineers to formulate the seismic elements of building codes.

By early January 1989 seismologists in Armenia had recorded more than 150 aftershocks at three or more stations for each; they ranged up to 5.1 in magnitude. (Data from at least three stations are needed to determine reliably the origin time and location of an aftershock.) The aftershock locations roughly defined a planar zone dipping to the north beneath Spitak, extending 35 km west-northwest and 15 km east-southeast of the city. The orientation of this zone was roughly consistent with the geologic observations, but the 50-km aftershock zone was much longer than the 8-km fault trace. Earth scientists had used both measures to estimate the subsurface extent of main-shock faulting in other earthquakes; in Armenia the 50-km dimension was more consistent with empirical and theoretical relationships between fault size and seismic-wave amplitudes.

Some Earth scientists suggested that the Armenian earthquake was tectonically analogous to the magnitude-6.5 San Fernando earthquake that struck southern California in 1971. After destructive compressional shocks on buried faults at Coalinga in 1983 and Whittier in 1987 (in central and southern California, respectively), this analogy gained added impetus from the point of view of seismic hazard prediction. These earthquakes surprised seismologists and caused them to reevaluate the traditional dominance of large strike-slip faults like California's San Andreas in seismic hazard estimates. (A strike-slip fault is one in which the direction of movement is parallel to the direction taken by the fault plane as it intersects the horizontal.) After the 1987 Whittier earthquake, seismologists at the University of Southern California analyzed 200 small earthquakes for evidence of other buried compressional faults in the Los Angeles basin. They identified two new structures and suggested that the associated earthquake potential was comparable to that of the major strike-slip faults—much greater than geoscientists had previously suspected.

Non-Newtonian gravity. Gravity surveying (the measuring of the differences in gravity force at two or more points) was one of the earliest and most successful methods in exploration geophysics. In the middle of the 20th century, gravity methods con-

Gravity meter is lowered into a 2,000-meter (6,560-foot) borehole in the Greenland ice cap. Its measurements suggested a small departure from Newton's inverse square law of gravity; two other groups obtained similar results.

tributed to vast new natural resource discoveries as geoscientists learned to measure minute variations in gravity over the Earth's surface and correlate them with buried hydrocarbon and mineral deposits. As the theory of plate tectonics developed in the 1960s, geophysics grew rapidly as an academic discipline by emphasizing areas of research that addressed questions of Earth dynamics—paleomagnetism, seismology, and rock physics. At about the same time, advances in computers and seismography pushed applied research toward seismic-exploration techniques, which, at least in theory, were capable of imaging the interior of the Earth with higher resolution than gravity techniques. Gravity methods in geophysics became tools that were accompanied by remarkable instrumentation and an elegant body of theory but were generally out of the research mainstream. It was in this context that one of the liveliest and most provocative sessions at the American Geophysical Union (AGU) meeting in San Francisco in December 1988 focused on some recent geophysical gravity measurements.

Nothing less than a fundamental tenet of classical physics was at stake: Newton's inverse square law of gravity, which states that the gravitational attraction between two bodies is proportional to the inverse square of the distance between them. In 1987 a team

led by geophysicists from the Scripps Institution of Oceanography, La Jolla, Calif., and the Los Alamos (N.M.) National Laboratory measured gravity in a 2,000-m (6,560-ft) borehole in the Greenland ice cap. After making precise corrections for topography below the ice and for local variations in ice density, they found a gravity anomaly that suggested a small departure from Newtonian gravitation. Two other groups reported similar results from separate experiments.

By the time of the meeting, however, the Scripps-Los Alamos team had reanalyzed their data and found that plausible density variations in the rocks below the borehole could explain the observed anomaly in a way that was consistent with Newtonian gravitation. Robert Parker from Scripps summarized the revised result in the following excerpt from his AGU meeting abstract. "When one indicts a venerable natural law, only the highest standards of evidence are acceptable. Because density variations in the crust also cause vertical gravity gradients, for the non-Newtonian explanation to be convincing, it must be shown that no acceptable density distribution can match the observed anomalies. . . . Conversely, if density variations of geologically permitted magnitude can mimic the measured results, exotic explanations relying upon new forces should be regarded with suspicion. . . . Grounds for doubt exist in all three experiments." The session ended in controversy, and most participants agreed that more measurements were needed to resolve the issue.

Seismic monitoring of nuclear tests. In 1986 the Natural Resources Defense Council, a nonprofit environmental organization in the U.S., and the Soviet Academy of Sciences began a series of joint experiments designed to address several technical questions related to seismic monitoring of nuclear bomb tests. Could seismic measurements discriminate nuclear explosions from earthquakes and, if so, what type of seismic networks were needed? How did geology at a test site influence the amount of seismic energy radiated from an explosion of a given yield; specifically, when U.S. seismologists estimate Soviet explosion yields, how should they modify formulas derived from Nevada test-site data to account for geologic differences at Soviet test sites? Finally, had each country complied in the past with the 150-kiloton test limit set by the (unratified) Threshold Test Ban Treaty (TTBT)? The Soviets claimed compliance, but the U.S. government consistently argued that Soviet tests had violated the TTBT. Lack of reliable seismic verifiability and alleged Soviet cheating were both used as arguments for blocking further test-ban negotiations.

Thus, a major goal of the experiments was to calibrate the relationships between geology, yield, and radiated seismic energy at the Nevada and Semipalatinsk test sites. Data collected and analyzed in 1987 and 1988 confirmed that seismic energy was radiated much more efficiently from the Soviet test site, presumably owing to relatively low seismic attenuation in the crust and upper mantle. Without correction for this site bias, computed yields of Soviet tests were 0.40 to 0.45 magnitude units too great. With the correction seismologists concluded that charges of Soviet cheating on the 150-kiloton TTBT limit were probably groundless. Data also suggested that nuclear explosions could be reliably verified through the use of only a modest network of seismic stations within each country, offering a practical and cost-effective alternative to intrusive on-site verification methods. These results succeeded in removing several stumbling blocks to future test-ban agreements.

Deep Earth structure. Since the first seismographs recorded distant earthquakes late in the 19th century, seismologists have tried to infer properties of the deep Earth by analyzing the travel times and amplitudes of seismic waves. Simple models with five seismically distinct layers (crust, Earth's surface to approximately 5–50 km; upper mantle, 5–50 to 670 km; lower mantle, 670 to 2,890 km; outer core, 2,890 to 5,150 km; and inner core, 5,150 to 6,371 km) were established, but progress in refining the models was slow and controversial. Then the plate tectonics revolution proved that the Earth's crust is surprisingly mobile. Those new ideas rekindled research interest into the structure and dynamics of the deep Earth, especially the forces that drive the crustal plates and the processes that generate the Earth's magnetic field. During the last few years advances in seismology, rock physics, and geomagnetism have led Earth scientists to some provocative new discoveries.

Employing large new data sets and powerful computers, seismologists have used tomographic techniques (similar to the medical computed tomography scan) to image the Earth's seismic structure with improved resolution. In order to apply seismic tomography, they first recorded many earthquakes at a number of stations on the surface of the Earth, and they then mapped zones of high and low seismic velocity by analyzing the travel times of waves along their crisscrossing ray paths. The results showed a remarkable spatial correlation between the seismic velocity structure of the mantle and surface manifestations of plate tectonics. For example, plate subduction (the descent of the edge of one crustal plate below the edge of another) around the Pacific margin generally correlated with high seismic velocities throughout the mantle, and tectonic "hot spots" generally correlated with low seismic velocities in the deep mantle. (A hot spot is a localized volcanic zone where the magma source is fixed in the mantle so that it appears to move relative to the drifting crustal plates; the islands of Hawaii and Iceland are examples.) In a separate study, seismologists used the travel times of deep seismic waves to measure topographic relief on the core-mantle boundary, a seismic discontinuity that partially reflects and partially transmits seismic waves. The researchers found that areas of low topography on the boundary correlated with zones of high seismic velocity in the overlying mantle, suggesting that the core-mantle boundary is dynamically suppressed by downwelling of cool mantle material.

These preliminary insights into deep Earth structure and dynamics were controversial but exciting, and this seems certain to be an area of vigorous geophysical research for years to come. Only when it is learned how the interior of the planet works, can the thermal and chemical history of the Earth as well as the current geologic processes on the Earth's surface be understood.

—Charles S. Mueller

See also Feature Article: PROFILING THE EARTH'S INTERIOR.

Hydrologic sciences

The severe drought that affected many areas in North America during the summer of 1988 stimulated research by hydrologists, who sought an explanation for this large-scale phenomenon. Other developments in the hydrologic sciences included experiments on groundwater contamination, continued research on deep-sea hydrothermal vents, and the use of satellites to study the topography of the ocean surface.

Hydrology. Drought was on the minds of many people during the past year. The Middle West in the United States suffered one of the worst droughts of the 20th century. Water levels in the Mississippi River were at historical lows. The drought had severe economic impacts on agricultural production and transportation systems. While most hydrologists agreed that the drought could be explained in terms of the expected natural cycle of wet and dry years, the possibility could not be immediately dismissed that it was not in some way related to the climate change that was predicted to result from the buildup of carbon dioxide, nitrogen oxide, methane, and other gases in the atmosphere. Much basic research remained to be done before the interplay of processes that lead to drought conditions could be understood and their occurrence and duration could be predicted.

One of the most exciting trends in hydrology is the effort to carry out large-scale, integrated field experiments in order to examine interactions between atmospheric and land-surface processes. The

Barges on the Illinois side of the Mississippi River near St. Louis, Missouri, in June 1988 are unable to proceed because of the low water level resulting from the severe drought in the Middle West.

data base used to describe hydrologic processes and the fluxes of water and heat on a spatial scale of 10 km to 100 km was very limited. At the 1988 spring meeting of the American Geophysical Union in Baltimore, Md., a symposium on large-scale field experimentation focused on the initial results of two projects. The World Meteorological Organization had established a program entitled Hydrologic-Atmospheric Pilot Experiments (HAPEX), with the goal of developing improved understanding and mathematical descriptions of exchange processes between the land surface and the atmosphere. The first project, HAPEX-MOBILHY, was carried out in southwestern France in 1986. It was designed to study the hydrologic processes and evapotranspiration in an area 100 × 100 km. Detailed ground-based networks for measuring surface, soil-moisture, and atmospheric parameters were augmented by atmospheric soundings and measurements from aircraft. Data collected in this monitoring program were being used to compare estimates obtained at different scales and with different instruments.

A second experiment was carried out under the sponsorship of the International Satellite Land Surface Climatology Program (ISLSCP). One of the objectives of this program was to better understand how water and energy fluxes and related hydrologic processes at the Earth's land surface can be measured by means of satellite-based sensors. The first ISLSCP field experiment took place near Manhattan, Kan., in the summer and fall of 1987. The study area, in a region of rolling topography covered by grasslands, measured 15 × 15 km. Several intensive data sets were collected during the growing season.

The experiment was designed to obtain simultaneous data via satellite, aircraft observation, atmospheric soundings and at numerous ground stations. Syntheses of the data were expected to be completed by the end of 1989.

New technologies that were expected to reach full development by the mid-1990s should enhance the ability of researchers to characterize large-scale hydrologic processes. These new technologies included high-resolution satellite sensors and NEXRAD, the new Doppler weather radar network. NEXRAD will provide the opportunity to obtain detailed measurements of rainfall intensity over a large area of the central U.S. for the first time. Such data would be invaluable in resolving basic relationships between the spatial and temporal characteristics of rainfall and the hydrologic response of watersheds.

Application of the concepts of fractals continued to provide new insight to hydrologic processes. On the basis of the analysis of digital elevation models of river basins, a group of researchers at the Massachusetts Institute of Technology presented evidence that the geometry of stream channel networks that drain a watershed is fractal. Fractals have the property that spatial patterns viewed at one scale are replicated statistically when viewed on other scales (this is called self-similarity). This observation suggests that the mathematical tools of fractal geometry will be helpful in quantifying the factors controlling the evolution of drainage networks.

In another application of fractals, Steve Wheatcraft and Scott Tyler of the Desert Research Institute in Nevada examined the spreading of a nonreactive solute transported through a heterogeneous porous medium. "Plumes" of solutes released into the subsurface expand in size as the mass is carried along by the groundwater flow system. This process is important in determining the changes in the concentration of solutes as the plume moves farther from its source. A considerable amount of research has been carried out to develop quantitative tools for predicting concentration distributions of solutes. Wheatcraft and Tyler assumed that the heterogeneity of a porous medium could be characterized as fractal. Their calculations revealed that if porous media are fractal, then the change in the rate at which a plume grows can be explained as a natural consequence of the structure of porous media.

Groundwater contamination continued to be the focus of many researchers. A field experiment carried out by researchers at the University of Waterloo, Ont., documented for the first time the manner and extent to which benzene, toluene, and xylene (major constituents of gasoline) are naturally attenuated by aerobic bacteria in the subsurface. Efforts were under way to develop computer models that simulate the transport and degradation of gasoline products and other organic compounds that may leak from underground storage tanks and potentially contaminate groundwater supplies. These models must be linked to those that describe microbial growth and decay, which in turn depend upon the availability and transport of oxygen and nitrate within the subsurface. While progress was being made in the formulation of such models, the lack of data on reaction kinetics was the greatest limitation in applying them as tools in site assessment and in the design of remedial strategies aimed at cleaning up contaminated groundwater.

Hydrologic research in support of plans for the permanent disposal of high-level nuclear wastes in underground repositories was providing opportunities for new insight in regard to groundwater flow in deep rock formations. Several European countries and Canada were evaluating the concept of locating underground repositories in crystalline rocks such as granite. The U.S., under the Nuclear Waste Policy Act of 1983, had in place a plan to evaluate three different geologic environments: bedded salt, basalts, and volcanic tuffs. In 1988, however, the U.S. program was redirected to study only one site as the potential location for the nation's first repository for commercial wastes produced in nuclear power plants. The site, at Yucca Mountain in Nevada, is in an area with a deep water table and limited groundwater recharge. The repository was to be located within the unsaturated zone above the water table. Research, therefore, was under way to gain a better understanding of the physical and chemical processes associated with groundwater flow and the transport of radioactive materials in an unsaturated, fractured rock mass.

The most important development in hydrology during the past year may not have been any single discovery. Rather, it may have been the concrete action hydrologists began to take to promote the scientific basis of their discipline. In recent years there had been an opinion growing in the hydrologic community that research was being hampered by perceived notions of hydrology as a subject centered on the applied issues of water supply and flood control. Some prominent hydrologists argued that this perception had a negative impact on funding of basic hydrologic research.

Efforts were, therefore, under way on several fronts to strengthen the recognition of hydrology as one of the fundamental Earth sciences. In the U.S. a committee organized by the Water Science and Technology Board of the National Research Council began the preparation of a report on opportunities in the hydrologic sciences. The committee was assessing critical topics at the frontiers of the science, identifying data requirements and the potential of emerging technologies for data acquisition, and evaluating educational programs for training hydrologists. This concern for the scientific stature of hydrology was not unique to U.S. hydrologists. Researchers in other countries, and in international organizations such as the International Association of Hydrological Sciences, reached similar conclusions.

The breadth of hydrology, beyond its applied base in water resources management, was perhaps best illustrated by the topics addressed by the National Research Council committee. They included hydrology and the Earth's crust, hydrology and land forms, hydrology and climatic processes, hydrology and weather processes, hydrology and surficial processes, hydrology and living communities, and hydrology and chemical processes. The committee expected to complete its work by the end of 1989. This effort, and those planned by other organizations, had as the long-term goal the promotion of scientific hydrology as a fundamental branch of the geosciences.

—Leslie Smith

Oceanography. *Drought of 1988.* One of the most exciting developments of the past year took place when oceanographers and meteorologists reported a possible link between ocean-atmosphere interactions in the tropics and the major drought that occurred in the summer of 1988. This understanding was based on study of the El Niño phenomenon, which is characterized by the appearance every few years of anomalously warm water along the Equator in the Pacific Ocean and the subsequent global climatic effects. The warm water suppresses the normal flow of nutrients from deep in the ocean and, therefore, also has a major effect on fisheries in tropical regions. The El Niño of 1982–83 had an enormous effect on the global economy, being implicated in declining fisheries, heavy rains and flooding on the west coast of South America, and severe drought in Australia and the Philippines.

The new studies showed that the appearance of warm water was just part of the story—in other years there appears to be anomalously cold water at the Equator in the Pacific. This cold phase is called La Niña. During 1988 cold water did appear at the Equator, pushing the normally warm water to the north. Accompanying this movement of the warm water was an intensification of atmospheric activity that apparently affected the North American jet stream, which flows through that region. The result was that the jet stream moved far north of its normal path over the U.S.—leaving room for a large, dry high-pressure system from the south and the subsequent drought.

As of 1989 the proposed links between tropical air-sea interaction and mid-latitude droughts were part of a theory that needed further testing. It is possible that global temperatures are affected by the warm and cold oscillations in the tropical Pacific.

World Ocean Circulation Experiment. Planning for new global programs continued. A major conference, attended by scientists from 48 countries, was held in Paris in late November and early December to plan the next steps for the World Ocean Circulation Experiment (WOCE). The conference was sponsored by the International Council of Scientific Unions, the Scientific Committee on Oceanic Research, the Intergovernmental Oceanographic Commission, and the World Meteorological Organization.

WOCE is to be one of the key elements of the World Climate Research Program (WCRP), which was established in 1980 to determine the degree to which climate can be predicted and the extent of human influence on it. The effect of the circulation of the world ocean is a major factor in the prediction of climate changes over periods of decades. WOCE is designed to be a global study that would provide the information necessary for understanding the large-scale movements of water, chemicals, and heat in the ocean. The worldwide scale of the WOCE experiment is made possible by the existence of new measuring equipment, including satellites and supercomputers. The major field phase is scheduled to begin in 1990.

One of the principal social concerns that provided an impetus for WOCE is the possible global warming produced by the increased concentrations of carbon dioxide and several other gases in the atmosphere. The ocean is a key element in determining these concentrations. One of the major WOCE objectives is to provide the information about ocean circulation necessary for understanding the role of the ocean in long-term climate changes.

Another likely effect of climate change in the coming decades would be a rise of sea level. WOCE data would permit understanding of sea-level change from several sources, including the melting of continental ice, an increase in ocean temperature, a decrease in the salinity of seawater, and movements of the Earth. Sea-level changes would have a direct social and economic impact on the large populations living near the coast.

Hydrothermal vents. The discovery in 1977 of hydrothermal vents in the deep ocean and the understanding of their role in recirculating water in the ocean (hydrothermal circulation) was one of the main recent advances in marine chemistry, and research continued at a rapid rate. The first year-long deployment of a camera to record the events near a hydrothermal vent was concluded in August. The time-lapse camera was deployed in September 1987 as part of the VENTS program sponsored by the U.S. National Oceanic and Atmospheric Administration. The camera was placed near a high-temperature hydrothermal system on the central Juan de Fuca Ridge off the northwestern coast of the U.S. The hydrothermal systems in this area are among the most extensively mapped and sampled in the world.

The camera took 260 sequential photographs with a frame interval of 30 hours. High-capacity lithium batteries were used to power the camera and its strobe flash. The time series of photographs provided a unique record of the structural and biologic changes in this system.

The deployment was the fourth of a successful set of time-series photography experiments that began in 1984. The longest set previously was just 26 days, and so the new year-long deployment provided a much better record. The area studied was venting high-temperature water (up to 283° C [541° F]) from at least six different orifices. A first look at the data revealed a rapid growth of spires, as fast as ten centimeters (four inches) per day, caused by the buildup of sulfides. When the area was first visited in 1984, it was entirely covered with the worms typical of such areas, called vestimentifera. The long-term photographic information showed that this population had been reduced to nearly 20% of its original size. The vestimentifera were apparently being replaced with a different population of marine worms, alvinellid polychaetes. The region was also visited frequently by deep-sea fish.

Since the process of hydrothermal circulation probably began early in the Earth's history, the vents were present in the oceans of the primitive Earth. Because of this, it was possible that these regions might be the area where life itself originated. During the year, however, biochemical evidence was presented that suggested otherwise. The synthesis of amino acids, necessary for production of the building blocks for life, appeared to be too inefficient at the high temperatures found in the vent regions. Whatever amino acids might be produced would most likely decompose within a few minutes. The same was true for the other building blocks of life, peptides and mononucleotides. Thus, the hypothesis of hydrothermal-vent origin of life appeared to be on shaky ground.

Satellite measurements. The U.S. Navy Geodetic Satellite (Geosat) began providing information on ocean surface topography in March 1985. The measurement of sea level is important for many purposes, as noted above in the discussions both of the El Niño studies and of the World Ocean Circulation Experiment. The new Geosat data revealed a dramatic improvement in resolution for measurement of sea-level changes along the Equator in the Pacific Ocean and of ocean eddies on a global scale.

The new data showed strong variability in the vicinity of the strongest ocean current systems, such as the Gulf Stream, the Kuroshio off Japan, the Brazil/Falkland Current off the east coast of South America, and the East Australian Current. The largest variability in sea level was found in the region south of Africa in the Agulhas Current, where sea-level changes during one year averaged 50 cm (20 in) or more.

Geosat data also clearly resolved for the first time several regions of high variability of the sea level, caused by currents flowing over topographic features on the ocean floor such as the South Tasmania Rise south of Australia, the East Pacific Rise, and the Kerguelen Plateau. The satellite was expected to last for at least two more years, providing oceanographers with a continuing data set for monitoring eddies and ocean currents. The U.S. Navy was also reported to be considering a second such satellite, to be put in orbit before the end of the Geosat mission. Having two such satellites in orbit would provide for the first time a real-time description of ocean variability.

Chemical oceanography. One of the unsolved problems for marine chemists and biologists in 1989 was how respiration takes place in the ocean's interior. Organic material in sinking particles was the accepted source, but recent measurements by Japanese scientists revealed that the amount of dissolved organic carbon may be larger than had been earlier suspected and was equally important in respiration. The measurements of dissolved organic carbon showed the same pattern with depth as the measurements of oxygen consumed, suggesting that deep-sea respiration was being fueled by the dissolved carbon compounds.

Because of the difficulty in calibrating the measurements, which involved understanding the chemical reactions in the different techniques for extraction of dissolved organic carbon, the measurements had not been fully reproduced as of early 1989. Should the measurements be confirmed, however, it appears that the mean production rate of carbon from the dissolved organic carbon pool could be comparable to the fluxes of carbon from sinking particulate matter. It was not known what constrains the amount of the dissolved organic carbon. If the amount were to grow or shrink, the uptake or release of carbon should be reflected in changes of atmospheric concentrations of carbon dioxide.

In April and May 1988 a joint U.S.-Turkey expedition was carried out in the Black Sea to study circulation, mixing, and biogeochemical processes. The expedition recovered sediment traps that had been set one year earlier and deployed new ones, traced the suspended particle layer throughout the southern Black Sea, and made a series of measurements in the sediments. The data provided new insights into changes occurring in the Black Sea. An unexpected result related to the layer that marked the transition between oxygen-rich and oxygen-poor water; it had risen to a much shallower layer than had been expected. The oxygen-poor layer, rich in hydrogen

sulfide, had risen into the zone of light penetration. One explanation for this change was that it was somehow related to the diversion of freshwater input from Soviet rivers. Measurements of the concentrations of chlorofluorocarbons were also made so that it could be determined how these compounds were being assimilated into the Black Sea.

Biological oceanography. Gradual ocean warming might be affecting the very existence of one of the most important marine resources in the tropics, the coral reefs. For example, in Puerto Rico more than 180 species of edible fish can be found on such reefs. The corals throughout the Caribbean Sea and neighboring waters were being affected both by "bleaching" and "white band" disease. Little was known about these ailments. Their recent outbreaks led scientists to believe that some unknown, long-term factor was affecting the world's reefs. One possible explanation for the bleaching was the unusually long period of high temperature of the seawater in 1987. If ocean temperatures continued to warm, then new bleaching episodes could occur before the corals had fully recovered from the previous one.

In order to assess in more detail what was actually happening, a comprehensive reef study supported by the U.S. National Science Foundation began to assess long-term changes in reef temperature and the conditions of the corals. The U.S. National Park Service provided funds for monitoring reefs within national parks.

The first results of a study on the biologic consequences of a major oil spill in the Caribbean Sea off Panama in 1986 showed significant long-term effects on the behavior and health of corals in the region. Scientists found that the organisms damaged by oil were more susceptible to epidemic disease and were more likely to grow and reproduce at slower rates than unaffected colonies. The longer-term effects of an oil spill may be more important than the initial mortality because the spill leaves the coral reefs vulnerable to disease and blight for years afterward.

Coastal studies. During the summer of 1988 a cooperative experiment, the Coastal Transition Zone Experiment, was held off Point Arena, Calif. The experiment involved a full range of techniques—ranging from satellite observations to shipboard surveys from four ships—for studying the physical and biologic processes present within the large, seaward-moving filaments that occur along the coast of California, particularly in the spring and summer.

The study produced a variety of results. Among the most interesting was the fact that surface properties of the filaments, such as chlorophyll, appeared to be inadequate indicators of filament size.

Ocean Drilling Program. The first four years of the international Ocean Drilling Program ended in 1988 as the drilling ship *JOIDES Resolution* completed its work in the Indian Ocean. A partnership of 19 countries supported the program. (JOIDES is the acronym for Joint Oceanographic Institutions for Deep Earth Sampling.) By 1989 the program had drilled in all the major ocean basins and had provided new insights into the evolution of the Earth's climate, plate tectonic processes, and the composition and properties of deep oceanic crust. The drilling revealed the complexity of the ocean-continent boundaries. New studies would require more lines of drill holes and the ability to drill deeper.

The Indian Ocean drilling provided new information about the large number of ridges and plateaus on the ocean floor. The data revealed that the most prominent of these are fundamentally volcanic features produced by "hot spots," the effects of convection activity in the deep mantle. Magnetic studies of the basalts and overlying sediments implied that these hot spots moved to the north about 8° of latitude some 45 million years ago. This suggests an episode of polar wandering during that period.

Technological advances were also made. Drilling on bare rock became almost routine. The logging facilities continuously recorded conditions at the site. In the fall of 1988 the *JOIDES Resolution* embarked on an extensive campaign of drilling in the western Pacific Ocean. Drilling there addressed a wide variety of scientific problems, including the processes of forming islands and mountains, paleoceanography and sediment history, and hydrothermal processes and sulfite deposit formation.

—D. James Baker

Electronics and information sciences

Although there were no outstanding breakthroughs during the past year, progress continued to be made in many fields of electronics and information sciences. Computer designers introduced a machine that blended the best characteristics of personal computers and scientific workstations. Newly developed flash semiconductor chips operated faster and more reliably than had previous memory chips. Unesco established the Office of Information Programs and Services, and the U.S. space shuttle returned to service after 32 months.

Communications systems

Telecommunications during the past year continued to change the ways in which people operated their homes and businesses. New concepts (ISDN, Intelligent Network, telecommuting), new tools (fiber optics, facsimile, voice mail), and new technologies (digital radio, wavelength division multiplexing)

Cathy Melloan

Facsimile (fax) machines gained wide popularity as fast and relatively inexpensive means of transmitting documents from one place to another.

were being employed as much of the world moved forward in this information age.

Because most advances require a marketing "pull" as well as a technology "push," the changes were generally slow and gradual. Most people were reluctant to accept changes that would abruptly disrupt their way of life. When a change was eventually seen to be of real value, however, either in time saved or benefits derived, then it was eagerly embraced.

Cellular radio. Cellular radio is an example of such a change. Mobile radio for decades had been a mostly unrealized dream. The cost and size of the radio itself, and the shortage of radio-wave spectrum, stunted any real enthusiasm for it. Indeed, until the advent of cellular radio, the metropolitan area of New York City was assigned only 12 channels; any 13th user at a particular time would receive only a dial tone.

Cellular radio changed that. Instead of using a single powerful transmitter, it used many low-power transmitters, each designed to serve only a small area. In fact, as the population in a particular area increased, the transmitter was made less powerful and, consequently, the area of coverage—the "cell"—became smaller. The advantage of this arrangement was that the same frequencies could be used simultaneously in different cells.

A second concept of cellular systems involved "handoff." For example, an automobile moving rapidly across a city almost certainly moved from one cell to another during a particular conversation. Microcircuits in the equipment constantly monitored signal strength at several sites, and when a vehicle moved to a location where a different cell frequency would be more appropriate, the electronics in the equipment issued instructions that caused the car radio to change frequencies, automatically and rapidly. A user, in fact, did not even know that this handoff had taken place.

The first cellular system (Chicago) began operations on Oct. 13, 1983; it, and all subsequent commercial systems, were analog, that is, based on a system in which the signal continuously varies in terms of voltage or current. Since that time, however, the world has moved to digital technology, and a rapidly growing service is dependent on an outdated technology. (Digital communications systems employ a nominally discontinuous signal that changes in time, amplitude, or polarity.) At some time the analog systems will be replaced by digital ones. Some experts predicted that it would not be until the mid-1990s that widespread implementation of digital cellular would be achieved.

Meanwhile, the growth rate of analog cellular radio continued to be remarkable. The Cellular Telecommunications Industry Association indicated that for the period of January 1 to June 30, 1988, new subscribers were being added at the rate of nearly 63,000 per month—or 2,100 per day. As of mid-1988, there were 1.6 million cellular subscribers in the U.S. This growth seemed certain to continue, and by the end of 1992 the number of subscribers was expected to be at least four million. If prices of the telephones themselves continued to drop (in many places they were below $500), it was likely that an even greater subscribership would be achieved.

Digital systems. The replacement of analog with digital systems was not unique to cellular radio; in recent years, "digital" had penetrated virtually every part of the telecommunications industry, including telephone switching systems, and audio systems. Digital television was on the horizon, and there were also reports of research on digital photography and digital X-rays. Digital systems were more compatible with computers and generally resulted in improved quality and speed.

Fiber optics. A transmission medium 1/10 the thickness of a human hair is able to carry one billion bits of data per second. Though this is hard to believe, glass fibers that transmit information in the form of light waves have achieved this capability. By 1989 fiber was the medium of choice for long-distance telecommunications transmission, and by the end of the year 99% of the 140 largest metropolitan areas in the U.S. would be connected by fiber.

The largest long-distance carriers in the U.S. relied heavily on fiber. At the end of the first quarter of 1988, AT&T Co. had 30,500 km (19,000 mi) of fiber in service; the total was expected to grow to 53,000 km (33,000 mi) by the end of 1990. U.S. Sprint Communications Co. started the year with 29,000 km (18,000 mi); by the end of 1988 this had grown to 30,500 km (19,000 mi) and represented 100% of the company's traffic.

During 1988 the concept of taking fiber to the home for such uses as videotex, security monitoring, remote meter reading, energy management, and interactive television had caught on. Bell South had a trial in operation in Heathrow, Fla.; Southwestern Bell at Leawood, Kan.; and GTE in Cerritos, Calif.

Another major opportunity for the application of fiber was with community antenna television (CATV). In 1989 the coaxial cable carrying CATV signals passed close to 80% of the homes in the U.S., and about 50% of those homes subscribed to the service.

The undersea market for fiber was also active during the past year. At least six new cable systems were planned for 1989–91:

Completion	Route
1989	U.S.–Bermuda–U.K.–Ireland
1989	California–Hawaii–Guam–Japan
1990	U.S.–Tokyo-spur to Alaska
1991	U.S.–Canada–U.K.–France–Spain
1991	Guam–Philippines–Taiwan
1991	Hong Kong–Japan–Korea

ISDN. For several years suppliers of products, providers of services, and users of both have been told of the wonderful promises of ISDN, the Integrated Services Digital Network. By 1989 the promises were beginning to become reality, not only in the form of field trials but also in actual commercial operations. This network, when finally deployed, will allow voice, high-speed data, slow-scan video, facsimile, and other types of data to be transmitted over the same pair of wires.

In order to do this, the suppliers and providers and users had to agree on standards—standards that deal with such aspects of the network as format structure, message protocols, and points of interface. This was no small task, but companies from around the world were working to achieve them. Electronic circuits were being developed to perform the functions dictated by these standards, and they were being incorporated in new terminals or in add-on adapters that allowed existing terminals to operate over the ISDN.

It should be emphasized that there were already means of implementing the promised features. Sophisticated private branch exchanges (PBXs) could perform many of the functions, especially when tied to private local-area networks or wide-area networks. However, each such arrangement was special and had to be custom engineered. ISDN, on the other hand, would be almost universally available.

One of the largest ISDN operations in the U.S. involved Southwestern Bell and Tenneco Inc. Approximately 2,800 ISDN lines were being used, and six Tenneco locations in Houston, Texas, were to be linked by means of both fiber and copper cable. Tenneco expected that the system would save the company 10 to 20% compared with conventional communications packages.

Intelligent networks. During recent years the providers of enhanced information services faced the problem of implementing them across the entire telecommunications spectrum. (One example of such a service is wide-area centrex in which a business is provided with the centrex services even if its various branches were not served by the same central office.) For example, they did not want to have to modify each of the 20,000 telephone exchanges in the country each time such a feature was introduced. Network providers for years hoped for a system that would prevent the need for such piecemeal solutions. By 1989 one had been found, the Intelligent Network (IN). It placed at logical points, or nodes, in the telecommunications network several large and sophisticated computers and data bases and made them available to all telephone central offices called upon to implement a particular enhanced service. The name given to these nodes was Service Control Points.

One of the most significant challenges in implementing an IN was the means to be employed in communicating with a Service Control Point. The solution selected was the use of a packet switching system (a system in which data are assembled into bundles or packets and transmitted at high speed toward the destination) and adherence to a signaling protocol designated Signaling System 7. The latter can also be used to implement out-of-band signaling, which allows long-distance telephone calls to be established without reserving and occupying a full voice channel until such time as one is sure that the call will be established. This will save precious seconds on each telephone call.

Regulation. Although technology plays perhaps the most important role in telecommunications, it must be recognized that government control or regulation is also significant. In the U.S., competition was greatly stimulated by the breakup of the Bell System in January 1984. Before that time the opportunity for other companies to achieve success in the U.S. was limited. By 1989, however, manufacturers from virtually every industrialized country had entered the U.S. telecommunications marketplace.

In other countries similar actions were being taken. In the U.K. British Telecom was shifted from government to private ownership, as was NTT in Japan.

—Robert E. Stoffels

Computers and computer science

During the past year computer scientists made advances in understanding the limits and possibilities of parallel computing, and a new computer was announced that blends the best characteristics of personal computers with the computing power of scientific workstations. Also, several groups were formed, each intent on defining an operating system standard for the industry.

Parallel processing. The Connection Machine, a novel computer architecture developed by Thinking Machines Corp., was in 1989 the only commercially available computer that incorporated more than 65,000 central processing units (CPUs) in one machine. The reason for doing this was simple: if all of those processors are put to work on a single computational problem, the time that it takes to compute the answer will be greatly reduced. In the ideal case the new machine should be able to compute an answer 65,000 times faster than a conventional computer that has only one CPU.

Unfortunately, the computations most users need do not fit the ideal case. Practical computations usually require that the problem be subdivided and that answers to the subproblems be combined to produce the overall answer. For example, one might consider how a computer might compute the sum of 16 separate integers. On a single processor the only possible solution requires at least 16 separate steps in which the computer fetches the first integer, adds the second to it, adds the third to the partial sum, and so on. On a parallel computer that has several processors the problem can be solved by pairing the integers and having eight processors simultaneously add the eight pairs in the first step, then pairing the partial sums and having four processors simultaneously add the pairs in the second step, and so on. Thus, it appears that the parallel computer could compute the total sum in only four steps. However, counting only the addition steps can be misleading because, in a real computer, additional steps are required for moving the integers to the correct processors. Thus, besides performing basic computation, a computer program that executes on a machine with multiple processors must spend some time controlling the processors, assigning them subtasks and incorporating the results into the overall computation.

Computer scientists have struggled for many years to understand the principles of parallel computation and to find practical ways to use computers that have multiple processors. By 1989 several general techniques had emerged, but none had produced good results. For example, one technique devoted one processor to overall control. This control processor divided the problem, assigned subpieces to other processors, and collected the results. Although using

Sandia National Laboratories

Supercomputer at Sandia National Laboratories contains 1,024 central processing units. Sandia scientists found that it could solve complex problems more than 1,000 times faster than could a computer with a single processor.

only one-half of one percent of a problem requires a sequential solution, then it would be impossible to solve the problem on a multiple-processor machine any more than 200 times faster than on a single-processor machine, no matter how many processors the former had.

To many in the computing community, Amdahl's proposition sounded like common sense; they saw no reason to doubt it. Others, who doubted at first, came to accept it gradually as the years passed, and no one found any practical problems that violated the rule. However, many computer science researchers never accepted the idea. Some worked to devise new multiple-processor architectures, while others even offered small cash prizes to anyone who could find a speedup of more than 200 for a practical problem.

During the past year a team of scientists from Sandia National Laboratories, Albuquerque, N.M., startled the computing community when they announced a speedup of more than 1,000 for three scientific problems. The team explored two ways of using multiple-processor computers. In one approach they devised a way to divide an existing problem into pieces, solve the pieces simultaneously on multiple processors, and then combine the results. They used a 1,024-processor N-cube machine from Intel Corp. and compared the time it took to solve the problem on a single-processor machine with the time it took to solve the problem on the multiple processor.

Using another approach, the scientists decided to fix the time available for a computation and compare the size of the problem that could be solved on a single-processor machine with the size of the same problem that could be solved on a multiple-processor machine in that same amount of time. The idea of using problem size as a measure is to provide a check against speedup techniques that work for only a few problem sizes and to show that the techniques work for large numbers of processors. Again, the results obtained were exciting. The ratio of problem sizes solvable in the same time was more than 1,000 to 1, showing that the new techniques provided computing capability approximately equal to the number of processors available.

While the techniques used by the computer scientists at Sandia Labs did not apply to all problems, they settled a long-running question and demonstrated that high-speed computing with multiple processors is possible and practical. The results are expected to stimulate researchers to look for other techniques that exploit parallelism as well as other problems that can use the techniques already discovered.

Personal computers and scientific workstations. During the year NeXT Inc. introduced a new computer that blends characteristics of personal computers and scientific workstations. In the past the differences between personal computers and work-

one processor for overall control worked with small numbers of processors, it had a major drawback—it did not work well for computers that had thousands of processors, like the Connection Machine. The trouble arose because the single control processor could not operate fast enough to keep the other processors busy. It became a bottleneck in the system, causing a computer with thousands of processors to execute at speeds not much faster than a machine with tens of processors.

In the past some computer professionals argued that the limitations of parallel processing are more fundamental than were generally suspected. They suggested that all problems of practical interest have inherent requirements that will prevent anyone from ever devising efficient solutions for multiple-processor machines. The informal statement of this proposition became known as Amdahl's law, named after computer architect and author Gene Amdahl, who formulated it in an article he wrote in 1967. According to Amdahl's law, if a program requires N computational steps on a single processor, the theoretically best solution on a machine with K processors will need only N/K steps. Amdahl argued, however, that such a speedup is possible only in theory because a few small parts of all practical problems require sequential solutions and those parts must execute as slowly on a multiple-processor machine as on a single-processor model. The subtle and surprising consequence of Amdahl's law is that if

Steven Jobs of NeXT Inc. introduces a new computer that combines the features of personal computers (a user-friendly interface) and workstations (a high-power processor, main memory, and large secondary storage).

alone. For most users, however, the differences in completion times of background activities are unimportant because the user is free to use the computer for other activities.

NeXT's new machine combines the characteristics of personal computers and scientific workstations. Like a PC, it has a friendly interface designed for users who may not be scientists or engineers. Like a workstation, it has a high-power processor (a Motorola MC68030), main memory (8 megabytes), and relatively large secondary storage (at least 256 megabytes). It also has a display device with higher resolution than the displays on many workstations. The machine can display shades of gray instead of merely black-and-white, thus providing images that have more detail than many workstations.

The speed of the central processor on the NeXT machine makes it unlike any previous personal computer. The sophisticated Motorola MC68030 CPU chip in the machine operates at a clock rate of 25 Mhz, meaning that it can execute approximately 4.5 million instructions per second. By comparison, the processor in the original IBM PC ran at approximately 6 Mhz. Processor speeds of 25 Mhz are currently considered high even for expensive scientific workstations; to find such speed in an inexpensive computer is unusual.

Most important, like a scientific workstation, the new machine includes an operating system that supports concurrent processing. Called Mach, it is a variant of the popular Unix™ time-sharing system. With Mach, developed by researchers at Carnegie-Mellon University, Pittsburgh, Pa., a user can conduct almost unlimited concurrent activity. For example, a user might begin work on a spreadsheet, suspend that work to find an entry in a data base, switch back to the spreadsheet, and stop to look up a word in an on-line dictionary. In the meantime, the computer could also be printing a document.

Despite its processing power and sophisticated operating system, the NeXT machine was aimed at a much broader cross section of computer users than are scientific workstations—faculty and students in all disciplines of colleges and universities. To demonstrate the potential usefulness of its machine in the academic environment, NeXT supplied more than the traditional amount of software. For example, the machine includes an on-line copy of *Webster's Collegiate Dictionary*, complete with illustrations. A user can identify a word anywhere on the screen and ask the system to display the definition of that word from the dictionary. The system automatically creates a new window in which to place the output from the dictionary and then displays the meaning of the word. Because the system supports concurrent processing, a user can leave the definition on the screen (moving it out of the way if necessary).

stations were dramatic. Personal computers, often called PCs, are usually small, inexpensive computers with limited main memory capacity, relatively slow processors, and small amounts of secondary storage. Intended for one person, PCs are designed to perform only one computation at a time and are typically used for nonscientific computing tasks such as personal finance and record keeping.

By contrast, scientific workstations are intended for scientists and engineers who perform such computational-intensive calculations as numerical solution of partial differential equations or numerical solution of linear equations. Compared with PCs, scientific workstations have large main memories, fast processors, and large secondary storage devices. In addition, the software used on scientific workstations resembles that used on midsize and large computers because it allows multiple concurrent activities. The need for concurrent computation on workstations has always been obvious because some of the large computations that scientists and engineers perform require hours or even days of processing time. If a scientist had to wait for each computation to finish before beginning the next, the machine would be unusable much of the time.

The central processing unit in a workstation works much like that in a PC—it consists of a single processor that executes instructions one at a time. In fact, the CPU in most workstations can perform only one computational activity at any given instant. When it is handling keystrokes, it cannot be solving linear equations. Inside the workstation, however, a complex program called an operating system manages to achieve the illusion of concurrent execution by switching the processor rapidly among all the computational activities. Thus, if a user begins multiple background computations, each of them will take longer to complete than if that computation ran

The NeXT machine also includes digital processing hardware that can be used for input or output of electrical signals, including speech from a microphone. Usually found only on PCs, this feature makes possible such new applications as voice mail, an electronic mail service in which users record and transmit audio messages instead of merely sending typed messages.

Perhaps one of the greatest innovations introduced with the NeXT computer is an optical disk drive used for secondary storage. One form of optical disk technology is already standard in the audio industry in the form of compact discs. A compact disc, which measures approximately 12.5 cm (5 in) in diameter, can hold approximately one hour of music or voice. It contains a digitized version of the sound etched into a continuous track that can be read by a laser. By 1989 versions of the compact disc had been used for data storage, but they all had the property that the disk could be written only once. The new disks introduced during the past year differ from the older ones in two important ways: first, they can be rewritten many times just like conventional disks, and second, they have much greater capacity than older ones.

Technically, the new optical disks should be called magneto-optical because they use a combination of magnetic and optical techniques to store and recall data. Because the first version of the disk requires three passes over an area to erase, rewrite, and verify it, the disk is slower than the fastest magnetic disks. Thus, recording data is more expensive than reading it. However, most experts expect that the mechanism will soon be improved to decrease the need for multiple passes.

One of the interesting pieces of software that NeXT developed to be used in its new computer is an automated interface builder. The idea of an interface builder is not new—researchers have been experimenting with flexible user interfaces in laboratories for many years. The idea behind automated interface construction is obvious: each user has preferences about the shape and placement and contents of windows, menus, and control areas on the screen. In the past a vendor who supplied software for a PC had complete control over the way the software chose to use the display. One vendor might create software that displayed sliders to be controlled with a mouse, while another might program software to respond to keystrokes. Some computer manufacturers tried to obtain uniformity by specifying guidelines that gave conventions for programmers to follow when building user interfaces. NeXT, instead of trying to specify a fixed format for interfaces, provides users with the ability to create their own interface for a program.

—Douglas E. Comer

Electronics

The outlook for the electronics industry in 1989 appeared to be good. U.S. companies had planned to spend about $415 billion on equipment and plant in 1988, a 6.5% increase over the previous year. Much of that investment was targeted for improved electronic automation and ways to increase productivity. Across all categories of the industry, such as electronic equipment, components, supercomputers, data-processing equipment, and software-testing equipment, projected sales levels were above those for 1987.

Technical and scientific workstations were among the growth segments of the industry, recording a 24% increase in sales over 1987 and expected to total approximately $3 billion in 1988. Their growth was aided by an explosive proliferation of programs that featured increased computational and graphic abilities. Some of these programs operated at ten million instructions per second (MIPS), while only a year earlier 4–5 MIPS had been the upper limit available.

Computer software sales increased 21% during 1988 to $16.7 billion. They were expected to grow by as much as 50% in the next few years in certain select areas and should overtake computer hardware revenues by the mid-1990s.

The proliferation of computers that process more information at ever faster rates caused large increases in the production of electronic testing equipment. From complex testing apparatuses that cost as much as $500,000 to such smaller devices as logic probes and digitizing oscilloscopes, sales increased by as much as 25%. Instruments that measure events in nanoseconds (10^{-9} seconds) were being replaced by those that can measure events in the picosecond (10^{-12} seconds) range.

Miniature solar cell mounted on a European bee is a prototype of transmitters that scientists hope to attach to Africanized "killer" bees in order to locate and track them when they enter the U.S.

Oak Ridge National Laboratory

The industrial sector of the industry also enjoyed a good year in 1988 owing to the continuing diversification of automated equipment in the automotive industry, aerospace, chemicals, food, beverages, and pharmaceuticals. This diversity, coupled with an increased need for quality control, boosted the sales of inspection systems by about 16% for the year.

Semiconductor sales grew about 20% in 1988. Among the leaders were memory chips; standard logic chips; RAM (random-access memory) chips, which grew at a 26% rate; and electrically erasable memory chips, which grew at a 50% rate. Many of the star performers in the field grew at the expense of chips that process information at slower rates and with smaller memories.

The electronic component industry profited from the overall healthy state of the electronics industry. Nontechnical developments such as the weakening of the U.S. dollar compared with the Japanese yen combined with technical factors such as the long-awaited spurt of local area networks (LANs) and a surge in sales of high-density printed circuit boards (especially of the multilayer variety) for a healthy growth. The sales of power supplies needed by computers increased by 13% for the year.

International developments. There were signs that the U.S. and Japan would cooperate more closely in the future. For the first time, the Japanese opened their research facility in superconductivity to non-Japanese companies. IBM Japan was invited by the International Superconductivity Technology Center in Tokyo to become its first foreign-owned member. This firm was responding to the Japanese demand for computers that run English-language software in Japan. The reason for the seemingly strange request was that there is a much greater variety of software available in English, and the Japanese did not wish to wait for it to be translated into Japanese. Also, the first electronic products resulting from U.S.-Japanese cooperation were completed during the year. Among them were integrated circuits used in telecommunications hardware, fiber-optic cables, intracomputer links, and various telemetric equipment.

The government-supported personal computer (PC) industry in Taiwan continued its healthy growth during 1988. Compared with 1987 the sales of PCs rose 58%, of disk drives 59%, and of monitors 42%. However, the industry was facing fierce competition in a market of increasing complexity. By itself the low price of the PCs manufactured in Taiwan was inadequate to secure Taiwan's place in the marketplace. The industry was squeezed between low-priced clones from Japan and South Korea and the emergence of technically sophisticated workstations. In response to this challenge, the Taiwanese planned to improve their own technology. Also, in an effort to entice new high-technology companies to move to Taiwan, the government offered a five-year tax holiday on all corporate income.

The investment made by South Korea during the mid-1980s in the development of electronic chips was beginning to pay off. The South Koreans were securing an increasing share of the world's chip market, mostly at the expense of the Japanese. The most direct impact was expected to take place in random-access memory, where the Japanese held the lead. The South Korean share of that market was estimated to be about $400,000 in 1988, a 400% increase over 1987. It seemed, therefore, that the South Koreans were doing to the Japanese what the latter had done to the U.S. about ten years earlier.

The Hindustan Computers Ltd. of New Delhi, India, in May 1988 became the first Indian company to produce a fault-tolerant computer. The deal between that company and Tolerant Systems of San Jose, Calif., gave the former the right to manufacture Tolerant's hardware and license its own TX software in India.

The European effort to cooperate in the manufacture of electronic chips, which resulted in the formation of a consortium similar to that of Sematech in the U.S. (the Joint European Submicron Silicon Initiative, or Jessi), was being foiled by national self-interest and probably would lessen Europe's chances of standing up to both U.S. and Japanese competition. Specifically, while Siemens of West Germany and Philips of The Netherlands agreed to develop high-density memory and logic chips by the 1990s, the Franco-Italian chipmaker SGS-Thompson, which wanted a share of that market, found itself excluded. That firm threatened to buy its needed chips from the Japanese, a move that it felt would hurt the entire European electronic community.

Chips. It appeared that a new development in memory chip design would provide the U.S. with a technological lead over other countries. Industry observers maintained that the new design, termed flash memory, would radically alter computer technology. Flash chips are programmable read-only memories that are built with single transistor cells, and it was expected that 64 million bits would be packed on one chip by the year 2000. This technology allows for denser packing and faster, more reliable operations than are possible with present-day memory chips. Industry specialists speculate that flash chips will replace magnetic disks for memory storage and will allow computers to be designed with all nonvolatile memories. The potential of the new chips technology appeared to be so great that Intel Corp. decided to concentrate on flash chip design. Also interested in the new technology were Seeq Technology Corp. and two Japanese companies, Toshiba Corp. and Kawasaki.

Supercomputers. In the computer segment of the electronics industry, supercomputers, minisuper-computers, and large-capacity workstations led the sales charts, followed by more traditional products, such as mainframes. While mainframe computers continued to represent the largest segment of the computer market, their annual growth rate of about 6% lagged by a considerable margin behind the 28% annual growth rate for supercomputers. The latter were becoming smaller yet smarter, cheaper, and more prolific. For "as little as" $1 million, in 1989 one could buy a supercomputer that outperformed any of its far more expensive predecessors. This decline in cost combined with their desired computational power and the increase of available software for them caused the sales of supercomputers to increase much faster than sales of other types of computers.

As the sales heated up, so did the competition. While U.S. companies had enjoyed a large share of the supercomputer market, competition from the Japanese companies of Futjitsu, Hitachi, and NEC was increasing. As of 1989 the U.S. continued to hold an advantage in software development; however, the maintenance of such a lead could not be taken for granted if the history of the electronics industry was any guide.

The difference in supercomputer architecture between the U.S. and Japan was interesting. The U.S. was moving toward the technology of parallel processing. That architecture involved placing a small number of the fastest available microprocessors onto a shared memory configuration. Typical of such an arrangement was the Cray Y-MP computer, which used eight processors in tandem. By contrast the Japanese preferred the traditional and simpler single-processor architecture. Their one-processor machines were the fastest machines of their kind in the world, thanks to their advanced semiconductor technology. It was only by parallel processing that the U.S. could match the computing speed of the Japanese machines. In 1989 Futjitsu was planning a parallel-processing supercomputer.

West Germany also was entering the supercomputer market. The Parsytec GmbH of Aachen, West Germany, unveiled two entries during the past year. One machine was a 64-processor model, while another had 256 processors in parallel configurations. The computing rates for these machines were 640 MIPS for the first and 2,560 MIPS for the second. Also, inherent in the parallel architecture of both machines was their capacity for expansion.

Computer networks. The U.S. communications industry expected an 11.5% increase in growth and sales, totaling about $4.9 billion, in 1988. Growth of LANs using fiber optics was particularly strong. When they are based on fiber optics, LANs are less

Laptop computer developed by the Japanese firm NEC weighs only 2 kilograms (4.4 pounds) but is four times faster than some personal computers. It has a main memory of 640 K (about 655,000 characters).

expensive than copper-based installations. Corporations also were increasingly interested in interconnecting their computers. For workstations, Ethernet by 1989 linked 10,000 computers in five continents.

The expansive nature of the network market impinged heavily on hardware developers. Thus, a growth of more than 34% in communications products took place in 1988.

Laptop computers. Laptop computer sales based on both the 80286 and 80386 microprocessor chips were estimated at close to one million units during 1988 and were projected at about 1.5 million units during 1989. Sales of such units for the next three years were expected to rise sharply, reaching close to two million units by 1990. By contrast, sales of laptop computers based on the older 8086 and 8088 microprocessors were expected to level off at about 300,000 units for the next three years.

Both Toshiba and NEC planned to capture a major share of the laptop market. In particular, Toshiba, which by 1989 held 25% of the market, was to introduce an 80286-based slim-line computer called the T1600 and an 80386-based unit named the T5200. NEC planned to market three new laptops, one based on the V-30 chip and the other two based on the 80286 and 80386 chips, respectively.

The sought-for assets in a laptop computer were its independence from an electrical outlet and its relatively light weight. A 2.7-kg (6-lb) laptop with a 20-megabyte disk, a modem, and a crisp display was an industry goal. However, until 1988 greater computing power and brighter displays required more battery power, which in turn required a larger and heavier battery. During the past year a new hard-disk technology developed by the Prairietek Corp. of Longmont, Colo., had a 20-megabyte hard disk that weighed only 255 g (9 oz) and could store about 10,000 pages of typed material. Aside from its small weight, which was about half that of existing 6.75-cm (3.5-in) disks, it featured ramp-loading, which significantly reduced its power requirements compared with current systems and therefore allowed a battery of reduced size and weight. Furthermore, ramp-loading allowed for repeated starts and stops of the computer without significant wear and tear on the magnetic surface of the hard disk.

Consumer electronics. An increase in the sale of color television sets, a resurgence of audio equipment, and the advent of camcorder systems and digital audio tape recorders/players boosted the sale of consumer electronics items by 5% in 1988 toward a $24 billion sales level. The sale of VCR (videocassette recorder) systems, however, grew only 2% for the year.

Casio marketed a combination TV-VCR, or TVCR, that displays all high-frequency and ultrahigh-frequency TV channels in addition to full VCR recording and playback on its 8.25 × 8.25-cm (3.3 × 3.3-in) liquid display screen. The unit, termed the VF-3000 and costing about $1,400, measured 32 cm (8 in) wide by 15 cm (6 in) high and 7.5 cm (3 in) deep. It weighed 2.2 kg (4.9 lb).

The Sony Corp. introduced its Video Walkman, weighing 1.1 kg (2.4 lb). It had a 7.5 × 7.5-cm (3 × 3-in) screen, was battery-operated, and cost about $1,000.

Making their appearance during the year were several electronic devices that for about $50 prevented a

Video Walkman, introduced during the year by Sony Corp., combines a videocassette recorder and a 7.5-centimeter (3-inch)-square full-color television screen in a unit weighing only 1.1 kilograms (2.4 pounds).

tap on one's phone or the listening to one's telephone conversations by unauthorized persons. Traditional protective devices insured one's telephone privacy by their electronic circuitry. However, accidental loss of telephone privacy could still occur. The new units left nothing to chance. Typical was the Tele-Privacy Guard unit developed by Measurements Specialities Inc. in Wayne, N.J. A user plugged the unit into the standard RJ-11 modular telephone plug and the phone, in turn, into the unit. An electronic circuit containing a silicon-controlled rectifier ensured an electronic mismatch between phone and eavesdropper. Should eavesdropping occur, or a tap be placed on a user's phone, the resultant current in the phone would be too small to operate both the user's phone and the eavesdropper's extension or the tap. As a result, the phone would simply go dead.

Customers could now consult a video screen to provide them with guidance to products and prices. With a touch of a button, a customer could even find out how he or she would look dressed in a particular garment or hairstyle.

New products. The prototype of a new computer screen minidisplay made its appearance during the year. In its demonstration, computer images were fed to a 56.7 g (2-oz), postage-stamp-sized viewing screen suspended via a headband in front of an operator. Such a technology could prove to be effective during a medical operation. It could, for example, provide a surgeon with all the needed information about the medical condition and pathology of a patient. The surgeon could obtain this without using his or her own hands while keeping the patient under direct observation. The device was based on plasma technology developed at the Massachusetts Institute of Technology and was actually built from standard components obtained at a local Radio Shack store.

The need for new kinds of sensors was becoming ever greater because modern electronic systems were allowing for more and more control of systems ranging from petroleum refineries to the glucose level inside a patient's blood vessels. The new sensors employed various technologies. Some used optical fibers in which a fluorescent dye gave off a reflected light depending upon the amount of oxygen in a patient's blood. Others employed piezoelectrical crystals in which the frequency of vibration was calibrated to the presence or absence of a substance to be monitored. Though the technology was promising, some major obstacles still remained. Among them were the rejection of sensors by the human body and the need to maintain accurate calibration of them under varying operating conditions.

Computers and art. Experimental programs to translate art objects into computer images were under way in various major art museums. Although these programs were controversial, enthusiasm for the new technology was running high. By means of the technology, a museum visitor could place art images side by side on a computer screen for comparison. He or she could zoom in on different details of the works and call other contemporary pieces up for comparison. Also, a viewer could change the color of a work to see its effects upon the finished product. In fact, a museum-goer could create his or her own art collection.

While in the past the written word was used in the description of a work of art, by 1989 the computer screen was providing a more direct visual description. Advocates of the new technology were enthusiastic about the interaction that it was making possible between works of art and their viewers.

—Franz J. Monssen

Information systems and services

As the complexity of the environment increased, ever more powerful and sophisticated information processing systems were needed to manage the many demanding tasks and activities that resulted from these changes. Within the U.S. there had been a widespread acceptance of computers and modern system technologies that provide the information needed to manage the government's activities and agencies.

The results of this acceptance were impressive and led to significant savings of time and money. However, the increase in the number of workers who had access to computer-stored information along with the widespread utilization of data bases created a possible threat to personal privacy. The U.S. government, therefore, took steps to ensure the security of its computer systems and data bases. A compre-

hensive policy, together with realistic and meaningful administrative and legislative actions, was needed to reassure a skeptical public that its interests were being protected and to shift the focus of information system planning toward the reduction of access barriers and improved public services.

Two significant changes in government personnel occurred. James H. Billington was appointed as the 13th librarian of Congress. A well-known author, historian, and educator, he planned as librarian to develop an expanded publications program, to make the library's resources more readily available, and to attract world-class scholars. The second appointment was Don W. Wilson, who was confirmed as the U.S. archivist, the first since the National Archives and Records Administration became an independent agency. Also a well-known historian, Wilson stated that one of his first tasks would be to review existing legislation to determine why significant quantities of federal records had not come under the control of the National Archives. He also announced plans for a major study on the impact of electronic technology on government records to understand how electronic records are retained and to prevent the potential loss of significant information.

Demographic projections for California indicated that soon after the year 2000 the state would be populated predominantly by black, Hispanic, Asian, and American Indian ethnic groups. In anticipation of this change, the California State Library and Stanford University sponsored a study, prepared by the Rand Corp., to examine the impact of California's changing ethnic character on internal library information policies and services. The study recommended that government officials, library directors, and other policymakers consider the implications of the forthcoming population changes and develop

VideOcart, a promotional device developed by Information Resources Inc., is triggered by an electronic scanner to flash ads and messages to the consumer about a product close at hand.

Michael L. Abramson—Woodfin Camp & Associates

new models for resource utilization that would help librarians provide needed services to all residents of the state.

Unesco was also responding to major changes that had taken place throughout the world and within the UN. A recent reorganization established the Office of Information Programs and Services (IPS), with four divisions, under the direction of Jacques Tocatlian. The IPS organization was given the responsibility for carrying out activities in the fields of scientific and technological information, documentation, libraries, and archives with an emphasis on the development of infrastructures, training, and regional cooperation in order to improve access to information for all member nations.

U.S. information systems. Applying for admission to the Georgia Institute of Technology became as easy as ABC if one used the school's Apply By Computer system. ABC allowed any student with a computer terminal and a modem to dial into the school's computer network and fill out an admissions application electronically. The University of Richmond, Va., had a similar program, called CAP (Computerized Application Process), that used floppy disks and did not require a modem. Instead of requesting a printed application form, the student applying for admission could request a CAP disk. When inserted into a personal computer, the program greeted the student with the University of Richmond's insignia and the school's fight song. After the last blank on the application form was filled in, the student mailed the disk back to the university along with an application fee. Both schools agreed that it was just a matter of time before other colleges provided similar programs, because applications by computer save time and money and improve the accuracy of the admissions process.

The National Information Center for Educational Media in Albuquerque, N.M., created a training media data base that provides references to more than 32,-000 programs on videotapes, audiocassettes, films, and filmstrips used for training and development in the workplace. The data base contained information culled from more than 25,000 catalogs representing more than 8,000 producers of the programs. Each data base reference listed the title, media type, educational level, key word descriptors, and an abstract plus the names and addresses of both the producer and distributor of the training media.

The SAE (Society of Automotive Engineers) Global Motility Database included reports on current research and technology related to automobiles and other self-propelled vehicles such as trucks, buses, aircraft, spacecraft, motorcycles, tractors, and construction, military, and marine equipment. The data base, which was updated quarterly, provided instant access to over 24,000 technical paper abstracts re-

lating to the design, composition, and propulsion of self-propelled vehicles.

The U.S. Public Law Updating Service (PLUS), a publicly accessible information service about legislation, was available 24 hours a day through the Office of the Federal Register. PLUS provided prerecorded information about new public laws and alerted callers to selected legislation that was awaiting approval and had not yet been received by the Office of the Federal Register.

The records of the Vietnam war, consisting of approximately 850 cu m (30,000 cu ft) of material created between 1954 and 1975 by the U.S. Army and Military Assistance Commands, were transferred to the National Archives. These records fully document the role of the U.S. Army and the U.S. Joint Commands in Vietnam. The staff of the Archives had to identify, describe, arrange, appraise, and review the records for declassification before they could be made available to the public.

AIDS-NET, a National AIDS (acquired immune deficiency syndrome) Network, was launched by the Public Health Foundation in cooperation with other public health organizations to provide federal, state, and local health personnel with the latest AIDS programs and research advances. The network's electronic mail and bulletin board services allowed AIDS coordinators to exchange information and messages by using their personal computers.

When planning to take a trip, one might first want to consult an on-line travel data base before making final arrangements. In addition to the usual data bases for flight-schedule information, there are others that provide information about tours, hotels, and restaurants in specific cities, states, and regions in both the U.S. and elsewhere. The Department of State Travel Advisory Service, maintained by the U.S. Department of State, offered advisories on visa requirements, travel restrictions, local customs, and news gathered from U.S. embassies and other agencies throughout the world. The Travel Security Guide (TSG) data base, available on line through U.S. Telecon, Inc., included descriptions of events about which tourists should be cautioned (such as terrorism, hijackings, and epidemics) and provided analyses of airport, railroad station, and surface route security.

International information systems. While the quality of European science was universally recognized, Europe's ability to promote economic growth by translating the results of its science and technology into new or improved goods, processes, and services remained a matter of concern. To address this issue the Commission of the European Communities proposed a number of specific programs for the dissemination and utilization of research results, including the establishment of a European newsletter, a technological consultancy service, and an "innovation diagnosis" system to assess the advantages, drawbacks, and risks of a technical project in target countries.

Ruralnet, a data base prepared by the Institute of Cultural Affairs International in Brussels, Belgium, aimed to consolidate a vast variety of experience in the management of local projects around the world. It enabled a user to find out where and when particular localities were faced with similar problems and to see how these were resolved. The data base was available in English, French, German, and Dutch.

TANDAM, a comprehensive information service on the theater, was housed in Munich, West Germany, and was jointly developed by Austrian, British, Danish, German, Italian, and Swedish institutions to aid theaters, publishers, tourist authorities, and the general public. Approximately 55,000 documents were referenced in the system and divided into separate files. A production file contained information from programs and press releases; an object file consisted of playbills, photographs, autographs, and similar items; a work title file contained descriptions of plays, translations, and adaptations; and a work catalog file comprised bibliographic records of play texts, musical scores, and librettos.

British Telecom demonstrated its experimental system for automatic speech translation. The system recognized spoken phrases (for example, from a speaker making hotel reservations) in English, French, or German and translated them, using a computer voice, into one of the other languages. Each word had to be pronounced slowly and distinctly. The vocabulary was stored on voice prints introduced by trained operators, and it contained more than 1,000 words and several hundred phrases.

The National Library of China (NLC), located in the western suburbs of Beijing (Peking), covered more than 7 ha (18 ac). With more than 14 million books in its possession, NLC was one of the best-stocked libraries in the world. Two large-capacity computers were to be installed soon—one for handling Chinese and Japanese characters and the other for 54 other languages. A staff of 1,625 assisted the 7,000–8,000 people who visited the library daily. When completed, the system would also function as a network center linking thousands of libraries throughout China.

Information science research. Such an enormous amount of textual information was available for scientific and engineering research that automated systems were needed to help manage this information resource, and research was needed to improve the effectiveness of information retrieval systems. A planning grant to study the feasibility of creating an industry/university cooperative Research Center in Information Management was given to the Geor-

gia Institute of Technology by the National Science Foundation (NSF). Both industries and universities recognized the need for information science research, but neither one could solve those research problems in isolation. The planning study addressed the varied interests of educational institutions and industry, the different policies and administrative procedures that could be used for operating a cooperative research center, and the potential for such a center to become self-sufficient.

The U.S. National Archives and Records Administration received a grant to develop a reliable accelerated test to determine whether the treatment of microfilm with selenium would increase the resistance of the silver image on the film to oxidation. This study was important because microfilms were being used to preserve information that might be lost because the paper on which books and newspapers had been printed had deteriorated. If both the paper and the microfilm deteriorated, then the information would be lost forever.

Loughborough (England) University of Technology received a grant from the British Library Research and Development Division to study ways in which the skills of information scientists could be used in the process of constructing expert systems (methods and techniques for constructing human-machine systems with specialized problem-solving expertise). Much of the study information was obtained through interviews with both developers and users of expert systems and library and information science professionals. Other researchers at Loughborough University studied the effect of information technology on the acquisition and use of personal information and the implication of such systems for education and training in the United Kingdom.

The Polytechnic of North London surveyed the information perceptions, literacy, and handling skills of information users in business and in the media. The project identified circumstances in which data bases were used to meet information needs, the effect of on-line services on the employees of a subscribing organization, and the main barriers to greater use of those services.

—Harold Borko

Satellite systems

Earth-orbiting satellites provide a variety of services of great economic, social, and military value. Such systems are called applications satellites, and there are three general classes: communications, Earth observation, and navigation. These satellites are developed, launched, and operated by individual nations, groups of nations, and private industrial concerns.

Launch vehicle services in 1989 were available from the U.S., the Soviet Union, Arianespace Inc.,

Japan, and China. Arianespace Inc. consisted of a group of European companies and banks.

In the U.S. the space shuttle returned to service after a 32-month hiatus following the January 1986 explosion of the *Challenger*. Successful manned flights were made in 1988 and 1989. Meanwhile, following government approval and encouragement, major U.S. aerospace industrial firms began offering competitive service on expendable launch vehicles.

Communications satellites. During the past year communications satellites continued their growth in size, complexity, and use. The International Telecommunications Satellite Organization (Intelsat), a commercial cooperative owned and operated by 116 member nations, during the year operated 13 satellites stationed in geostationary orbit above the Atlantic, Pacific, and Indian oceans. (A geostationary satellite orbits the Earth from west to east at such a speed as to remain fixed over a given place on the Equator at an altitude of about 35,900 km [22,300 mi]). Total full-time traffic grew to 118,000 channels, a 12.5% increase over the previous year. At the end of 1988 there were more than 800 Earth stations accessing Intelsat. They provided transoceanic telephone and television services as well as transmission of facsimile, digital data, and telex through 1,840 Earth-station-to-Earth-station paths. In addition, many thousand "receive-only" small terminals were using Intelsat capacity. More than 5,000 such terminals were in operation in China. The Chinese as of early 1989 owned two transponders and leased another from Intelsat. The national Ministry of Education programmed about one-half of this capacity in educational lessons ranging from elementary- to university-level courses.

The next generation of satellite design was to be Intelsat 6. Built by Hughes Electronics Corp., each satellite would be able to relay at least three television channels and 120,000 telephone calls simultaneously. The first two Intelsat 6 spacecraft were scheduled to be launched in 1989–90, as needed, by Martin Marietta Corp. In October Intelsat placed orders with Ford Aerospace Corp. for five high-capacity Intelsat 7 spacecraft, with delivery to begin in 1992–93.

Satellite transmission was increasingly being used to relay entire newspapers electronically to a distant printing plant. Thus, *The Financial Times* of London was able to provide same-morning delivery in two dozen cities in the U.S. and Canada. Major U.S. newspapers utilizing daily satellite transmission to other cities in the U.S., Europe, and the Far East included the *Christian Science Monitor*, the *International Herald Tribune, USA Today*, and the *Wall Street Journal*.

At the close of 1987 the West German TVSat 1 direct-broadcast satellite was in trouble, unable to de-

ploy its solar panels after being launched into orbit. By March, after various attempts had been made, the latches remained immobile, and the loss of the high-powered satellite was accepted. Total value of the satellite was about $230 million. Of this amount less than one-fourth was covered by satellite insurance.

In October the French government launched the TDF-1 direct-broadcast television satellite. Capable of transmitting five television channels, TDF-1 was almost identical to TVSat 1. However, no problems occurred during the deployment of the solar panels on the TDF-1, and the 2,130-kg (4,695-lb) satellite was placed successfully in geostationary orbit. The high-power (230-watt) channels were designed to deliver high-quality imagery and sound to home receivers equipped with relatively small antenna dishes.

In the U.S. many rural areas were unable to receive adequate television reception from distant urban transmitters, and cable TV was not available. As a result, there was a tremendous growth in home TV reception direct from satellite transmissions. Large antennas were generally required. During the past year 19 C-band-frequency satellites provided some 150 channels of regular TV programming of news, education, and entertainment. About 30 stations transmitted all-sports programs. In addition, more than 50 radio stations could be received, offering a wide variety of music, news, and other programming.

Throughout much of the rural U.S., one could see TV receiving dishes aimed at the satellites ringing the Equator in geostationary orbit. Costs of purchase and installation of TVRO (television receive-only) antennas dropped rapidly during the past several years. At the same time many technical design improvements were made. Antennas by 1989 were able to track and lock onto specific satellites by remote control from one's living room. The cost of such an installation varied considerably, depending upon location and terrain.

Mobile communications using satellite systems continued their development throughout the past year. The International Maritime Satellite Organization (Inmarsat) expanded air-to-ground communications services. Maritime telephone, telex, facsimile, and data communications services were under evaluation. Inmarsat granted Communications Satellite Corp. (Comsat), the U.S. member of Inmarsat and Intelsat, permission to lease satellite capacity to Aeronautical Radio, Inc. (Arinc). Arinc, a U.S. airline-owned communications services firm, was engaged in a joint venture with its foreign counterpart, SITA (Société Internationale de Télécommunications Aéronautiques). SITA provided communications for 314 foreign airlines.

Three Inmarsat 2 spacecraft with an L-band spectrum assigned for aviation use were scheduled to be launched by early 1990. Meanwhile, two British

Tracking and Data Relay Satellite (TDRS) is positioned in the payload bay of the space shuttle Discovery *just before being launched into orbit in September 1988. Together with the TDRS launched in 1983, it is expected to provide message-relay capability to 85% of the Earth's surface.*

Airways 747 aircraft were fitted with equipment that would allow them to use Inmarsat's existing Atlantic satellite for operational evaluation. Passengers on these airplanes would be able to dial virtually any telephone number and talk for about $10 per minute. Long awaited, such "aerosat" communications would provide continuous voice communication to aircraft. All radio telephone in current use is limited by "line of sight" restrictions, resulting in loss of signal in transoceanic service.

Inmarsat conducted a test and demonstration of mobile satellite communications with the use of a mobile home traveling on a 5,600-km (3,500-mi) circuit of cities from Prague, Czech., to Berlin by way of Hungary, Yugoslavia, Bulgaria, and the U.S.S.R. Hundreds of text messages were sent and received between the moving vehicle and Inmarsat headquarters in London. Transmissions were carried via the Inmarsat operational satellite orbiting over the Atlantic Ocean.

A major task in the September mission of the space shuttle *Discovery* was the launch of the massive Tracking and Data Relay Satellite (TDRS) into geostationary orbit. Weighing more than 2,700 kg (5,000 lb), the satellite joined the first TDRS, launched in 1983. The second TDRS was lost in the shuttle tragedy of 1986. The two satellites, positioned at longitudes 41° W and 171° W, were designed to provide message-relay capabilities to 85% of the Earth's surface. Before the TDRS system, low-orbit spacecraft could communicate with Earth only when they were in sight of one of several ground tracking stations, typically less than one-sixth of an orbit.

Earth-observation satellites. This category of applications satellites consists of three major types: weather (meteorologic), Earth resources, and military reconnaissance.

Weather satellites. Continuous global weather observations were obtained from U.S., European Space Agency, Soviet, and Japanese weather satellites in geostationary orbits above the Equator. Supplementing this capability were the two U.S. satellites in polar orbits.

The U.S. normally had two Geostationary Operational Environmental Satellites (GOES) stationed at longitudes 75° W and 135° W to provide eastern and western coverage of the U.S. and the Western Hemisphere. They continuously tracked the movement of clouds, weather fronts, and storms and transmitted a new image each half hour.

Having exceeded its five-year life expectancy, GOES-West developed instrument problems in 1988. The National Oceanic and Atmospheric Administration (NOAA), operator of U.S. weather satellites, consequently made plans for a probable return to a one-GOES system some time in 1989. NOAA was one spacecraft short because of the destruction during launch failure of a new GOES in 1986. The first of a new family of GOES satellites was scheduled for launch in 1990.

During 1988 a new ozone-monitoring TIROS polar-orbiting satellite, NOAA 11, was launched from Vandenberg Air Force Base, California. Among its instruments was a sensor that mapped the global distribution of the Earth's protective ozone layer. It was designed to provide data important to scien-

The first Ariane 4 of the European Space Agency lifts off from Kourou, French Guiana, on June 15, 1988. It placed into orbit one weather and two telecommunications satellites.

tists studying ozone depletion in relation to possible global climate changes.

Earth-resources satellites. In the U.S. the Earth Observation Satellite Co. (Eosat) continued to manage the Landsat satellite system under contract from NOAA. The commercial sale of images from the Landsat 4 and Landsat 5 satellites had not been successful, partly because the resolution of surface features was limited to 30 m (98 ft).

The competing French Spot satellite imagery had a resolution of 10 m (33 ft). Likewise, in the Soviet Union the Soyuzkarta organization offered surface imagery of 5–10-m (16–33-ft) resolution. During the year exploratory discussions were held by officials of NOAA and CNES (Centre Nationale d'Etudes Spatiale), the French national space agency, on the possibility of a merger of the Landsat and Spot systems.

Military reconnaissance satellites. The prime purpose of this category of satellites is to provide intelligence concerning military troop movements—tanks, ships, and submarines—and missile activity. Long the province solely of the U.S. and the Soviet Union, a satellite recovery pod for reconnaissance was recently developed by China. Such satellites

may record not only optical images of the Earth in a variety of spectra but also electronic emissions of terrestrial and airborne communications and radar systems.

The space shuttle *Atlantis,* launched in December, carried a secret military satellite payload. It was believed to have been deployed successfully in low orbit. The satellite had a reported span of 45 m (150 ft) and might have both optical and radar imaging capability. Radar transmission penetrates cloud cover and is valuable for both ocean and land surveillance.

Navigation satellites. Mobile satellite communications for position determination and navigation were undergoing rapid development. In 1988 a Washington, D.C., commercial firm, Geostar, launched on two satellites (Spacenet 3R and G-Star 2C) a position-locating service for trucks, trains, and boats called "radiodetermination satellite system" (RDSS). Positions were derived through comparison with loran C units. (Loran C is a low-frequency radio navigation system that determines position by measuring the difference in the times of reception of synchronized pulse signals from two fixed transmitters.) Geostar reported that more than 5,000 position fixes per day were provided to commercial customers via small RDSS terminals installed in more than 1,000 vehicles, mostly trucks.

In June the first intergovernmental agreement concerning the Sarsat/Cospas global satellite search-and-rescue system was signed in Paris. The agreement bound four nations—the U.S., Canada, France, and the Soviet Union—to cooperate for 15 years in the Sarsat/Cospas system. At their summit meeting late in 1987, Soviet leader Mikhail Gorbachev and U.S. Pres. Ronald Reagan had endorsed this agreement to "institutionalize" the system.

Started in 1982 under a working agreement among technical agencies of the four nations, the system employed U.S. and Soviet satellites to relay emergency radio messages from downed fliers and shipwrecked sailors throughout the world. Twelve other nations later decided to cooperate in the system. In 1988 the U.S. Coast Guard required all U.S. commercial fishing vessels to carry Sarsat/Cospas radio beacons. During the year the International Maritime Organization of the UN voted to require lifeboats of all merchant vessels weighing more than 300 tons to carry them.

With four satellites in operation, a distress signal from anywhere on Earth could be received and its position determined (by the Doppler shift) within about two hours. By 1988 Sarsat/Cospas had proved its value. Despite a high percentage of false alarms, more than 1,100 persons in distress had been rescued.

—F. C. Durant III

See also Feature Article: MACHINES OF INNER SPACE.

Energy

Concerns about energy generally decreased during the past year. Belief in the return of oil prices to the heights of 1980 nearly vanished, but rising prices early in 1989 revived fears of a return to high levels. The perennial concern about what the members of the Organization of Petroleum Exporting Countries (OPEC) intended to do remained. However, even this inspired less attention than it had in the early 1980s.

Nevertheless, the experience with OPEC had profoundly altered many aspects of energy. One major change was the discovery that many options were available both to augment energy supplies and to reduce consumption.

New elements in the energy business. Major changes in the conduct of energy business were taking place. The participants and the ways in which they dealt with each other were changing radically. Arrangements long alleged to be indispensable vanished without causing perceptible problems. Five terms—disintegration, commoditization, restructuring, privatization, and deregulation—were being used to describe key elements in this change.

Disintegration refers to the lessening emphasis on having the same company involved in several parts of the supply chain. Given the differences among fuels, the previous integration had taken different forms in oil, gas, coal, and uranium. Integration in oil involved extracting, transporting, refining, and retailing. For gas, pipeline companies continued to be major producers. Major coal users owned mines. Several electric utilities ventured into ownership of uranium mines.

Commoditization refers to a moving away from securing raw materials through integration or long-term contracts that impose limits on price movements. Instead, arrangements are made in which prices are more flexible. Restructuring is simply the selling of energy or other business. Privatization is the newest word for the goal of those who argue that government ownership should cease because it does more harm than good. Growing interest in privatization, however, cannot be attributed to the coining of a catchier phrase. The roots lie in the recognition that performance by private energy firms has often been more impressive than government action. Deregulation involves the removal or at least the lessening of government regulation of industry. All these changes reflect the basic principle that whatever arrangements are adopted must reflect economic realities.

The most profound disintegration occurred in the international oil business. Companies from the United States and Western Europe ceased managing oil operations in the Middle East, North Africa, and Venezuela and also stopped marketing the output. Companies and countries learned that while advantages existed for the old arrangement, they were different from what the companies and the U.S. and many Western European governments had believed. For much of the 20th century those companies and governments thought that producing abroad provided them with a favorable business position. Thus, in times of travail the company would have greater access to oil and could favor its home country in the allocation of supplies. This belief, however, was not borne out in practice. The interests of both the company and the country in which production occurred were such that the choice between supplying the oil to the refining subsidiaries of that company or supplying it to another customer was based upon which was more profitable. In practice, even the home-country government did not actually seek supply favoritism. Such favoritism generated opposition in the country of production and in the other countries that were deprived of the oil. Political alliances between such countries as the U.S., the U.K., France, and The Netherlands and companies heavily involved in international oil also stimulated those nations to encourage sharing of supplies.

What the oil companies contributed was production and marketing expertise that the oil-producing countries could not secure as cheaply elsewhere. While the advantage of reliance on the companies decreased as the countries became more sophisticated, some nations—notably Iran and Iraq—may have excessively reduced their reliance on foreign expertise.

Integration by gas pipelines, steel companies, and electric utilities was designed to isolate them from the presumably harmful effects of open-market purchases. However, two special conditions must prevail for such integration to be profitable. First, open-market prices must be increasing because of depletion. Second, the integrating firm must have a better ability to forecast those developments than the present owners of the resource and all rival buyers. If the owners of such properties foresee the profit rises, they will refuse to sell unless they are paid an amount equivalent to the expected profits. And if others in the market forecast the depletion-induced price rises, competitive bidding will force the prices of attractive properties up to the point that the landowner is offered an amount equivalent to the profits expected by other bidders. If such buyers are more optimistic about price rises than the landowners, their offers may exceed the minimum price that the landowner would have accepted.

Steel companies long prided themselves on the astuteness with which they recognized the value of high-grade coal resources and acquired them. As steel output fell and technology lessened the importance

Bullwinkle, at 490 meters (1,615 feet) the world's tallest offshore oil-drilling and oil-production rig, is towed through the Corpus Christi (Texas) Ship Channel to the Gulf of Mexico, where it was to be installed off the coast of Louisiana.

of high-grade resources, however, such acquisitions no longer seemed so desirable. Several electric utilities also greatly reduced and even ceased coal production. Fears by the steel firms and utilities about high prices and dependency on rigid supply chains for the coal proved unfounded.

Contracts cannot shelter the parties from market realities even if the explicit terms seem to provide such a shield. A common form of contract is one that bases prices on a formula that ties them to movements in cost indicators such as government indexes for wages, supplies, and equipment costs. When actual costs differ radically from the prices determined by such formulas, pressures predictably arise to change the formula. Sellers cannot survive with prices below costs; buyers are unwilling to pay prices grossly in excess of cost.

In fact, neither side will tolerate a price radically different from prevailing market rates. When market prices show a persistent tendency to differ radically from those determined by formulas in contracts, formula-based contracts are abandoned. Contracting is ended, contracts are shortened, or the contract price is based on some sort of market price indicator.

Commoditization refers primarily to the first of these alternatives—shifting from contracting to spot buying. However, a range of responses has developed. In oil, commodity markets in London and New York each trade a particular crude oil. These commodity exchange prices provide indicators of general market trends. These indications are used as the basis for pricing the crude oils actually traded by brokers who arrange spot deals and those who contract for oil.

As of 1989 such formal exchanges had not been developed for other fuels. In coal, for example, substantial adjustments were made on the basis of direct negotiations between buyers and sellers. Such adjustments date back at least to the rise of energy

prices in the early 1970s. Without much publicity, energy consumers agreed to reflect the new realities by paying prices above those required in the contracts. The 1980s then produced price reductions; among the best documented cases are those in the U.S. and Japan.

In the U.S. many separate rearrangements were undertaken. Specific utilities broke specific contracts. Starting in the late 1970s the Japanese started negotiating prices annually. Separate discussions were held by the steel and electric-power industries. In both cases the industries and their suppliers exchanged proposals seeking to establish an appropriate price. This practice began as a means of responding to producer demands for greater responses to the rising prices of the late 1970s and early 1980s. In the mid-1980s, however, it was used to allow consumers in Japan to benefit from falling prices. The Japanese now annually negotiate prices with all but a few suppliers.

Associated with the changes in the oil industry were numerous mergers between leading firms. Thus, the deal in which British Petroleum Co. was to acquire the majority of the shares of Standard Oil Co. of Ohio was followed by a complete takeover of Standard Oil by British Petroleum (the company was renamed BP America Inc.). Chevron Corp. bought Gulf Corp.; Texaco Inc. purchased Getty Oil Co.; and Occidental Petroleum Corp. acquired Cities Service Co. Royal Dutch/Shell Group bought out the publicly held shares of the U.S. Shell Oil Co.

Largely independently, some oil companies shed or reorganized ventures into coal and other minerals. Thus, Royal Dutch/Shell acquired a half interest in the U.S. coal producer A. T. Massey Coal Co. in 1980, but the firm was split in half in 1987. The half held by the other owner—Fluor Corp.—retained the Massey name, and the portion assigned Shell was merged with the coal operations of U.S. Shell.

Some of the largest changes in coal occurred in Australia. Broken Hill Proprietary Co. Ltd. (BHP), a leading Australian mining company, acquired the controlling interest in two major Queensland companies from U.S. firms. First, Peabody Coal Co. sold its controlling share in what is now called Thiess Dampier Mitsui Coal. Then BHP purchased Utah International Inc., which was the controlling owner of the largest coal-mining company in Queensland. More recently, CSR Ltd., a diversified Australian firm, sold most of its coal interests.

Privatization in 1989 remained mainly a slogan for the energy business outside the United Kingdom. U.S. efforts faltered. The general preference in the U.S. for private enterprise did not translate into an ability to turn major energy ventures over to the private sector. The principal exceptions were small municipal electric companies; for example, a problem-plagued nuclear plant owned by the municipal utility in Sacramento, Calif., was a prime candidate in 1989 for the first significant case of privatization.

Barriers to privatization have existed for many decades. During the administration of U.S. Pres. Dwight Eisenhower (1953–61), an effort was made to allow a private company to build a power plant that would have substituted for expansion by the federal government's Tennessee Valley Authority (TVA). An effective campaign was mounted to discredit the proposal, and TVA was allowed to expand unchallenged.

By 1989 TVA's image as a lodestar had been tarnished. Environmentalists and other social critics dismissed the agency as just another power company, and its nuclear plants were shut down over concerns about the quality of construction and operation. Nevertheless, privatization remained elusive in the U.S. Efforts early in the administration of Pres. Ronald Reagan to sell a modest amount of public land failed badly. A 1988 study of privatization that proposed the sale of hydroelectric dams in the Pacific Northwest, among other things, attracted little attention and produced no action.

Britain's retreat from socialism, however, involved privatization of the government-owned gas and oil companies. Steel, coal, and electricity may follow.

While many other countries adopted government ownership for electric power, the U.S. depended largely upon regulation to control the industry. Similar logic was applied to oil and gas pipelines and to natural gas production. The economic literature on such regulation long has held that while it might be a means of reducing the exercise of monopoly power, it often protects vested interests. Some writers, including the authors of leading textbooks on the subject, considered regulation to be so essential or politically necessary that reform within the regulatory system was the best or at least the most feasible approach.

Criticism of regulation led in the 1970s to the deregulation of airlines and to the loosening of the regulation of other forms of transportation. A phased program of removing price controls on most U.S. production of natural gas was incorporated in the Natural Gas Act of 1978. However, deregulation did not prove a major thrust of the Reagan administration, which limited itself largely to appointing regulators who adopted an approach that critics considered less vigilant and supporters called less intrusive.

Since the early 1970s, however, observers have complained that regulation was endangering the survival of the electric-power industry. The failure of rate increases to match cost increases reduced the profitability of some utilities to the point that their credit ratings were severely reduced. There were improvements in this situation during the 1980s, but doubts remained about whether the alleviation was permanent.

Part of the improvement was achieved by cutting back on expansion of production capacity and, in many cases, by shifting from reliance on large plants built by the utilities to smaller facilities often built by independent companies. Some observers contended that this new pattern was a sensible way

Technician inspects some of the more than 8,000 batteries comprising the world's largest battery-energy-storage facility. The facility, located at Chino, California, can store up to ten megawatts of electricity.

Courtesy of Southern California Edison Co.

to respond to slower growth, rising capital costs for large plants, and environmental problems. Others suggested, however, that the shifts were a costly way to lessen regulatory pressures. Their concern was that small plants were not really less costly but merely more acceptable to regulators.

Under standard regulatory practice, rates include an allowance for return on investments in plants. Although some states allow a phase-in of charges for such investments while the plants are under construction, the usual practice is to adjust rates only after the plant has been completed. Thus, completion of a large plant built over many years leads to a large abrupt change in rates. Steady additions of smaller plants cause rates to rise in smaller but steadier steps. Whether this results on balance in lower costs and rates remained unclear.

In any case, the U.S. Federal Energy Regulatory Commission proposed simplification of its rate-setting process to encourage the development of small independently owned generating facilities. This was labeled by some as a step toward deregulation. Others feared that it was only a modest, inadequate effort to prevent total collapse from occurring.

Evolution of energy market patterns. An examination of world energy data reveals that major changes have occurred since the 1973 oil price rises (and since 1965, the first year reported by the data compilation used here). Industrialized countries in North America and Western Europe experienced slower growth in energy consumption than the rest of the world and thus accounted for a smaller percentage of world energy use. North American use in 1987 was less than in 1978 and only slightly above 1973. The rest of the non-Communist world had the fastest energy consumption growth.

Another major change that took place throughout the non-Communist world was the decline of the share of oil in total energy consumption after 1973. In the Communist bloc the shares of oil in total energy consumption dropped after 1978 but remained well above the 1965 percentage.

For the world as a whole natural gas and nuclear power displayed regular increases in shares in energy consumption. The share of coal rose after 1978 but remained well below the 1965 proportion, and there

was little change in the total for hydroelectricity.

North America, Australia, and New Zealand were the main exceptions to this basic pattern. In North America the coal share in 1987 was above that of 1965; the 1987 natural gas share was below 1965. The 1987 coal share in Australia and New Zealand was closer to its 1965 level than for any other region except North America.

In the U.S. several forces were at work. The long-run tendency toward using an increasing part of energy as electricity was reinforced. Industrial, residential, and commercial users reduced their direct use of fossil fuels but continued to increase electricity consumption. The electric power sector, in turn, drastically reduced oil use and cut gas consumption as well. Coal and nuclear power replaced oil and gas to generate electricity. The transportation sector continued to rely on gasoline and other oil-derived fuels and thus brought oil consumption levels above the prior peaks reached in the late 1970s.

OPEC in the 1990s. As had been true since 1973, OPEC during the past year sought to stabilize oil prices. Nevertheless, the price seesaw of the 1980s seemed destined to continue. The conflicts that had persisted throughout the 1980s continued through 1988 and into early 1989. Another round of price erosion was reversed in 1988 by a Saudi Arabian threat to institute another price cut.

The problems of reconciling conflicting member country objectives worsened with the end of the Iran-Iraq war. The end of that conflict meant that instead of disrupting each other's production and expansion of capacity, the two countries could work to raise output. This was expected to exert downward pressures on oil prices for at least the remainder of the 20th century.

The barriers to capacity expansion caused by the war seemed more critical to world oil prices than the

Table I: Share of Fuels in World Energy Consumption
(percent)

Fuel	1965	1973	1978	1987
Oil	38.8	47.3	45.9	37.6
Coal	39.1	28.2	27.7	30.6
Gas	15.9	18.1	18.1	19.9
Hydroelectric	6.0	5.6	6.0	6.7
Nuclear	0.2	0.8	2.3	5.2

Source: British Petroleum, *BP Statistical Review of World Energy,* diskette version. London, 1988.

Table II: Role of Selected Countries in World Energy Consumption
(Millions of tons of oil equivalent)

Country	1965	1973	1978	1987
United States	1,331.0	1,812.9	1,893.1	1,849.3
Canada	121.2	190.9	217.9	231.9
France	116.4	186.1	191.8	196.6
Italy	81.1	137.9	145.4	147.9
United Kingdom	190.7	224.8	211.4	205.4
West Germany	187.0	264.9	270.0	266.4
Australia and New Zealand	42.1	64.6	79.6	100.0
Japan	152.0	347.7	354.5	377.8
China	229.9	362.5	487.9	700.1
U.S.S.R.	592.3	874.1	1,104.9	1,444.4
Other Communist nations	305.4	431.3	530.2	595.9
Total world	3,941.3	5,914.4	6,712.9	7,811.0

Source: British Petroleum, *BP Statistical Review of World Energy,* diskette version. London, 1988.

pressures to utilize available capacity fully. The traditional OPEC disputes between the countries with large populations and the low-cost producers over how to share output seemed likely to become more vigorous now that Iran and Iraq no longer were paralyzed by warfare.

The maneuvering of the past probably would continue. The countries discontented with their production quotas would try to exceed them. Saudi Arabia would have to lower its output and accept slightly lower prices if it tried to limit the effect of higher output elsewhere. At some point the downward pressures on Saudi Arabia would become intolerable, and it would insist on greater self-control by other OPEC members. Saudi Arabia's production increases in 1986 showed the other OPEC countries that it was willing as well as ready and able to expand output and force down world prices if the rest of OPEC refused to restrain production.

OPEC learned enough from the 1986 experience to pay more attention to Saudi needs. However, the lesson remained imperfectly absorbed. OPEC countries in 1989 appeared to be afraid to provoke the Saudis severely but still were probing to test the limits of Saudi tolerance. The result was periodic successes at bolstering oil prices followed by erosions of a few dollars a barrel because of increased output, Saudi complaints, and yet another accord to prop up prices.

Past experience inspired caution about future developments. As long as conditions did not change radically and unexpectedly, the most likely outcome would be steady oil-price erosion. The dominant force, as noted, would be the expansion objectives of Iran and Iraq.

The often-heralded deterioration of non-OPEC supplies seemed unlikely to emerge. First, the argument had been too narrowly focused on oil and gas. The ability of coal and nuclear energy to displace oil in electricity generation received inadequate attention. The potential for continued substantial oil output in Britain and even more substantial rises in North Sea gas supplies was also underplayed. The Soviet Union might be improving its energy-supply position more than had been anticipated. The latest data suggested that the U.S.S.R. might be able to halt the decline in oil and coal output and thus not have to rely only on natural gas for increased energy supplies. Given these developments, OPEC would be less dominant than some have contended.

—Richard L. Gordon

Environment

Perhaps the single most disturbing set of environmental news items during the past year concerned the large number of marine animals that were washing up dead on beaches in widely separated parts of the world. In the Adriatic Sea during the summer of 1988, phosphates and other pollutants produced an outbreak of algae that starved the water of oxygen. As a result, fish were killed along a 1,600-km (1,000-mi) stretch of the Italian coast. Off the coast of California, sea lions from Santa Barbara to San Luis Obispo were afflicted with a mysterious illness that sent them into sudden, violent seizures. About one of every four sea lions affected by the illness died. The tentative diagnosis was poisoning by heavy metals. One sea lion had very high concentrations of lead, while another had chromium, zinc, and copper levels ten times higher than normal. In the St. Lawrence River about a dozen white beluga whales were washing ashore every summer, their bodies loaded with deadly toxic chemicals, including PCBs (polychlorinated biphenyls), DDT, Mirex, and mercury. Autopsies revealed that the animals had tumors, cancers, lesions, ulcers, and blood diseases. In mid-1988 about 7,000 harbor seals died off the coasts of West Germany, The Netherlands, Norway, Denmark, and Sweden. Another estimate put the total seal deaths in northern Europe at 11,000 from April to December 1988. Various published and unpublished estimates placed North Sea harbor seal deaths at 50 to 90% of the entire population. Within the last two years, the deaths of marine organisms off the Atlantic coast of North America have also attracted attention.

There are two ways that this list of incidents can

Table III. Oil Output in Leading Producing Countries
(Thousands of barrels per day)

	1973	1979	1987	Sept. 1988
Algeria	1,097	1,224	985	985
Iraq	2,018	3,477	2,079	2,700
Kuwait	3,020	2,500	1,361	1,660
Libya	2,175	2,092	972	1,050
Qatar	570	508	304	300
Saudi Arabia	7,596	9,532	4,207	5,260
United Arab Emirates	1,533	1,831	1,541	1,965
Arab OPEC	18,009	21,164	11,448	13,920
Indonesia	1,339	1,591	1,311	1,220
Iran	5,861	3,168	2,426	2,500
Nigeria	2,054	2,302	1,340	1,500
Venezuela	3,366	2,356	1,741	1,880
Total OPEC	30,989	30,998	18,594	21,505
Canada	1,800	1,496	1,514	1,650
Mexico	465	1,461	2,540	2,390
United Kingdom	2	1,568	2,473	2,114
United States	9,208	8,552	8,349	7,900
China	1,090	2,122	2,690	2,710
U.S.S.R.	8,329	11,187	11,792	11,675
Other	3,690	5,039	8,240	8,833
Total non-OPEC	24,584	31,425	37,598	37,272
World	55,573	62,427	56,191	58,777

Source: U.S. Department of Energy, *Monthly Energy Review.*

be interpreted. One way is to argue that all animal species, including humans, on occasion experience serious epidemics, such as the Black Death of the 14th century, which killed one-quarter to one-third of the population of Europe. From this point of view the recent series of global occurrences would be interpreted as an improbable but possible set of unrelated coincidences. The other interpretation is that all of these cases are somehow linked. Specifically, it would argue that epidemic diseases in marine organisms are occurring more frequently than in the past because the background level of pollutants in the marine environment has risen to a level at which the immune systems of organisms are significantly depressed, rendering them more vulnerable to pathogens.

During 1988 groups of scientists began to develop information allowing them to make an educated guess about which hypothesis was more probable. In September Alfred D. M. E. Osterhaus and Elizabeth J. Vedder reported on tests of serum samples from harbor seals collected at the seal orphanage in Pieterburen, Neth. They found a correlation between the onset of the mysterious disease in the seals and the presence in their serum of canine distemper virus. An urgent program to develop a vaccine was under way by late in the year.

No direct link was found between the seal epidemic and pollution, but the possibility remained that pollution played an important role in making the animals more vulnerable to infection. By the end of the year an international team was investigating links between pollution and the seal disease. In November Seamus Kennedy and five associates reported on the discovery of the canine distemper virus in two common porpoises found dead on the coast of Northern Ireland. They suggested that this discovery might explain the decline in recent years of porpoise and dolphin populations in European waters.

Jerome O. Nriagu and Jozef M. Pacyna reported on "a quantitative assessment of worldwide contamination of air, water and soils by trace metals." Their study allowed scientists to estimate the severity of the global environmental contamination, which may be the common causative factor underlying the deaths of marine organisms throughout the world. They discovered that the concentrations of trace metals in lakes and rivers are probably being elevated manyfold by the products of civilization. For example, human-generated emissions into the atmosphere of arsenic, cadmium, nickel, and zinc are greater than those from natural sources by at least a factor of two. Emissions of lead are about 17 times those from natural sources. In short, human civilization is now the major factor determining the concentrations of chemicals in the atmosphere. Therefore, it seems highly likely, if not certain, that civilization

Medical wastes were brought by ocean waves to Midland Beach on Staten Island, New York. Many Atlantic Ocean beaches in New York and New Jersey suffered similar pollution during the past year.

is the root cause of the toxic oceanic environment. It is possible that at some time pollution of the ocean may reach the level at which people become sick because of depression of their immune systems, leaving them more vulnerable to any pathogens to which they might be exposed.

If there should be major biologic and economic consequences of a poisoned ocean for humans, it is reasonable to argue that the first evidence would appear off the coasts of regions with the highest human population densities coupled with the most intense industrial activity. To illustrate that, in the United States the state with the highest human population per square kilometer is New Jersey. It also has a high density of industrial activity. Therefore, it is not surprising that the New Jersey shore has experienced the consequences of ocean pollution. For two weeks in July, raw sewage rolled in with the waves. Many beaches were inundated with infectious hospital wastes, including dirty needles and vials of blood tainted with the AIDS (acquired immune deficiency syndrome) virus. Clearly there needs to be much tighter legal and legislative control of those responsible for management and disposal of the wastes of civilization.

Climate change. During 1988 climate change became a major issue worldwide. It would be an understatement to note that there was an astonishing discrepancy between the picture one would form, on the one hand, from articles in the popular press and from statements to and by legislators at congressional hearings and, on the other, from the data tables and scientific literature. For example, the discourse at congressional hearings seemed to suggest that there was a consensus among scientists that warming of the Earth was occurring at a faster rate than ever before in history. This point of view seemed uninfluenced by the following facts. During 1988 F. B. Wood, a senior information science expert in the Office of Technology Assessment of the Congress, published two articles pointing out (1) that seven independent studies had shown that between 1938 and 1983 the temperature at rural sites in the United States had cooled significantly; (2) that there was a problem in logic with the procedure for correcting for the urban heat island effect, or differential warming of cities relative to the surrounding countryside (incomplete correction for the effect eroded the basis for the contention that the world was warming); and (3) that climate change is a phenomenon of great complexity, involving inadequately explored linkages between many types of phenomena. The U.S. media failed to point out that on days when they devoted great attention to global heating, while it was very hot in parts of the United States, it was cold elsewhere. In short, a local, short-term heating was being misread as a long-term global phenomenon.

A major stimulus to the congressional and media concern about the greenhouse warming phenomenon was the United States heat wave in the first three weeks of July 1988. On July 17, for example, San Francisco was 103° F (39° C), which broke the record for that day since records began 114 years ago. Many other parts of the United States were extraordinarily hot and had been for three weeks. What the U.S. media did not notice was that on July 18 the highs for the day were 23° F (a range of 1° F = a range of 0.56° C) below the long-term normal for the day in Lisbon, 6° F below normal in Amsterdam, and down 11° F in Bonn, West Germany, 5° F in Casablanca, Morocco, 8° F in Edmonton, Alta., 9° F in Martinique, 6° F in Sydney, Australia, and 4° F in Tokyo. Furthermore, statistical analysis of those U.S. benchmark stations that the National Weather Service had identified as useful for drawing inferences about long-term climate trends revealed that annual temperatures from 1980 to the end of 1986 were unusually cold. These benchmark stations were characterized by declining temperature trends since 1940 where any trend was detectable at all.

This should come as no surprise to careful observers of events around them. For example, K. A. Miller and M. H. Glantz noted in a scientific article on freezes in northern Florida citrus groves that these occurred in 1981, 1982, 1983, and 1985. That is an unprecedentedly high incidence of freezes,

given the history of the industry since 1894, and seems scarcely reconcilable with the notion of the 1980s as an extraordinarily hot decade.

Once one realizes that the recent hot weather is due to cities' heating differentially with respect to the surrounding countryside and is masking a pronounced rural cooling since 1940, an entirely different view of the recent global environment is suggested. The rural cooling is causing a decrease in the photosynthetic rate in forests in northern latitudes; consequently, the rate at which these forests draw down the levels of carbon dioxide in the atmosphere is also declining. Indeed, during 1988 there was a growing awareness of the role of trees in the global carbon dioxide problem, leading to an increased discussion of the value of mass tree-planting programs. Many people began calculating the number of trees that would have to be planted to counteract the buildup of carbon dioxide in the global atmosphere. For example, Norman Myers, a senior fellow at the World Wildlife Fund, calculated that 3 million sq km (1.9 million sq mi) of trees must be planted to absorb the carbon dioxide in the air; Gregg Marland of Oak Ridge (Tenn.) National Laboratory calculated that 7 million sq km (4.3 million sq mi) were needed. These amount to the area of Zaire and Australia, respectively.

Another linkage between climate and the environment was reported during the year by James S. Clark—the effect of climate change since 1240 on the frequency of forest fires in northwestern Minnesota. He found that the probability of forest fires fluctuates, with high probabilities appearing in multiples of the 22-year drought cycle. He also discovered that, given this cycle, the probability of fires decreased dramatically with the onset or intensification of periods of unusually cold, wet climate. Thus, warming or cooling climatic trends will have implications for the likelihood of widespread natural fires.

AIDS and population projections. The statistical data base for AIDS improved during the year, allowing projections to be made with somewhat more confidence. Experts on the epidemic cautioned that all the figures may be low by a factor of at least two because of underreporting. When this is taken into account, computer projections of the cumulative number of AIDS cases worldwide suggest that if present trends continue there will be about 1 million cases in 1992, 10 million in 1998, 100 million by 2006, and 1 billion by 2016. As might be expected, such experts on mathematical models of the epidemic as R. M. Anderson, R. M. May, and A. R. McLean began pointing out the demographic consequences of the disease, particularly for less developed countries. In those nations the disease has the potential to convert population growth rates from positive to negative within the next few decades.

Forecasters of future national economic statistics and of demand for energy, transportation, and all other commodities, manufactured goods, and services need to take AIDS projections into account. Almost all projections assume that national and world population will grow as far into the future as anyone can see, an assumption that any examination of the AIDS forecasts would render suspect.

A changing discipline. During 1988 it became clear that environmental studies was evolving and changing as a discipline and was no longer neatly bounded within the biologic and physical sciences. A new international society for ecological economics was founded during the year, and it was to begin publishing a new journal, *Ecological Economics*, in 1989. In fact, the domain covered by that new field is much larger than the journal title would indicate since it draws together not only ecology, environmental studies, and economics but also theories, data, techniques, and methods from mathematics, statistics, computing, engineering systems analysis, political science, history, and many other fields.

Two important documents that appeared during the year suggest the direction that the new synthesis might take. The first of these was by H. T. Odum, who presented a set of four simple, yet ingenious and insightful, equations that describe the dynamics of systems with respect to the energy sources that drive them and the resulting cycles of production and consumption. One striking feature of these equations is that they can be used to produce long-run trends in production and consumption that mimic not only biologic systems but also economic ones and long-term historical patterns, as in the rise and fall of entire civilizations.

The pattern generated by Odum's four equations is a repeating cycle; low production and low consumption are followed by a gradual increase in production until more is being produced than is needed for short-term needs. Consumption then increases sharply in order to use up the excess production, whereupon consumption and production both decline sharply, with production leading consumption down.

The significance of Odum's theories was made clear in a new book by Joshua S. Goldstein, a political scientist who was interested in discovering the connections between war cycles and economic cycles. From previous studies and his own analyses, he synthesized a theory of the root cause of long historical cycles. The connection between Goldstein's theory and that of Odum becomes clear when it is seen that war represents a virtual orgy of resource consumption, particularly of fuel. For example, fuel consumption in the U.S. increased 60% from 1938 to 1944, and coal production in Germany increased 79% from 1932 to 1940. In Goldstein's theory production growth turns downward in the 50-year cycle

10 to 15 years before a price peak. Within roughly three years investment also declines, and about five years before the price peak, the rate of innovation turns upward. Just before the price peak is the peak probability for war. After the price peak there is an extended period of stagnation. During this time production, war, and prices are all stagnant, but innovation grows briskly. Roughly 15 years after a war there is a trough for production and then for investment, after which both again begin to rise. The trough implies a depression or serious recession.

There are deep parallels between the theories of Odum and Goldstein. As Goldstein explained, the heart of his theory is that there is a two-way causality between war and production in which economic growth generates war and then is disrupted by it. If one substitutes "production" for "economic growth" and "consumption" for "war," then it appears that the theories of Odum and Goldstein are identical. At the deepest possible level of interpretation production is stimulated by the increased availability of energy resources but then is choked off by excessive production, which creates market saturation and excessive consumption. Consumption is stimulated by production but then is choked off when it becomes excessive. The result is a long-term pattern of cyclical or wavelike behavior.

The writings of Odum and Goldstein suggest a new perspective for scholars seeking to improve the theoretical foundation for forecasting, planning, and management in all fields. According to their views, the ability to make accurate predictions is not improved by generating computer models of staggering complexity, those with very large numbers of equations and variables. Rather, the ability to formulate realistic visions of the future is improved by a deepened understanding of the fundamental forces that produce historical patterns of change. This understanding can be expressed by means of rather simple sets of equations that focus on linkages between very different types of system components, such as energy resources, patterns of capital investment, and the effects of war on trends in production and consumption.

Diversity and stability. An issue of great interest to many environmental scientists and the public is the relationship between diversity and stability. For a long time many scientists believed that a high level of species diversity had an intrinsic value in a natural community, as in a lake or a forest, because if one food species became rare or extinct, species that ate it could switch to an alternative food supply.

This notion is deeply imbedded in popular culture, as in "Don't put all your eggs in one basket." Scientists also refer to it as "spreading the risk." The larger the number of alternative means one has to supply a critical need, the lower the probability that all of them will fail simultaneously. This principle is the basis for "fail safe" system designs in engineering systems and the logic underlying the operations of insurance companies. Thus, it came as a surprise several years ago when Robert May and others showed that the larger the number of connections of any systems component to other system elements, the lower its stability, all other things being equal. This appeared to fly in the face of the widespread perception that more complex, that is, species-rich, communities appeared to be more stable over long periods than more simple (species-poor) communities. On the basis of recent experience, however, it appears that May and his colleagues are correct. It is obvious, for example, that the U.S. economy has become more vulnerable to instability as it has made more connections to remote sources of potential instability, such as foreign suppliers of crude oil.

One approach to dealing with this apparent paradox has been to explore the possibility that as systems become more complex, the average intensity of the connections between each component and each of the other components becomes weakened. Thus, one means by which systems could minimize vulnerability to instability as the complexity and diversity of component elements increase would be to divide the system into functional subcomponents, or compartments, such that there would be minimum

Oil spreads from the Exxon Valdez *across the surface of Prince William Sound in Alaska after the tanker collided with a reef and spilled some 240,000 barrels (10.1 million gallons) of its cargo.*

AP/Wide World

average interaction strength between the subcomponents. During the year J. C. Moore and H. W. Hunt offered a convincing empirical demonstration that in real-world ecosystems very high diversity was accompanied by diminished average interaction strength between different system subcomponents. Thus, systems of very high diversity, or species richness, can maintain themselves over long periods in the face of environmental perturbations, such as population explosions of a predator.

Toxic waste. During the year there were several revelations about widespread toxic-waste dumping in Africa and illegal dumping of wastes from industrialized nations in other countries or international waters. Driving forces behind this phenomenon were the sharply increased cost of waste disposal and the immense positive financial impact of fees charged by poor nations receiving the waste relative to their other prospective sources of income. In the U.S. the cost of waste disposal in landfills rose from $15 per ton in 1980 to $250 a ton in 1988, and incineration costs increased to $1,500 per ton. This contrasted startlingly with the $2.50 a ton Benin was offered to accept five million tons a year of foreign waste or the $40 a ton Guinea-Bissau was offered to bury drums of toxic waste.

Other developments. Most naturalists have noticed that animals are unevenly distributed on the Earth's surface. Some areas are remarkably barren of life, whereas others have almost unbelievable concentrations of animals. One example of the latter is the large herbivores of Africa, which often concentrate in very large numbers in certain locations on that continent. S. J. McNaughton discovered that areas where animals concentrate have plant food of unusually high mineral content, which in turn results from elevated mineral nutrient concentration in the soil. Thus, magnesium, sodium, and phosphorus appear to be particularly important as determinants of high concentrations of animals.

An environmental news story of the last few years that has aroused considerable curiosity concerned gas bursts from lakes in Cameroon. On Aug. 21, 1986, about 1,700 people were killed by a sudden emission of gas, mostly carbon dioxide, from Lake Nyos. As this phenomenon was explored, it was discovered that there are many crater lakes in Cameroon that already have released, or eventually will release, gas bursts. During the year Michael Pourchet and associates reported that two of these lakes, including Nyos, have lake sediments characterized by unusually strong radioactivity, a flux of radon out of the sediment, and gas content very close to gas saturation.

On March 24, 1989, the tanker *Exxon Valdez* collided with a reef in Prince William Sound on the southern coast of Alaska. The collision tore a hole in the ship's hull, causing some 240,000 bbl (10.1 million gal) of oil to flow into the water—the worst oil spill in U.S. history. Several days later the resulting oil slick covered approximately 2,300 sq km (900 sq mi) of the Sound and washed onto the shore in many places. Critics charged that efforts to clean up the spill did not begin soon enough after the accident. Marine life suffered; 25% of the sea otters in the Sound may die.

—Kenneth E. F. Watt

Food and agriculture

Despite a 1.6% decline in per capita world food production in 1988, the United States and the European Communities (EC) entered a new era of trade wars triggered by increased European production and artificially high price supports. Even with drought conditions and other factors reducing U.S. production of some commodities by as much as 45%, few inroads were made in the stockpiles of some crops, such as sugar and wheat. More producers were competing for fewer export markets, raising the possibility of a food trade war between the U.S., the EC, and possibly Japan.

An increasingly health-conscious public was placing new demands on the U.S. research community to find tasty low-calorie, low-fat, high-fiber foods in an ever increasing variety. Several new foods were identified. Environmental concerns over the increase in pollutants and the decrease in stratospheric ozone raised environmental quality to a high level of priority among agricultural scientists.

Agriculture

The 1989 agricultural outlook was for smaller crop supplies and higher prices worldwide. The 1988 drought caused world production to decline by 6%, largely because of sharp reductions in U.S. and Canadian crops. Crop prices continued to reflect small supplies early in the year, but expanded production later led to some adjustments. Large world supplies of animal products resulted in lower livestock prices. Meat production rose 1%. Global feed grain production was down by 10% in 1988–89, and oilseed production fell 3%. The wheat harvest was steady despite production declines in North America, mainly because of increased production levels in the EC, Eastern Europe, and several other areas.

Demand for both crop and animal products was bolstered by continued world economic expansion and population growth. Despite increased supplies and higher prices, world trade in wheat, feed grains, and soybeans combined declined only about 4% in fiscal year 1989. Trade in wheat and soybeans was

Farmer in eastern Pennsylvania in July 1988 kneels next to his corn, which has been stunted by the severe drought that was affecting much of the United States and Canada at that time. Many crops were lost.

down, but coarse grain exports were boosted by larger Soviet imports. A large rice crop bolstered trade in that commodity. The early 1989 world prices for wheat, corn, and soybeans—commodities affected by the U.S. drought—were their highest since 1985. World sugar production in 1988–89 set a record for the third straight year. Sugar was consumed in record amounts, but sugar stocks fell only slightly.

In the U.S. feed grain and soybean production declined, as did that of beef, but bigger supplies of poultry and pork helped keep total meat prices stable. Retail beef prices rose nearly 5% in 1988 and continued to increase in 1989. Climbing production costs, decreased production of some products, and stiff world competition meant less net cash income for U.S. producers. Figures were incomplete, but farm income was slightly higher than the 1987 high of $57 billion. Direct government payments to farmers were falling.

Trade wars. It was predicted that the value of U.S. agricultural exports in 1989 would increase by nearly $1 billion to $36.5 billion. A rise of nearly $2.5 billion for grain and feed exports offset declines in cotton and oilseeds. Exports of high-value products were expected to be close to the fiscal 1988 record of $16.5 billion. Overall, however, the total volume of U.S. farm exports declined by at least 8%. Behind the figures lay a tale of continuing U.S. and European protectionism, turf wars, and a trade "showdown" over beef and other commodities as well.

The latest skirmish concerned the EC ban on imports of beef from animals treated with hormones, which went into effect Jan. 1, 1989. Most U.S. farmers treat their livestock with hormones, and U.S. scientists insist the practice is safe. The U.S. claimed the ban was not a matter of health but just another trade barrier aimed at American products, and in retaliation it imposed sanctions against some $100 million of EC farm exports, including canned tomatoes, boned beef, hams, and fruit juices. The EC threatened countermeasures against such U.S. exports as dried fruit and walnuts, but in February, after two days of intensive negotiations, the two sides agreed to refer the matter to a task force, which was to report in 75 days. Meanwhile, the U.S. would export to the EC some beef certified as hormone-free.

The background of this international food fight was the so-called Uruguay round of negotiations within the General Agreement on Tariffs and Trade (GATT). The GATT talks, aimed at reducing barriers to trade in products and services, began in September 1986 and were scheduled to continue into 1990. A major stumbling block in the talks was the question of whether price supports to farmers result in an unfair distortion of international trade in agricultural products. U.S. officials argued that under the EC's common agricultural policy small farmers sometimes receive as much as 300% above world prices, thus encouraging overproduction. However, the U.S. also had price supports to protect farmers from price declines and, depending on the negotiated definition of "trade-distorting," U.S. farmers as well as their European counterparts could stand to lose. In both the U.S. and the EC farm subsidies were highly sensitive politically, making negotiations even more difficult. The basic problem was that farmers were producing more food than was needed worldwide. Even those countries that still imported much of their food were, in many cases, not importing any more than they had in the past.

Biotechnological advances. Public interest in biotechnology continued to increase, but alarmists appeared to be having less effect on national policy than in earlier years. The U.S. Department of Agriculture (USDA) developed guidelines that, in essence, extended the long-standing National Institutes of Health laboratory guidelines to include field testing. In addition, regulatory agencies, principally the Environmental Protection Agency and the USDA, issued regulations covering the products of biotechnology. The guidelines and regulations allowed industrial groups to proceed with due caution.

A significant advance was marked by the sale by Du Pont of mice with cancer-causing genes inserted into their cells. The mice—trade name OncoMice—were the first to be commercialized under the first patent ever granted for genetically engineered animals. The mice were expected to be useful for studies of cancer development, screening of anticancer drugs, and testing of compounds for carcinogenicity. The first mice in the strains were created by Harvard Medical School geneticists who cloned the oncogene-promoter (tumor-inducing) DNA sequence in bacteria cultures, injected the DNA into fertilized mouse ova, and inserted the ova into the uteri of surrogate mothers.

In other developments scientists at Auburn (Ala.) University, the University of Maryland, and Johns Hopkins University, Baltimore, Md., were conducting field experiments involving insertion of the gene for rainbow trout growth hormone into the common carp. Texas A&M University scientists removed a gene segment from *Brucella abortus*, making it less virulent. The technique was used to make a vaccine to prevent infectious abortions in cattle.

One of the major issues relating to biotechnology centered on the 1987 U.S. Patent Office decision that if a biotechnology company adjusts animals' genes to produce a line that has different characteristics from the original animal, the inventor can be granted a patent protecting the discovery. This triggered concerns over ownership of the offspring of the genetically altered "superanimals." On the one hand it was argued that the inventor owns the offspring, especially if they are exact genetic copies of the superanimal. On the other hand environmentalists, legislators, and representatives of the farming community insisted that rights to animals belong to

Farmer in Morocco dumps dead locusts onto the ground. Billions of desert locusts ravaged crops in North Africa and the Middle East in late 1987 and 1988 in the worst plague of these insects in 30 years.

Blondin—© Sipa Press

the farmer who raised them. It was expected that the issue would be addressed by legislation in several countries over the next few years.

Looking to the future. Traditionally, Americans have not been very adventurous eaters, but they have become increasingly health conscious, and this has led to dietary changes. Thus, Americans have substantially increased the quantity of fish and shellfish in their diets despite the fact that seafood prices have risen considerably faster than those of some major competing sources of dietary protein. Between 1980 and 1987 U.S. per capita consumption of fishery products increased 18%. Although domestic wild harvests and imports are the main sources of fishery products, aquaculture production grew by 20% during that same period and by 1989 was the fastest growing source of fish and shellfish for the U.S. market. Catfish farming was the largest aquaculture industry, followed by salmon and trout. It was increasingly apparent that aquaculture had become an important part of the U.S. agricultural industry.

The national obsession with cholesterol led scientists to focus increasingly on bran research. Recent studies found that oat, barley, and rice bran can lower blood cholesterol. What they have in common is soluble fiber. Researchers at the Montana State University Agricultural Experiment Station found that both barley and oats significantly reduce total and low-density lipoprotein cholesterol. A high level of low-density lipoprotein is considered to be a risk factor in heart disease. Unlike oats, in which the bran is the key cholesterol-reducing ingredient, barley should be eaten whole because its innermost part—the endosperm—plays the primary role. USDA researchers noted that rice bran, if stabilized so that its oils do not break down, also contains cholesterol-reducing properties.

Noting that consumers love convenience foods but dislike greasy coatings, New York Agricultural Experiment Station scientists at Cornell University developed a batter that is 85% egg albumen (egg white). Without the yolks these batters are high in protein and low in calories and fat. Other new foods include a "superonion" the size of a grapefruit, developed at the Texas Agricultural Experiment Station by a cloning process. It is more resistant to disease and more prolific than many other varieties and is sweet enough to be eaten like an apple.

Low-input sustainable agriculture (LISA) was becoming part of the agriculturalists' vocabulary. In the late 19th century cattlemen and sheep producers in the West considered themselves to be bitter enemies, but now it is known that cattle and sheep can graze well together. Similarly, environmentalists and farmers, once worlds apart in their approach to fundamental issues such as pesticide use, were coming together to focus on the resolution of problems. The

USDA held a series of significant conferences cooperatively sponsored by the fertilizer and chemical industries as well as by groups dedicated to organic farming and environmental quality.

The USDA was sponsoring a program for schoolchildren designed to give them some understanding of food and agriculture. Called "Ag in the Classroom," it was aimed at students from kindergarten through 12th grade. At the collegiate level a national agribusiness education project brought deans of business and agricultural colleges together to develop cooperative curricula that would prepare tomorrow's farmer to operate in the business world.

—John Patrick Jordan

Nutrition

In 1985 the U.S. National Heart, Lung, and Blood Institute sponsored the National Cholesterol Education Program, with the aim of contributing to the prevention of coronary heart disease by reducing the prevalence of high blood cholesterol levels in the population. A panel of experts from various disciplines, including epidemiology, nutrition, and pediatrics, was organized early in 1989 to consider feasible and effective means of reducing the level of cholesterol and other lipids in a segment of the U.S. population as related to available food choices and eating practices. The institute also arranged for a panel in 1989 on the "Treatment of Children and Adolescents," which would recommend guidelines for management of high blood cholesterol levels in people 19 and under.

The Adult Treatment Panel placed major emphasis on patients with elevated blood levels of low-density lipoproteins (LDL), considered a major risk factor in cardiovascular disease. In contrast, people at high risk of cardiovascular disease have been shown to have low levels of high-density lipoproteins (HDL). Clearly, all forms of cholesterol do not have the same effect on the body. However, popular literature has tended to ignore these research results and to concentrate on attacking high levels of cholesterol in general. The Adult Treatment Panel raised the question of whether HDL as well as total cholesterol should be measured in adults as part of a general health assessment. Another question is whether adults found to have a reduced HDL level should enter active therapy to raise it.

Children's diets. Cardiovascular disease remained the principal cause of death in the U.S., giving rise to discussions about the need for preventive measures during childhood. There was disagreement over whether the sodium and fat content of an infant's diet should be restricted after the baby was weaned from breast milk. Such a practice was criticized by some as unnecessary or even unsafe. Dietitians,

The importance of a proper diet for children was emphasized by research which showed that such ailments as cancer, heart disease, and hypertension may be initiated during childhood.

nurse practitioners, and pediatricians were surveyed to determine what dietary recommendations they gave to parents and the source of their information. Of 252 usable responses (76% of those surveyed), 54% of professional pediatricians had no preference for any one of the three most popular commercial infant formulas. However, professional groups differed significantly in the choice of whole, low-fat, or nonfat milk for both one-year-old and six-year-old children. Dietitians and pediatricians with nutrition expertise recommended milk with a higher fat content than was recommended by other professional groups.

Opinions also varied on the efficacy and safety of sodium- and fat-modified diets during childhood, indicating the need for additional research. In cases of obesity in children or where there was a family history of hyperlipemia (presence of excess fats or lipids in the blood), professionals generally tended to recommend restricting the sodium and fat content of the child's diet. However, in the case of infants, dietary formulas were chosen on the basis of gastrointestinal tolerance rather than fat or sodium content.

Increasing evidence has been given to the idea that childhood may be the time when such conditions as cancer, heart disease, and hypertension are initiated and that the eventual outcome can be influenced by eating habits. Research has shown that children will select and eat an adequate diet when they are offered a variety of nutritious foods—foods that provide the necessary nutrients as well as having taste, texture, and shape appeal. However, some foods on the market that are designed to be attractive to children are high in fats and low in protein, vitamins, and the mineral elements required for growth and health. Informed adults must supply guidance in food selection and the formation of healthful eating habits. Exces-

sive permissiveness can result in the development of eating habits that will lead to disaster later in life.

Nutrition education. With the increasing emphasis on prevention as a vital component of health care, organizations of health professionals continued to step up their efforts to inform people of the need for a healthful life-style. Leaders of the U.S. health and medical professions had made considerable strides in convincing the general public that reduced calorie intake, combined with a regular exercise program, is the way to "the good life." All health-oriented publications contain monthly reports on research, analyses of data from laboratories and research centers, and recommendations for achieving and maintaining health throughout life.

John Foreyt, director of the Diet Modification Clinic at Baylor College of Medicine, Houston, Texas, reported in *Calorie Control Commentary* that a true "miracle diet" is one "with sensible portions from all food groups combined with a regular exercise program." The amount of weight loss depends on the reduction of calories and the duration and effort of the exercise. Both must be practiced each day for a week or longer, depending on the amount of weight involved. No diet or food is "magic," and quick weight losses are the result of dehydration, which can be dangerous if the body's water balance is not restored rapidly. Liquid formula diets for weight reduction should be used only under the supervision of a physician and should not be used by children or teenagers. Such diets can help persons who are severely obese, making it possible for them to lose as much as 20 kg (45 lb) in 12 weeks. However, a major concern is that the weight loss is very difficult to maintain, and a rebound occurs in most patients. A slower weight loss, especially when accompanied by changes in life-style as well as diet, is far more

359

likely to be maintained. The problem with diets that reduce weight quickly is that behavioral modification is not usually part of the weight-loss regime.

Calorie control. Jack L. Smith of the University of Delaware and J. P. Heybach of the NutraSweet Co. analyzed data from a USDA food and nutrition survey of 1,500 women conducted in 1985, which showed that 25% of the women questioned had consumed aspartame, or NutraSweet, on the day of the survey. The diets of these women contained, on average, 165 fewer calories than the diets of other women in the survey. For ages 25 to 50, the difference was a reduction of 215 cal. Much of the reduction was due to lower carbohydrate intake, while protein and fat intake remained unchanged. This research supported other studies on the effectiveness of calorie reduction through the use of low-calorie sweeteners.

The columnist Erma Bombeck has written that "one third of the world is on a diet. Another third just fell off a diet. And the remaining third is going on one next Monday." Surveys indicate that about seven of ten women want to maintain their weight or to lose no more than 4.5 kg (10 lb); they use the topic as diversionary conversation. However, people with dietary disorders, such as anorexia nervosa or bulimia, or who are grossly overweight have serious problems. Chronic dieters tend to spend an inordinate amount of time thinking about food—whether

Moderate regular exercise such as brisk walking can halt bone deterioration, reduce the arthritic changes in hip joints, and help arthritic persons retain a full range of movement.

Cathy Melloan

to eat, what type of food to eat, and where to eat it. Often they end up not eating at all or going on a binge of indiscriminate stuffing. Such cases call for professional help and personalized therapy over an extended period of time.

Exercise has come to be considered a counterbalance for diet, and some persons equate the amount of food eaten to kilometers of jogging or other exertion. Jane Brody, health columnist for the *New York Times,* reported that "no matter when in life a person starts to exercise, improvement can occur. Exercise by middle-aged and older people can turn back the clock as many as 10 to 25 years." Roy J. Shephard said, "You'd have to go a long way to find something as good as exercise as a fountain of youth."

Muscle and bone deterioration can be retarded by moderate regular exercise. Studies have shown that exercise can halt bone deterioration, reduce the arthritic changes in hip joints, and help the arthritic person keep a full range of movement. A sedentary person should start an exercise program gradually in order to avoid experiencing muscle soreness and "burnout" without noticeable benefit. About a month is needed to adjust the muscles and joints to a significant change of behavior. Brisk walking is probably ideal for most people, provided smooth paths and cushioned walking shoes are available. Shephard suggests that brisk walking for 30 minutes at a time, three or four times a week, will provide ten years' worth of rejuvenation.

The adequacy of a diet can be gauged by comparing the nutrients it contains to the recommended levels. Natural foods are still the most reliable sources of the ingredients needed for a nutritious diet. The abundance provided by U.S. agriculture has made a nation of basically healthy people. However, safety from additives, introduced either in food production or in processing, remained a cause for concern and required control by health-oriented governmental agencies.

The superiority of organically grown foods had long been promoted by various groups and continued to have some support. In the U.S. 33 states had no laws specifying what the term organic means or governing the types and amounts of pesticide that may be used and the allowable residue that may remain on the food. In a reversal of policy the U.S. Environmental Protection Agency (EPA) recently allowed the use of pesticides that present a negligible risk, namely, "a one-in-a-million chance of causing cancer after a lifetime (70 years) of eating foods treated with these chemicals." The EPA considered the resulting benefits of an increased food supply to outweigh the health risks from the pesticides. Organically grown fruits and vegetables can cost from 20 to 100% more than conventionally grown ones, according to the January 1989 issue of the *Diet and*

Nutrition Newsletter of Tufts University, Medford, Mass.

The American Dietetic Association was scheduled to open a nutrition information center in Chicago in 1990 to process orders for its numerous booklets on nutrition and other health-related topics. Its client education pamphlets cover a wide range of topics related to health and dietetics.

—Mina W. Lamb

Life sciences

Among developments of special significance in the life sciences during the past year were the granting of the first U.S. patent on a genetically engineered animal, the introduction of a new nutritionally improved variety of maize (corn), and a controversial report suggesting that bacteria may somehow be able to influence mutations in their own genes in order to better survive environmental challenges. Molecular biologists continued to unravel the complexities of gene expression in embryonic development and adult tissue and took some first steps toward constructing "designer proteins." During 1988 a mysterious epidemic killed thousands of seals in the North and Baltic seas, leading researchers to a possible new strain of infectious agent related to canine distemper virus.

Botany

Newsworthy events in botany during the past year included consideration of the effects of great forest fires and tropical forest exploitation, continued use of recombinant DNA in basic botanical research and practical applications, and ongoing programs to explore all aspects of plant structure and function.

Forests. One of the big concerns in forestry during 1988 involved the epidemic of gigantic fires in many North American forests brought on by widespread drought conditions. At one time late in the year, the Boise (Idaho) Interagency Fire Center estimated that more than 72,000 fires had broken out in the U.S. and that more than two million hectares (five million acres) were bounded by the fire areas (although not all of this forest had actually burned). Even before the fires were out, serious questions were raised about the U.S. government's policy of "natural burn," which allows fires to burn as long as people, certain property, special sites, or endangered wildlife are not at risk. The policy is based on the ecological theory that forest fires occurred naturally for millions of years before humans developed means to control them and that maintenance of forest ecosystems should reflect this natural process. Moreover, control of fire encourages the buildup of combustible materials on the forest floor, which actually increases the danger of severe fire.

One focus of critics was Yellowstone National Park, which with seven surrounding national forests accounted for more than a quarter of the nationwide damage. National Park Service scientists defended the present policy and contended that unusual weather patterns including low humidity and high winds would have resulted in severe fire regardless of the control policy in effect. Even the mosaic nature of the forest failed to retard progress of the fires. Such mosaics are forest stands of various ages and compositions caused by natural burns and windthrows (uprooting and overthrowing by the wind) of former times. Some of these stands do not have understory characteristics to support a crown fire; *i.e.*, burning tree tops. Nevertheless, the high winds and low humidity in 1988 allowed movement of fire through the canopy in an unexpected way. Whatever the effect on policy, Yellowstone and other burn sites would serve as gigantic laboratories for observation of the natural recovery process. More than 120 scientists were interested in studying the Yellowstone ecosystem.

The relationship of weather and climate to forest fires captured the interest of researchers. It was known that in 1910 much larger fires had occurred in Idaho and Montana under conditions similar to those of 1988. James S. Clark, then at the University of Minnesota, studied core samples of annually deposited lake sediments to gain evidence of severe fires of the past. He made thin sections of the cores and searched for the comparatively large fragments of charcoal that would indicate local fire. Comparison of the dated sediment layers with known climatic data led Clark to conclude that periods of great forest fires were a response to climatic changes in the past. He suggested that warmer and drier periods account for a certain periodicity seen in fire occurrences, particularly when coordinated with the accumulation of fuel after the previous fire. Absence of charcoal in layers deposited since 1910 substantiated his method since that was the year fire-suppression policy was instituted in the U.S.

Continual exploitation of tropical forests remained a major concern for foresters. Some of its characteristics and implications have been discussed in past yearbooks (see *1987 Yearbook of Science and the Future* Year in Review: LIFE SCIENCES: *Botany* and *1988 Yearbook of Science and the Future* Year in Review: ENVIRONMENT) and include matters of biodiversity, economics, and ecology. Recently its effect on the carbon cycle was being given increased attention. Since it was estimated that at least 11 million hectares (27 million acres) of tropical forest were being destroyed annually for agriculture, ranching, and similar purposes, plus another 4.5 million to 5.3

Fire-darkened stumps rise in the aftermath of a forest fire at Yellowstone National Park, part of a spectacular epidemic of fires that ravaged North American forests during the summer of 1988. From aerial photographs it was estimated that by September 178,000 hectares (440,000 acres) of Yellowstone area timber had burned to some degree.

million hectares (11 million to 13 million acres) for timber, the decreased potential of the world's forests to recycle atmospheric carbon dioxide (CO_2) via photosynthesis needed to be considered. Although the magnitude of the effect was yet to be understood, it seemed reasonable that ongoing deforestation does contribute to elevated levels of CO_2, which have been implicated with other substances in producing global warming by means of the so-called greenhouse effect.

While some researchers worked to understand the effect of deforestation on global warming, others attempted to forecast the effect of global warming on forests. One approach was to reconstruct the history of single tree species over a period of climatic warming, and an example of this was the work of Steven P. Hamburg of the University of Kansas and Charles V. Cogbill, then at the Center for Northern Studies in Wolcott, Vt. The investigators studied surveyors' records for several sites in New Hampshire, some dating back to the 1770s. Such records yield information about the presence of tree species since surveyors used and recorded "witness trees" in documenting corners of plots and other points. The investigators also studied pollen records, and both methods indicated a decrease in populations of red spruce (*Picea rubens*) over a long period of time. Other recent work had suggested that decline of the red spruce—at least the death of older trees—in the Appalachian Mountains is due to acid rain. Hamburg and Cogbill, however, contended that mid-elevation forests in New Hampshire have been losing red spruce for a long time as a part of climatic temperature changes. Whereas pollution effects may have enhanced recent trends in this loss, the population decrease extends much farther back in history than does acid rain.

Another approach to predicting forest changes was by means of computer simulations, a recent exam-

ple of which came from the work of John Pastor of the University of Minnesota and W. M. Post of Oak Ridge (Tenn.) National Laboratory. The researchers modeled climatic changes resulting from increased atmospheric CO_2 and the effects of these changes on forest composition in northeastern North America. When CO_2 levels were doubled and the interrelationships between temperature, moisture, nitrogen availability, and water-holding capacity of soil were modeled, the simulation predicted certain forest

A new species of tiny phytoplankton was found living in Atlantic Ocean waters. Its pigments and internal structure suggested a relationship to previously known prochlorophytes, putative ancestors of the photosynthetic chloroplasts of green plants.

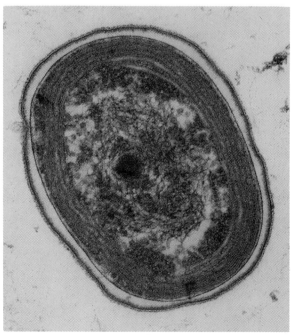

changes over the next 200 years. With soil water above wilting point, forests at the boreal-northern hardwood border would transform from the spruce-fir-northern hardwood composition of today to only hardwoods in a band from the western Great Lakes to the Atlantic. Temperature changes, however, would not be great enough to cause replacement of the boreal forests in northern Quebec.

Algae, fungi, and lichens. Fascinating findings about algae continued to come from the sea. For about a decade, the existence of tiny marine phytoplankton (picoplankton) called prochlorophytes has fueled speculation that they are the ancestors of chloroplasts, the photosynthetic organelles of the cells of green plants. Chloroplasts are thought to be descended from photosynthetic microorganisms that once took up symbiotic residence within other cells, and they share with prochlorophytes certain characteristics—similar pigments, for example. Recently a Massachusetts Institute of Technology researcher and her associates detected new species of prochlorophytes in such places as the Gulf of Mexico, the Caribbean, and the North Atlantic. Collecting samples deep in the euphotic zone (zone of light penetration sufficient to support plant life), Sallie W. Chisholm found these algae to be very small (0.6–0.8 μm, or 0.000024–0.000032 in) and very abundant. The biologic relationships of these picoplankton were yet to be confirmed; they contain forms of the pigments carotene and chlorophyll that differ from those in other known prochlorophytes and thus from those in higher plants. They do occupy an important ecological niche, however, since they are such abundant producers in the food chain.

John H. Martin and Steve E. Fitzwater of Moss Landing (Calif.) Marine Laboratories carried out experiments on phytoplankton in a portable laboratory aboard ship. They collected samples from the 20-m (66-ft) level at a northeastern Pacific subarctic site and investigated various aspects of mineral nutrition in these algae, which seem to have limited growth even in the nutrient-rich waters of the collection site. They were able to show that the limiting factor was not nitrogen, as is often the case, but iron. Addition of small amounts of dissolved iron was sufficient to cause the algae to take up more of the available nitrogen compounds and also resulted in increased chlorophyll production.

An interesting discovery from the world of fungi was reported by John E. Hamer and associates of the Du Pont Co., Wilmington, Del. They found that the fungus responsible for rice blast disease, *Magnaporthe grisea*, produces a specialized mucilage for a novel use. To investigate the mechanism by which spores of the fungus lodge on leaf surfaces prior to germination and infection of the plant, the researchers grew the fungus on artificial surfaces—Teflon-PFA film, for example. They discovered that the spores attach themselves quite readily even to smooth Teflon surfaces by the extrusion of a mucilage from the spore tip in the presence of water and that this attachment makes the spores resistant to removal by water flow. They assumed that the spores attach in this way to rice leaves and suggested that the method may be an adaptation to the wet environment in which rice grows.

Two investigators in Israel continued their observations on lichen reproduction. Lichens are important and abundant constituents of many plant communities, where their usual method of reproduction is thought to be vegetative, by mechanical dissemination of parts of the thallus, or body. Since the thallus is really a symbiotic arrangement of at least one fungal type and one algal type, sexual reproduction would seem to be difficult. Jacob Garty and Jacob Delarea of Tel-Aviv (Israel) University studied the way lichens establish themselves on roof tiles of old houses. They broke the tiles into small pieces and observed them with a scanning electron microscope. They found that *Lecanora dispersa* and several other lichens produced ascospores just as the fungal component of the lichen would do. They also observed some of the spores growing germination tubes toward free-living algal cells of the type associated with the fungus in the lichen. The actual association of the germinating fungus and algal cells had yet to be documented, but the study appeared to reveal a way in which at least one element of a lichen may reproduce sexually.

Genetics. One of the more significant developments in economic botany was reported by the U.S. National Research Council: a new maize (corn) variety called quality-protein maize (QPM) and developed by workers at Mexico's Centro Internacional de Mejoramiento de Maíz y Trigo (CIMMYT). Maize varieties currently in wide use lack two essential amino acids, lysine and tryptophan; consequently, the 200 million people who rely heavily on maize risk a deficient diet. The story goes back to 1963 when researchers at Purdue University, West Lafayette, Ind., discovered a mutant strain, opaque-2 maize, which contained the desired amino acids but had undesirable qualities as well. The painstaking process of crossing, selecting, and recrossing finally produced strains that combine the quality-protein feature of opaque-2 with desired qualities of traditional maize. Tests of QPM in third world countries were under way to identify other limitations of the new maize that would need to be remedied genetically. Seed was available commercially in Guatemala; tests were proceeding favorably in such countries as China, El Salvador, Brazil, and Senegal; and the NRC report predicted that QPM would be grown worldwide before the turn of the century.

Heterosis, or hybrid vigor, in which offspring often outgrow the parent plants, is a commonly observed result of the crossing of dissimilar parents. Although the phenomenon has been important for agriculture and other economically centered pursuits, its actual mechanisms are not well understood. The role of a class of plant hormones well known for growth promotion, the gibberellins, was under investigation by a number of researchers: Stewart B. Rood of the University of Lethbridge, Alta.; Richard I. Buzzell of the Agriculture Canada Research Station, Harrow, Ont.; Lewis N. Mander of the Australian National University, Canberra; and David Pearce and Richard P. Pharis of the University of Calgary, Alta. They reported on crosses of maize involving inbred lines and hybrids. The inbreds represented some of the most widely used strains for the production of commercial hybrids in North America. In each case in which male and female parent plants from the same inbred strain were crossed, levels of endogenous gibberellin (gibberellin produced by the plants themselves) in offspring were low. By contrast, endogenous gibberellin levels were higher in hybrid offspring of crosses between different inbred strains. In addition, application of exogenous gibberellin (gibberellin made elsewhere and often synthetic) to inbred plants enhanced growth. The researchers concluded that hybrid vigor is at least partly due to higher gibberellin levels. The exact mechanism by which gibberellins promote growth was still subject to verification, but the researchers suggested that the hormones are active in the genetic control of enzyme production. Hybrids may have the capacity to produce allozymes (different forms of the same enzyme), which promote biochemical processes over a broadened range of developmental and ecological conditions.

The continued emphasis on agricultural crop productivity was turning increasingly to genetic engineering as a means of developing resistances to viruses, insects, fungi, and herbicides. Improving herbicide resistance was of special concern because certain crop plants may be harmed by the very treatment used to benefit them by means of weed control. It has been suggested that recombinant DNA introduced to crop plants could boost herbicide resistance in at least three ways, all of which involve the target in the plant cell where the herbicide acts: (1) by coding for overproduction of the herbicide-sensitive target, (2) by coding for a defective, herbicide-insensitive target, or (3) by coding for a substance that inactivates the herbicide before it reaches the target. Examples of the first two approaches were reported recently, and during the past year David M. Stalker and co-workers at Calgene, Inc., Davis, Calif., succeeded in producing an example of the last one by introducing into tobacco plants a gene that confers resistance to bromoxynil, a herbicide affecting photosynthesis. First, from the soil bacterium *Klebsiella ozaenae* they isolated a gene, *bxn*, that codes for an enzyme that breaks down bromoxynil to harmless metabolites. Next, they transferred the gene by means of recombinant DNA techniques to tobacco cells growing in tissue culture. When these preparations were grown into mature plants, some of the plants possessed varying levels of resistance to bromoxynil and also varying levels of the foreign enzyme. Crossing experiments with the altered plants revealed that the enzyme levels and corresponding resistance were inherited as a dominant trait.

Photosynthesis. Noteworthy discoveries about environment-photosynthesis relationships were reported during the year. William K. Smith and Gregory Carter of the University of Wyoming showed that certain high-elevation conifers of the Rocky Mountains use needle packing to increase photosynthetic efficiency in cold temperatures. The investigators employed a portable device to test branches of Engelmann spruce (*Picea engelmanni*), subalpine fir (*Abies lasiocarpa*), and lodgepole pine (*Pinus contorta*) for temperature and photosynthetic activity. Laboratory experiments were used to corroborate findings. At comparatively cold locations, it was found that branches growing in the sunlight tend to grow their needles closer together, thus raising their local temperature above that of the surrounding air. The extra warmth allows a higher rate of photosynthesis than would otherwise be possible, perhaps an important adaptation to living at colder elevations.

Jonathan P. Comstock and James R. Ehleringer of the University of Utah reported on photosynthesis in plants growing in quite a different environment, the Mojave and Sonoran deserts in the southwestern U.S. There many plants have not only leaves but also stems that are photosynthetic. The investigators raised plants in a greenhouse that simulated natural conditions to compare the processes in both organs of *Hymenoclea salsola*, a desert shrub. They found that both leaves and stems contribute significantly to the productivity of these plants, although leaf photosynthesis is about 50% more efficient under well-watered conditions. Structure and placement of leaves are far superior to those of stems for photosynthesis, Comstock and Ehleringer surmised, but when the transport, storage, and support functions of stems are considered, the addition of photosynthetic capacity is a real bonus even when efficiency is decreased by a structure optimized for the other functions. Of course, stem photosynthesis is a great advantage when leaves are lost from these plants.

Vines growing in a deciduous forest often are found in low-light environments. To discover whether certain climbing mechanics are related to this environment, Gregory A. Carter and Alan A. Teramura of the University of Maryland studied eight species at the Beltsville (Md.) Agricultural Research Center. Three species are exotic, originating elsewhere, and five are considered to be native. The scientists found that vine species that produce tendrils (threadlike structures for grasping) tend to have the mechanical and photosynthetic capabilities for growing up through the low-light environment of the forest understory and for taking advantage of full sunlight when the canopy is reached. Observed plants with these characteristics are greenbrier (*Smilax rotundifolia*), frost grape (*Vitis vulpina*), and Virginia creeper (*Parthenocissus quinquefolia*), the last of which has adhesive-disk tendrils. Two plants, poison ivy (*Rhus radicans*) and English ivy (*Hedera helix*), use adventitious roots (roots growing from the stem), which limit their support to trunks and larger stems, and thus do not achieve a position in the canopy. Virgin's bower (*Clematis virginiana*) has touch-sensitive leaf petioles and occasionally reaches the crown of small trees. Two major weedy species in the southeastern U.S.—kudzu (*Pueraria lobata*) and Japanese honeysuckle (*Lonicera japonica*)—have been introduced from Asia. Both are vigorous twining vines, but kudzu is not shade-tolerant and grows destructively on shrubs and trees with open canopies. Japanese honeysuckle is more shade-tolerant but is limited to twining on small-diameter structures and thus will not thrive in mature forests.

—Albert J. Smith

Microbiology

Microorganisms have contributed greatly to the advancement of biology as a whole. It was through the use of microorganisms that much of the present understanding of cellular physiology and metabolism, whether of procaryotic microbial cells or eucaryotic plant and animal cells, was acquired. It is of special significance that since the 1950s the study of microbial genetics, by providing concepts and methodology, has paved the way for the study of genetics in cells of all types and has led to modern advances in molecular biology, recombinant DNA techniques, and biotechnology.

The advantages of using bacteria for studies of basic biologic processes are due to the simplicity of the bacterial cell. Bacterial cells lack compartments for the nuclei, mitochondria, chloroplasts, and vacuoles of eucaryotic cells. The DNA of bacteria is organized as a single chromosome, which makes DNA isolation easy. Thus, the expression of a gene in the microbial cell can be correlated relatively easily with the gene product in a cell-free system composed of purified components.

Contributions to "mainstream" biology. The microorganism that has been most widely studied is the bacterium *Escherichia coli*, whose normal habitat is the gut of warm-blooded animals. Several books have been written about this organism alone. One would think that after nearly 50 years of intensive study, *E. coli* would hold no more surprises. Nevertheless, workers from West Germany, France, and the U.S. independently reported the discovery of a new type of transfer RNA (tRNA) in *E. coli* that incorporates the amino acid selenocysteine into a protein during translation (construction of a protein from the message carried in messenger RNA [mRNA]).

Selenium is a trace metal found in certain enzymes in the form of selenocysteine in both microorganisms and higher forms of life. The new work not only showed how selenocysteine becomes incorporated into the *E. coli* enzyme formate dehydrogenase but also, more importantly, uncovered a previously unknown tRNA. The anticodon of this tRNA—*i.e.*, the triplet of nucleotide bases on the tRNA that recognizes and binds to a specific, complementary triplet of bases (codon) in mRNA—was complementary to the UGA codon of mRNA. UGA (shorthand for the nucleotide base sequence uracil-guanine-adenine) is one of three "nonsense" codons in that, until now, no known tRNAs could bind to them. The normal role of UGA and the other nonsense codons is a signal for termination of the synthesis of a completed protein during the translation process. Future work was expected to show that selenium is incorporated into enzymes of more complex eucaryotic cells in ways similar to that found for *E. coli*.

Another surprising discovery, made by scientists from Utah, was the presence of an untranslated region of 50 nucleotides in the DNA of gene 60 of the *E. coli* bacteriophage T4. (Bacteriophages are viruses that attack bacteria.) It was already known that certain other genes of this bacteriophage code for mRNA that cuts out regions of its own nucleotide sequence by means of a self-splicing mechanism previously thought to be characteristic of higher eucaryotic cells. In the case of gene 60, however, it appeared that the translation apparatus bypassed a region of the message by a mechanism yet to be determined. When this mechanism finally is elucidated, it no doubt will result in a better understanding of protein synthesis in all types of cells.

Evidence was presented during the year by U.S. scientists that bacteria may be able to alter their genes when faced with changes in the environment. If true, this would be the first evidence for directed mutagenesis (*i.e.*, the ability of an organism somehow to influence mutations) in contrast to the process of random mutations by which evolution is held to proceed. The work was carried out with *E. coli* bacteria that had been genetically altered such that they were unable to use the sugar lactose. The bacteria were introduced into a lactose-containing medium in which other nutrients were so sparse that in order to survive the organisms had to use lactose. Over the course of the experiment, the number of survivors greatly exceeded the number of organisms predicted to regain the ability to use lactose through random mutations. This outcome was taken as evidence for directed rather than random mutation—a conclusion that many biologists disputed. Obviously, further research would be needed to confirm these preliminary observations.

An area in which results from research on microorganisms were expected to contribute greatly toward an understanding of biologic processes and genetic events is that of cellular differentiation. Among the bacterial species and the types of bacterial cellular differentiation on which considerable research was under way are (1) *Bacillus subtilis,* whose cells can differentiate to form spores, which in turn can differentiate again into vegetative cells; (2) *Caulobacter crescentus,* whose multiplication depends on a transition between swarmer (highly motile) cells equipped with a flagellum and stalked sessile (permanently attached or not motile) cells; (3) species of myxobacteria, which occur as a multicellular mass but can aggregate to form fruiting bodies and then segregate into myxospores; and (4) cyanobacteria (formerly and improperly called blue-green algae), some of which differentiate into heterocysts when grown with molecular nitrogen as the sole source of nitrogen.

The cyanobacterium *Anabaena,* for example, has a filamentous appearance in that its cells form chains. When filamentous *Anabaena* is deprived of a source of nitrogen compounds from the environment, about every tenth cell in the chain develops into a heterocyst having special characteristics that provide an anaerobic (oxygen-free) environment required for nitrogen fixation. (Nitrogen fixation is a metabolic process peculiar to certain microbial species in which atmospheric, molecular nitrogen, which cannot be used by the majority of living cells, is converted into nitrogen-containing compounds that can be used by living cells.) This cellular differentiation by *Anabaena* results in the activation, or turning on, of genes whose products are enzymes responsible for nitrogen fixation. The activation involves rearrangements of genetic material similar to that observed in genes coding for antibodies (immunoglobulins) in eucaryotic cells. Thus, the same type of molecular mechanism is used both in a procaryotic bacterium and in eucaryotic vertebrate cells.

Another microorganism that was rapidly gaining favor as a successful model system for understanding eucaryotic biology at the cellular and molecular levels is the eucaryotic yeast *Saccharomyces cerevisiae* (baker's yeast) and its close relatives. The reasons for the use of *Saccharomyces* are much the same as

Agricultural scientist tests a solution of a newly discovered strain of Bacillus thuringiensis *(Bt) against Colorado potato beetles. Bt and its toxin have been studied and exploited as a natural control for crop pests for more than two decades.*

those for which *E. coli* has been such a successful model system: ease of handling when molecular genetic methods are applied in work to associate genes with specific proteins and with functions within the cell. Single-celled *Saccharomyces* turns out to be a surprisingly typical eucaryote. Moreover, it is extremely well known, having been used since antiquity in making bread and alcoholic beverages.

A somewhat different role was played recently by another microorganism in the advancement of biology. The 1988 Nobel Prize for Chemistry was awarded to three West German scientists, who carried out their research both in West Germany and the U.S., for the crystallization and structural determination of the photosynthetic reaction center from the membrane of the bacterium *Rhodopseudomonas viridis.* These results have broad implications in furthering the understanding of the way in which light energy is converted to chemical energy by means of the photosynthetic apparatus not only of this bacterium but of eucaryotic green plant cells as well. (*See* SCIENTISTS OF THE YEAR.)

Applied and environmental microbiology. Epidemic deaths of harbor seals in the North and Baltic seas occurred during the year. At first the deaths were attributed to the effects of pollution, but later a virus identified initially as canine distemper virus (CDV) was blamed as the causative agent. Further studies suggested that the virus was sufficiently different from CDV to be considered a new virus. How the harbor seals acquired the viral infection was not known. Harp seals were abundant in the North Sea at the time, and it is possible that they transmitted the virus to the harbor seals. This begs the question, however, because even the harp seal appeared to be an unlikely host for the virus. To further the mystery, a CDV-like infection was identified in dead porpoises found on the coast of Northern Ireland. (See *Zoology,* below.)

Until the 1970s the primary producers in nature were considered to be photosynthetic organisms that use light energy and that fix, or convert, carbon dioxide into organic carbon compounds. That this concept is not exclusively true became apparent with the discovery of deep-ocean hydrothermal vent communities. In these Atlantic and Pacific habitats, the primary producers were found to be chemolithotrophic bacteria. These autotrophic organisms (those needing only simple inorganic compounds and an energy source to make their own food) are able to gain energy from the oxidation of reduced sulfur compounds and to fix carbon dioxide. Both substances are acquired from the surrounding seawater. Higher organisms in the communities, including giant mussels and tube worms, depend on the chemolithotrophs for their nutrients.

Recently a similar situation was found in communities of mussels associated with hydrocarbon seeps off the coast of Louisiana. In this case the mussels contain symbiotic autotrophic bacteria that use methane seeping from the seafloor as the sole source of carbon and energy. The mussels in turn derive nutrients from the bacteria, which live in cells of the animals. Whether the mussels obtain nutrients through digestion of the bacteria or through a transfer of nutrients from bacteria to host had yet to be determined. The latter explanation was favored.

Scientists from The Netherlands learned how the bacterium *Pseudomonas putida* promotes the growth of such plants as potatoes. Living in the rhizosphere of plants are species of bacteria and fungi, some beneficial and some harmful. The rhizosphere is that region of soil immediately outside the root and where microbial activity is high. *P. putida* was found to produce an iron-binding compound, named pseudobactin, whose physiological role is to capture iron from the environment for use by the bacterium. Pseudobactin is a more efficient iron-capture compound than that produced by harmful species of microorganisms. Growth of harmful species, therefore, is suppressed because they are unable to compete efficiently for needed iron.

It seems likely that genetically engineered organisms will be used in the future to improve plant growth. In 1988 work was under way to alter genetically, and thus improve, the bacterium *Rhizobium,*

the symbiotic nitrogen-fixing organism that forms nodules on the roots of legumes. It is likely, too, that other beneficial bacteria and fungi living in the rhizosphere of plants will be subjects for genetic manipulation.

Field trials were under way on a genetically altered form of the bacterium *Pseudomonas fluorescens.* This organism was given harmless, easily detectable genes that code for enzymes involved in utilization of the sugar lactose. The objective of the research was to devise a system for tracking and evaluating the effectiveness of microorganisms genetically engineered for applications in agriculture. *P. fluorescens* naturally colonizes the root system of many plants. If the present trials are successful, then the organism, when appropriately genetically engineered, would be a likely candidate for delivery of growth promoters, pesticides, and fungicides to plants.

Through collaboration of U.S. and French institutes, a genetically engineered rabies vaccine was ready for field trials in France, Belgium, and the U.S. The recombinant vaccine consists of a harmless vaccinia (cowpox) virus containing a rabies gene that codes for the protective antigen of the rabies virus; *i.e.,* a viral protein component that stimulates formation of protective antibodies. Bait containing the recombinant vaccinia virus was to be placed in fields to be fed upon by wild animals, particularly raccoons and skunks (the prime transmitters of rabies in the wild). In this way the animals should become immunized against rabies, thus limiting its spread.

Another recombinant vaccine ready for field trials was one for rinderpest, prepared by inserting rinderpest virus genes into the vaccinia virus. Rinderpest, or cattle plague, is prevalent in Africa and Asia, and its control would have major economic, ecological, and social benefits.

—Robert G. Eagon

Molecular biology

One measure of the dramatic expansion in the number of genes whose complete sequence of nucleotides has been determined is the work load of the world gene sequence data bases. These facilities are located at Los Alamos (N.M.) National Laboratory and at the European Molecular Biology Laboratory in Heidelberg, West Germany. There, workers scan the world literature and transfer published nucleotide sequences to computer files, copies of which are made available to anyone who needs them. The files are particularly useful to people who have determined the nucleotide sequence of a newly cloned gene. The new sequence can be compared, via computer programs using suitable algorithms (step-by-step mathematical procedures), with all the known sequences in the data base. Where similarities are observed, one obtains clues to the possible function of the newly cloned gene and to its relationship to previously described genes.

During the past year the rate of publication of new sequences was so high that the interval between publication and transfer of the sequences to the data bases became unacceptably large. Moreover, the gap was increasing inexorably. To remedy the situation, several major journals, such as the *Proceedings of the National Academy of Sciences* of the U.S., introduced a new requirement of authors: when a paper submitted for publication contains nucleotide sequences, the data must be sent, at the same time, on a computer-readable disk to the gene banks. The paper cannot be published until the gene bank has acknowledged that the sequence has been deposited.

Regulation of gene expression. A stunning example of the uses to which such sequence banks can be put is the discovery of similar regions (domains) in proteins that regulate expression of genes in insects, frogs, and mammals. While it was still too early by the end of 1988 to comprehend the full implications of these recent results, they put researchers on the threshold of understanding the molecular mechanisms for early embryonic development as well as for the function of specialized genes in adult tissue such as antibody-producing white blood cells.

To begin, it will be useful to recall that genes consist of defined sequences of molecular building blocks, called nucleotides, in DNA. For a gene to be expressed, the enzyme RNA polymerase binds to a specific sequence of nucleotides located next to the sequence carrying the instructions for the sequence of amino acids that constitute the gene's ultimate product, a protein. For simplicity scientists call the sequence to which RNA polymerase binds a pro-

moter. In some cases it is sufficient for RNA polymerase to bind to a promoter; transcription (synthesis of messenger RNA, whose nucleotide sequence corresponds to that of one of the gene's two DNA strands) then follows without the need for participation of other factors. The messenger RNA transcript (after processing and, in the case of eucaryotes, transport from the nucleus to the cytoplasm) then associates with ribosomes and is translated to produce the protein encoded by the gene. The protein could be any of the thousands that distinguish one cell from another.

Regulation of gene expression is accomplished, in the simplest cases, by the interaction between RNA polymerase and the promoter. In bacteria such as *Escherichia coli,* the promoter has been defined as two sequences of six nucleotide pairs that are centered 35 and 10 nucleotide pairs, respectively, before the nucleotide at which transcription starts. (A shorthand way of expressing the locations is −35 and −10, the minus signs signifying positions before the start of transcription.) Although the three-dimensional structure of RNA polymerase is not known, it has been established that the enzyme molecule is long enough to cover at least 40 nucleotide pairs of DNA. Thus, scientists envision that it makes contact with the DNA helix in the −35 and −10 regions and then inserts itself between the two DNA strands, in order to make available the hydrogen-bonding specificities of the DNA nucleotides for determining the sequence of the synthesized RNA (*see* Figure 1). For some promoters this "melting in" of the RNA polymerase can occur spontaneously. For other promoters (whose nucleotide sequence in the −10 or −35 regions differs slightly from the consensus) the structural transition required for initiating RNA syn-

Figure 1: Position of transcription elements just before transcription

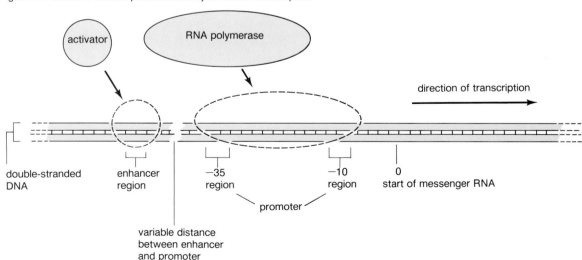

thesis after RNA polymerase has bound is not spontaneous. In these cases a second protein must bind to the DNA slightly farther from the gene than the promoter region. The second protein may be called an activator; the DNA sequence it recognizes is an enhancer. The detailed mechanism of gene activation by the activator-enhancer complex is not known. However, on the basis of incisive experiments in the laboratory of Sydney Kustu at the University of California at Berkeley, it is believed to include some kind of association between the activator protein and RNA polymerase and the facilitation of the melting in of the polymerase.

Activation provides a means for coordinated regulation of families of genes. Consider a set of genes whose products are required by the cell only under certain circumstances—elevated temperature or nutrient starvation, for example. The entire set could be turned on together if each gene's promoter was flanked by an enhancer that responded to a single activator protein. In one exceptionally well-studied example, the Ntr system in enteric bacteria, the environmental cue is starvation for ammonia or a related source of nitrogen. The activator protein, called NtrC, binds to enhancers that activate transcription of genes required for transport and catabolism (breakdown) of alternate nitrogen sources or for nitrogen fixation itself.

The Ntr system has an additional feature of truly vast implications. The NtrC protein, as it is newly minted, is not a functional gene activator. It is converted to full activity by another protein, NtrB, which is a kinase, an enzyme that adds phosphate groups from the molecule adenosine triphosphate (ATP) to certain amino acid side chains of other proteins. The kinase function of NtrB in turn is regulated by the nitrogen status of the cell, possibly through the action of yet another protein that monitors the ratio of concentrations of two small molecules, one rich in nitrogen, the other poor.

How does this regulatory cascade work? It begins with a molecular sensor, a protein, that discovers a deficit in the concentration of the nitrogen-rich compound glutamine within the bacterial cell. The sensor "tells" NtrB. The NtrB protein then phosphorylates (adds a phosphate group to) an aspartic acid residue on the NtrC protein. The phosphorylated NtrC protein binds to enhancers associated with the genes needed for nitrogen source transport and catabolism, activating their expression (transcription) by RNA polymerase (see Figure 2).

Bacteria have many regulatory systems, similar to Ntr, in which two proteins are required for gene activation. In each case one protein senses the environmental situation and phosphorylates the second; the second protein in its phosphorylated form binds to an enhancer and promotes transcription by RNA polymerase. To date, such two-component systems have been described for phosphate metabolism, outer-membrane protein synthesis, chemotaxis (orientation or movement in relation to chemical agents), transport of dicarboxylic acid, and plasmid mobilization (transfer of small DNA molecules from one bacterial cell to another). In some cases the systems overlap somewhat. These systems provide a background for considering the mechanisms by which

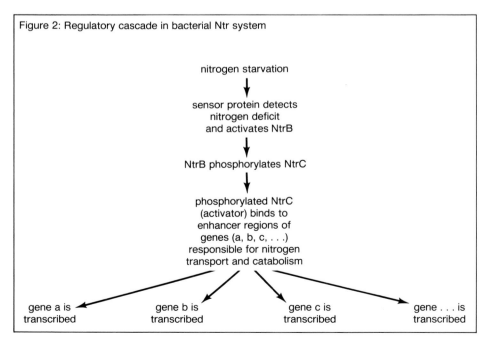

Figure 2: Regulatory cascade in bacterial Ntr system

nitrogen starvation

↓

sensor protein detects nitrogen deficit and activates NtrB

↓

NtrB phosphorylates NtrC

↓

phosphorylated NtrC (activator) binds to enhancer regions of genes (a, b, c, . . .) responsible for nitrogen transport and catabolism

gene a is transcribed   gene b is transcribed   gene c is transcribed   gene . . . is transcribed

transcription is regulated in cells with nuclei; *i.e.,* in organisms other than bacteria.

One of the central problems in developmental biology is the way in which a single fertilized egg gives rise to all the different tissues of an adult organism. The cells of blood, liver, brain, muscle, and other tissues and organs differ from each other in terms of the proteins that each synthesizes. This means that at least some genes are expressed in one group of cells but not in another. But how is this regulation accomplished? And how does an embryo determine which cells to commit to a particular task? Answers to these questions were provided in part during the past year by the convergence of independent lines of investigation in the areas of genetics and biochemistry. The data banks figured importantly in this convergence, signaled by the discovery of similarities in the amino acid sequence of proteins that control embryonic differentiation, on one hand, and proteins that control transcription of genes in specialized adult tissues, on the other.

The fruit fly *Drosophila* has been the object of genetic analysis for many years. In the field of development, *Drosophila* mutants of particular interest are those in which differentiation has gone awry. The *Drosophila* adult is segmented; it consists of a head, three thoracic segments, and eight abdominal segments. Normally each of the thoracic segments produces one pair of legs, and only the middle thoracic segment produces a pair of wings. Mutations in single genes, however, can result in the duplication of an entire thoracic segment, yielding a fly with four wings, or in the production of complete legs where antennae should be or of complete wings where eyes should be. These mutations, which result in the transformation of one body part into another, are said to occur in homeotic genes. The homeotic genes are clearly master control genes that in turn regulate the large numbers of genes that define the body parts. If one considers the bacterial model described previously, one might suppose that the products of homeotic genes are activators of the transcription of sets of genes, perhaps acting on enhancers that are common to the various sets.

A number of homeotic genes of *Drosophila* have been cloned, and their nucleotide sequences have been determined. In the laboratory of Walter Gehring at the University of Basel, Switz., it was noted that the homeotic gene products share a stretch of 60 amino acids called the homeobox. On the basis of similarity of sequence to other known proteins, it could be predicted that the homeobox region of the homeotic gene products would fold into a structure having a part that can recognize and bind to specific sequences in DNA. The distribution of the products of genes containing homeoboxes (maternal effect genes, segmentation genes, and homeotic genes) in

Drosophila eggs and embryos can be determined by staining sectioned material with labeled antibody to the gene products or by in situ hybridization with DNA probes to detect messenger RNA. The individual genes are found to be expressed in specific locations: maternal effect genes (responsible for the general spatial organization of the body) in small regions of the egg, segment-specifying genes in individual embryo segments, and so on.

The convergence with biochemistry resulted from work in many laboratories on transcription-promoting factors from mature cells of frogs, worms, and mice. In each case the purification of small amounts of a protein factor that bound to an enhancer and activated transcription of a specific gene led to the isolation of the gene encoding the protein factor. The gene sequence yielded in each case a homeobox. Thus, at the risk of extreme oversimplification, it can be suggested that the homeobox genes play a role not only in segmentation of the embryo but also in regulating gene expression in fully differentiated tissue. Further, they accomplish this by binding of their products to enhancer elements, which activates transcription of single genes or sets of genes. Of course, there remains the entire question of the regulation of the homeotic genes themselves. Following the bacterial analogy, one would expect these genes to be activated by environmental cues, which could be as primitive as their position in the egg or as complex as activation by a hormone-triggered cascade.

Designer proteins. As was described above, genes control the properties of cells by determining which

In early 1988 scientists reported direct observation of native, uncoated DNA with the scanning tunneling microscope. In the image of a DNA loop below, the helical coiling of the double strands is clearly visible.

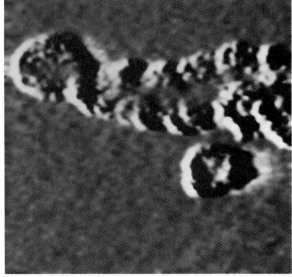

Lawrence Livermore National Laboratory and Lawrence Berkeley Laboratory

of the many possible proteins a cell actually makes. The gene, in fact, can specify only the sequence of amino acids in a given protein. For the protein to function as an enzyme, a receptor, or a structural element, it has to fold up into the correct three-dimensional conformation and find its way to the correct place, either inside the cell in which it was made or outside, in the case of proteins destined to be secreted. For many proteins the amino acid sequence is sufficient to determine the final folded structure. This principle was established in the 1950s by a simple and elegant experiment carried out at the U.S. National Institutes of Health by Christian Anfinsen. He studied the enzyme ribonuclease, which cuts up RNA into nucleotides. It was shown that the enzyme could be unfolded (denatured), completely losing its enzyme activity, and then allowed to refold, resulting in complete restoration of enzyme activity. Since no cellular component other than the enzyme itself was present during the entire experiment, the information for correct folding had to reside in the sequence of amino acids of the enzyme protein.

The principle that amino acid sequence determines folding and specifies the final three-dimensional structure of a protein has wide and far-reaching implications. If, for example, the rules that relate sequence and structure could be discovered, it would be possible to design proteins for a particular purpose and make them by synthesizing genes encoding the correct amino acid sequence.

Some progress has been made in elucidating the rules. More than 100 different structures of globular proteins have been determined by X-ray diffraction studies of protein crystals. Statistical analysis of these structures has permitted researchers to formulate rules for medium-range folding (so-called secondary structure). Using these rules one can predict, on the basis of an amino acid sequence, which regions of the polypeptide chain are likely to form such structures as α-helices, β-sheets, or reverse turns or no defined structures at all. These secondary-structure predictions are likely to be correct only about 80% of the time. Moreover, since these interactions involve amino acids distant from each other in the sequence, they cannot predict at all how the local domains interact with each other. On the other hand, the 100 known structures do provide some generalizations about long-range interactions. For water-soluble proteins, for example, the hydrophobic (water-avoiding) amino acid side chains are predominantly buried inside the structure, and the hydrophilic (water-seeking) side chains are on the outside.

An alternate approach to the relationship between protein sequence and structure, gaining significantly in importance in the past year, is to design synthetic peptides or proteins. Clearly such an approach depends heavily on the information obtained in the structural analyses described above, but evolution indicates that there is considerable leeway in protein design. Comparison of the amino acid sequences of the same protein from many different species shows that the same function and structure can be achieved in spite of numerous amino acid substitutions. It might therefore be possible to design, as a starting point, a simple polypeptide whose folding could be predicted and whose functional properties could be exploited. This general approach was used with great success to study the interactions of peptide (small protein) toxins and hormones with their cellular receptors by the late E. T. Kaiser of the Rockefeller University, New York City. Progress in extending the methods to larger proteinlike molecules was reported last year by W. F. DeGrado, Z. R. Wasserman, J. D. Lear, and L. Regan of the Du Pont Co., Wilmington, Del.

Two examples illustrate the power of this approach. A local structure termed an α-helical coiled coil is thought to be an important feature of proteins that span (penetrate the full thickness of) biologic membranes, such as the membranes that surround cells. Among such membrane-spanning proteins are some that function as ion channels, selectively conducting protons (hydrogen ions) or sodium or potassium ions into or out of the cell (see *1986 Yearbook of Science and the Future* Year in Review: LIFE SCIENCES: *Molecular biology*). On the basis of the structures and properties of known ion-channel proteins, DeGrado and his co-workers designed several peptide models for an ion channel. One such peptide has 21 amino acids with the sequence leucine-serine-leucine-leucine-leucine-serine-leucine repeated three times, ending with an amide group ($-CONH_2$). When mixed with model membranes (phospholipid bilayers), this peptide forms ion channels that conduct protons but exclude alkali metal ions. Another peptide, in which the third amino acid of the repeating group of seven is changed from leucine to serine, packs differently in the membrane, conducting protons, alkali metal ions, and small organic cations (positively charged ions). Physical methods of analysis suggest that the first peptide forms a tetramer—*i.e.*, a larger structure made up of four of the peptides as subunits—in the membrane, while the second forms a hexamer— a six-peptide structure—with a wider channel. These results are remarkable in many ways. They indicate the correctness of the generalizations relating structure and function of known proteins. As the number and kind of modifications to the simple peptides that now can be introduced is vast, so are the possibilities for both new insights and useful applications.

The structure-determining principles were also used to design a water-soluble protein containing 74 amino acids that folds into a defined, globular, three-dimensional conformation containing four tightly packed α-helices. This work was at a very early stage in 1988, with crystallography still to be done, but it is still possible to anticipate that such a protein will provide a suitable framework on which to hang specific binding or catalytic sites. This protein is conveniently made by designing a gene with the correct nucleotide sequence and then producing the protein in recombinant bacteria. However, it is also small enough to be synthesized chemically, which opens the possibility of substituting amino acids not normally used in protein synthesis by living cells. For the biochemists who have worked so hard and so long to understand the rules relating protein structure and function, the success of the "minimalist" approach to protein design must be particularly satisfying.

—Robert Haselkorn

Zoology

Survival of the species served as a unifying theme during the past year for studies of such diverse animals as the African elephant, a striking blue-colored frog of South America, and the California condor. Zoologists found that cooperative hunting is practiced by a bird of prey and marveled over the discovery that the hawksbill turtle thrives largely on a diet of glassy needles and poisonous substances. Brain tissue transplanted from quail to chickens was demonstrated to transmit behavioral traits; a thumb-sized embryonic skeleton of an ancient reptile was found; and a sixth specimen of *Archaeopteryx* turned up in a private collection in West Germany.

Endangered species. The high price of ivory in the world market and the consequent poaching of elephants in African wildlife preserves continued to have devastating effects. According to Diana McMeekin of the African Wildlife Foundation in Washington, D.C., the elephant population of Kenya decreased from 130,000 in 1973 to fewer than 20,-000 in 1988, and the rate of decrease was accelerating. Even greater losses of elephants were observed in Tanzania. Although the African elephant was not in imminent danger of extinction, the growing practice of killing females—since few large males remained—appeared to be unexpectedly and seriously disrupting elephant society. Cynthia Moss, director of the Amboseli Elephant Research Project in southern Kenya, pointed out that young elephants have a 12-year childhood during which they learn from their mothers and herd leaders how to live and behave. The massive loss of females meant that large numbers of young elephants not only might fail to learn the essentials of survival but also might lack the knowledge needed for normal interaction in the elephants' complex society.

The poison arrow frogs of South America are a group of small, brilliantly colored species that inhabit the rain forests. Although certain of them had been bred successfully in captivity at the National Aquarium in Baltimore, Md., the blue poison arrow frog until recently had failed to produce fertile eggs. Finally, after five years' effort, National Aquarium herpetologist Jack Cover reported success in raising six adults from eggs laid by captive frogs. The key to this success lay in providing pairs of frogs with an enriched diet, a humid climate, and private breeding nests made from the bottoms of two-liter plastic bottles. Such breeding studies were important not only for the blue poison arrow frog but also for the future survival of many small amphibians threatened by the continuing destruction of the rain forests.

Another hopeful note was sounded when scientists associated with the condor breeding program at the San Diego (Calif.) Wild Animal Park announced the hatching of the first California condor that had been conceived in captivity. Named Molloko, after an Indian word meaning "condor," the chick joined the other 27 known members of its species, all in captivity at the San Diego institution or the Los An-

The blue poison arrow frog was recently bred for the first time in the U.S. at the National Aquarium in Baltimore, Maryland. The threatened South American species is named for its brilliant warning coloration and the nerve toxin it secretes.

National Aquarium in Baltimore; photo, George Grall

geles Zoo. If the breeding program succeeded, the California condor would be reintroduced into the wild. To prepare for that event, related Andean condors from South America were taken to California, fitted with radio transmitters, and released. Scientists were tracking these birds to learn as much as possible about the survival of future releases of California condors.

Behavior. One of the more intriguing studies of animal behavior was under way at Shark Bay in Western Australia. Over a period of several years, certain members of a large population of bottle-nosed dolphins (*Tursiops truncatus*) had spontaneously acquired a friendly interest in the humans who visited the beach. They swam into extremely shallow water, allowed beach visitors to touch them, accepted handouts of food, and even occasionally returned the favor by tossing a fish or piece of seaweed to the people. These "habituated" dolphins offered a unique opportunity for behaviorists, particularly those who study wild chimpanzees, to observe the behavior and society of a wild population of dolphins and to compare them with those of anthropoids.

Dolphins possess a very large brain. Relative to body size, their brain is smaller than the human brain but twice as large as that of the great apes. Dolphins, apes, and human beings all have extensive convolutions on the surface of the brain and a large neocortex. All three undergo a prolonged period of training and development after birth. The clear water and approachability of the Shark Bay dolphins provided an unparalleled opportunity for making extensive observations of the dolphins. Studies at Shark Bay were initiated in 1982 by graduate students Richard Connor and Rachel Smolker. Later the two were joined by experienced primatologists Barbara Smuts and Richard Wrangham, both of whom had worked with chimpanzees at the Gombe Stream Reserve in Tanzania.

Smuts reported that the dolphins have a home territory but live in temporary social groups; however, associations of males with one or two male companions may persist for long periods of time. Females often assist each other in the care of young. Sexual activity is frequent and appears to be an important aspect of "recreation." Many of these traits are shared with chimpanzees. A detailed comparison of these two very complex animal societies promised fascinating revelations.

Cooperative hunting, in which two or more animals hunt together in a coordinated manner and share caught prey, has been demonstrated for only a few mammals, such as the lion and the wolf. James C. Bednarz of the University of New Mexico recently documented similar activities by Harris's hawk (*Parabuteo unicinctus*). These birds live in family groups of two to six individuals and consistently hunt as a group. Their tactics appear to fall into three general approaches. In one, members of the group take turns diving at their prey—for example, a desert cottontail rabbit or a blacktailed jackrabbit—until it becomes sufficiently tired and confused to be caught. In another tactic, used when the prey takes cover in brush, one bird lands, walks into the brush, and flushes the prey, which can then be taken by another bird. In the third and most common tactic, when the prey is in the open, several birds may dive almost simultaneously, usually with success. In all cases, the catch is consumed by all members of the hunt. In addition to increasing hunting success, cooperation allows the hawks to take animals—like the jackrabbit—that are larger than a single bird could subdue, to consume all of the catch, and to protect the catch from scavengers while it is being eaten.

The hawksbill turtle (*Eretmochelys imbricata*) lives in tropical marine waters around the world. While studying this species in the Caribbean, Anne Meylan of the American Museum of Natural History, New York City, found it to have a very unusual diet. The hawksbill feeds primarily on several species of large silicious sponges. As their name indicates, the sponges possess large numbers of glassy needlelike protective spicules, some of which may reach five centimeters (two inches) in length. Examination of the intestines of the turtles yielded masses of these spicules, many embedded in the intestinal wall. In addition, the sponges contain a variety of toxins, some of which are fatal in other vertebrates. How the turtle manages the spicules and toxins was yet to be understood. Since the turtle consumes large quantities of sponges, opening up space for other sessile animals, it probably plays an influential role in determining the species composition of tropical reefs.

Nervous system. In an attempt to determine the paths taken by migrating nerve cells of the brain during embryonic development and to see if transplanted brain tissue affects behavior, a group of investigators transferred brain tissue between early embryos of chicken and Japanese quail. The nuclei of the cells of the two birds are distinctly different, allowing the origin of the cells to be discerned after the transplanted quail tissue and host chicken tissue have intermingled. Evan Balaban, Marie-Aimée Teillet, and Nicole Le Douarin of the Institute of Cellular and Molecular Embryology of the National Center for Scientific Research and the Collège de France observed both radial and tangential movements of the transplanted cells during development. Of particular interest was the behavior of certain of the chicks after hatching. The mixed-brain chicks were able to walk, peck, eat, and interact with other animals. Twenty of the chicken hosts were given testosterone implants to induce early crowing. Of these, 15 produced normal sounds, while 5 produced quail-like sounds. All of the latter had received transplants from the middle regions of the quail brain and had developed brains in which either the telencephalon, diencephalon, and mesencephalon or the rhomben-cephalon, mesencephalon, and diencephalon consisted entirely of quail-derived cells. This case was apparently the first in which brain-cell transplantation was demonstrated to transmit behavioral traits, and it provided an experimental approach to aspects of behavior, embryology, and immunology.

Chickens and quail played a role in studies of the ear as well. Hair cells are the receptors for sound in the inner ear of vertebrates. They can be destroyed, with a consequent loss of hearing, by excessively loud noise—a common and supposedly irreversible cause of hearing loss in humans. In 1988 two independent reports, one involving work with chickens by Jeffrey T. Corwin of the University of Hawaii and Douglas A. Cotanche of the Boston University School of Medicine and the other involving work with quail by Brenda M. Ryals of the Veterans Administration Medical Center, Richmond, Va., and Edwin W. Rubel of the University of Washington, offered evidence for regeneration of hair cells in the inner ears of these birds. After inducing acoustic damage to the ears, Corwin and Cotanche injected radioactive thymidine into young chickens to identify the cells that produce new hair cells. The thymidine was taken up into the DNA of dividing cells, allowing them to be identified by autoradiography. The researchers found that new hair cells appeared in areas where previously existing ones had been totally destroyed. Both the new cells and their supporting cells showed the presence of radioactive thymidine, indicating that the supporting cells or their precursors were the likely source of the new hair cells.

Regeneration of hair cells was originally thought to occur only in young animals, but Ryals and Rubel demonstrated that acoustically destroyed hair cells in the adult quail would also regenerate. Using an approach similar to that of Corwin and Cotanche, they found that over a period of 60 days the hair cells gradually returned to a normal condition. The studies suggested the possibility of finding a means of reversing the hair-cell loss that results from damage or aging in human beings.

Unusual parasites. Larvae of the mosquito *Aedes sierrensis* and the ciliate protozoan *Lambornella clarki* commonly occur together in water-filled tree holes on the western coast of North America. In the absence of the mosquito larvae, the ciliate is free-living and feeds on bacteria. If mosquito larvae hatch in the water, they feed on the ciliate and can greatly reduce its numbers. Jan O. Washburn and co-workers of the University of California at Berkeley found that the ciliates can counter this predation with a surprising defense based on an ability to detect and respond to a water-soluble substance released by the larvae. In the presence of this material, the ciliate begins to undergo cell division, but instead of reproducing the free-living form (trophont), the daughter cells become parasitic theronts. Theronts have a morphology different from that of the trophont and form cysts on the exoskeleton of the mosquito. The cysts break through into the body cavity of the mosquito, where they feed, multiply, kill the larva, and release both theronts and trophonts. The theronts are obligate parasites and will die if they cannot enter a mosquito. This novel defensive tactic, in which prey metamorphoses into predator, is quite effective and can eliminate mosquito larvae from a tree hole. The water-soluble substance that triggers transformation of the ciliates had yet to be identified.

Like other members of the hymenopterous insects, sex in wasps is determined by chromosome number; an offspring that has the full diploid complement of chromosomes is female, whereas one that has only half the number is male. Normally, sex determination is controlled by the female wasp as she lays eggs. The female stores sperm received in an earlier copulation and can deliberately allow an egg to be fertilized (and thus made diploid) or not be fertilized as it is laid. In this way she controls the sex ratio in her young. For some years it had been known that males of the small parasitic wasp *Nasonia vitripennis* could carry a genetic factor, named *psr* (for paternal sex ratio), that forces offspring to become males even though the egg is fertilized. Originally *psr* was thought to be a virus that somehow prevents the expression of the male chromosomes in a fertilized egg, thus causing the egg to function as if unfertilized and consequently to produce a male.

During the past year Uzi Nur, John H. Werren, Danna G. Eickbush, William D. Burke, and Thomas H. Eickbush of the University of Rochester, N.Y., showed that this factor is a supernumerary (extra) chromosome carried in sperm cells. It produces its effect in a fertilized egg by causing all the male chromosomes, except the supernumerary, to clump and fail to reproduce during cell division. The result is a male wasp whose chromosome complement derives from the female parent except for the addition of the supernumerary chromosome from the male parent. This chromosome assures its continued existence and future transmission by destroying the genetic material of the male that carries it. Such genetic material was interpreted by some as "parasitic" or "selfish" and, as such, represented the most extreme case known. The structure of the chromosome suggested that it may be the result of unsuccessful hybridization between closely related species of *Nasonia*.

New blood vessel constrictor. The endothelium is the innermost lining of blood vessels. It consists of a single cell layer that is continuous throughout the circulatory system and forms the entire wall of capillaries. Only recently have scientists come to realize that the endothelium is more than just a physical separation between the blood and tissues. During the past year Japanese researcher Masashi Yanagisawa and colleagues at the University of Tsukuba, the Fermentation Research Institute in Ibaraki, and the University of Tokyo isolated a peptide that is 21 amino acids long from cell cultures of pig endothelium. They found this substance, which they named endothelin, to be the most potent vasoconstrictor known. The structure of the peptide is unlike any known physiological peptide but does resemble certain neurotoxins that alter the permeability of cell membranes to sodium ions. At about the same time, closely related compounds were isolated from the venom of an African burrowing viper (*Atractaspis engaddensis*) by Y. Kloog and co-workers of Tel-Aviv (Israel) University. These sarafotoxins are all 21-amino-acid peptides having a high degree of resemblance in their structure to endothelin. They act on blood vessels and the heart and can be rapidly fatal. The Tel Aviv researchers found that the toxins activate an enzyme system that causes a rapid rise in intracellular calcium. The close similarity in structure of endothelin and the sarafotoxins is surprising since one is a normal component of the body and the others are extremely powerful poisons.

Paleontology. Dinosaurs and other ancient reptiles are usually pictured as large, imposing creatures, but during the year one of the more interesting new developments occurred at the opposite end of the size scale. P. Martin Sander of the University of Zürich, Switz., described an almost complete embryonic skeleton of a pachypleurosaur from the Middle Triassic Period, about 230 million years ago. The embryo, a nothosaur of the genus *Neusticosaurus*,

has a body length of only 51 mm (2 in) and was the smallest skeleton of an extinct reptile yet discovered. The nothosaurs were small amphibious reptiles (230–370 mm [9–14.5 in] in adult length) that lived in shallow coastal marine waters. The fossil is in a typical head-to-tail curved fetal position. There was no evidence of an eggshell, but it remained uncertain whether the animal gave live birth.

The sixth and largest fossil of *Archaeopteryx* surfaced in Solnhofen, West Germany; it was found misidentified in a private collection. Peter Wellnhofer of the Bavarian State Collection of Paleontology and Historical Geology, Munich, West Germany, recognized the nature and importance of the fossil. The skeleton is nearly complete except for portions of the skull and tail. The specimen closely resembles one in the British Museum, London, and shows impressions of feather shafts extending from the left wing.

Another fossil bird found in Cuenca, Spain, by J. L. Sanz of the Autonomous University, Madrid, J. F. Bonaparte of the Argentine Museum of Natural Science, Buenos Aires, and Antonio Lacasa of the Institut d'Estudis Ilerdencs, Lérida, Spain, helped fill the gap between *Archaeopteryx* and modern birds. The bird, 120 million to 130 million years old, is about the size of a small robin and has both advanced and primitive features. Its structure supported the contention that adaptation for flight was a primary and early driving force in the evolution of birds.

Among other important finds was that of a well-preserved group of jawless fish from rocks 470 million years old in southern Bolivia, discovered by an expedition led by Phillipe Janvier of the French National Research Center, Paris. The fossils imply that vertebrate diversity at that time was greater than expected and that vertebrate evolutionary history must extend considerably farther back in time than gen-

Honors for the oldest known land animal in North America went to a recently discovered fossil, from the Early Devonian, of an insect known as a bristletail. Microscopic examination of the head capsule and mouthparts (left) indicate that the insect had large, bulging, compound eyes and probably ate soft plant material.

From "Early Insect Diversification: Evidence from a Lower Devonian Bristletail from Quebec," C. C. Labandeira, B. S. Beall, and F. M. Hueber, *Science,* vol. 242, no. 4880, pp. 913–916, Nov. 11, 1988, © 1988 AAAS

erally believed. John R. Bolt of the Field Museum of Natural History, Chicago, R. M. McKay and B. J. Witzke of Iowa's Geological Survey Bureau, and M. P. McAdams of William Penn College, Oskaloosa, Iowa, reported a large fossil bed in Iowa containing the remains of amphibians that reached 0.9–1.5 m (3–5 ft) in length. These salamander-like animals lived about 335 million years ago in the Carboniferous Period. The extremely primitive nature of certain of the specimens may help shed light on the origin and development of terrestrial vertebrates from fish.

Conrad C. Labandeira of the University of Chicago, Bret S. Beall of the Field Museum of Natural History, and Francis M. Hueber of the Smithsonian Institution, Washington, D.C., found the oldest known land animal in North America. The fossil is that of an insect from Early Devonian deposits on the Gaspé Peninsula of Canada. About 390 million to 392 million years old, the insect shows features that identify it as a bristletail, a member of a primitive group of insects still in existence. Its mouthparts indicate that it probably lived on soft plant material. Its presence during the Early Devonian suggested that the enormous diversification of insects that later followed may have had its start simultaneously with the appearance of vascular land plants during the Silurian (between 430 million and 395 million years ago).

Ancient human ancestors. Traditionally, the use of hand tools by hominids had been associated exclusively with members of the genus *Homo*. Randall L. Susman of the State University of New York at Stony Brook presented evidence that newly discovered hand fossils of the hominid *Paranthropus robustus* from Swartkrans, South Africa, have a structure indicative of manipulation rather than power grasping. According to Susman, muscle insertions and the round fingertips of the fossils are much more like those of modern humans than of the apes. Crude stone implements found in association with other remains of *Paranthropus* had been assumed to belong to the contemporaneous species *Homo habilis* or *Homo erectus*, but they actually may have been produced by *Paranthropus*. This idea raised interesting questions concerning possible tool use by other hominids and suggested that lack of tool use was not the cause of the extinction of *Paranthropus*.

Recent advances in genetic analysis and the discovery of new paleontological remains were stimulating debate over the relative merits of theories of the origin of modern humans (*Homo sapiens*). One theory, the multiregional theory, states that widespread populations of prehumans, by means of gene exchange at the peripheries of their separate localities, all gradually evolved into modern humans roughly simultaneously. By contrast, the single-origin theory states that *Homo sapiens* arose in one restricted area and then spread from there, displacing other pop-

ulations along the way. A published review article by Christopher B. Stringer and Peter Andrews of the British Museum considered the evidence for and against each theory and concluded that the evidence strongly favors the single-origin theory. Comparison of the molecular structure of mitochondrial DNA, nuclear DNA, and proteins all indicated that the varieties of human beings living today are very closely related. If the degree of genetic differences in various populations is traced, the point of origin appears to be in sub-Saharan Africa. Although fossil evidence thus far was limited, the absence of convincing intermediates between *Homo sapiens* and the populations that it replaced did not suggest a widespread, gradual change of those populations into modern humans. If correct, the interpretation would indicate that in Europe the Neanderthals were displaced by modern humans and contributed little, if any, to the genetic composition of *Homo sapiens*.

First patented animal. In April 1988, for the first time, a U.S. patent was issued for an animal, specifically one genetically engineered for cancer studies. The highly controversial award was made to Harvard University for, as the patent stated, a "transgenic nonhuman eukaryotic animal." Although mice are usually used for the purpose specified, the broad language of the patent could include any animal into which foreign genetic material had been implanted so as to make it especially susceptible to cancer. The implications of patenting genetically engineered animals were still being widely discussed.

Mass seal deaths in Europe. During the year a catastrophic disease killed nearly two-thirds of the estimated 15,000 harbor seals living along the coasts of The Netherlands, West Germany, Denmark, Sweden, and Norway. Initially the cause of the deaths was puzzling and was attributed by some to serious pollution in the North Sea. A breakthrough occurred when Swedish scientists Anders Bergman and Brendt Klingeborn of the National Veterinary Institute in Uppsala reported that the symptoms shown by seals closely resembled those shown by dogs with canine distemper. Confirmation came when a Dutch group led by Albert Osterhaus of the National Institute of Public Health and Environmental Protection, Bilthoven, and Elizabeth Vedder of the Seal Orphanage, Pieterburen, isolated the infectious agent. They identified it as either the canine distemper virus or a very closely related one. An attempt was under way to develop a vaccine to protect seals in sanctuaries, but little help was seen for wild populations. The source of the infection remained unknown, but it could have been transmitted by Arctic foxes on Baffin Island or diseased huskies on Greenland. If the disease continued to spread, it could devastate seal populations throughout the Atlantic Ocean.

—J. R. Redmond

Materials sciences

New high-temperature ceramic superconductors were discovered and developed during the past year as researchers continued their efforts to find applications for these materials. Intermetallic alloys captured the attention of metallurgists because of their strength at high temperatures, and a search was under way for new sources of platinum.

Ceramics

Significant progress was made in many aspects of ceramics. These included high-temperature ceramic superconductors, synthetic diamonds and diamond-like coatings, and ceramic composites.

High-temperature superconductors. Progress in the area of high-temperature superconductors was highlighted by the discovery of new, higher temperature materials that were easier to process than the previous materials, the development of several theories that tried to account for their behavior and explain the relationship between their structure and properties, and processing efforts aimed at improvements in their current-carrying capabilities. French scientists at the University of Caen had reported superconductivity in a bismuth-strontium-copper oxide at about 22 K in 1987. (To convert Kelvins [K] to degrees Celsius, subtract 273; thus, 22 K = −251° C. To convert this figure to Fahrenheit, multiply it by $9/5$ and subtract 32 [−419.8° F].) On Jan. 22, 1988, Hiroshi Maeda and co-workers at the National Research Institute for Metals, Tsukuba, Japan, announced that they had obtained a critical temperature of transition to the superconducting state, T_c, of 120 K in a bismuth-strontium-calcium-copper oxide. Their results were verified within days by Paul Chu and his group at the University of Houston, Texas.

That same day, Jan. 22, 1988, Zhengzhi Sheng and Allen M. Hermann of the University of Arkansas announced the discovery of still another high-T_c superconductor, a thallium-barium-copper oxide with a T_c of about 80 K. They soon found that additions of calcium raised T_c to about 106 K. On March 3 researchers at IBM Almaden Research Center announced that they had found a thallium-calcium-barium-copper oxide with a T_c of 125 K.

The compositions based on bismuth and thallium had several immediately interesting features. From a practical standpoint these new high-T_c materials appeared to be more stable and easier to produce than the yttrium-barium-copper oxides discovered earlier. Particularly important is the fact that they did not seem to require careful oxygen annealing treatments.

From a more theoretical standpoint it is interesting that the chemical structures of the new high-T_c materials do not contain the one-dimensional copper-oxygen chains that many thought might be responsible for the high-T_c superconductivity of the yttrium-barium-copper oxides. They do, however, contain a greater number of two-dimensional copper-oxygen planes per unit cell of the structure. Researchers have suggested that T_c may increase in direct proportion to the number of copper-oxygen planes, with a probable upper limit for T_c in those materials of about 180–200 K. The materials based on bismuth and thallium were further modified during the year by additions of lead, and by November 1988 reports had appeared of high-T_c superconductivity in still another group of materials, the lead–strontium–rare-earth–copper oxides.

Much of the effort in the development of high-T_c superconductors was aimed also at a theoretical explanation of the superconducting state in these new materials. Theoretical advances would be extremely valuable in guiding further efforts to improve these materials by compositional, structural, and processing variations.

Most theorists agreed that superconductivity in the high-T_c materials most likely arises from spin or charge fluctuations, rather than the phonon interactions involved in conventional low-temperature superconductors. In the Bardeen-Cooper-Schrieffer (BCS) theory of low-temperature superconductivity, electrons that would otherwise repel one another are bound into pairs by their interaction with the lattice vibrations of the ions (phonons) of suitable materials, and those pairs then move without any resistance.

General Electric scientists examine bars of SILTEM copolymer, a new kind of plastic created by combining silicones and polyimides. It is strong, flexible, and resistant to both abrasions and flames.

G.E. Research and Development Center, Schenectady, N.Y.

In the high-T_c superconductors such pairs also form, but their origin is different. Researchers suggested several possibilities. The pairing might be due to unusual, strongly anharmonic phonon interactions capable of binding pairs more tightly. Other explanations were based on interactions not with the lattice vibrations of the ions but with fluctuations in the electronic charges. The most favored theories involved interactions with fluctuations in the spins of electrons within the lattice. Such spins are effectively magnetic, and spin fluctuations (magnons) could lead to tightly bound electron pairs that might be responsible for the high-T_c superconducting state.

An interesting feature of these theories was their ability to predict and explain important aspects of the behavior of high-T_c superconductors. For example, William A. Goddard III at the California Institute of Technology used his magnon-pairing theory to determine the likely upper limit for T_c in structures based on copper-oxygen planes and found a value of about 200 K. The theories also generally arrived at small spatial extents (coherence lengths) for the pairs in these high-T_c materials, and it was suggested that these short lengths might be the source of a number of their troublesome features, including the suppression of superconductivity near grain boundaries (the surfaces between individual grains).

Although initial estimates following the discovery of these high-T_c superconductors had projected huge commercial impacts in areas such as electronics, power generation and distribution, and transportation, recent efforts to overcome some of the material, processing, and fabrication problems necessary for their realization suggested that most of these large-scale applications were probably 15–20 years in the future. For example, most applications would require these ceramic superconductors to be able to carry electrical current densities of the order of 10^5 to 10^6 amp per sq cm, often in the presence of very high magnetic fields. While substantial progress had been made in this direction, none of the present high-T_c superconductors came close to achieving these current densities in the bulk ceramic forms that would be needed for many large-scale applications, and even the thin-film forms that would be useful in electronic and sensor applications were only now beginning to come close.

Sumitomo Electric Industries in Japan recently reported 1.9×10^6 and 3.2×10^6 amp per sq cm in bismuth- and thallium-based thin films at zero magnetic field. Typical values that could be achieved reproducibly in production, however, would be considerably lower, and the critical current density in these materials generally drops rapidly with increasing magnetic field. Current bulk forms, which appear to be particularly susceptible to weak links in the superconducting paths at the grain boundaries,

generally have current density values of the order of 1,000 amp per sq cm.

Progress was made, however, in the fabrication of film and multifilament wire and tape. Particularly notable were advances at Sumitomo, Mitsubishi Electric, and Hitachi in the fabrication of wires and tapes that contain large numbers of very fine high-T_c filaments embedded in metal, typically silver, sheaths. The resulting wires and tapes were capable of carrying several thousand amperes per square centimeter at 77.3 K in zero field.

While long-term applications of these superconductors for such purposes as motors for electrically driven cars and ships, power-distribution and power-storage devices, and large high-field magnets remained in the future, near-term applications seemed likely in Josephson junction devices, superconducting quantum interference devices (SQUIDs), and, perhaps, semiconductor interconnects or even new hybrid semiconducting/superconducting devices themselves. Josephson junctions operate by the tunneling of electron pairs between two superconductors through a very thin, "weak link," nonsuperconducting barrier. They are especially promising for digital electronic systems, including new classes of powerful supercomputers, because they can be used as extremely fast, low-power-consumption switches. They are also the essential ingredient of SQUIDs. When two Josephson junctions are connected in a ring, the current flow in the resultant SQUID is so sensitive to the magnetic flux through the ring that magnetic fields as small as those associated with human heart or brain activity can be measured. High-T_c ceramic SQUIDs operating at liquid nitrogen temperatures could provide long-life satellite-based sensors for many geophysical- and defense-survey applications.

Synthetic diamonds. Synthetic diamond and diamond-like materials formed by low-pressure gas phase and ion-deposition processes have been receiving increasing attention in recent years for a variety of applications, ranging from wear-resistant coatings on cutting tools to use as high-temperature, radiation-resistant semiconductors. Recent research more clearly delineated the mechanisms of formation and the chemical bonding and structural relationships in vapor-grown diamonds, diamond-like hydrocarbons, and diamond-like carbons. As more was being learned about their structure and properties, the diamond-like hydrocarbons were emerging as an interesting class of materials that vary with hydrogen content from ceramic-like materials with hardnesses greater than silicon carbide to much softer, polymer-like materials.

Synthetic, low-pressure, vapor-grown diamond itself was becoming especially attractive. Intense efforts throughout the world spanned the spectrum from quite slow growth methods aimed at fine-

Space Felt, a high-purity alumina-silica material created by Standard Oil Engineered Materials Co., can be easily formed into complex shapes. It was developed as an insulator for aerospace applications.

grained, smooth, continuous films for electronic and optical applications to some recent very rapid growth-rate methods (film thicknesses of tens of micrometers per hour) suitable for many wear-resistant and abrasive grinding applications.

Composites. Because of their potential usefulness in high-temperature structural applications, ceramic composites continued to receive most of the attention in the structural ceramics area. While much remained to be done in improving the stability and long-term properties of these materials at still higher temperatures, fiber-reinforced glass and glass-ceramic matrix composites for use at temperatures up to about 1,000° C were developed with fracture toughnesses as high as 25–30 MPa-m$^{1/2}$ (megapascal-square root of meter). These values were twice those of other tough ceramics, such as partially stabilized zirconia, and about as high as some advanced, high-strength alloys currently in service.

Interesting advances were also made in the processing and fabrication of ceramic composites. They were normally made by a variety of sintering, hot pressing, and vapor-infiltration techniques. Recently researchers at the Lanxide Corp. in Delaware described openly for the first time processes they had been working on for several years that offered significant fabrication advantages.

Lanxide found several years ago that when molten metals are suitably alloyed, they react with a gas phase in such a way that the ceramic reaction product grows quite rapidly. It is an unusual process in which molten metal is continuously drawn up to the gas phase through continuous microscopic channels in the ceramic until either the process is stopped or all of the molten metal has been consumed.

While this process is intriguing in itself, Lanxide was able to show that it could be adapted to the fabrication of composites. The firm's researchers demonstrated that when a reinforcement or filler phase (an arrangement of continuous or chopped fibers, whiskers, or powders) prepared in a shape called a preform is placed in contact with a suitably alloyed source of molten metal, the ceramic grown by the Lanxide process can be made to grow into the reinforcement phase, forming high-strength, high-performance ceramic composites. The use of the process in the commercial fabrication of automotive parts, heat exchangers, aerospace parts, and protective armor was anticipated.

—Norman M. Tallan

Metallurgy

Rising prices and increased demand for platinum caused metallurgists to seek new sources for this metal. Research continued on intermetallic alloys, which showed great promise for use in high-temperature operations.

Sources of platinum. Market prices of more than $21 per gram ($600 per ounce) and the resumption of strategic stockpiling by the U.S. government intensified interest in new sources of platinum. Prior to the opening of the Stillwater mine and mill in 1987, the Soviet Union and South Africa were the only countries producing platinum group metals. The Stillwater Mining Co., located in southern Montana, received strong support from the U.S. government as it eased concerns over U.S. reliance on South African production. At the end of its first full year of production, the Stillwater mill was capable of producing 840,000 g (33,000 oz) of platinum and 3.2 million g (114,000 oz) of palladium annually.

Of the platinum group metals (platinum, palladium, iridium, osmium, rhodium, and ruthenium), platinum and palladium (about $7 per gram) were the most abundant. Nearly 98% of the dollar value of the Stillwater production was accounted for by recovery of platinum, palladium, and rhodium from a concentrate produced in the mill. The concentrate was smelted and refined into the pure form of the precious metals in Antwerp, Belgium, and then returned to the U.S. for marketing.

The production process at the Stillwater Mining Co. starts in the underground mine from which ore containing 6 g platinum, 20 g palladium, 0.2 g rhodium, and 0.2 g gold for every metric ton is transported to the milling operation. As of early 1989 the mine was producing approximately 600 tons of ore per day from five tunnels, with plans to reach nearly

1,000 tons per day. Although continuous assays were to be made as to the economic return of further mining, the mine was expected to remain viable for over 20 years.

At the mill the ore is crushed and milled into a fine powder. The valuable minerals that contain the elements sought in the recovery process are separated from a slurry of the fine powder by means of chemical additions. These enhance the adherence of the valuable minerals to air bubbles, which carry the fine particles of the minerals to the surface for skimming. These concentrates are filtered and dried and sent to Belgium for further refinement. Future plans for the operation may include on-site smelting and refining of the ore concentrate.

Environmental concerns about the operation of the Stillwater mine and mill were raised because of its location within the Custer National Forest and its close proximity to Yellowstone National Park, only 56 km (35 mi) to the south. Therefore, the milling process and monitoring procedures were carefully chosen to minimize environmental effects. The quality of surface water and groundwater, the effect on the bighorn sheep living near the mine, and other environmental impacts were evaluated. As a result of these concerns, fine tailings from the mill operation were pumped to a plastic-lined pond for recovery. In addition, surface locations damaged by mining were scheduled to be replanted after the areas are no longer in use.

Another possible source of platinum is recovery from objects that contain platinum and are no longer functional. One example is the catalytic converter. Federal legislation adopted in the 1970s mandated reductions in the level of hydrocarbon emissions from automobile exhausts. U.S. auto companies chose to use catalytic converters to achieve these reductions. Consequently, in the U.S. junked automobiles account for more than 2.5 million kg (5.5 million lb) of catalyst annually. Approximately 0.04% of the catalyst weight was platinum and 0.015% was palladium, roughly $25 million of scrapped platinum group metals per year. In fact, the concentration of platinum was much higher than in the Stillwater mine discussed above. Annually, the U.S. scraps more platinum than it produces.

Unfortunately, recovery of the platinum group metals from the catalyst is difficult and expensive. In a catalytic converter the platinum group metals are found in a thin film on an aluminum oxide substrate. This film assists in oxidation of the complex hydrocarbons that are a major source of exhaust pollution from automobiles. The catalytic converter, located in a stainless steel cylinder between the exhaust manifold and the muffler in an automobile exhaust system, consists of a group of pellets or a honeycomb of a ceramic coated with a thin film of platinum-palladium. The passages between the pellets or honeycomb serve to maximize the contact area of the auto exhaust gases, thereby filtering the exhaust as it passes through the catalytic converter. For recovery of platinum and palladium, the stainless steel canister must be removed from the junked vehicles, cut open, and then processed to separate the precious metals from the support materials. In the recovery of one gram (0.035 oz) of platinum from a typical pellet catalytic converter, more than 3,000 g (105 oz) of 100% hydrochloric acid is consumed. Disposal of the residuals produced from this dissolution method of platinum recovery is difficult because the acidic by-products must be neutralized. Also, used catalytic converters can contain up to 10% lead from the use of tetraethyl lead in gasoline. Processing of catalyst containing lead results in a need to control lead emissions.

An alternative to the liquid dissolution method is the possibility of using copper or nickel smelters for recovery. Direct introduction of the catalyst into the smelter would permit the platinum and palladium to be dissolved into the copper or nickel. Subsequent refining could be used for recovery of the platinum and palladium with only moderate modifications in current smelting practice.

Those undertaking process development for recovery of platinum group metals from catalytic converters must presume that these devices will remain a viable technology for the reduction of automobile hydrocarbon emissions. New developments in engine design may eventually eliminate the use of catalytic converters and, therefore, this source of platinum recovery, as well as reduce the demand for the use of platinum and palladium.

High-temperature applications of intermetallic alloys. As the proposed operating temperatures for jet engines increased, the main design limitation remained the performance of available materials. Although ceramics and carbon-carbon composites were in the running for such applications, intermetallic alloys were also under consideration. Intermetallics, which are metal-metal compounds, are found in many existing alloys as hard particles that strengthen the alloys. The high-temperature, nickel-based superalloys used in most jet turbines are one example. In these superalloys blocky precipitates of a nickel aluminide, Ni_3Al, assist in maintaining high-temperature strength and resistance to the high-temperature deformation mode called creep. Creep is a slow mode of failure in parts exposed to greater than half the melting temperature of the alloy. Some advantages of the intermetallic alloys such as Ni_3Al include good oxidation resistance, light weight, and strength at high temperatures. Ni_3Al is unusual in that its strength increases with increasing temperature up to 600° C.

Like ceramic materials, intermetallics are difficult to process. The high melting temperatures of many intermetallic alloys preclude the use of conventional casting techniques for production since mold materials that can withstand such high temperatures are either very expensive or have very limited lifetimes. Instead, powder metallurgy techniques are commonly used to produce intermetallic alloys. Typical powder metallurgy processing of intermetallics requires a starting powder of the alloy. Often these powders are produced through a rapid-solidification technique.

Rapid-solidification production of powders is performed by the formation of drops from a molten alloy stream or by the rapid cooling of a molten alloy stream on a cooled plate. The fine powders that can be produced by these techniques are compacted in a stainless steel can that is subsequently sealed. The can is extruded (compressed) at high temperatures to consolidate the powder into a solid alloy. The can is then removed, leaving behind a bar of the intermetallic alloy.

Because intermetallics are not very formable at room temperature and are difficult to machine, the remaining steps in making a useful object can be quite expensive. Any engine components with internal passages or other complicated geometries are difficult to produce from the extruded intermetallic alloy. On the other hand, production of sheet materials for outer surfaces of atmospheric reentry vehicles might be a possibility. The titanium-based intermetallics, TiAl and Ti_3Al, have quite high possible operating temperatures, nearly 1,000° C. In comparison with their current competition, the carbon-carbon composites, the titanium aluminides are more oxidation resistant.

Once produced, intermetallic alloys must also perform predictably. The strictly ordered bonding in intermetallics that provides the benefit of strength at high temperatures also limits ductility and toughness (energy for fracture). In addition, the reported susceptibility of intermetallic alloys such as Ni_3Al to grain-boundary embrittlement raises more concern about the toughness of these alloys. For nearly every aspect of research on intermetallics, the primary mechanisms that enhance high-temperature performance are also those that make the material more difficult to produce and inhibit its performance under other conditions. Prime examples of this are the beryllium intermetallics. Because they have melting temperatures as high as 1,800° C, these materials have a potential for operation at very high temperatures. Unfortunately, their production is inhibited by the high toxicity associated with the processing of beryllium. Thus, it is certain that further research into the processing and performance of intermetallic alloys will be needed.

—Keith J. Bowman

Mathematics

Several notable discoveries, together with a "near-miss," took place in mathematics during the past year. A team of mathematicians used a supercomputer to help show that there is no finite projective plane of order 10; another team pooled just their personal computers to factor a "most-wanted" 100-digit number; and a perspective from information theory showed that randomness lies at the heart of mathematical provability. Finally, a claim of a proof of the famous Fermat's last theorem turned out to be premature.

Projective plane. At the end of 1988, Clement W. H. Lam and colleagues at Concordia University, Montreal, announced that they had solved—with the aid of thousands of hours of U.S. supercomputer time—one of the leading problems of combinatorial mathematics. Lam and his colleagues studied a finite projective geometry; in such a geometry every pair of lines intersects just once in a single point, and every pair of points determines a unique line. It turns out that each line must contain the same number of points, and each point lies on the same number of lines. Figure 1 illustrates a projective plane with seven points and seven lines. A finite projective plane is said to be of order n if each line has exactly n + 1 points, in which case there are in the geometry exactly $n^2 + n + 1$ lines (and the same number of points). The figure, then, illustrates a projective plane of order 2, since $2^2 + 2 + 1 = 7$.

Figure 1. A projective plane of order 2 consists of seven points and seven lines. The seven lines are denoted by letters and the seven points by numerals. An "x" denotes that the point in question lies on the line indicated (or, from the point of view of the line, that the line passes through the point indicated). Each point lies on three lines, each line passes through three points, and every pair of lines has a point in common.

				lines			
	A	B	C	D	E	F	G
1	X	X		X			
2		X	X		X		
3			X	X		X	
4					X	X	X
5	X			X	X		
6		X				X	X
7	X		X				X

0	4	1	7	2	9	8	3	6	5	0	7	8	6	9	3	5	4	1	2
8	1	5	2	7	3	9	4	0	6	6	1	7	8	0	9	4	5	2	3
9	8	2	6	3	7	4	5	1	0	5	0	2	7	8	1	9	6	3	4
5	9	8	3	0	4	7	6	2	1	9	6	1	3	7	8	2	0	4	5
7	6	9	8	4	1	5	0	3	2	3	9	0	2	4	7	8	1	5	6
6	7	0	9	8	5	2	1	4	3	8	4	9	1	3	5	7	2	6	0
3	0	7	1	9	8	6	2	5	4	7	8	5	9	2	4	6	3	0	1
1	2	3	4	5	6	0	7	8	9	4	5	6	0	1	2	3	7	8	9
2	3	4	5	6	0	1	8	9	7	1	2	3	4	5	6	0	9	7	8
4	5	6	0	1	2	3	9	7	8	2	3	4	5	6	0	1	8	9	7

Figure 2. Two mutually orthogonal Latin squares of order 10.

What the Lam team showed is that there is no projective plane of order 10; such a geometry would have to have 111 points, with exactly 11 on each of 111 different lines. Also, in a separate but related result, Lam and a student showed that there are exactly 4 distinct projective planes of order 9.

What is remarkable about this discovery is that the question was first posed, in an equivalent form, more than 200 years ago by the preeminent 18th-century mathematician Leonhard Euler (1707–1783). Euler brought up the problem in 1779 in terms of what are now called Latin squares (so called because Euler labeled them with Latin letters). A Latin square is a square array of cells, each of which is occupied by a symbol so that each symbol appears exactly once in each (horizontal) row and exactly once in each (vertical) column. Figure 2 shows two different Latin squares of order 10, in which the symbols are the digits from 0 to 9.

Figure 3. Order 10 Graeco-Latin (or Euler) square.

00	47	18	76	29	93	85	34	61	52
86	11	57	28	70	39	94	45	02	63
95	80	22	67	38	71	49	56	13	04
59	96	81	33	07	48	72	60	24	15
73	69	90	82	44	17	58	01	35	26
68	74	09	91	83	55	27	12	46	30
37	08	75	19	92	84	66	23	50	41
14	25	36	40	51	62	03	77	88	99
21	32	43	54	65	06	10	89	97	78
42	53	64	05	16	20	31	98	79	87

Latin squares are important in statistics in the design of efficient experiments. For example, in an agricultural experiment the rows could be strips of land in a plot, and the columns then could be strips at right angles to the row strips; the symbols in the square correspond to treatments applied to the smaller plots at the intersections of the rows and columns. In an industrial experiment the rows could correspond to particular machines, the columns to days, and the symbols to individual workers.

The two Latin squares in Figure 2 have the property of being mutually orthogonal; that is, if the two are superimposed (as in Figure 3), each symbol from the first square pairs up once and only once with each symbol from the second. For the two order-10 Latin squares exhibited, this feature shows up as each of the two-digit pairs from 00 to 99 occurring exactly once in the combined square, which is known as a Graeco-Latin (or Euler) square.

The oldest known example of a Graeco-Latin square is found in a 1623 puzzle by Claude-Gaspar Bachet de Méziriac (1581–1638), in which the reader is asked to arrange in a square the aces, kings, queens, and jacks from an ordinary deck of playing cards so that no row or column contains more than one card of each suit and one card of each rank (Figure 4). (Bachet de Méziriac added the condition that the main diagonals should also have this property.) Today Graeco-Latin squares are widely applied in the design of experiments.

Euler too was concerned with the existence of mutually orthogonal Latin squares. With increasing amounts of effort, his predecessors had shown that there are no such squares of order 2 and that there are two of order 3, three of order 4, and four of order 5. In his 1779 paper Euler posed the problem of finding two mutually orthogonal Latin squares (or one Graeco-Latin square) of order 6 in terms of the ranks and regiments of 36 military officers (*see* Figure 5). Euler conjectured that no such Graeco-Latin square existed for orders 6, 10, 14, . . .

In 1901 Gaston Tarry, aided by his brother, settled the conjecture for 6 by brute force; they constructed all order-6 Latin squares and then examined all possible pairs for a Graeco-Latin square. Only in 1959 were investigators able to show that 6 is exceptional; Euler's conjecture was wrong in the other cases. For all orders except 2 and 6, there are Graeco-Latin squares. The Graeco-Latin square of order 10 in Figure 3 was discovered by E. T. Parker, one of those investigators.

For some orders it is possible to find more than two Latin squares that are mutually orthogonal. For order n there can be at most n − 1 mutually orthog-

Charles Cegielski

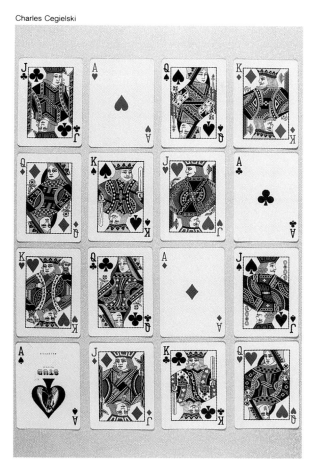

Figure 4. Oldest known example of a Graeco-Latin square.

onal Latin squares. It is exactly in this latter circumstance that there exists a finite projective plane of that order. In fact, the table for the point and line incidences of the projective plane can be built directly from the Latin squares (and vice versa). Therefore, Tarry's result showed that there can be no projective plane of order 6. The question of the existence of a projective plane of order 10 is the same as the question of whether there exists a collection of nine mutually orthogonal Latin squares of order 10.

Since Parker's discovery of the two mutually orthogonal Latin squares of order 10, shown in Figure 3, no one has been able to find even three such squares. The Lam team result showed that there cannot be as many as nine.

Figure 5. Euler's 36-officers problem.

Each of six different regiments has six officers,
one belonging to each of six different ranks.
Can these 36 officers be arranged in
a square formation so that each row and file contains one
officer of each rank and one of each regiment?

Lam began his work on the problem in 1979. The final results required more than two years of time on a supercomputer. Because of the vast computer resources used, the proof cannot be checked easily in all its details, and there is always the possibility of computer error. Consequently, some mathematicians remained skeptical about whether a mathematical proof with so much computer aid should be considered a proof at all. Others likened such a proof to a laboratory experiment, whose credibility would be enhanced by replication.

Distributed factoring. A related development during the past year involved teams of mathematicians using many microcomputers to factor large numbers. One group at the University of Georgia used 140 microcomputers to factor the 95-digit number remaining when 17 and 11,953 are divided out of $2^{332} + 1$. Another group, using hundreds of computers dispersed throughout the U.S., The Netherlands, and Australia, divided up the work of finding the factors of $(11^{104} + 1)/(11^8 + 1)$.

These results showed that supercomputers are not critical in factoring; more important is the algorithm (step-by-step procedure for solving a problem) that is used. In addition, it should be susceptible to division into parts that can be worked on at the same time by different computers.

Fermat's last theorem. A 350-year-old problem managed to maintain its status as unsolved despite a serious challenge. Yoichi Miyaoka of Tokyo Metropolitan University outlined a proof of the conjecture known as Fermat's last theorem, but his proof was soon shown to have a gap in it that could not be patched. Fermat's last theorem was jotted down by Pierre de Fermat (1601–65), a lawyer by trade but also a serious amateur mathematician, in the margin of his copy of Diophantus's *Arithmetica*, with the note, "I have discovered a truly remarkable proof, but this margin is too small to contain it."

Tantalizingly, Fermat never elaborated further on his claim that there are no natural numbers x, y, and z such that $x^n + y^n = z^n$ in which n is a natural number greater than 2. (The case $n = 2$ corresponds to numbers that satisfy the well-known Pythagorean relation among the sides of a right triangle, as in $3^2 + 4^2 = 5^2$.) Leonhard Euler showed that there are no solutions for $n = 3$, and Ernst Kummer proved it for all n up to 100. In the 1970s Samuel Wagstaff showed that there are no solutions for n less than 125,000. Therefore, if there is a solution, the numbers involved are astronomically large. In 1983 Gerd Faltings was able to show that for any n there can be at most a finite number of fundamentally different solutions.

Euler had also extended Fermat's conjecture. While Fermat's last theorem says that no·number raised to the fourth power can equal the sum of two other numbers at the fourth powers, Euler suggested that no number at the fourth power can equal the sum of three other fourth-power numbers. Late in 1987 Euler was shown to be wrong, there being an infinite number of counterexamples, the smallest of which is $95,800^4 + 217,519^4 + 414,560^4 = 422,481^4$. In light of Wagstaff's result, however, Fermat's last theorem will not yield to so simple a refutation.

Randomness and Gödel's proof. In 1930 Kurt Gödel showed that any axiomatization of arithmetic (reducing arithmetic to a system of axioms) must be incomplete; there must be arithmetic truths that cannot be deduced from the axioms. During 1988 Gödel's proof was reinterpreted and proved again by Gregory Chaitin (of the IBM Thomas J. Watson Research Center, Yorktown Heights, N.Y.) in terms of algorithmic information theory, with a surprising twist that pulls randomness into the picture.

The algorithmic information content, or complexity, of an object (such as a string of digits) is the size in bits of the smallest program for computing it. A sequence of digits is random if its information content is equal to its length, so a random sequence cannot be described by a recipe shorter than the sequence itself. With this definition a number such as π (3.14159265 . . .) is not random, since arbitrarily many digits of π can be generated from any of a number of algorithms of fixed length.

Much more difficult would be to prove that a sequence of digits is random, since that task would involve showing that there is no short program to generate the sequence; also, generally it is more difficult to show that an object does not exist than that it does. Chaitin demonstrated that there can be no such proof that an infinite sequence is random. In effect, the information content of the axioms and rules of inference can be encapsulated in a single (enormous but finite) program that prints out all (infinitely many) theorems and their proofs. No sequence whose complexity exceeds that of this program can be proved to be random. As with Gödel's incompleteness theorem, simply adding more axioms to the system to increase its complexity will not allow one to elude the fundamental difficulty.

The major consequence of Chaitin's work for mathematicians is that even arithmetic contains randomness. He exhibits a sequence of equations and asks whether each has a finite or infinite number of solutions; the answer "is indistinguishable from the result of independent tosses of a fair coin." Says Chaitin, "These questions are completely beyond the power of human reasoning. Mathematics cannot deal with them. . . . This does not mean that the universe and mathematics are lawless, it means that laws of a different kind apply: statistical laws."

Milestones. The year 1988 was marked by a number of events, both regular and irregular. The American Mathematical Society celebrated the 100th anniversary of its founding with a gala evening at the State Capitol in Rhode Island. The U.S. team in the high-school International Mathematical Olympiad competition finished fifth, its lowest placing ever. The first high-school team ever to enter the international undergraduate Mathematical Competition in Modeling, from the North Carolina School of Science and Mathematics, was one of the eight winners.

Two of the three winners of the 1988 Kyoto Prizes ($340,000 each) for accomplishments in technology, science, and the arts were researchers with strong connections to the mathematical sciences: mathematical linguist Noam Chomsky and artificial-intelligence authority John McCarthy. In early 1989 still another international assessment of mathematics and science achievement, this time of 13-year-olds, showed U.S. students placing last.

—Paul J. Campbell

Medical sciences

Isolation of the protein from a gene present in many cancers of the lung, colon, and pancreas led to hopes of improved treatments for these often fatal diseases. A newly developed catheter that can remove fatty deposits from within clogged arteries was showing promise as an effective way to prevent heart attacks and strokes. The U.S. appeared ready to embark on a major research project, the determination of the exact order and makeup of the human genetic endowment. Dental researchers found that many kinds of cheese can help prevent the development of dental plaque acids that cause cavities, and veterinary scientists isolated a virus that killed thousands of seals in the North and Baltic seas in the summer of 1988.

General medicine

Genetics. While the technology for transferring genes from one organism into another is relatively straightforward, getting the new genes into the right position on the target chromosome is not. The ability to aim the genes with precision could be crucial to gene transfer, since a gene that incorporates itself randomly could interrupt another, vital, gene or could turn on another gene at an inappropriate time.

Various methods of targeting were described during the past year, the most elegant and efficient developed by Suzanne Mansour, Kirk Thomas, and Mario Capecchi of the University of Utah. Their method involved linking the gene to be transferred to two other genes, one that confers resistance to an antibiotic compound and another that makes its bearer sensitive to an antiviral compound. When this triple gene sequence lines itself up near a chromosome that bears the gene intended for replacement, it inserts itself in place of that gene, shedding the gene that causes sensitivity to the antiviral compound. When the cells are exposed to the antiviral compound and the antibiotic compound, all those that have failed to pick up the new gene with its antibiotic resistance attachment, as well as those that have the new gene in the wrong place (meaning they still have the antiviral sensitivity gene), die, leaving only those cells that have the new gene in the right place. The researchers developed the system in mouse cells but believe that it should be applicable to any gene.

The U.S. moved closer to initiating a massive project to determine the exact order and makeup of the human genetic endowment. It is estimated that such a project will cost $3 billion and take 15 years to complete. The task is an enormous one. There are approximately 100,000 genes along the 46 chromosomes in human cells. By early 1989 only 1,400 had been roughly located, and only 600 of those had been defined at the level of the individual "rungs" along the DNA (deoxyribonucleic acid) ladder. There are about three billion rungs along the ladder. A report by the U.S. Office of Technology Assessment, the research arm of the U.S. Congress, suggested that the government move ahead on the project. The National Institutes of Health (NIH) appointed James Watson, who shared the 1962 Nobel Prize for Physiology or Medicine with Francis Crick for their elucidation of the structure of DNA, to head up a sequencing project.

Meanwhile, several European governments were also involved in the effort to sequence the human genome. France was financing research and data processing development; the U.K. set up a committee to coordinate research; West Germany was holding meetings and studying the issue; and the Italian government planned to allocate about $10 million to sequence a chromosomal fragment associated with mental retardation. Also, scientists from the U.S., Europe, the Soviet Union, and Japan met in Switzerland and organized a committee, the Human Genome Organization (HUGO), to coordinate research efforts.

Regulatory committees within the U.S. scientific establishment spent much of the year considering a proposal by researchers W. French Anderson, R. Michael Blaese, and Steven A. Rosenberg of the NIH to perform the first gene transfer experiment in humans. The transfer was not meant to be therapeutic but was intended as research for an experimental cancer therapy. The transferred genes would serve as markers on the patients' own cells, which would be removed from the body, stimulated with a growth factor, and reinserted. Tracking the cells would allow

Researchers W. French Anderson, Steven A. Rosenberg, and R. Michael Blaese (left to right) of the U.S. National Institutes of Health sought permission during the past year to perform the first gene transfer experiments in humans.

the researchers to determine whether the boosted cells persist in the body. The experiment passed its last regulatory hurdle in early 1989.

While geneticists and the public focused most of their attention on the genetic material packed into the nucleus of the cell, researchers at Emory University, Atlanta, Ga., found a defect in the genetic material contained in mitochondria, the intracellular organelles that supply energy to the cells and carry their own genes. Douglas C. Wallace found a defect in a mitochondrial gene carried by people with a hereditary form of blindness and suggested that other diseases could also be due to defects in mitochondrial DNA.

Homeopathy. The medical world was thrown into a bit of a furor by the publication of an article in the respected scientific journal *Nature*. The article described a finding for which, in the words of *Nature* editor John Maddox, "there is no physical basis." The study was conducted by a French laboratory and repeated by Italian, Canadian, and Israeli biologists. It supposedly provided biochemical evidence for homeopathy, a medical approach that holds that drugs that can cause particular symptoms—for example, fever—are capable of reversing those symptoms when used in minute amounts.

The experiment, headed by Jacques Benveniste of the Inserm Laboratory in Paris, involved an antibody that stimulates white blood cells. The researchers found that even after they diluted the antibody solution to less than one molecule of antibody for every 10 to the 120th power (1 with 120 zeros after it) molecules of solution, the solution was still capable of causing a reaction. Three weeks after the article was published, however, John Maddox, Walter Stew-

385

Stanford University scientists display a mouse that has been injected with immune system cells from an aborted human fetus in order to test the effects of new drugs and vaccines on the human immune system.

art of the NIH, and magician James Randi spent a week observing and conducting their own experiment in Benveniste's laboratory and concluded that the study had been shoddily conducted and there was "no substantial basis for the claim." Benveniste countered that the investigation itself was flawed and that if his group was wrong, they were wrong in good faith.

Immunology. Two groups of researchers, one at the Medical Biology Institute in La Jolla, Calif., and the other at Stanford University transferred key elements of the human immune system into mice. This feat was expected to enable a more detailed study of the human immune system than would be possible in humans because researchers would be able to test new drugs and vaccines on mice instead of humans.

Both groups used a special breed of mice that lack their own immune systems. The Stanford researchers injected the mice with cells taken from aborted human fetuses; the tissue came from the organs that produce immune system cells. The Medical Biology Institute researchers took a different approach. They injected mice with immune cells from adult humans. In both cases the immune system grafts produced human antibodies in the mice.

Cancer. At the molecular level, Sung-Hou Kim of the University of California at Berkeley built a model of a gene that plays a key role in cancer. Called *ras,* the gene in its normal form directs cell division. As an oncogene (a gene that causes cancer), however, it is found in 90% of all pancreatic cancers and in many lung and colon cancers. Kim and an international group of co-workers isolated the protein produced by the oncogene and took an X-ray picture of it from which they were able to make a structural model. Using their analysis, they hoped to find a drug capable of blocking the protein's activity.

Citing cost and difficulty, the U.S. National Cancer Institute canceled a multiyear, multimillion-dollar study aimed at determining whether a low-fat diet can protect women from breast cancer, a relationship that researchers suspected from epidemiological studies but had not yet proved. A small-scale study at two Toronto hospitals suggested that the diet-cancer connection might be true. The researchers studied 180 women at high risk of breast cancer because of precancerous conditions revealed by their mammograms. Half the women were assigned to a diet in which only 15 to 20% of the calories came from fat; the remaining women ate a typical diet containing 37% fat. After a year two women on the low-fat diet and five women on the normal diet had developed cancer. In a second study at Laval University, Quebec City, researchers found an association between the amount of fat in a woman's diet and the possibility that her cancer had spread to her lymph nodes. In addition, they found more lymph-node involvement among women with a high intake of saturated fat compared with unsaturated fat.

Heart attacks and strokes. The major weapons of cardiologists fighting the fatty buildup of plaque inside coronary arteries have been drugs, tiny balloons that push aside the plaque, and a bypass operation to route blood around the clogged areas. By 1989, however, researchers were turning to devices that cut out the plaque. One such tool, invented by John B. Simpson of Sequoia Hospital in Redwood City, Calif., uses a screw-type catheter to shave and remove fatty deposits from within clogged arteries. He reported encouraging results with 33 patients.

Other researchers at several institutions in the U.S. and abroad were using a miniaturized drill that blasts through the hardened plaque, breaking it up into tiny pieces that are carried away by the bloodstream. The "rotoblator" worked well on 40 patients at Stanford University.

Using a principle borrowed from 3rd-century BC scientist Archimedes, Texas Heart Institute surgeons took a new approach to an artificial heart. Rather than fabricating a bulky pump sewn onto the heart's atria, they threaded a tiny screw into the heart via a 7.5-cm (3-in) incision in a patient's groin. The screw, which spins continuously rather than beating, pulls 2.8 liters (6 pt) of blood a minute through the heart. Normal heartbeats circulate 3.8 to 4.7 liters (8 to 10 pt) a minute; this Hemopump, developed by Richard Wampler, can keep people alive for several days until their hearts are healthy enough to take over. The pump made the difference in 5 of 13 patients who were near death.

The fight against deaths from heart disease moved from the hospital to the streets as researchers experimented with the best way to administer drugs that disrupt the clots that cause most heart attacks. In France physicians rode in ambulances to pick up suspected victims of heart attacks. If they thought the person was having an attack, they administered a drug called anisoylated plasminogen streptokinase activator complex (APSAC) to 54 patients and a placebo to 56, who received APSAC about an hour later, after they had arrived at the hospital. The drug improved heart function but did not affect the person's chances of being alive after a year. Israeli physicians found essentially the same result with a different drug, tissue plasminogen activator (t-PA). In the U.S. researchers in Seattle, Wash., began testing the ability of paramedics to deliver a clot buster.

Aspirin. During the past year the *New England Journal of Medicine* and the *British Medical Journal* published several articles evaluating the ability of aspirin to prevent heart attacks. The *New England Journal of Medicine* study involved more than 22,000 physicians, all of whom had never had a heart attack. Half took one aspirin every other day, and the rest took placebos. After about five years 189 members of the placebo group had suffered a heart attack, compared with 104 members of the aspirin group; aspirin had cut the heart attack risk by 47%. This result so convinced the researchers who conducted it that they cut the study short in order to announce the results. Critics claimed, however, that the study should have been continued to determine if aspirin's protective effect against heart disease was offset by an increased incidence of stroke. Indeed, there was a higher rate of stroke among those receiving aspirin—80 of them had strokes, primarily the type caused by intracranial bleeding, compared with 70 in the placebo group—although these figures were not held to be statistically significant.

Both heart attacks and strokes were counted in one of the *British Medical Journal* studies. In 5,000 healthy British physicians aspirin did not affect overall deaths from heart attacks and stroke. It did, however, prove advantageous for people who had already had a stroke, reducing the subsequent stroke rate by 18%, presumably by preventing the blood clots that can block off vessels in the brain.

As cardiologists tried to determine which of various drugs best break up the clots that cause heart attacks, aspirin proved that it too could help. A 16-nation study showed that ordinary aspirin taken within 24 hours of a heart attack cut the death rate by 23%. When used with streptokinase, the results were even better, the death rate dropping by 42%.

By preventing strokes, aspirin may also help prevent the dementia that results from multiple strokes. Stroke-related dementia was second only to Alzheimer's disease in causing a loss of intellectual function in the elderly. Researchers at Baylor College of Medicine, Houston, Texas, gave 70 people who suffered from multi-infarct dementia either one aspirin a day or no aspirin treatment. Over the three-year course of the study, the aspirin group's IQ tests improved 18%, while the untreated group's scores fell 5%. Approximately 40% of the nonaspirin group had recurrent small strokes during the trial, while only 19% of the group on aspirin did; there were four times as many deaths in the nonaspirin group. Because aspirin can increase the chances of suffering the type of stroke caused by spontaneous bleeding in the brain, however, people should consult their physicians before putting themselves on medication.

If aspirin can handle heart attacks, can it not also be effective against flu? Richard T. C. Huang and Ellen Dietsch of the Free University in West Berlin found that aspirin stopped the growth of influenza viruses in culture. Whether it eliminates the flu virus in people remained to be seen.

AIDS. The human immunodeficiency virus (HIV), the virus that causes AIDS (acquired immune deficiency syndrome), does more than just kill a key immune system cell. Components of the virus can wreak havoc in at least two other ways. Research from the NIH indicated that a protein on the virus's membrane is capable of killing nervous system cells. This finding may explain why some HIV-infected individuals appear to be outwardly healthy but nevertheless develop dementia. National Cancer Institute (NCI) researchers, along with researchers at the University of California at Davis, found that one of HIV's genes, called *tat,* on its own can cause Kaposi's sarcoma, a cancer that often occurs in people with AIDS.

While zidovudine (azidothymidine, or AZT) remained the only drug generally accepted as being able to slow the course of AIDS, researchers searched for alternatives. The NIH laboratory that first determined zidovudine's value found that alternating it with a similar medication, dideoxycytidine, appeared to help people. Both drugs block the replication of the AIDS virus, but both, when used alone, have side effects that limit their use. Researchers from the University of Texas and Genentech, Inc., capitalized on the virus's habit of placing a marker, a protein called gp120, on the surfaces of cells it has infected. They used a protein that attaches itself to gp120 and linked the protein to another molecule, ricin A chain, one of the most powerful toxins known to humans. In test-tube experiments this molecule selectively attacked HIV-infected cells. NIH scientists also worked with gp120. They fused the gene from a *Pseudomonas* bacterium that produces a powerful toxin with a gene that makes a protein that hooks onto gp120 and implanted the hybrid gene in *Escherichia coli* bacteria. These *E. coli* pumped out a protein that the researchers found could, at least in the test tube, seek out and destroy HIV-infected human white blood cells while leaving noninfected white blood cells alone.

Another approach to treatment is to imbue target cells with the ability to fight off the virus. Alan Friedman, Steven Triezenberg, and Steven McKnight were able to make cells immune to a herpesvirus; the system, they believed, should also work with HIV. They took a herpesvirus gene that produces a part of a protein necessary for the virus to infect a cell successfully and put this gene into cellular targets. When the virus itself entered the cell to produce its own protein, its action was blocked by the already present protein fragment, which was not infectious by itself.

The search for a treatment was greatly hampered by the lack of an animal that becomes infected by HIV, gets sick, and dies. An animal model would give researchers the chance to test a wide spectrum of drugs and help determine what makes the disease progress rapidly in some people and slowly in others. The Stanford University researchers who developed the mouse model of the human immune system (see *Immunology,* above) reported that they were able to infect those mice with AIDS. Malcolm Martin of the NIH essentially built his own model by injecting the AIDS virus into mouse embryos. Some of the offspring of those mice carried the virus in their cells, and some of them sickened and died of an AIDS-like disease. Unfortunately, the air supply to the mice, which were housed in a highly secure laboratory to ensure against escape, was accidentally cut off temporarily, and all but three of the mice died. The researchers planned to retrace their steps.

Vaccines. The specter of malaria continued to haunt much of the third world. In Africa, for example, it was responsible for about a quarter of the deaths in children between one and four years old. Researchers from Bogota, Colombia, led by Manuel

E. Patarroyo of the Universidad Nacional de Colombia, moved from monkeys to humans with a vaccine, one of several candidate malaria vaccines. The vaccine was made by linking proteins synthesized in the laboratory. These proteins were copies of proteins carried by the parasite at the stage in which it resides in red blood cells.

The researchers injected the protein into 13 volunteers from the Colombian military forces and found that it delayed or suppressed the establishment of infection. A useful vaccine was still years away, however. The Colombian vaccine was made from only one of the four major species that cause malaria, and even within that species there is enough variation that the vaccine might not be effective against all types.

While vaccines are generally thought of as preventing disease, they can also sometimes fight already existing ailments. Jean-Claude Bystryn of New York University announced promising results for a vaccine against malignant melanoma. The vaccine, made from melanoma cell lines, boosts the body's ability to destroy melanoma cells. In a test of the vaccine, nearly half of 75 patients with advanced melanoma mounted an immune response, and they tended to remain free of the disease longer than people who did not get the vaccine. A trial using a different vaccine, produced by the Merieux Institute in France, also generated an immune response, but both vaccines were in their early stages, and it was too early to tell if they would be curative.

There was bad news for a new whooping cough vaccine. In a small number of children the conventional vaccine, made of killed whole pertussis bacteria, causes brain damage or death, and so scientists in several countries were working on new formulations. A Swedish vaccine that contained only parts of the pertussis bacterium was found to be less effective than the whole-cell vaccine. In tests on 3,800 children one formulation of the new vaccine protected 55% of the recipients, and another form protected 70%. The unprotected children who got whooping cough did, however, suffer less serious effects than the children who received no vaccine.

Birth control. A conflict involving the French government, a drug company, and groups for and against abortion flared over an antipregnancy pill called mifepristone or by its brand name, RU-486. The pill counters the effects of the female hormone progesterone. Progesterone's actions are necessary for maintenance of a pregnancy. If a woman takes RU-486 within five weeks after conception, her uterus will bleed and expel the embryo. In studies on more than 5,000 French women, the pill proved 85% effective, and it was more than 95% effective when used in conjunction with other drugs that stimulate uterine contractions. Soon after the French

The French antipregnancy pill RU-486 counters the effect of the female hormone progesterone. Taken within five weeks after conception, RU-486 causes a woman's uterus to bleed and expel the embryo.

government approved the pill, however, manufacturer Groupe Roussel-Uclaf announced that because of pressure from antiabortion groups, it would not market the drug. The French government, a partial owner of the manufacturer, ordered it back on the market.

Meanwhile, other researchers continued their search for a vaccine that would block conception. Several vaccines that cause the destruction of fertilized eggs were being tested in women in India, Europe, South America, and Australia. In a study in Australia a vaccine developed by an Ohio State University researcher was shown to have no major side effects. The vaccine produced antibodies to a hormone that must be present in order for a fertilized egg to implant itself in the uterus. University of Connecticut researchers announced encouraging results on a vaccine that blocks conception itself, a prospect that may prove more acceptable to antiabortion advocates. The vaccine is a protein from the male sperm. When injected into both male and female guinea pigs, it stimulated the immune system to produce antibodies against the sperm and successfully sterilized both the males and females. The effect also proved reversible. The researchers were attempting to find a similar protein in human sperm.

Microbes. The salmonella bacterium proved potent enough to lead to the ouster of a British public health official after she claimed that people who ate eggs in the U.K. were putting themselves at real risk of infection. The bacterium was also linked with several outbreaks of food poisoning in the U.S., but the risk, said the U.S. Centers for Disease Control expert who chronicled the problem, was low. Only 3 in every 1,000 eggs were likely to be infected, and cooking or proper handling of those eggs would reduce the likelihood of illness.

A small biotechnology company in New York was studying a possible answer to the salmonella problem. The company, Applied Microbiology, Inc., modified a protein produced by bacteria to kill the bacteria's competitors. Called Ambicin-N, the antibiotic proved its ability to kill four types of bacteria, including one strain of salmonella. Whether it would work on all 1,800 strains and be safe and effective remained to be seen.

The mysterious non-A, non-B hepatitis virus may have been identified. Named for what it is not (hepatitis caused neither by type A nor by type B viruses, both of which are well characterized), the microbe is the major cause of transfusion-associated disease in countries where blood is already screened for the AIDS virus. Researchers from Chiron Corp. and the Centers for Disease Control cloned parts of the non-A, non-B virus, made antibodies to it, and used the antibodies to detect the virus in blood. The discovery could lead to a method of screening blood for the virus and possibly to a vaccine against it.

Dermatology. An article in the *Journal of the American Medical Association* generated much excitement among people worried about looking old. The research, done at the University of Michigan, showed that a vitamin A derivative is capable of mitigating wrinkles. The drug, Retin-A, was already on the U.S. market for treating acne. The product, made by Ortho Pharmaceutical Corp., causes a rash or dryness in many people who use it, but that was not enough to stop people from rushing to their drugstores.

Meanwhile, the incidence rate of malignant melanoma continued to rise, and younger people were getting it. While it used to be rare for anyone under 40 to develop this potentially lethal form of skin cancer, physicians were now seeing people in their 20s and 30s with the disease. In the U.S. there was a 93% increase in the annual number of diagnosed cases since 1980, and 16 other countries showed a similar rate of increase.

Ethics. As other countries experimented with human fetal tissue, the U.S. grappled with the ethics involved in such research. Theoretically, fetal tissue, which is less likely to be rejected than adult tissue, could be used to treat Parkinson's disease and other neurological conditions, immune disorders, and blood diseases. After a three-day meeting, an advisory committee to the NIH deemed the use of fetal tissue "morally acceptable" and suggested that the U.S. government lift its ban on providing funds for fetal tissue research.

Implants of fetal tissue into the brains of people with Parkinson's disease had been disappointing as of early 1989. Swedish researchers reported that surgery there had not been successful. A University of Colorado researcher said that experiments in which fetal pancreatic cells were placed into adult diabetics showed some potential benefit, as had similar surgery done in China, but transplants in Australia had failed to work.

—Joanne Silberner

Dentistry

There was cheerful news for U.S. schoolchildren during 1988: half of them aged 5 to 17 had no cavities in permanent teeth, thus continuing a remarkable decline in tooth decay that was first documented in 1980. The credit for this accomplishment goes in large measure to the guidance of the men and women who worked in the laboratories and offices of the National Institute of Dental Research (NIDR) in Bethesda, Md., which celebrated its 40th anniversary during the year. Forty years ago tooth decay was the bane of American youth—or some of them at least—and tooth loss was accepted as an inevitable consequence of aging, like wrinkles and gray hair. Then in 1948 U.S. Pres. Harry Truman signed a bill establishing the NIDR as part of the National Institutes of Health. This act was to have profound effects on dental health across the U.S. and throughout the world. In a study of almost 40,000 children during the 1986–87 school year, NIDR researchers found

Dentist uses a probe to scan model's teeth, shown on the screen, during a demonstration of the computer-aided-design and computer-aided-manufacturing (CAD/CAM) system of dental restoration.

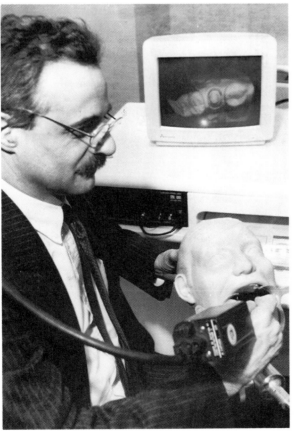

AP/Wide World

36% fewer cavities than in a 1980 survey. This decline led Harald Löe, NIDR director, to predict "the beginning of the end" for tooth decay.

The latest figure for the U.S. showed a total of 147,200 practicing dentists, or 60 dentists for each 100,000 persons. This was not only the highest dentist-to-population ratio ever but probably the highest it would ever be. "We are in reasonable [supply and demand] balance," said Tullio Albertini, a principal author of the U.S. government's newest dental-manpower report. It was not always so. In the 1960s and early 1970s there was concern that the supply of dentists and other health professionals was insufficient to meet the nation's health care needs. Beginning in the early 1980s there were some indications of an oversupply of dentists, but this trend peaked in 1983. The actual number of dentists would continue to increase into the 1990s, but the dentist-to-population ratio would steadily decrease, according to government projections.

Lasers in dentistry. In medicine lasers were replacing scalpels, and it seemed only a matter of time before dental drills also became a thing of the past. According to Leo Miserendino at the Marquette University Dental School, Milwaukee, Wis., "Lasers are well suited for dentistry because so much of the work dentists do calls for precision." He told the annual meeting of the Academy of General Dentistry in Chicago that lasers have been used successfully on soft-tissue surgery. A laser leaves a precise cut and does not disrupt adjacent tissue; thus, there is little scar tissue. This helps lower a patient's postoperative discomfort and the possibility of infection. "You can do things with a laser you can't do with a scalpel, like going around the corners to remove tissue. Certain areas of the mouth are just very difficult to get to with a scalpel," Miserendino noted.

A laser sterilizes the tooth as decay is removed and quickly cleans out the decay without the sound of the drill. Decay seemed less likely to reappear when removed by laser. Lasers were also being used to sterilize other tooth surfaces infected by periodontal (gum) disease and root-canal infections.

Cheesy dental attack. At least a dozen kinds of cheese can help battle dental plaque acids in the mouth and thus limit cavities, a University of Iowa Dental School researcher reported. In 1984 Mark Jensen discovered that aged cheddar, Swiss, and Monterey Jack cheeses help fight tooth decay. Although the way in which they do so remained unknown, he and his co-workers confirmed that another nine cheeses—Edam, Gouda, Münster, mozzarella, Port du Salut, Roquefort, Romano, Stilton, and Tilsit—also help curb decay.

When carbohydrates such as sugar become trapped in plaque—a film on tooth surfaces that harbors cavity-fostering bacteria—they are converted to acids that can destroy teeth. When researchers implanted electrodes between the teeth in five volunteers, however, they found no significant increase in the acidity of plaque when a sucrose (table sugar) rinse followed the consumption of any of the 12 cheeses. All the types of cheeses tested were able to neutralize an acid attack that was already in progress.

In an experiment involving only cheddar, Jensen found that those who ate this cheese four times a day for two weeks experienced a 20% remineralization (tooth-surface rebuilding) in synthetic toothlike materials temporarily attached to root areas and a 5–10% remineralization in materials similar to tooth-crown enamel. These studies indicate that the 12 tested cheeses, when eaten as snacks, do not promote the formation of cavities. Also, when eaten— or chewed without swallowing—before a sweet meal, they might limit tooth decay by preventing the formation of acids that demineralize teeth.

Hopeless teeth. A study at Hebrew University–Hadassah School of Dentistry in Jerusalem proved that extraction of teeth termed hopeless or untreatable is essential to prevent deterioration of adjacent teeth and to promote the patient's well-being. Extraction of hopeless teeth, which could not be treated because of severe bone loss, was becoming common practice in dental offices throughout the world. Recently, however, several studies questioned the validity of this procedure and claimed that even an untreatable tooth should be left in place as long as it did not cause discomfort. The purpose of the Hadassah study was to determine whether this claim was valid and if, indeed, a patient would fare better untreated. The study, which was conducted over four years, involved 71 patients with hopeless teeth that were retained throughout the experiment and 58 patients with equally damaged teeth that were extracted.

Results clearly showed the advantage of extraction of untreatable teeth. The teeth-dependent bone that serves as a base for the roots and also the teeth in the vicinity of the "bad" tooth were in much better condition in patients who underwent extraction. Those whose teeth were left untouched showed severe bone loss in the vicinity of the damaged teeth. These findings confirmed that the common practice of extracting a hopeless tooth, even if it was not causing pain, was the correct approach.

Gum disease. A significant amount of adult gum disease may be inherited, a University of Minnesota School of Dentistry researcher told the annual meeting of the International Association for Dental Research in Montreal. Preliminary results from a study of 30 pairs of fraternal and identical twins suggested that genetics may account for 50 to 75% of chronic adult periodontal disease. The study was continuing to gather additional data from twins reared together

and reared apart to learn how genetics and the environment contribute to gum problems.

A new method for detecting periodontal disease was also described at the Montreal meeting. Successful clinical trials of a temperature probe that rapidly detects gum disease were reported by scientists from the Forsyth Dental Center of Boston and ABIOMED, Inc., of Danvers, Mass. The device is a microprocessor-based probe with a disposable tip that measures gum temperature, correlating minute temperature differences with the presence of periodontal disease. The researchers predicted that the device would enable dentists to detect gum disease before extensive damage had occurred. The machine also monitors the decrease in periodontal disease following antibiotic treatment.

Realigning teeth can help prevent and treat periodontal disease in susceptible individuals, according to University of Pennsylvania orthodontists. Their research showed that the movement of teeth during orthodontic treatment disrupts bacterial colonies that cause periodontal disease. Robert L. Vanarsdall told the annual meeting of the American Dental Association that some of the disease-causing bacteria thrive on an absence of oxygen. "Once the teeth move during orthodontic treatment, these anaerobic bacteria have difficulty recolonizing, which makes treating the periodontal condition easier and more effective."

Immune system disorders, particularly neutrophil dysfunction, seem to be major factors in the development of gum disease, Neutrophils are white blood cells that normally eliminate infections but are impaired in children with an advanced form of gum disease known as juvenile periodontitis, according to Robert Genco, professor and chairman of the department of oral biology at the State University of New York at Buffalo. Neutrophils are also impaired in people who have recurring periodontal disease.

Genco also described advances in stimulating bone regeneration and reattachment of the gum tissue to the teeth in severe cases of periodontal disease. Following mechanical removal of bacteria by deep scaling (scraping), the tooth root surface is roughened with an acid solution to foster reattachment of periodontal ligaments. A plastic membrane also is placed over the site to prevent a cellular lining known as epithelium from forming and interfering with reattachment. "When etching and epithelial control are combined, reattachment and bone regeneration are more successful," Genco concluded.

Fluorides. School-based tooth-decay-prevention programs may soon reflect new findings that will determine which fluoride treatments or combination of treatments works best at fighting cavities in areas where community water fluoridation is not available. NIDR researcher Ruth Nowjack-Raymer compared the amount of tooth decay in children receiving weekly fluoride rinses, daily fluoride tablets, or both procedures combined. Those children who received the combined treatment experienced almost one-third less tooth decay than did children who merely rinsed with a fluoride solution. Although the children who received fluoride tablets experienced more tooth decay than those who received the combined fluoride treatment, the differences between those two groups were not large enough to be considered statistically significant.

These findings indicate that for communities without fluoridated water supplies, the fluoride tablet procedure alone is the most cost-effective strategy for preventing cavities in schoolchildren. Tablets alone are also easier to administer than a combined fluoride rinse and tablet treatment.

There might be another role for fluoride—as a new ingredient in chocolate milk to keep both children and their parents happy. A two-year study by Louisiana State University found that fluoride prevents tooth decay whether in water or chocolate milk. The students who drank the fluoridated chocolate milk for lunch had 77% less tooth decay than those children who did not. Thus, it may be the best alternative for communities without fluoridated water.

—Lou Joseph

Veterinary medicine

The American Veterinary Medical Association (AVMA) selected its first congressional fellow, Martha Gearhart, a private practitioner from Kingston, N.Y., in 1988. Gearhart was to spend a year working as a special legislative assistant to U.S. Sen. Kent Conrad (Dem., N.D.), who chairs the research subcommittee of the Senate Committee on Agriculture.

The fact that the first AVMA congressional fellow was a woman reflected not only on the excellent credentials of Gearhart but also on the "gender trend" in veterinary medicine. Thirty years ago having as many as three women in a veterinary class was unusual. By 1989 over half of the beginning students were female. Of the 4,200 applicants to the 27 U.S. veterinary colleges in 1988, 60% were women and 40% were men. The percentage of women in 1987 was 57%. Reasons suggested for this shift included the fact that women were encouraged rather than discouraged from applying for admission and also that women appeared less influenced by the fact that veterinary medicine offered a lower earning potential and took more years of education than did engineering and computer science.

The presence of more women in veterinary practices focused attention on the potential hazards of the workplace for veterinarians. Safety considerations involving reducing exposure to anesthetic gases, X-rays, drugs, chemicals, and diseases transmissible from animals to people were being implemented more rigorously than before the gender shift.

Of the male and female 1988 veterinary medical college graduates responding to a survey, 88% of the males and 78% of the females had received at least one employment offer exclusive of postgraduate study programs. Of the respondents, 51% were men and 49% were women. Nearly twice as many women as men entered advanced study programs. The 1988 mean starting salary for females ($22,616) was only 3.3% less than the 1988 mean starting salary for males ($23,396). The number of women entering fields other than private practice nearly doubled between 1983 and 1987.

Enrollment. Overall a 42% decline in the number of applicants to U.S. veterinary colleges had occurred since 1980, although in 1988 there still

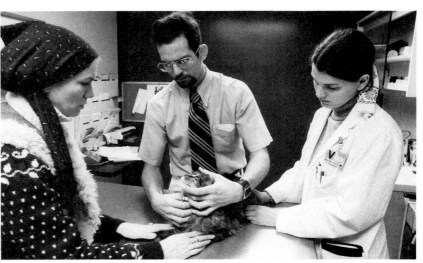

Veterinarian (center) and student (right) examine a cat. By 1989 more than half of the beginning students in U.S. veterinary schools were women.

existed 1.91 qualified applicants for each student opening. A decline in applicants was also noted in the other health professions, including medicine, dentistry, nursing, and pharmacy. The decline was partly an indication of the increased attraction to careers such as business, engineering, and computer science, which were offering higher starting salaries with fewer years of college training. The increasing cost of veterinary education was also a factor.

The Koret School of Veterinary Medicine at Hebrew University in Israel opened its enrollment to as many as ten students from outside Israel beginning in 1988. Lectures to enrolled U.S. students would be in English for the first year and in Hebrew during the remaining three years of the program leading to the degree.

Veterinary drugs. A major advance in the veterinary profession occurred when the U.S. Congress passed the Generic Animal Drug and Patent Term Restoration Act of 1988. The act contained an amendment that provided for proper statutory recognition of a veterinary prescription drug category. The U.S. Food and Drug Administration (FDA) had been authorized by law to control human prescription drugs, but it had regulated veterinary prescription drugs without clear legal authority and had been challenged a number of times in court. The new act also was expected to enhance the FDA's ability to reduce illegal sales of veterinary prescription drugs by nonveterinarians.

An additional provision of the act was concerned with patents. It allowed animal-drug sponsors up to five additional years of patent protection based on time lost from the life of a patent due to the FDA regulatory approval process. This provision should encourage development of new animal drugs. Drugs available to veterinarians for treatment of animal diseases were limited because profits in veterinary drug markets were often very small compared with those in human-drug markets and also because the expenses of the animal-drug-approval process, particularly when it involved food-producing animals, were very high.

A University of Georgia College of Veterinary Medicine researcher demonstrated that cyclosporine, an immunomodulating drug used for the suppression of tissue rejection in transplant surgery, dramatically improves aqueous tear production in canine keratoconjunctivitis sicca, or "dry eye." Without treatment the disease can severely damage the eyes. An early success in the use of the drug was the university's mascot, a bulldog named UGA-IV, who, prior to treatment, had advanced corneal scarring and sight loss resulting from chronic "dry eye."

Veterinary boards. The AVMA Advisory Board on Veterinary Specialties recommended provisional recognition for the American College of Veterinary

Dentistry and the American College of Veterinary Nutrition. Provisional approval of the American College of Veterinary Emergency Medicine and Critical Care remained under consideration. The American College of Zoological Medicine was granted a change in status from provisional to full recognition. The 14 AVMA veterinary specialties had a combined membership of 3,205 veterinarians as board-certified diplomates as of Jan. 1, 1988.

Veterinary clinical nutrition was being viewed as a new veterinary medical specialty. Recently, clinical nutrition residency programs were initiated at some veterinary colleges. With increasing recognition of the importance of nutrition in veterinary medicine, demand for veterinarians with postgraduate training in nutrition was increasing in academic veterinary medicine, industry, and private practice. An endowed professorship of nutrition was established at Texas A&M University's College of Veterinary Medicine in honor of Mark L. Morris, a pioneer in veterinary nutrition.

Veterinarians involved in the use of lasers established a national Veterinary Laser Society. At North Carolina State University's School of Veterinary Medicine, veterinary surgeons began using lasers several years ago for a variety of purposes, including removal of tumors from the throats and nasal passages of horses, locations relatively inaccessible to standard surgical procedures. The Beckman Laser Institute and Medical Center at the University of California at Irvine opened its doors to local veterinarians two days a month. The program not only provided veterinarians with access to state-of-the-art laser technology for animal treatments but also gave veterinarians the opportunity for training in the use of this new technology for animal surgery.

The Veterinary History Society met at the Old Library of Queens' College, Cambridge, in June 1988. Veterinary books dating back to 1686 were among the library's collection of 20,000 books.

Veterinary education and accreditation. An Australian Veterinary Boards Committee (AVBC) was established to conduct accreditation evaluations of Australian veterinary schools. It was possible that this would result in mutual recognition of schools by the Royal College of Veterinary Surgeons (RCVS) in Britain and the AVBC without the requirement of visitation of each other's schools. In the U.S. the AVMA continued to have responsibility for accreditation of the 27 U.S. schools and colleges of veterinary medicine and also accredited the four Canadian colleges of veterinary medicine.

The inaugural meeting of the newly formed European Association of Establishments for Veterinary Education (EAEVE) was held in Paris on May 27, 1988. Representatives of the six British veterinary schools attended. The aims of the EAEVE were to develop and strengthen cooperation among veterinary schools throughout the world with special emphasis on the 45 schools of the 16 member countries. Areas of mutual interest to be explored were to include information exchange in teaching and research; student mobility; teacher exchange; and training at the basic, continuing, and postgraduate levels. A comparative study of the curricula of the European veterinary schools was planned.

The Veterinary Record was founded a century ago (1888). This British publication was and is the only weekly journal in veterinary medicine. The *Norsk Veterinaertidsskrift,* a Norwegian scientific and professional journal of veterinary medicine, also celebrated its 100th anniversary in 1988.

Grants. Researchers at the New York State College of Veterinary Medicine at Cornell University were awarded an $8.9 million grant by the U.S. National Institutes of Health. The grant was to support research that would focus on the link between hepatitis (inflammation of the liver) and liver cancer, using woodchucks as the animal model. The Cornell scientists had observed that high rates of liver cancer occurred in woodchucks and that woodchuck hepatitis B virus could be isolated from most of the affected animals. The woodchuck hepatitis virus is similar to the human hepatitis B virus. The researchers hoped to learn more about the key molecular genetic events involved in the development of the cancer and to break the relationship between the virus and cancer by using an antiviral drug.

The United States Agency for International Development (USAID) awarded the University of Florida's College of Veterinary Medicine and Institute of Food and Agricultural Sciences a $5 million, five-year grant. Scientists would use genetic engineering techniques to develop vaccines and to improve diagnostic tests for the livestock diseases anaplasmosis and babesiosis. Anaplasmosis causes an estimated $100 million in livestock losses in the United States each year, as well as losses in other countries. Babesiosis was eradicated from the U.S. in the 1940s but could again spread there by means of infected cattle in Mexico and the Caribbean.

Animal diseases. A new $10.9 million veterinary diagnostic laboratory began operation in the fall of 1988 on the campus of the University of California at Davis. The laboratory was designed to provide diagnostic services for state agencies responsible for animal-disease control, food-animal industries, and the general public. Construction of the facility was delayed by a fire, which caused more than $4.6 million in damages and was thought to have been set by animal-rights activists.

During the summer of 1988 more than 7,000 North Sea and Baltic seals died of a mysterious disease. A veterinarian at the Common Seal Rehabil-

Dutch veterinarian and an assistant vaccinate a seal. During the summer of 1988 more than 7,000 North Sea and Baltic seals died of a virus, possibly related to one causing distemper in dogs.

itation and Research Center at Pieterburen, Neth., reported that more than 90% of the orphaned seal pups in the rehabilitation program were suffering from the disease, which was frequently fatal. Efforts to determine the cause of the ailment led to the discovery of a virus that is either the canine distemper virus or a closely related, previously undescribed morbillivirus that has tentatively been called "phocine distemper virus." If the cause is the canine distemper virus, one theory of its origin is a distemper outbreak in Greenland that killed thousands of husky dogs.

The number of reported cases of Lyme disease in dogs more than quadrupled between 1983 and 1988. Dogs are more susceptible than people to this tick-borne illness. In a survey of dogs at pounds it was found that 5 to 15% of the dogs were carriers of the organism causing the disease.

A new disease caused a significant number of British dairy cows to collapse; many subsequently died or had to be put to death. The cause of the disease was unknown, but because it severely damages the cow brain, it was named bovine spongiform encephalopathy (BSE). As of early 1989 the disease had been restricted to the U.K., although a suspect virus was infecting mink in the U.S.

High-rise syndrome in cats reflected the need for owners of cats living in multistory buildings to better limit their pets' access to open windows and patio doors. The Animal Medical Center in New York City reviewed 132 cases in which cats fell from 2 to 32 floors. Amazingly, 90% of the cats survived, and 60% required minor care or no care at all. A superb "internal gyroscope" was thought to be involved in enabling cats to survive falls from great distances by preventing their tumbling and thus minimizing the impact of the head with the ground.

An Auburn (Ala.) University veterinarian developed a canine hearing aid. Because dogs were living longer, problems such as hearing loss were increasing, and owners were becoming interested in finding help for their afflicted pets. The design of the hearing aid so that it would fit a dog's ear canal was completed successfully, but difficulty was encountered in training dogs to tolerate the aids, a process that generally required about three weeks.

The Cambridge Veterinary School received funding for a new cancer treatment center that would be equipped with a linear accelerator having a wide range of radiation therapy capabilities for all species. The Colorado State University Teaching Hospital initiated operation of a new computed tomography (CT) scanner in 1988. The scanner was expected to enable better determination of size, location, and condition of brain tumors and other cancers and to improve monitoring of tumor changes during therapy. Veterinarians at the U.S. Department of Defense Military Working Dog Center began using two-dimensional, real-time ultrasound equipment for routine diagnostic procedures as part of a preventive medicine program for military dogs during and after training.

—John M. Bowen

Optical engineering

Many small achievements rather than a few revolutionary changes marked the past year in optical engineering. New consumer products such as automated cameras and interactive video compact discs appeared. Electro-optical systems for military purposes prospered, but the emphasis upon laser weapons was much diminished. Some new applications of lasers to medicine occurred, including clinical trials of an approach to eliminating eyeglasses by sculpturing of the cornea of the eye with a laser.

The development of new lasers produced new opportunities in optical engineering. The ability to obtain moderate power outputs at a number of wavelengths by using solid-state lasers pumped by diode lasers permitted the development of very compact, reliable replacements for most conventional flash lamp-pumped lasers.

Diode lasers continued to increase in power and shorten in wavelength. During the year diode lasers emitting visible red radiation became commercially available. It seemed likely that these lasers would soon replace helium-neon gas lasers as sources in the bar code scanners used in grocery stores and other locations. There were reports that green diode lasers had been demonstrated in some laboratories, but as of early 1989 none had been marketed commercially.

Among the most interesting semiconductor lasers were the diode arrays that were demonstrated in several laboratories. A conventional diode laser is limited in its power level by the small exit aperture from the lasing cavity, which necessitates a very high energy density at the surface in order to obtain high power levels. The surfaces of the lasers are prone to thermal damage at these localized high energy densities, limiting practical single-diode lasers to no more than one watt of output power. However, the development of a semiconductor chip containing an array of some 20 active diodes that are electrically and optically coupled to operate together permits the coherent summing of the outputs of the individual lasers to produce several watts of effective power. In addition, this coupling effectively produces a large emitting region on the diode array; this reduces the beam divergence, making it easier to concentrate the laser radiation by using conventional optics.

These high-power arrays are expected to replace many of the less dependable flash lamp-pumped or gas lasers used for material processing in precision machining applications. During 1988 a 1.6-diode array with a conversion efficiency from electrical power to light power of 32% was reported by Lincoln Laboratories and McDonnell Douglas Corp. Spectra Diode Laboratories announced the development of a 5-w 200-element diode array at the end of 1988.

Consumer products. The digital audio compact disc continued to be the most successful optical consumer product. These discs were adapted to permit the addition of video data in order to produce "music videos." Also interesting was the prospect of making hybrid disks that contain text data accessible by a computer, audio tracks, and interactive video images. The addition of these options would not require modification of the basic optical techniques used in reading the disks but would require some additional electronic decoding options.

A major area of interest during the year was the use of holographic optical elements for directing laser radiation in various optical devices. It has long been recognized that a hologram that contains the proper

A computer CD, a union of a personal computer and a compact disc, displays real estate properties in Florida. A disk just 11.98 centimeters (4.72 inches) in diameter can provide maps showing the locations of 520,000 such properties.

distribution of grating elements (periodic structures that redirect light by diffraction) has the possibility of replacing lenses, both for directing energy and for forming images. The simplest analogy to holographic lenses is the well-known Fresnel lens, in which lens action is obtained on a flat surface through the use of a series of shaped circular grooves that direct the light passing through the surface by refraction and diffraction. If a hologram is produced by placement of laser sources at specific points related to the desired object and image positions and by exposure of the interference fringes (light and dark bands produced by the interference of light waves) formed by these sources on a glass substrate covered by a light-sensitive coating, a form of diffraction lens with good correction of any optical aberration (deviation from a perfect image) can be produced.

By suitable choices of the interfering sources that produce the gratings, diffraction analogs to many optical components, such as prisms, beam splitters, and polarizers, can be fabricated. This leads to the possibility of producing an entire assembly of optical components upon a single substrate. Once the master has been fabricated by recording the interference fringes that are produced by the appropriately located sources, other methods can be used to manufacture the optics in quantity. In order to produce assemblies in large quantities at low cost, plastic molding techniques or semiconductor manufacturing techniques may be used, depending upon the goals of the assembly.

For application to an optical disc head, these holographic components can be incorporated into an integrated optical system that transfers radiation by means of optical waveguides, devices whose physical construction guides the propagation of light waves along predetermined paths. The complete optical system, including sources and detectors, may then be produced on a single semiconductor chip. The first suggestion of such devices was made in 1987, and a

demonstration of hybrid devices with some limited capabilities took place in 1988.

Conventional optics were not being ignored. New designs of cameras with a zoom lens, shutter and viewfinder, and autofocus system in a single assembly were marketed in 1988. An examination of the details of these designs revealed that the optical engineers responsible for the cameras were able to take advantage of the ability of the computer in the camera to respond rapidly to changes in the relative aperture during focusing and zooming in order to reduce greatly the complexity of the lens and, consequently, reduce the weight of the camera. It appeared that the autofocus camera would become the standard type of camera, even when used on a through-the-lens viewing system.

One of the products that by 1989 had not yet made a major impact on the marketplace was the electronic still camera. The only major consumer application using electronic image recording was the video tape recording camera. These devices reached a high degree of sophistication, with zoom lenses and significant automated electronic components. Little interest seemed to have developed in a counterpart still camera, however, perhaps because of its high cost and minimal advantage over conventional photography. The availability of rapid "one-hour" processing of print film probably made the electronic still camera an uninteresting product.

Medical applications. Optical fiber probes used for imaging systems in conjunction with delivery of laser power through other fibers in the same cables led to major applications in noninvasive surgery. Many such applications were approved and demonstrated in routine use during the past year. One of the most important was the removal of deposits blocking arteries adjacent to the heart. Removal of the blockage by snaking a fiber probe to the site of the blockage and using a laser to destroy the blockage replaced the need for many bypass operations.

Demonstrated in 1988 and probably destined to become a major application for medical optical systems was the sculpturing of the shape of the cornea of the eye by use of a short-wavelength blue or ultraviolet laser. The action of such a laser in chemically altering the structure of the cornea and removing material in proportion to the exposure time and intensity of the laser beam as it is scanned over the eye led to the possibility of changing the shape of the cornea to permit the correction of most types of visual defects. As of 1989 this use was experimental, with permission to treat humans on a trial basis granted to only one company.

The long-term payoff of this development would be the ability to correct most types of refractive abnormalities that are now corrected only by the use of eyeglasses. The laser technique had considerably greater flexibility and certainty of success than vision correction by radial keratotomy, in which tiny excisions are used to alter the shape of the cornea. Even with this procedure, optics provides an alternative in that the excisions can be produced by means of a laser.

Telescopes. Several large telescope programs moved ahead during the year. The European Southern Observatory obtained funding to proceed with the construction of a linear array of four telescopes, each one eight meters in diameter. A decision was made to use for the primary mirrors thin mirror blanks with several hundred supports whose forces and position are electronically controlled by servomechanisms positioned behind each mirror, but the detailed design for the telescopes was still being developed. A half-scale model of one of the telescopes using this primary mirror technology was nearing completion in early 1989. The primary mirror itself was completed to excellent quality by the West German firm Carl Zeiss, thus demonstrating the practicality of the approach.

Work on the ten-meter-diameter Keck telescope continued, with progress being made on the fabrication of the mirror segments and completion of the dome for the observatory in Hawaii. The Arizona telescope projects received a major boost toward realization with the fabrication of a 3.5-m-diameter primary mirror blank made of glass; a rotating furnace was used to produce a surface within a few centimeters of the required final surface shape.

Military applications. Optical systems used by the military changed in nature, with increasing interest in observation and ranging systems and greatly reduced emphasis on the use of lasers as weapons. The Airborne Laser Laboratory, designed to demonstrate the application of a gas dynamic high-power laser beam projector in an aircraft, reached the end of its life and was decommissioned in May 1988. During the 11-year existence of this laboratory, the feasibility of putting a high-power laser in a moving vehicle, tracking an incoming missile, and destroying the missile by directed laser radiation was demonstrated. The complexity of the entire system was sufficiently great, however, that no near-term application of this technology seemed likely.

The program under the Strategic Defense Initiative (SDI) to produce a practical, deployable, directed-energy weapon using lasers in space was much reduced in scope during the past year. In an attempt to carry out the demonstration in space of all of the technologies required for deployment, the SDI office initiated the Zenith Star program for using the existing four-meter-diameter segmented LAMP primary mirror in a beam director along with the megawatt-level deuterium fluoride gas dynamic laser developed under the Alpha laser program. At the end of 1988 a demonstration sometime in the mid-1990s seemed to be possible. The Alpha laser had been operated in a test but had not yet demonstrated its applicability to space.

The use of a ground-based laser system using a free-electron laser had been proposed earlier, and two possible configurations for the laser were actively under development. A free-electron laser uses a high-energy electron accelerator to provide a high-flux stream of electrons that are passed through a magnetic wiggler (a series of transverse, periodic electromagnetic fields) to produce coherent radiation with a wavelength in the near-infrared region. During the past year demonstrations at low power of laser radiation or amplification of laser radiation were accomplished by prototypes of these devices, but a large increase in power was required for a practical system.

—Robert R. Shannon

Lightweight, palm-sized still-video camera can convert images into electronic signals and store as many as 50 shots on an erasable, reusable five-centimeter (two-inch)-diameter floppy disk. Sharply defined pictures are produced when the system is plugged into a television set.

Mario Ruiz—Time Magazine

Physics

Success in proving or disproving the reality of two unusual physical phenomena continued to evade investigators during the past year. Elementary-particle physicists readied new facilities in anticipation of settling some unresolved problems in their theoretical picture of matter, while nuclear scientists made progress in understanding the behavior of atomic nuclei subjected to increasing temperature and spin. In early 1989 a report of fusion in the laboratory at room temperature generated a flurry of excitement and controversy and set hundreds of laboratories racing to verify or refute the claim.

General developments

Significant progress continued to be made during the past year in the capture, trapping, and detailed scientific study of clouds of atoms, both neutral and charged. In addition, two types of unusual physical phenomena, both of which had first appeared in earlier experiments and which had been expected to "disappear" as more and better experiments were done, remained stubbornly observable even in experiments designed to disprove their existence.

"Wind chill" for trapped atoms. Since the mid-1970s scientists have been using lasers to slow and trap atoms for studies. To slow neutral atoms they train a laser beam on the atoms from a direction opposite to that of the atoms' flight. They also tune the frequency of the laser so that photons in the beam interact only with those atoms that are moving rapidly toward the laser. Each time an atom in the beam absorbs a laser photon, the momentum of the absorbed photon causes the atom to slow down a little. To hold the slowed atoms in place, scientists arrange several lasers coming from different directions to make an optical trap. (See *1988 Yearbook of Science and the Future* Year in Review: PHYSICS: *General developments*.) In a sense, the atoms in the trap are being "chilled" almost motionless by the constant "wind" of photons blowing at them from all directions. The instant an atom gains energy and starts to move, the laser photons stop it in its tracks, in effect keeping it at an extremely cold temperature.

The minimum temperature that can be reached depends on the laser and the atom. For sodium the lower practical limit to the temperature thought possible was about 240 microkelvins (240 millionths of a degree above absolute zero). This is about the energy a sodium atom would gain if it dropped one centimeter (about 0.4 in) in the gravity field of the Earth. Recently, however, William Phillips at the U.S. National Bureau of Standards (NBS), Gaithersburg, Md., and co-workers observed a trapped collection of atoms that behaved as if it were at 40

microkelvins, six times colder than the practical limit and close to the one-photon limit, the energy given to the atom by one kick of a laser photon.

A similar experiment on helium atoms was then carried out by Alain Aspect and co-workers at the Laboratoire de Spectroscopie Hertzienne de l'École Normale Supérieure et Collège de France. For helium the practical limit was 23 microkelvins, and the one-photon limit was 4 microkelvins. Aspect's group used some unique characteristics of the helium atom to find a way around the one-photon limit and measured cooling to two microkelvins—only two millionths of a degree above absolute zero.

If the atoms being cooled are ionized (have an excess or deficit of electrons), the resultant ions carry an electric charge and can be trapped easily with electric and magnetic fields. In the past such ion traps were used successfully to hold single barium ions for long periods of time. (See *1986 Yearbook of Science and the Future* Year in Review: PHYSICS: *General developments*.) Recently Herbert Walther and co-workers from the Max Planck Institute for Quantum Optics, Garching, West Germany, and David J. Wineland and co-workers at the NBS, Boulder, Colo., studied clouds of as many as 15,000 ionized atoms collected in a trap and laser-cooled to temperatures of about ten millikelvins (ten thousandths of a degree above absolute zero). Under laser cooling, these ions assembled into regular patterns similar to the way atoms in an ordinary liquid freeze into a solid crystalline array below the melting point. In the case of the ion clouds, however, the spacing between ions was thousands of times larger than that in normal crystals. In the larger clouds studied by the NBS group, the cooled ions arranged themselves in concentric shells of different radii that allowed liquidlike motion of the ions within the shell but had solidlike barriers preventing motion of ions between shells.

The fifth (and possibly sixth) force. For many years Australian scientists had been measuring the gravity of the Earth in mine shafts. They found that

Clouds of laser-cooled beryllium ions trapped with magnetic and electric fields were found to crystallize into concentric shells. The 5- and 11-shell clouds (below) each have a diameter measured in the hundreds of micrometers and contain about 1,000 and 15,000 ions respectively.

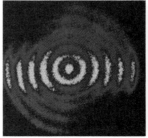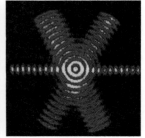

Photos, Ion Storage Group of the Time and Frequency Division, National Institute of Standards and Technology, Boulder, Colo.

398

the measured value of the gravitational attraction of the surface layers of the Earth was about 1% lower than the calculated value, suggesting a short-range repulsive (antigravity) force—soon dubbed the fifth force (to distinguish it from the four known fundamental forces of gravity, electromagnetism, and the strong and weak interactions). Later, reanalysis of gravity data taken between 1889 and 1908 by Hungarian scientist Roland Eötvös and colleagues found additional evidence for such a force. These findings inspired several different experiments by various groups that attempted to verify or disprove the reality of this unexpected deviation from Newton's law of gravity. (See *1988* and *1989 Yearbook of Science and the Future* Year in Review: PHYSICS: *General developments*.) One of the experiments involved raising a gravity meter up a 600-m (2,000-ft) television tower in North Carolina. To the surprise of the initially skeptical experimenters from the U.S. Air Force Geophysical Laboratory, Hanscom Air Force Base, Massachusetts, the experiment produced evidence for both a short-range, repulsive fifth force and an intermediate-range, attractive sixth force.

Because most of the error in measurements down mine shafts and up towers is believed to be the error in calculating the gravity effect of the local variations of density in the Earth's surface, researchers are interested in geographic regions comprising smooth layered plains that are geologically well known (such as in North Carolina). The polar ice caps are even more homogeneous, and the density of the ice with depth is well known. The ice caps are also thick, which means that the rocky bottom, with its unknown gravity variations, is far away.

In 1988 an international team of 22 scientists from the U.S. and England reported on their measurements a year earlier of the gravity down a 2,033-m (6,670-ft) borehole in the Greenland ice cap about 60 km (37 mi) south of the Arctic Circle. They measured the gravity at eight positions 183 m (600 ft) apart from 213 to 1,673 m (699 to 5,489 ft) down the borehole. They also made gravity measurements on the surface of the ice at 25 stations spaced in concentric circles around the borehole in order to obtain an estimate of the gravity variations due to the bedrock below. They found an anomalous variation in gravity with depth over that calculated from Newton's law and the measured density of the ice with depth. The data indicated an attractive sixth force—or, as some have interpreted it, an additional short-range component of Newtonian gravity—having a range on the order of one kilometer (0.6 mi) and a strength of a few percent of the Earth's gravity.

Robert Parker, a geophysicist from the Scripps Institution of Oceanography, La Jolla, Calif., who worked with the Greenland team, was quick to point out that it was possible to explain the observed measurements in the borehole and on the surface by assuming a certain configuration of density variations of the rock formations under the ice. These configurations would require surprisingly large intrusions of high-density lava into the lower density bedrock near the site of the experiment. In addition, the percentage of high-density lava in the bedrock near the test site would have to be significantly larger than that seen along the Greenland coast where the bedrock with its lava intrusions is exposed. An aeromagnetic survey around the borehole region to map the iron-bearing lava intrusions was being considered.

Further experiments to check on the reality of the fifth and sixth forces were in the planning stage in early 1989. Some of the more ambitious involve lowering gravity meters into the deeper parts of the ocean. The difference between the gravity on the surface and the gravity at the bottom, say, five kilometers (three miles) away, is in effect a measurement of the gravity of a five-kilometer column of seawater. The density of seawater with depth is well known, and the variations are so slight that they should not affect the results of the experiment. With repetition of the experiment at different locations over a wide area, the effect of the density variations of the sea bottom can be taken out. The results of these and other planned experiments should provide excitement and entertainment at scientific conferences in the next few years.

Mystery particles from the sky. Some of the brightest stars in the sky are invisible to the human eye. They emit intense radiation in the X-ray region of the electromagnetic spectrum and can best be seen with X-ray or gamma-ray telescopes. Three of the most prominent are Tau X-1, Cygnus X-3, and Hercules X-1. Tau X-1 is better known as the Crab Nebula pulsar, a rapidly rotating neutron star (formed by a supernova explosion in AD 1054) that emits pulses of cosmic rays, X-rays, and visible light. Cygnus X-3 and Hercules X-1 are also rotating neutron stars that emit pulsed radiation, but in addition they each orbit a more massive normal star to form a binary system.

In 1986 mysterious particles were observed among the pulses of cosmic rays coming from the direction of Cygnus X-3. (See *1987 Yearbook of Science and the Future* Year in Review: PHYSICS: *General developments*.) When an incoming cosmic ray strikes an atom in the Earth's upper atmosphere, the collision energy is transformed into a narrow cone-shaped cascade of various subatomic particles, which can be timed and measured by large detector arrays spread over the ground. From the arrival time, number, and energy of the particles in the cascade, scientists can determine the direction and energy of the initial cosmic ray. From the types of particles produced, they can determine whether the cosmic ray was a photon (gamma ray), a lepton (neutrino or electron), or a baryon (proton or neutron). The showers that were traced to pulses of cosmic rays from Cygnus X-3 were rich in muon particles, indicating the initial particles were massive and thus eliminating the neutrino and gamma ray. Since they appeared to come straight from the direction of Cygnus X-3, they were not deflected by the interstellar magnetic fields and so had to be uncharged. This condition eliminates the electron and proton and leaves only the neutron. Outside the atomic nucleus, however, the neutron has a lifetime of only about 15 minutes; even allowing for a significant increase in the lifetime of an extremely high-velocity neutron due to the relativistic time-dilation effect, a neutron would have decayed into a charged proton and charged electron long before it reached the Earth.

With the neutron also out of the picture, some scientists postulated a new particle, dubbed the cygnon or cygnet, that would be electrically neutral and stable, would be able to interact strongly with atoms in the atmosphere to make numerous muons, and would have a rest mass less than 100 times that of the electron (otherwise it would lag too far behind Cygnus X-3's pulses of radio waves, which travel at the speed of light). No such particle is known to exist. Most physicists were dubious about the early Cygnus X-3 results and believed that the anomalous events would "go away" or prove to be the effect of a more mundane phenomenon.

In 1988, however, three different research groups detected cygnets coming from Hercules X-1, while other groups confirmed the cygnets from Cygnus X-3. The total number of observed events was small, and they were detected in short bursts separated by months of no signal, making it extremely difficult to collect reliable data. To date, scientists were uncertain about what the small number of detected events meant. The most important clue was that, although the Crab Nebula pulsar produces cosmic rays with an energy level equivalent to that from the binary systems, only the binary systems produce the occasional burst of cosmic rays carrying the unusual properties of the cygnet. There was speculation that an interaction between the pulsar and matter from the normal companion star somehow changes the pulsar's cosmic rays from ordinary particles into cygnets—but just what cygnets are remained a puzzle.

—Robert L. Forward

High-energy physics

Since the discovery in 1983 of the intermediate vector bosons, the $W^{\pm}$ and Z particles, and the refinement of the standard model of subatomic particles and their interactions to include the unification of the electromagnetic and weak interactions into a single theory, high-energy elementary-particle physics has

Table I. The Elementary Particles

Generation	Lepton		Charge	Mass[1]
1	electron	(e)	−1	0.51 MeV
	electron neutrino	(v_e)	0	0 (less than 50 eV)
2	muon	(μ)	−1	106 MeV
	muon neutrino	(v_μ)	0	0 (less than 0.5 MeV)
3	tau	(τ)	−1	1,784 MeV
	tau neutrino[2]	(v_τ)	0	0 (less than 160 MeV)

Generation	Quark		Charge	Mass
1	up	(u)	⅔	about 300 MeV
	down	(d)	−⅓	about 300 MeV
2	charmed	(c)	⅔	about 1,500 MeV
	strange	(s)	−⅓	about 500 MeV
3	top	(t)	⅔	? (not yet observed)
	bottom	(b)	−⅓	about 5,000 MeV

[1]Mass is expressed in millions of electron volts (MeV).
[2]Only indirect evidence exists for the tau neutrino.

remained in somewhat of a holding pattern while awaiting completion of new accelerator and detector facilities. Recent advances, although interesting, have been more in the nature of improvements to the standard model and of clarifications of already known enigmas than of major discoveries.

The standard model holds that all matter comprises quarks and leptons and that interactions among them proceed through three forces—the strong, the electroweak, and the gravitational interactions. Each force is propagated via fields having associated particles, the bosons. Quarks and leptons are organized into three generations; each generation includes two different quarks (each quark being further differentiated by one of three quantum states—red, blue, or green), a charged lepton, and an associated neutrino. The particles and some of their properties are listed in Table I, and the forces in Table II.

Historically, one milestone in establishing what is now understood as the three generations of particles was an experiment at Brookhaven National Laboratory, Upton, N.Y., in 1961, which demonstrated that the neutrino associated with the muon is not the same as that associated with the electron. The 1988 Nobel Prize for Physics was awarded to the physicists, then at Columbia University, New York City, who carried out this experiment—Leon Lederman, Jack Steinberger, and Melvin Schwartz (see SCIENTISTS OF THE YEAR).

Recent results. In spite of claims made a couple of years earlier, the top quark remained experimentally

Table II. The Basic Forces or Interactions of Physics

Force	Field particle and rest mass	Strength relative to strong force at 10^{-13} cm distance	Particles that experience force
electro-magnetic[1]	γ (photon); 0	10^{-2}	all electrically charged particles; all quarks and all charged leptons
weak[1]	$W^{\pm}$; 81.8 GeV Z^0; 92.6 GeV	10^{-13}	all particles
strong	g (gluon)[2]; 0	1	quarks and hadrons (particles composed of quarks)
gravita-tional	G (graviton)[3]; 0?	10^{-38}	all particles with mass

[1]The electromagnetic and weak forces are now understood as special cases of a more general electroweak interaction.
[2]The gluon has been identified indirectly but has not been, and perhaps cannot be, isolated.
[3]The graviton has not yet been experimentally observed.

unobserved by the end of 1988. Best estimates of the lower limits to its mass, about 30–35 GeV (billion electron volts), were derived from experiments done at the Tristan electron-positron colliding-beam facility at the KEK Laboratory near Tokyo. (Positrons are the antimatter counterparts of electrons.) No direct observation of the tau neutrino was made either, although the indirect evidence for its existence was quite strong. Of the forces, the most difficult to handle theoretically has proved to be the force of gravity, although it was the first recognized, by Isaac Newton in the late 17th century. There was yet no direct observation of the graviton, the presumed field particle of the gravitational field, and quantization of the gravitational field has also proved more difficult theoretically than the corresponding problems with the strong and electroweak interaction.

On the other hand, the manner in which quarks are combined into the known hadrons (e.g., protons, neutrons, and mesons) was becoming very well understood. Recent experiments at Brookhaven on rare decays of kaons (K mesons) provided further agreement with the finer details of the standard model. In addition, kaon decays that violate both charge conjugation and parity conservation (referred to as CP-violating decays) were studied systematically and again could be understood, within the precision of the data, by the standard model. In particular, these measurements appeared to rule out some theories that would introduce a new "superweak" force to explain such decays. The CP-violating decay experiments were done at the Fermi National Accelerator

Laboratory (Fermilab) near Chicago and at CERN near Geneva.

In mid-1988 the Fermilab Tevatron began a productive experimental run, colliding beams of 900-GeV protons with antiprotons (antimatter counterparts of protons) of the same energy. Although the facility had been operated initially about two years earlier, only in 1988 were the luminosity (rate of interaction) and the detector such that serious definitive research could be undertaken. Thus far, the data from the Tevatron have further confirmed details of the standard model, such as the energy dependence of the production of the intermediate vector bosons and the scattering of the colliding particles' constituent quarks (producing jets of particles). These data set much more definitive limits than the CERN experiments on the existence of postulated new (supersymmetric) particles. In spite of having run a much shorter time than the CERN (antiproton-proton) collider, the better limits were set because the energy of the Tevatron is two and a half times greater.

The detector operating with the Fermilab Tevatron collider is the Collider Detector Facility (CDF). It consists of more than a thousand tons of iron, a superconducting solenoidal coil (for producing a magnetic field), sophisticated gas-filled tracking chambers (for visualizing, via computer readout, the particle trajectories), and thousands of channels of digitized electronics. A team of about 200 physicists from Japan and Italy, as well as a number of U.S. institutions, worked for several years to construct the detector and then to collect and analyze data from it.

Physics as a "social" science. The detector typifies what is becoming the dominant manner of doing high-energy physics with colliding-beam accelerator facilities. Physicists are learning to work together in a large team organized to develop a major detector, which is designed to gather as much data as possible from beam-beam interactions in a collider accelerator. The scale, cost, complexity, and work required for bringing one of these detectors into operation is well beyond the scope of even the largest university or national laboratory research group; hence, many groups join together under the leadership of a prominent physicist to undertake the task.

The largest such collaboration, the L3 experiment at the CERN Large Electron-Positron Collider (LEP) facility, which was scheduled for completion in mid-1989, involved about 400 physicists from 33 universities and institutes in the U.S., several Western European countries, Bulgaria, East Germany, the Soviet Union, China, and India. The cost of the detector was perhaps $200 million, although it was difficult to reckon in Western bookkeeping terms, as many of the contributions have been in materials, labor, and infrastructure costs.

Such a way of conducting fundamental physics research seems a far cry from the traditional image of the lone scientist laboring in a quiet laboratory over a piece of equipment that fits comfortably on a tabletop. However, the challenges to individual creativity and the potential for reward and recognition are at least as great, and the probability of contributing to truly frontier research is significantly greater than for the isolated researcher. On the other hand, the scientists involved must work more cooperatively, adhere to an established schedule, and sacrifice some of the autonomy of the traditional scientist. Physics thus seems to be evolving into a "social" science, with an attendant spectrum of assets and liabilities.

New facilities. As of the end of 1988, the Fermilab Tevatron collider was the latest facility to begin productive operation. The Tristan electron-positron collider in Japan, in operation for a few years, was gradually increasing the energy of each beam to more than 30 GeV. The CERN antiproton-proton collider, with up to 400 GeV in each beam, has run since about 1983. It should be noted that a given energy for an electron-positron collider is equivalent to several times that energy for a proton-proton (or proton-antiproton) collider because in the latter case the important collisions are between the constituent quarks, which each carry only about one-sixth the energy of the nucleon in the collisions.

Meanwhile, in the U.S. the Stanford Linear Collider (SLC) was tuning up with beams of 50 GeV electrons and 50 GeV positrons to pursue many of the same physics goals as LEP. This facility operated with a lower luminosity than LEP and provided for only one experiment to operate at a time (compared with LEP's four), but it was completed sooner and in early 1989 produced the first Z bosons from electron-positron collisions.

In Hamburg, West Germany, a facility for colliding 800 GeV protons with 30 GeV electrons was nearing completion in late 1988, and in the Soviet Union work was progressing on UNK, a 3,000-GeV (3-TeV [trillion-electron-volt]) proton accelerator that would provide the capability of colliding two proton beams of this energy (providing 6 TeV in the center of mass) in the 1990s.

In the U.S. the major focus on new facilities was on the planned Superconducting Super Collider (SSC), which was to be a ring of almost 10,000 superconducting magnets 83 km (53 mi) in circumference. They were to carry counterrotating beams of 20 TeV each to produce collisions at six points along the ring of 40 TeV in the center of mass. The U.S. Department of Energy endorsed this project and proposed to construct it near Dallas, Texas. Construction authorization was being sought in Congress.

Unresolved problems. It is appropriate to note some of the problems that the new facilities seek to address. Although the standard model is quite successful as far as it goes, many questions remain. It is crucial to verify the existence of the top quark and to know its mass. It is also desirable to detect the tau neutrino. Beyond these obvious questions are others. Are there more than the three known generations of quarks and leptons? This should be answered through careful studies of the decays of Z bosons at LEP and SLC. Might there be heavier intermediate vector bosons—a W', Z', or both? In spite of the lack of evidence to date, many theorists are intrigued by the possibility of supersymmetrical partners to known quarks and leptons. These would be spin-0, more massive analogues of known quarks (called squarks), leptons (sleptons), and neutrinos (sneutrinos), as well as spin-½ field particles that are counterparts of the photon (photino) and so on.

One major focus of new searches involving higher energies is the Higgs particle. Theory suggests that the Higgs field associated with this particle may be responsible for the observed masses of the quarks and leptons as well as of the W and Z bosons (see *1989 Yearbook of Science and the Future* Year in Review: PHYSICS: *High-energy physics*). No firm predictions exist for the mass of the Higgs, but it could not be much greater than 1 TeV and produce the effects ascribed to it. Hence, it should be detectable at the SSC and perhaps at LEP or the Fermilab Tevatron if its mass is low enough. In this context it is interesting that particle physicists are beginning to go beyond questions of "what" and "how" and are beginning to ask, in a meaningful way, "why."

Other questions have to do with understanding why the spontaneous decay of the free proton, predicted in theories linking the strong and electroweak interactions, has not been detected and why it has not been possible to detect free magnetic monopoles, particles having a single south or north magnetic pole. Another obvious question is the possible internal structure of the quark. Until the past two decades, every state of matter previously thought to be fundamental or elementary has turned out to be composite. Thus, crystals, atoms, protons, and quarks in turn have been believed to be fundamental. There are conjectures that all quarks are made of a smaller number of entities called preons. There is yet no evidence for such an internal structure, and existing data are compatible with quarks and leptons being point particles; *i.e.*, having no detectable finite size.

It is interesting in this context to note how humankind's perception of the complexity of nature has oscillated from the ancient Greek idea that all nature is made up of earth, air, fire, and water, through the alchemists' identification of pure substances (compounds), to the discovery of chemical elements and the periodic table, and later to the discovery of the component nuclei and electrons of atoms. All nuclei subsequently were found to be made up of protons and neutrons, but in the 1950s and 1960s, a flood of newly discovered mesons and other particles raised the number of fundamental entities again until it was learned that these in turn are composed of a small number of quarks. Today there are new questions. Are there more kinds of quarks? Do quarks have an internal structure, or do physicists now have the final answer to the number of constituents of nature? This history is depicted graphically in the figure below.

The progress described above can be given a perspective by noting that physicists believe that nature is fundamentally simple, however elegant. Thus, whenever the number of seemingly "fundamental" entities proliferates too far, it suggests that physicists' understanding is on the wrong track and that they must seek an underlying order and simplicity. So far this intuition has proved correct.

A second conjecture of physicists is that everything either exists or is forbidden to exist. There is a compulsion, for example, to search for physical magnetic monopoles or to understand why they are not possible. Earlier, free quarks were sought in every conceivable way until theorists understood why they should be forbidden to exist.

Finally, there is the quest for a grand unification wherein all forces, interactions, and particles will be understood to arise naturally out of a single underlying force law or equation and the observed different masses and forces to be due to the pervasion of space by a phenomenon like the Higgs field. Thus, it is presumed that a fundamental interrelatedness exists among all of the forces and particles and that if, for example, the mass of the electron and the velocity

of light are given, everything else can be derived from the equation.

While known questions and problems are sufficient motivation for building the SSC and other new facilities, the prospect of quite unanticipated discoveries provides added incentive. In a lecture at Fermilab, Nobel laureate Tsung-Dao Lee of Columbia University summarized the dozen or so most important experimental discoveries of the past three decades of research with high-energy accelerators. He noted that only two of them—the intermediate vector bosons and the antiproton—had been anticipated and had been a consideration in the design and parameters of an accelerator. High-energy elementary-particle physics thus remains an exciting, lively field pressing constantly on the most fundamental questions about the nature of matter and energy—both known questions and questions yet to be asked.
—Lawrence W. Jones

Nuclear physics

During the past year nuclear physicists made striking progress in understanding the behavior of the nucleus as its temperature is raised and as it is subjected to ever increasing angular velocity. Theoretical understanding of the quantum excitations of intrinsically asymmetrical nuclei was extended to the quantum excitations of the nucleon (proton or neutron) and heavier hadrons (particles built from quarks and thus experiencing the strong nuclear interaction), creating the possibility of an entirely new spectroscopy in physics and new insight into the role of quantum chromodynamics in describing the strong nuclear interaction. The year also was marked by

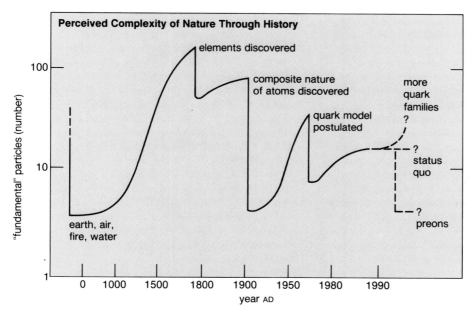

Physics

development of new instrumentation for studying all aspects of the nuclear domain—ranging from neutrino astronomy to the study of nuclear structure and dynamics to probing the equation of state for nuclear matter in new and powerful ways. Through it all, the boundaries between nuclear physics and elementary-particle physics—artificial to begin with—continued to crumble, to the benefit of both disciplines.

Super- and hyperdeformation in nuclei. Since the pioneering work of Aage Bohr in 1952 concerning the collective behavior of nuclei, for which he and Ben Mottleson received the 1975 Nobel Prize for Physics (shared with James Rainwater), the attention of nuclear physicists has focused on the behavior of relatively "cold" nuclei (those near their ground energy states) whose deformations—departures from the spherical shape characteristic of closed nucleon shells—were relatively modest. In both prolate (football-shaped) and oblate (doorknob-shaped) configurations, the major axes of the nuclear spheroids were typically at most 15–20% greater than the minor axes. Theoretical work of Sven Gösta Nilsson of the University of Lund, Sweden, in the late 1950s predicted that nuclei having much greater deformation—with ratios of major to minor axis of 2:1 or even 3:1—would have special stability if ways could be found to produce them. It was not until 1986 that Peter Twin and his associates at the Daresbury (England) Laboratory using the new TESSA 3 gamma-ray detector system, showed that a rotational band of excitations having 2:1 axis ratios (now referred to as superdeformation) existed at high excitation in the nucleus of dysprosium-152 (^{152}Dy). (See *1988 Yearbook of Science and the Future* Year in Review: PHYSICS: *Nuclear physics.*) Finally, in 1987 C. J. Lister and his collaborators at the University of Manchester, England, showed that nuclei like zirconium-80 (^{80}Zr), far removed from stability, have such a superdeformed ground state.

A convenient way of representing the shape behavior of nuclear systems is to plot the potential energy of the system as a function of two parameters that describe its shape. In such a three-dimensional plot, the stable configurations would be those lying at minima, *i.e.*, in the depressions, in the potential-energy surface. Such a surface calculated for a spin of 80 units in the nucleus of ^{152}Dy is shown in Figure 1. (The usual unit of angular momentum is Planck's constant divided by 2π.) The minimum in the foreground corresponds to normal deformations in which the axis ratio is less than 6:5 and is rather broad, encompassing a range of shapes. The second minimum is more sharply defined and corresponds to an axis ratio of 2:1; nuclei in this minimum are termed superdeformed. The third minimum is even more sharply defined and corresponds to an axis ratio of 3:1; any nuclei in that minimum would be

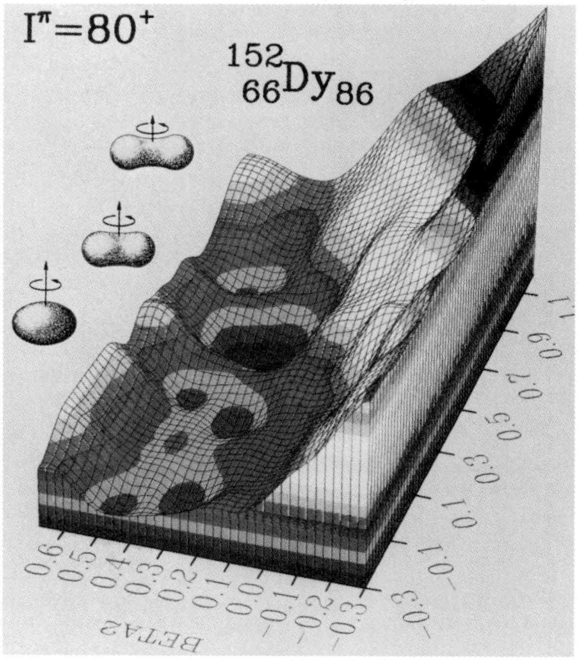

Figure 1. A calculated potential-energy surface for the dysprosium-152 nucleus having a total angular momentum of 80 units is shown above. The surface depressions, or mimima, from front to back correspond to normal deformation, superdeformation, and hyperdeformation.

called hyperdeformed. On the left of the plot are an artist's conceptions of the appearance of nuclei in these three categories of deformation.

Since the 1950s nuclear physicists worldwide have explored extensively the nuclei in the first minimum. In the late 1980s exploration of superdeformed nuclei in the second minimum has become a major focus of attention, as has the search for the predicted hyperdeformation. The exploration of this new domain in the nuclear quantum system has been made possible by the development of new heavy-ion accelerators giving beams of increasing heavy nuclear projectiles at higher energies and the development of high-multiplicity gamma-ray detectors capable of detecting and unraveling the cascade of gamma rays emitted by nuclei in superdeformed configurations as they relax toward the nuclear ground state.

A new spectroscopy. The nuclear shapes just described all have axial symmetry; moreover, all are symmetrical about a plane perpendicular to the symmetry axis through the nuclear center of mass. Such symmetries characterize the majority of nuclear systems. In some regions of the nuclear domain, however, nuclei that do not possess this so-called reflection symmetry have been studied in recent years as examples of dipole and octopole deformations. One of the characteristic signatures for this lack of

404

reflection symmetry is the occurrence in the spectrum (energy plotted against angular momentum) of quantum excitations in the form of close-lying pairs of states (doublets) having the same angular momentum but opposite parity; *i.e.*, they behave in opposite sense when reflected about the plane perpendicular to their symmetry axis. Recently Francesco Iachello of Yale University noted that the quantum excitations of the nucleons themselves, which are made of three quarks, and of the excited meson states called deltas, which comprise only up and down quarks, show this same effect in their low-spin spectra, while the lambda particle and such heavier hadrons as the sigma particle (both heavy relatives of nucleons) show this pairing of opposite parity states to a lesser extent. Iachello recognized that these spectra provided a signature for the underlying symmetries of the quark structure of these fundamental hadrons.

In its low-energy states, for example, a proton or neutron can most readily be considered as comprising three quarks located at the vertices of an equilateral triangle and bound by means of the strong force through the exchange of gluons. Such a structure does not have reflection symmetry but does have rotational symmetry; turning it through a 120° angle reproduces the original structure. On the basis of the well-understood picture of nuclear structure, this particular quark structure would be expected to give rise to precisely the excitation spectrum that is observed for the nucleon. The doublet states seem to disappear with increasing spin, a phenomenon that can be taken to indicate that, with increased angular velocity, two of the three quarks in the nucleon tend to move closer together and away from the third one, thus changing the symmetries involved. In the future it should be possible, from much more detailed study of these spectra than is available to date, to interpret the location and structure of their states in terms of the underlying quark behavior and, in particular, in terms of the mechanism, described by quantum chromodynamics, that governs the gluon exchange and thus the fundamental behavior of these systems.

Parity doubling is considerably less evident in the lambda and sigma systems. This observation is simply a reflection of the fact that the strange quark present in them is substantially heavier than the up or down quark and thus breaks much of the symmetry that is present in the nucleon and delta systems.

For probing these hadronic excitations, the method of choice involves the use of high-energy electron beams and high-resolution spectrometers to isolate and study the structure of the individual quantum excitations. In 1988 such equipment was under construction at the Continuous Electron Beam Accelerator Facility (CEBAF) at Newport News, Va.

Sudbury Neutrino Observatory. Over the past several years in nuclear physics, the question of the mass of the neutrino, which traditionally has been thought to be zero, has continued to attract attention. Although a number of experiments have reported nonzero neutrino masses, none has made this discovery unambiguous. The best current upper limit for the mass is 11 eV (electron volts), with an uncertainty that still makes a zero value entirely possible. The consequences of a nonzero mass would be dramatic and would include violation of lepton number conservation, the possible existence of right-handed as well as left-handed neutrinos, and the existence of spontaneous neutrino oscillations wherein neutrinos of one type would change over time into other types.

Such neutrino oscillations have long been postulated as the underlying cause of the so-called solar neutrino problem. Simply stated, the problem reflects the measurements since the late 1960s by Raymond Davis of Brookhaven National Laboratory, Upton, N.Y., and later of the University of Pennsylvania of the flux of electron neutrinos from the Sun, which has been a factor of three to four lower than can be accommodated in any current model of the Sun's nuclear burning that is consistent with all other data. The problem is fundamental inasmuch as an inability to understand our own star weakens the approach to more general questions of stellar physics.

The existing experiments are less than entirely satisfactory in that they detect only neutrinos from a minor branch of the energy-generation cycle in the Sun and are insensitive to the branch that produces by far the greatest fraction of solar energy. Moreover, they detect only electron neutrinos. If in their traversal of the material of the Sun and their subsequent eight-minute flight to the Earth the electron neutrinos were to convert spontaneously to muon or tau neutrinos (the two heavier species currently known), the Davis detector would not be sensitive to them, thus possibly explaining the observed deficit.

To overcome these limitations, the Canadian and U.S. governments in 1988 were jointly considering a proposal that would exploit a fortunate circumstance of nature in the construction of the so-called Sudbury Neutrino Observatory (SNO) at the International Nickel Mine in Sudbury, Ont. It is generally believed that the ore body at this mine is the relic of a gigantic nickel-iron meteorite that plunged into the Canadian Shield many millions of years ago. According to the proposal, 1,000 tons of heavy water (deuterium oxide [D_2O]) on loan from the Canadian government would be installed in a cavity excavated some 2,000 m (6,600 ft) below the surface of the ore body to provide unparalleled shielding against cosmic radiation, which otherwise would interfere with the detection of the desired neutrinos. This heavy water detector has the tremendous advantage of sensitivity to all types of neutrinos and to low-energy neutrinos from the dominant energy-genera-

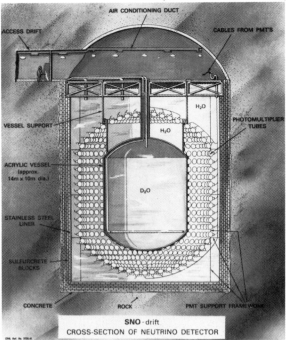

Figure 2. In a schematic cross section of the Sudbury Neutrino Observatory, 1,000 tons of heavy water (D_2O) are enclosed in an acrylic container and surrounded by ultrapure ordinary water (H_2O) and other shielding.

tion process in the Sun. As shown in Figure 2, the heavy water will be enclosed in an acrylic vessel and surrounded by 4 m (13 ft) of ultrapure ordinary water, as well as by additional shielding to avoid the detection of radiation from the surrounding ore body. The mass of heavy water will be observed by some 2,000 high-efficiency photomultiplier tubes searching for the Cerenkov radiation from charged particles produced in neutrino-induced interactions. If funded, SNO would begin operation in 1993.

Large electrostatic accelerators. Although the energies of their charged-particle beams are intrinsically limited by the direct-current (DC) voltages attainable in them, large electrostatic accelerators have remained the instrument of choice for precision investigation on nuclear systems. The combination of DC beam characteristics, wide-ranging availability of beam species, high geometric beam quality, and energy resolution better than one part in 10,000 makes possible the use of these beams in "microsurgery" on nuclear systems. In 1988 the three largest facilities of this type were those at the Daresbury Laboratory, the Holifield Heavy Ion Research Facility of the Oak Ridge (Tenn.) National Laboratory, and the A. W. Wright Nuclear Structure Laboratory at Yale University. All three are designed to operate at voltages as high as 20 million to 25 million volts.

During the past year the Yale facility (*see* Figure 3) became operational; it features an open inter-shield electrode designed to stabilize the electrostatic gradients in the insulating gas in the accelerator (the first of the so-called ESTU-model electrostatic configurations). These new machines are large and complex and are highly complementary to the even larger but intrinsically less precise machines of elementary-particle and nuclear physics.

Continuous Electron Beam Accelerator Facility. Because the electromagnetic force is the most thoroughly understood in physics, high-energy electron beams provide a very important powerful probe for nuclear behavior. To illustrate, one can compare the expected responses for electrons scattered from a typical nucleus and from a nucleon, the proton, as a function of the energy lost by the electron in the scattering event. In the case of the nucleus, for no energy loss there occurs strong elastic scattering of electrons from the nucleus as a whole, while for low energy loss the electrons excite the low-energy quantum states of the nuclear system. At somewhat higher energy loss the electrons excite the nuclear giant resonances wherein the neutron and proton fluids within the nucleus move coherently with respect to one another because the electrons couple directly only to the charges of the protons. At still higher energy loss there is evidence that the component neutrons and protons are being excited to their own higher quantum states (the Δ and N^* excitations), and at still higher loss there occurs the so-called EMC (European Muon Collaboration) effect, wherein the observed interactions appear to depend on the underlying quark structure of the nucleons, and the nucleons themselves begin to melt in a transition from hadronic matter to an entirely new form, quark matter. This transition is extremely complex, but probing it with high-energy electrons can provide

Figure 3. View inside Yale University's ESTU-1 accelerator shows the electrostatic column. The horizontal and vertical foreground structures help support the high-voltage terminal running down the center of the 30-meter-long steel pressure tank. D. Allan Bromley (right) and others provide scale.

unique access to important aspects of the nuclear equation of state.

The entire behavior described above reflects the underlying behavior shown for electron scattering on a single proton. In this case no inelastic scattering appears until the Δ excitation at just over 300 MeV (million electron volts), which is followed by the N* resonances and finally the so-called deep inelastic effect in which the electrons scatter not off the proton as such but rather off the individual charged quarks within the proton.

When completed, CEBAF will feature a racetrack-shaped area containing the two 0.4-GeV (billion-electron-volt) superconducting linear accelerators through which an electron beam will be circulated five times before being brought to one of three target areas. The largest of the target areas will have two high-resolution magnetic spectrometers (HRS) for precision spectroscopic work of the kind described above. A second one will have a large acceptance spectrometer (LAS) designed to search for rare processes, and the third target area will have a variety of more specialized research instruments. All of this instrumentation will be used extensively by scientists from laboratories worldwide after it becomes available in 1993.

Because CEBAF is designed to have an essentially 100% duty factor (its beam is present virtually all of the time it is operating) and 100 microamperes of beam current at energies as high as 4 GeV, even in its initial configuration, it will be a completely unique facility for nuclear research. If and when required by the research program, its maximum energy can be increased to 16 GeV through the installation of additional linear accelerator sections on the long sides of the racetrack and additional dipole bending magnets in the circular arcs connecting them.

—D. Allan Bromley

Condensed-matter physics

During the past year condensed-matter physics continued experiencing a major revival as a consequence of the recent discoveries of new materials that exhibit unusual physical phenomena in the condensed phase of matter and that have technically significant properties. Ongoing development of powerful instruments for probing matter and new experimental methods contributed to the rapid progress.

Another reason for the vitality of the field was its tendency to be more and more interdisciplinary, with a particularly strong coupling to the materials sciences and chemistry. Condensed-matter physics, which evolved from solid-state physics, began by using "simple" materials in the form of single crystals of the elements to understand basic physical phenomena in these ideal systems. By contrast, some of the latest new materials—for example, the class of high-temperature superconductors—are exceedingly complicated, far removed from the ideal single crystal with perfect regularity. It therefore has required the combined expertise of chemists, materials scientists, and physicists to synthesize, process, and characterize these materials. The field of materials was also rapidly growing into a vital technical area and was often ranked number one in technical importance for the 1990s.

The major challenges in condensed-matter physics remained centered on the 1986–87 discovery of high-temperature superconducting materials, mixed metal oxides that allow resistance-free flow of electric current at temperatures well above the 77 K boiling point of liquid nitrogen. (Subtracting about 273 from a temperature in kelvins [K] gives its equivalent in degrees Celsius; thus, 77 K = −196° C, or −321° F.) The challenges existed on all fronts, from experimental efforts to find materials that superconduct at even higher temperatures to theoretical attempts to explain the high-temperature phenomenon and to development of the materials for technical applications. Nevertheless, by early 1989 there appeared preliminary reports of another scientific discovery that, if proved true, could overshadow even the revolutionary superconductors. The new claim, which involved the use of materials in an imaginative way, promised major consequences for the production of energy.

Room-temperature fusion? At a press conference in March 1989 two chemists at the University of Utah and the University of Southampton, England, reported observing signs of the fusion of deuterium nuclei under normal laboratory conditions in a cathode made of palladium metal in an electrolytic bath. Deuterium (hydrogen-2) is a heavy isotope of hydrogen, with a nucleus consisting of a proton and a neutron. Water in which deuterium replaces the regular hydrogen isotope is called heavy water. If two deuterium nuclei are brought close enough together to let the attractive but short-ranged nuclear force overcome the repulsive Coulomb force (the electrostatic repulsion of like charges), the two nuclei will fuse to form a new kind of nucleus—usually either helium-3 (two protons and one neutron) and a neutron, or hydrogen-3 (tritium; one proton and two neutrons) and a proton. A large amount of energy is released in the fusion process, which is the basic mechanism in a hydrogen bomb explosion and the primary energy source in the Sun and other stars.

Palladium is known for its ability to store large amounts of hydrogen. The small hydrogen atoms can be stacked in so-called interstitial positions in the palladium crystal lattice. In the reported experiment a palladium metal electrode was used as the cathode in an electrolytic bath of heavy water. When current passed through the bath, oxygen was released at the anode and deuterium was released at the cathode. Since a palladium cathode was used, the liberated deuterium moved into the metal and was stored in the interstitial sites. As the lattice became saturated with deuterium, continued electrolysis squeezed the deuterium nuclei ever closer together. According to the scientists who conducted the experiment, the packing eventually forced some deuterium nuclei close enough for fusion to occur in the cathode. Although the reports were sketchy, the experimental evidence took the form of excess heat and the release of neutrons. Previous techniques for creating forces strong enough for fusion to occur have used the power of an atomic bomb as the initiator for a hydrogen bomb; a powerful laser beam to raise the temperature in a small pellet of tritium; or the strong forces that exist in a plasma (hot ionized gas) confined with strong magnetic fields.

It would be remarkable, of course, if the claimed discovery proved to be real. Within weeks of the announcement, hundreds of laboratories all over the world were trying to repeat the experiment. Early reports were nearly all negative, prompting many scientists to express skepticism about the initial claim. Whatever the truth, one is reminded of the strange ways that science sometimes progresses. The current scene is not much different from that at the end of 19th century, when it was commonly believed that most of the basic physics had been discovered and only refinements were left. Now, a hundred years later, one can say that instead of being at the conclusion of an era, condensed-matter physics and the materials sciences are more likely on the verge of a new revolution.

High-temperature superconductivity. The phenomenon of superconductivity, *i.e.*, no electrical resistance, above the boiling point of liquid nitrogen was first observed in materials composed of atoms of yttrium (Y), barium (Ba), copper (Cu), and oxygen (O) at a transition temperature (T_c; the temperature below which the material is superconducting) near 100 K. Subsequently, in the search for materials with even higher transition temperatures, several new classes of high-temperature superconductors were found. In particular, two systems containing the elements bismuth (Bi) or thallium (Tl) showed transition temperatures above 100 K. The highest reported and verified T_c as of early 1989 was 125 K, from a research group at the IBM Almaden Research Center, San Jose, Calif., for a thallium- and calcium (Ca)-containing compound, a Tl-Ba-Ca-Cu oxide. Claims for even higher transition temperatures (up to room temperature) were not yet verified.

In all these systems of materials, it appeared that sheets of copper and oxygen atoms, which are characteristic of the compounds, are important struc-

tural elements for superconductivity. The thallium and bismuth compounds were proving particularly valuable as model systems for understanding the mechanism behind the high-temperature transition. In these systems one can vary the number of Cu-O sheets in the unit cell. The T_c increases with the number of sheets, being 20–95 K for one sheet and as high as 125 K for three sheets. Unfortunately, it appeared to level off for four sheets and to decrease for five and more sheets.

The search for materials without the Cu-O sheets yielded another class of oxides containing elements barium, potassium (K), and bismuth but no copper. Although the T_c is a modest 29 K, the discovery could provide more clues to the basic mechanism of the phenomenon of high-temperature superconductivity.

Despite enormous effort to find a theoretical explanation for the new superconductors, the results have been disappointing. Normal superconductivity in metals and alloys is described by the Bardeen-Cooper-Schrieffer (BCS) theory, in which the electrical carriers are electron pairs, with the pairing being provided by phonons, or quantized vibrations of the material's crystal lattice. It was known that the new superconductors also demonstrate pairing, although pairs of holes (mobile, positively charged locations in the lattice due to the removal of electrons) may be the most important charge carriers. To date, however, no theory satisfactorily explained the pairing mechanism for the Cu-O high-temperature superconductors in the same way that the BCS theory

Figure 1. Superconductors are characterized by three critical parameters: temperature (T_c), magnetic field (H_c), and current density (J_c). Superconductivity can occur only within the shaded region of the diagram.

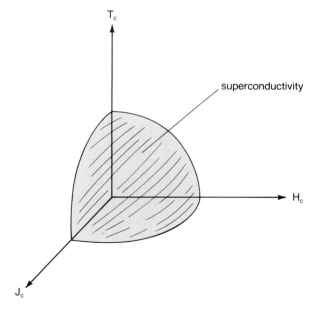

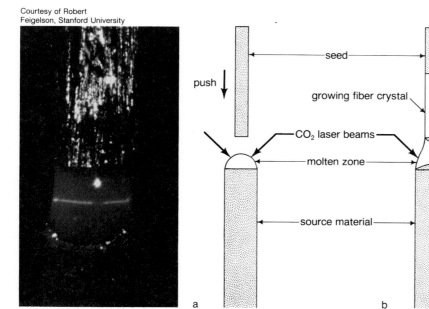

Figure 2. A technique for growing fibers of the new high-temperature superconductors is diagrammed (left). The top of a rod of source material is kept continually melted with laser beams. A seed crystal of the same material is dipped into the melt (a) and then withdrawn at a controlled rate (b). In the photo (far left) the melt appears between the growing superconducting fiber above and the starting material below.

does for conventional superconductors. A number of so-called quasiparticles (the phonon is one) were suggested as the enabling agent for the pairing, but so far the theories that incorporate them lacked the consistency that could verify and eventually predict experimental results.

While work progressed to increase fundamental knowledge of these new materials both in experiments and in theory, large efforts were under way to explore their technological applications. A superconductor is characterized not only by its T_c, the critical transition temperature below which electrical resistance disappears, but also by its critical magnetic field (H_c), which is the highest magnetic field the superconductor can sustain without going into its normal, resistive state, and its critical current density (J_c), which is the highest current density (amp/sq cm) that a superconductor can carry. The relationship among these three values is illustrated in Figure 1, a three-dimensional plot with the three critical parameters as axes. Superconductivity can occur only within the shaded volume. Both the T_c and H_c of the new materials are high enough to make them attractive for certain technical applications. The critical current density, however, is still too low to allow broader technical and commercial use.

Most crystal-growth techniques have been used to prepare single crystals of these materials for study. By applying techniques for making single-crystal optical fibers, researchers at Stanford University were able to grow fibers of a bismuth-strontium-calcium-copper oxide that are superconducting in liquid nitrogen coolant. A focused laser beam causes local melting of the material, which then can be drawn as a thin fiber (*see* Figure 2). This method could prove

important in the manufacture of wires of the materials. (For additional discussions of high-temperature superconductors, *see* Year in Review: CHEMISTRY: *Inorganic chemistry;* MATERIALS SCIENCES: *Ceramics.*)

Scanning Tunneling Microscopy. The scanning tunneling microscope, described in the *1984* and *1988 Yearbook of Science and the Future* Year in Review: PHYSICS: *Condensed-matter physics (Solid-state physics* in the 1984 edition), has made astounding progress since its introduction in the early 1980s. It has become the most powerful tool for studying the microscopic structure of clean surfaces of metals and semiconductors. One drawback of early versions of the STM was the limited area of observation of a few hundred atoms—indeed a "tunnel vision." Subsequent improvements have expanded the area of observation to more than ten million atoms, thus allowing researchers to get an initial overview of a surface with its many features, such as defects and adsorbed atoms, and then zoom in on a smaller area for close investigation.

One of the more interesting applications of the STM for condensed-matter physics is the study of adsorbed atoms on a surface. Figure 3 illustrates the ability of the instrument to image iodine atoms adsorbed on a single crystal face of platinum. Many technical uses of this feature suggest themselves. For example, a reliable technique for controlling and detecting individual atoms or molecules on a surface could be developed into an information-storage system having an enormously high information density.

The STM can be used to investigate not only the geometric atomic structure of a surface and its adsorbed atoms but also the electronic structure of the surface (by analyses of the tunneling current).

409

Figure 3. Scanning tunneling microscope images depict atoms of iodine adsorbed on a platinum crystal face. The two images distinguish different structural geometries assumed by the adsorbed iodine and provide information about the bonding forces between iodine and platinum.

Accordingly, it is feasible to measure the atomic and molecular orbitals of adsorbed atoms and molecules. Even biologic samples can be studied with the STM under conditions similar to their normal environment; *e.g.,* immersed in water. In a recent study at Stanford University and the University of California at Santa Barbara, the origin of blood clotting was revealed under the STM. Although not condensed-matter physics, it is a good example of the growing versatility and power of the instrument.

Fractional quantized Hall effect revisited. Two recently discovered phenomena, the integral quantized Hall effect and the fractional quantized Hall effect (FQHE), were discussed in the *1985 Yearbook of Science and the Future* Year in Review: PHYSICS: *Solid-state physics.* Both effects occur for electrons that are confined to a thin layer in a semiconductor and at low temperatures and high magnetic fields. The terms integral and fractional refer to the fact that the so-called Hall resistance becomes quantized under these conditions and can be expressed as integrals or exact rational-fraction multiples of the ratio h/e^2, in which h is Planck's constant and e is the unit charge of the electron.

The integral effect is explainable in terms of the two-dimensional movement of single electrons in a strong magnetic field. The FQHE, however, is a many-body effect, caused by a new condensed phase of highly correlated electrons. This phase behaves like a liquid. If the liquid is energetically excited, the excitations behave like quasiparticles that have an electric charge of a rational fraction of the electron charge, $1/3$, $2/3$, $2/5$, $2/7$, $3/7$, and so forth. It should be noted that all the denominators are odd numbers. The existing theory, although complex and still in need of further experimental verification, predicts only such odd-denominator fractional charges. It therefore was astonishing when an even-denominator excitation was found. The newly discovered state

has a charge of $5/2$. Whether this could be explained by the accepted theory remained to be seen.

Although the described effect is complex and esoteric, it is a good reminder that scientific understanding of condensed matter is far from complete. The new superconductors and the FQHE both indicate that the simple picture of a solid consisting of individual electrons that move around in a lattice of nuclei is not entirely realistic.

Metal superlattices. Modern deposition techniques for thin films, such as molecular beam epitaxy (MBE), allow control of the deposited films to a precision of one atomic layer. These techniques have been used primarily to fabricate new semiconductor materials. An example is the superlattice of GaAs and $Ga_xAl_{1-x}As$, which has found practical applications in solid-state lasers and other modern electronic devices. In such superlattice materials, alternate layers of two different compounds are deposited to build up a macroscopic crystal, sometimes called an artificially structured material. More recently MBE and other thin-film-deposition techniques have been used to make artificially structured metals and metal alloys. The thickness of the layers, again controllable to a precision of an atomic layer, can vary from a few atomic layers to several hundred layers.

Such metal-film materials have already found use in devices like X-ray monochromators, which are designed to isolate a narrow band of X-ray wavelengths from a broader spectrum for experiments or other purposes. Conventional X-ray monochromators use natural crystals like quartz for filters. The crystal must have a spacing between the atomic planes that matches the wavelength of the X-rays desired. This necessity puts a severe limitation on the use of natural crystals, particularly for long-wavelength X-rays. The ability to make metal-film superlattices allows one to tailor the spacing in these synthetic crystals to fit the needed X-ray wavelength. With the rapidly increasing use of synchrotron radiation sources, which are the most powerful X-ray sources available and which produce a continuous spectrum of X-rays, the demand for such man-made X-ray monochromator crystals was growing.

When properly fabricated, multilayer metal films also can yield unusual physical and chemical properties; such qualities as hardness and chemical resistance to corrosion can be increased beyond the levels exhibited by materials made of the individual constituents of the layers. Hence, another concept that began as a curiosity among condensed-matter physicists has quickly blossomed into a technology of atomically engineered materials.

—Stig B. Hagstrom

See also Feature Articles: THE ARROW OF TIME; CHAOS: DOES GOD PLAY DICE?; MACHINES OF INNER SPACE.

Psychology

Conditioning, cognitive development, and the relationship between environmental conditions and physiological responses were among the major subjects of research in psychology during the past year. Also, the American Psychoanalytic Association agreed to allow a larger number of psychologists to be trained as analysts, and the member nations of the European Communities signed a directive that provided for the mutual recognition of professional qualifications across national frontiers.

Experimental psychology. Pavlovian, or classical, conditioning is the more or less mechanically acquired capacity of a new conditioned stimulus (such as a tone or a bell) to produce a conditioned response (such as salivation) that was initially evoked by some other, unconditioned stimulus (such as meat). This occurs when the two stimuli are paired over a number of trials. During the past year psychologist Robert Rescorla of the University of Pennsylvania pointed out the inadequacy of this "stimulus substitution" view, still widely accepted within psychology in spite of the many contradictory research results of the past two decades.

Rescorla's alternative interpretation is that conditioning is rather "the learning of relations among events so as to allow the organism to represent its environment." A simple illustration of this can be seen in a basic comparison made by Rescorla over two decades ago. A laboratory rat is exposed to both a tone that lasts two minutes and a brief electric shock. If the tone and shock are unrelated in time so that no information about their relationship is given, no conditioning occurs (that is, the rat will display none of the escape responses to the tone that it makes to the shock). If, however, shocks are presented *only* during the tone stimulation, conditioned responses do occur when the tone is presented (that is, the rat makes escape responses when it hears the tone).

According to the cognitive theory, the crucial difference between these two situations is the information provided to the animal in the second case. This fundamental proposition is well supported by many more elaborate experimental results. As Rescorla noted, "A useful shorthand is that organisms adjust their Pavlovian associations only when they are 'surprised.' "

Attacks on psychological research by some of the approximately ten million animal-rights activists were becoming a fact of life in many U.S. research centers. A compromise position was suggested during the year by psychologist Earl Hunt of the University of Washington. He proposed that computers be more widely employed as supplements to actual animals in order to reduce the number of animal subjects, which for psychologists were mainly laboratory rats and pigeons. The reduction would be achieved mainly by computer modeling so that as few subjects as possible would be needed in the research. One should note that Hunt recognized the necessity of using some live animal subjects and did not propose, as some had, complete dependence on "computer simulations" in lieu of actual animals.

A recent National Research Council special report on this problem also emphasized the necessity of using animal subjects in behavioral and biologic research and supported Hunt's suggestions. The difficulties involved in finding acceptable resolutions of the basic problem were emphasized in the report. It was pointed out, for example, that some of the measures proposed by the critics of animal research, such as not permitting the use of pound animals, would be self-defeating; for example, that prohibition would mean that "instead of using . . . 10 million pound animals that will be destroyed [anyway], different animals are used for research."

In human experimental psychology there was a marked increase in the acceptance of the distinction between explicit (conscious) and implicit (unconscious) learning. In the U.K., for example, Elizabeth Warrington and Lawrence Weiskrantz demonstrated that amnesiacs who do poorly on direct (explicit) tests of memory nonetheless can do as well as normal subjects when asked to perform a task requiring long-term memory. As an example of the latter, implicit task, a subject is shown a series of words and then asked to respond to fragments of those words by giving the first complete words that come to mind.

Psychologist Henry Roediger and his colleagues at Rice University, Houston, Texas, used this distinction to develop a new systematic interpretation of memory that emphasizes process rather than the orthodox systems. They distinguished between processes driven by concepts (meaning) and those driven by data (perception), the former relating to explicit tests and the latter to implicit tests. In one experiment people who were bilingual in Spanish and English studied a mixed list of Spanish and English words. They were then given either a standard free-recall (concept-driven) or a word-completion (data- or perception-driven) test with fragments of English words. In the free-recall test some superiority was found for the Spanish words, which was hardly surprising because Spanish was the dominant language of the subjects. However, a different result occurred in the word-completion test; English-word translations of studied Spanish words were not better recalled, indicating the perceptual specificity of the data-driven or implicit test.

Development. A somewhat revolutionary new concept appeared in the literature on infantile development. Called "emergent literacy," it refers to the initial reading efforts that were being identified in preschoolers as young as two years. The notion was introduced in 1967 by New Zealand educational psychologist Marie Clay, who hypothesized that reading skill is a long-term, continuing process that starts well before formal study begins in the first grade. The idea that reading skill starts earlier and develops gradually is contradictory to the orthodox notion of "reading readiness," which assumes that a certain degree of maturation is necessary before a child can be taught to read. The work of contemporary researchers can be found in a recent book, *Emergent Literacy,* edited by educational researchers William Teale of the University of Texas and Elizabeth Salzby of the University of Michigan.

A major component of the recent research concerns the ability of children to learn about reading and writing when stories are read to them. Psychologist Grover Whitehurst at the State University of New York at Stony Brook manipulated the amount of open-ended questioning used by parents as they read stories to their two- and three-year-old preschoolers. Half of the 30 parents in the study were instructed to intersperse such questions as "There's Eeyore. What's happening to him?"; while the other half simply read the stories in the usual manner. Tests administered one month later revealed an 8½-month advantage in vocabulary for the children who answered the questions and then were praised or given corrective feedback.

The importance of sensory and cognitive activities during the early phases of development was also demonstrated in animal studies. Robert Sapolsky of Stanford University reported that giving even a minimal amount of handling to infant rats (merely removing them from their cage to a bed of wood shavings for a brief period) resulted in improved maze learning as long as 2½ years later. Sapolsky interpreted the advantage of briefly handled rats over nonhandled controls as a kind of "brake" that the treatment put on the stress response so that there was less production of glucocorticoids, hormones that are known to kill brain cells crucial to cognitive function. This hypothesis was supported by autopsies that showed fewer destroyed neurons in the handled animals.

Further support for the interaction of environmental conditions and physiological responses came from a series of studies by Yale University psychologist Judith Rodin and Harvard University psychologist Ellen Langer. They first studied, in rats, the harmful behavioral effects of "learned helplessness," a condition in which experimentally imposed stress cannot be avoided or escaped. They were able to show that suppression of the immunologic system is a major consequence of such loss of control.

In more recent research, reported during the past year by Rodin at a meeting of the Society of Behav-

ioral Medicine, she and Langer used human subjects to test the hypothesis that loss of control resulting from environmental stressors has a strong negative impact on older persons. In a study of nursing-home patients, one group of elderly persons was encouraged by the staff to exercise control of everyday events by making their own choices, while an "attention control" group was made to feel that the staff would attend to them and satisfy their needs. Both immediately and after 18 months, the subjects who had been encouraged to take more responsibility were judged to be more alert and reported feeling happier. They were also assessed as healthier than the controls. The same positive results were evident in mortality statistics; twice as many control subjects (30%) died during the 18 months following the differential treatment. This result is especially important because many deaths in elderly people are attributed to reduced immunologic capability.

In a subsequent study Rodin and Langer interviewed 300 elderly individuals (62 to 91 years of age) living in south-central Connecticut. They concluded that such factors as perceived helplessness and generally pessimistic attitudes predicted disabilities. Rodin interpreted the results as revealing "a far more optimistic view about the aging process than those purely biological views that assume the inevitability of decline." Rodin also pointed out that loss of control is a function not simply of aging but also of environmental factors that lead to self-concepts in which age and helplessness are associated.

Personality and clinical psychology. The big news in clinical psychology during the past year was the opening up of psychoanalytic training by an out-of-court settlement of the antitrust lawsuit brought by four psychologists against the American Psychoanalytic Association. Although Freud himself did not insist on medical training as a prerequisite for psychoanalysis, for many years the American Psychoanalytic Association accepted only a very small number of nonmedical applicants. Under the terms of the new agreement, about 40% of the training slots will be filled by psychologists and other nonmedical applicants. The association also agreed to drop a rule that prevented its M.D.-trained analysts from participating in institutes operated by psychologists and to pay the very large legal fees incurred by the plaintiffs during the three years of legal action.

The four plaintiffs claimed to act for the 2,500 members of the American Psychological Association's Division 39 (Psychoanalysis), many of whom will no doubt become applicants for psychoanalytic training. The economic stakes in this issue are enormous; a 50-minute analytic session costs between $75 and $150, and four or five such sessions per week typically extend over four to seven years or more. Each client thus represents an eventual income of $60,000–$275,000.

Contributions that have been and are being made by psychologists to alleviate the devastating effects of the AIDS (acquired immune deficiency syndrome) epidemic were summarized in a special issue (November 1988) of the *American Psychologist*. A total of 25 articles plus sectional introductions covered clinical, social, and scientific facets of the behavioral problems posed by AIDS. Another issue of the same journal, published exactly four years earlier, had included six articles on AIDS. At that time there were 5,000 AIDS cases in the U.S.; at the time the later, more comprehensive issue appeared, the number had grown to 75,000. The new issue should be consulted by those concerned with preventing the spread of the epidemic.

There was another new twist in the continuing saga of the "Type A" personality. Psychologist Edward Suarez at the Duke University Medical Center, Durham, N.C., studied the "cynical hostility" component of this classification. He found that persons with high hostility scores did indeed show the expected physiological responses while performing scrambled-word problems, but only if they were deliberately antagonized by an experimenter (for example, if they were told to "stop mumbling" or to "earn the payment" they were receiving). This interaction helps to explain some earlier reported failures of high-hostility but unharassed subjects to exhibit the predicted bodily responses; apparently some kind of interpersonal relationship is necessary for the hostility to be exhibited.

Psychologist Timothy Smith of the University of Utah further analyzed the interpersonal relationships involved. Looking at data from one of the original Type-A studies, he found that the men who were categorized as more likely to have heart trouble were those who were married to more assertive, better educated women, suggesting the presence of recurring competition.

Ever since Freud and his older associate, Josef Breuer, first demonstrated the efficacy of catharsis—the so-called "talking out" cure—mental health workers have been concerned with finding ways in which clients can express their reactions to personal problems and thereby relieve them. During the past year psychologist James Pennybaker of Southern Methodist University, Dallas, Texas, reported beneficial results from a relatively simple and straightforward "writing out" procedure. He and colleagues asked undergraduate students to write for 20 minutes either about traumatic personal events that they had not shared with anyone or, as a control, about trivial events. The writing continued for four successive days. Questionnaires designed to assess moods and physical symptoms were filled out by the students just before and after the writing exercise. Also, blood samples were taken on the day before the exercise started, on the last day, and six weeks later.

The blood samples taken on the last day showed facilitation of the immune response in students who had written about traumatic personal events that they had not previously shared. Moreover, this trend persisted over the following six weeks, suggesting that this simple, readily implemented procedure merits closer experimental attention.

A systematic, multifaceted attack on the problem of depression was mounted by psychologist Martin Seligman of the University of Pennsylvania. In his G. Stanley Hall lecture at the American Psychological Association's 1988 annual meeting, Seligman attributed the disturbingly great increase in the incidence of depression since World War II in large part to the "waxing of the individual and the waning of the commons." By "waxing" he meant overemphasis on the self and individual achievement; by "waning," the breakdown of support from such traditional institutions as the family, the nation, and the church.

There was overwhelming statistical support for such a sharp increase in the incidence of depression, quite apart from its theoretical interpretation. In two large-sample epidemiological studies, the Alcohol, Drug Abuse, and Mental Health Administration determined that people in the U.S. born after 1945 are ten times more likely to suffer depression than those born 50 or more years earlier.

There was also suggestive evidence implicating the role of "Westernization" in the increase in depression. "Primitive" cultures typically show much less and sometimes even no depression. In the U.S. the Amish of Lancaster County, Pa., an essentially rural and nonindustrialized society, demonstrated one-fifth to one-tenth as much depression as was found in the city of Baltimore, Md. This contrast is especially impressive because no difference was found in the incidence of manic-depressive psychosis.

—Melvin H. Marx

International developments. The governments of member nations within the European Communities reached a "common position" on a directive that would become law within the EC during 1989. The directive covered the mutual recognition of professional qualifications across national frontiers and included psychology and most other professions. Once the directive became law, all member nations would be required by 1991 to implement procedures that would greatly facilitate the freedom of psychologists to practice in any member nation of the EC.

Currently it can be quite difficult for a psychologist trained in one member nation, for example, France, to have his or her professional qualifications in psychology recognized in another, such as West

The Amish people of Lancaster County in Pennsylvania, essentially rural and nonindustrialized, demonstrated only 10–20% as much depression as did the residents of nearby Baltimore, Maryland.

Germany. The directive would change this situation by requiring a "competent authority"—that is, the nationally recognized controlling professional body that determined entry to the profession of psychology within the member nation—to recognize the psychological training given in a different member nation. However, this "competent authority" would also have the power to require migrants to pass certain limited tests of ability or to undergo a period of up to three years of supervised practice in the new country. The European Federation of Professional Psychologists Associations (EFPPA) welcomed the forthcoming directive but sought and gained assurances that member countries would also be able to require proof that a migrant psychologist was fluent in the language of the host nation before being licensed to practice there.

Although the directive went no further than requiring the mutual recognition of qualifications across national boundaries within the EC, the EFPPA began tackling the more ambitious task of attempting to harmonize training requirements and standards across Europe. This was a sensitive and difficult task, as there were major differences in what was judged to be the central content of the discipline of psychology in the different countries. For example, in France clinical psychology training was largely psychodynamic in orientation, emphasizing psychoanalysis as the way to treat neuroses; by contrast, in the U.K. and The Netherlands, clinical psychol-

ogy training followed a more eclectic approach with an emphasis on cognitive and behavioral methods of treatment.

The International Union of Psychological Science (IUPsyS) held its 24th International Congress of Psychology in Sydney, Australia, in September 1988. The Nigerian and Indonesian psychologists' associations were admitted into membership in the International Union, and a resolution was passed by which the U.K. became represented by a British National Committee for Psychological Science under the aegis of the Royal Society, the British national academy for science; the British Psychological Society had formerly been the representative. Similar committees had earlier been established in the U.S. and Canada to represent those countries within the IUPsyS. These changes symbolized the way that psychology was now unambiguously recognized as a science by the national academies of science within the countries of the developed Western world and by the International Council of Scientific Unions, to which all the national academies adhered.

The IUPsyS fostered six international network projects encouraging collaboration between researchers in different countries. These projects covered human development and child research; psychology-based man-computer interaction research; behavioral ecology and environmental psychology; cognitive science, artificial intelligence, and neuroscience; psychology and health; and communication studies and psychology in the third world. Under this final heading, a workshop was prepared for discussion of how social values and cultural characteristics had influenced management styles and organizational forms in third world countries.

—Colin V. Newman

Space exploration

The return of the U.S. space shuttle to flight status, along with the launching by the Soviet Union of twin probes to Mars and the unveiling of their version of the space shuttle, highlighted the past year.

Manned flight

Reaffirming directions for the future in space, the U.S. government on Feb. 11, 1988, released a new "Space Policy and Commercial Space Initiative to Begin the Next Century." Its major components were meant to establish "human presence and activity beyond Earth orbit into the solar system," create opportunities for U.S. commerce in space, and continue the national commitment to the space station. James C. Fletcher, administrator of the National Aeronautics and Space Administration (NASA), said the policy "stresses that civilian space activities contribute significantly to enhancing America's world leadership" and "lays the necessary groundwork for the decisions of the next century."

Where space science should be going at that time was outlined by the National Research Council (NRC) in its long-awaited *Space Science in the Twenty-First Century—Imperatives for the Decades 1995 to 2015.* In it the NRC requested that the "present ordering of priorities in the national space program be changed" from manned and large engineering projects "for their own sake." The NRC recommended instead that "the advance of science and its applications to human welfare be adopted and implemented as an objective no less central to the space program."

The battle over the space station budget led to strong warnings from NASA administrator Fletcher. Of particular concern was a $1 billion difference between House and Senate budget bills for NASA. Fletcher threatened that if the lower bill was passed, he would recommend terminating the space station program lest it suffer from inadequate funding. Congress restored a "bare minimum" amount, $900 million, with $515 million held until May 15, 1989, when the new president was to decide his priorities in space. The total NASA appropriation for fiscal 1989 was $10.7 billion.

At a summit between the two superpowers on May 31, 1988, U.S. Pres. Ronald Reagan and Soviet leader Mikhail Gorbachev signed an expansion of the 1987 U.S.-Soviet Cooperative Agreement on the Exploration and Use of Outer Space for Peaceful Purposes. It endorsed exchanging flight opportunities, including the placement of instruments on another nation's spacecraft, and sharing data on missions to the planets.

Space shuttles. The U.S. space shuttle made its first flight in almost three years when *Discovery* was launched on September 29 with five astronauts aboard. The near-perfect mission reflected hundreds of design changes totaling $2.4 billion since the 1986 *Challenger* accident, which killed seven astronauts and grounded the program.

Most of NASA's redesign effort focused on the shuttle's solid-propellant rocket boosters, which give it the thrust to climb through the atmosphere for the first two minutes of flight. A leak in a joint between the segments of one of the boosters led to the destruction of *Challenger.*

Tests went well until a demonstration firing on Dec. 23, 1987, when a portion of the boot assembly in the exhaust nozzle collapsed. NASA decided to proceed with an older boot design, which had been successfully tested, but this delayed the shuttle launch from June 2 to between July 15 and August 15.

Three more solid-rocket motor (SRM) firings in 1988 cleared the way for the shuttle to return to flight. Qualification motor firings (QM-6 and -7) on April 20 and June 14 were followed by a production-verification motor (PVM-1) firing on August 18. The QM-7 firing was the most rigorous because it took place in a new test stand equipped with hydraulics that simulated flight loads during the most demanding portion of ascent. PVM-1 was the ultimate test of the SRM since it incorporated the largest number yet of deliberate flaws.

Dozens of modifications were also made to the shuttle's main engines, external tank, and winged orbiter. In March NASA concluded testing on an escape-pole system for the shuttle crew. The escape pole, like a fire fighter's pole, would help the crew slide clear of the shuttle when bailing out during level flight between 3,000 and 6,000 m (10,000 and 20,000 ft). The orbiter was not expected to survive a crash landing or ditching. Tests were conducted by navy parachutists aboard a military cargo jet. The pole replaced a rocket extraction system that had been considered in 1987.

The U.S. space shuttle Discovery lands at Edwards Air Force Base in California on Oct. 3, 1988, after an almost flawless mission that marked the return of the U.S. to manned space flight after the Challenger disaster of January 1986.

NASA

Discovery was finally taken to the launch pad on July 4. The shuttle had been scheduled to be launched August 22, but a number of minor problems caused a series of small delays that pushed launch to September 4. Yet another launch delay was threatened by a leak in a relief valve for one of two main maneuvering rockets. Facing a delay of months if they had to send *Discovery* back to the hangar for repairs, engineers devised a way to cut a hole in the aft cargo bulkhead and clamp a seal around the leak without taking the spaceship off the launch pad.

The shuttle was finally launched from the Kennedy Space Center in Florida on September 29, 32 months after the *Challenger* disaster. Ironically, it was delayed for another hour and 38 minutes because of good weather; winds aloft were lighter than expected and in the wrong direction, which meant that flight loads might have pushed structures too far. The countdown was resumed when the winds appeared to become more favorable. Lift-off, at 11:37 AM Eastern Daylight Time, was perfect; a brief flash of light, which appeared to mimic those preceding the *Challenger* accident, was believed to have been caused by exhaust gas recirculating below the external tank. The flight was manned by five veteran astronauts: Comdr. Frederick Hauck, Pilot Richard Covey, and Mission Specialists George Nelson, David Hilmers, and John Lounge.

Six hours after launch they deployed a tracking and data relay satellite (TDRS-C) identical to the one lost aboard *Challenger*. The remainder of the mission was spent performing various mid-deck experiments and testing the improved systems aboard *Discovery*. The shuttle landed at Edwards Air Force Base in California on October 3. Postflight analyses showed that *Discovery* performed almost perfectly, although a small crack developed in a main engine as it cooled down after cutoff. Examination of the booster rockets also revealed a flawless performance.

On December 2 another shuttle, *Atlantis,* was launched. Although details of the four-day flight were not released by the government, it was widely believed that *Atlantis* carried a radar spy satellite dubbed La Crosse. The crew comprised Comdr. Robert Gibson, Pilot Guy Gardner, and Mission Specialists Richard M. Mullane, Jerry Ross, and William M. Shepherd. Nine flights were to follow in 1989 as NASA gradually built the flight rate to 14 a year. Many would carry science payloads.

Discovery was again launched into orbit from the Kennedy Space Center on March 13, 1989. The mission had been delayed for almost a month because of technical problems with the orbiter. The crew included Comdr. Michael Coats, Pilot John Blaha, and Mission Specialists James Buchli, Robert Springer, and James Bagian; only Coats and Buchli had previously flown in space. During the mission the astronauts successfully launched another tracking and data relay satellite (TDRS-D) and monitored scientific experiments. *Discovery* landed at Edwards Air Force Base on March 18.

The Soviet space shuttle, *Buran* ("blizzard"), was unveiled in October 1988 and launched on November 15. The 60-m (200-ft)-tall vehicle was remarkably similar to the U.S. shuttle in shape and size, even down to the pattern of heat-shield tiles on the winged orbiter. There were marked differences, though, including the placement of all the main rocket engines in the launch vehicle (the *Energia*). The unmanned first flight completed two orbits of the Earth and landed 3 hours 25 minutes after lift-off.

Space stations. Soviet cosmonauts Vladimir Titov and Musa Manarov set a new space duration record of 366 days (breaking the previous record of 326 days) when they returned to the Earth on Dec. 21, 1988, from the *Mir* space station. They, along with Anatoly Levchenko, had been launched to Mir aboard Soyuz TM-3. Levchenko, one of two test pilots in training for the *Buran* shuttle, returned with Yury Romanenko on Dec. 29, 1987, and died at age 47

Buran, *the first Soviet space shuttle, awaits its launch by the heavy booster* Energia. *The unmanned craft completed two orbits of the Earth on November 15 and landed 3 hours 25 minutes after lift-off.*

Tass/Sovfoto

on Aug. 9, 1988, of a brain tumor. Titov and Manarov broke the endurance record by spending a full year in space.

The Soyuz TM-4 flight on June 7–17 carried Viktor Savinykh and Anatoly Solovyov of the U.S.S.R. and Alexander Alexandrov of Bulgaria on a visit to *Mir* before returning to Earth. It was the second manned flight for Bulgaria.

That space travel is risky at any phase of a mission was made apparent when the crew of Soyuz TM-5, returning from *Mir,* was almost marooned in orbit by equipment and crew errors. Vladimir Lyakhov and Valery Polyakov of the U.S.S.R. and Abdul Ahad Mohmand of Afghanistan were launched on August 29 and spent the next eight days aboard *Mir.* Polyakov, a physician, stayed aboard *Mir* to monitor the health of cosmonauts Titov and Manarov, who had been aboard since December 1987. On September 6 Lyakhov and Mohmand left *Mir* aboard their Soyuz spacecraft. The first attempted retro-rocket firing was aborted when a piece of attitude-control equipment malfunctioned. The crew attempted a second firing three hours later, but it lasted only 6 seconds instead of the necessary 230 because the onboard computer had not been properly reset. Lyakhov briefly refired the engine manually, a move that he later admitted was an error and that complicated reentry calculations because of changes in the orbit. A third firing was postponed a day to let ground controllers analyze the problem. The crew had only 48 hours of air and water when they left *Mir,* but they were in only modest danger since they could have made a manually controlled reentry almost anywhere, if necessary.

Agreements to develop a U.S. space station, now named *Freedom,* were completed during the year. International agreements were finally signed in October by the U.S., the European Space Agency, Canada, and Japan to formalize those nations' commitments to the space station. About the same time, final contracts were signed with Boeing Aerospace, McDonnell Douglas, General Electric, and Rocketdyne to build major components of *Freedom.*

Space probes

Only two planetary probes were launched during 1988—both headed for Mars—but preparations were under way for several missions in 1989–90 to explore the inner and outer solar system. A major step taken by the United States was the resumption of the space shuttle missions in September 1988.

Venus. The first planetary mission to be launched by the shuttle was Magellan, the Venus radar-mapping mission, scheduled for the spring of 1989. Because of the large number of missions requiring a shuttle launch, Magellan was to spend 14 months

instead of the normal 4 to reach Venus. In order to have a four-month journey Magellan needed to be launched in October 1989, but that time was required for the Galileo mission to Jupiter. Magellan was delivered to the Kennedy Space Center during the year for final tests and assembly. A small fire broke out when a battery contact was shorted, but no major damage occurred.

After first grazing the orbit of Venus and then returning past the Earth, Magellan was scheduled to arrive at Venus on Aug. 10, 1990. It would then be inserted in a three-hour orbit ranging from 250 to 7,550 km (155 to 4,690 mi) in altitude. This was selected rather than a lower, circular orbit because the spacecraft's low-cost design had to make use of existing hardware and had one high-gain antenna (left over from the Voyager program) for both radar mapping and communications. During the low point of Magellan's orbit the antenna would combine several images of the surface to achieve the resolution of a much larger antenna. During the high point the spacecraft would rotate so as to point at the Earth and transmit the data. In this manner Magellan was expected to map 70% of the surface of Venus at resolutions ranging from 30 to 120 m (100 to 400 ft). Its primary mission was scheduled to last 243 Earth days, or one Venusian day; thus, the entire planet would rotate under the spacecraft. The remaining 30% of Venus's surface would be mapped after the planet passed behind the Sun.

Interest in Venus was strong because that planet is considered to be Earth's geologic sister. About two-thirds of the surface is covered by highlands; the remaining basins are smaller and shallower than similar basins on Earth. The presence of lightning indicates that there may be active volcanoes, and radar maps hint at crustal activity similar to plate tectonics on Earth. Such activity in turn implies convection in the mantle, as on Earth, but without an Earthlike magnetic field.

Scientists estimated that the mission would return 100,000 times as much data as did the first flight past Venus, Mariner 2 in 1962, and would produce maps with a resolution ten times better than the Venera probes launched by the U.S.S.R. They also hoped that the mission could be extended through four or five mapping cycles.

Meanwhile, the Pioneer Venus Orbiter marked its tenth anniversary in space on May 20, 1988. The radar altimeter aboard the orbiter provided the first medium-resolution maps of the planet. The high proportion of heavy hydrogen (deuterium) to hydrogen (100 times richer than on Earth) indicated that any water formerly on Venus had been lost as sunlight dissociated the water's molecules, leaving the hydrogen free to escape the planet.

Mars. The Soviet Union during the past year

417

launched its first space probes to Mars since 1973 but soon lost one of the pair to an apparent computer problem on the ground. Phobos 1 and Phobos 2, so named for one of the tiny Martian moons they were designed to explore, were launched on July 7 and 12, 1988. Phobos 2 was equipped with a "hopper" spacecraft designed to descend to the surface of Phobos for closeup inspections. Phobos 1 carried additional scientific instruments for investigations during the cruise to Mars and while in Mars orbit.

Unfortunately, in September Phobos 1 apparently was ordered to commit suicide by a computer error that commanded it to aim its solar arrays away from the Sun and its main antenna away from Earth. Once it turned away from the Sun, it quickly ran its batteries down and died. Despite repeated attempts to recontact it, Phobos 1 did not respond and soon was written off as lost. Although Phobos 2 carried the landers, the failure of Phobos 1 caused the loss of several scientific opportunities, including stereoscopic observations of the solar corona with the use of instruments aboard Phobos 1 and the Earth-orbiting Solar Max satellite.

Phobos 2 soon experienced problems with its on-

The space probe Magellan is prepared for its scheduled launch in the spring of 1989. It was designed to orbit Venus and use its radar to map the planet's surface at resolutions ranging from 30 to 120 meters (100 to 400 feet).

NASA

board scientific instruments. The 6,225-kg (13,700-lb) spacecraft entered Mars orbit on Jan. 29, 1989. Ranging in altitude from 950 to 120,000 km (600 to 75,000 mi), its three-day-long orbit allowed observations of the Martian surface and a series of maneuvers that brought the Phobos 2 orbit within 50 km (30 mi) of the orbit of Phobos itself, the larger of Mars's two moons. Phobos is a potato-shaped rock that may be a captured asteroid. If this is so, it represents primitive material almost unchanged since the formation of the solar system.

To study Phobos the probe was to fly within 50 m (165 ft) of the surface for a period of about 20 minutes and deploy two 45-kg (100-lb) spacecraft, the long-duration lander and the hopper. Phobos 2 would then return to a 5,950-km (3,700-mi) equatorial orbit around Mars. The lander was designed to take measurements from one spot on Phobos, while the hopper would use spring-loaded legs to jump roughly 20 m (65 ft) at a time in the extremely low gravity of the small moon. (*See* Feature Article: IN QUEST OF MARS.)

Although this was primarily a Soviet mission, the international scientific community was participating in it as well. The Deep Space Tracking network of NASA was to measure precisely the distance from Earth to the lander and, from these data, of the rotation and orbit of Phobos and the motion of Mars around the Sun. In return, a number of U.S. scientists were named as coinvestigators on the Soviet scientific team for the spacecraft and landers.

Instrumentation aboard the main spacecraft included a high-resolution, solid-state TV camera; infrared spectrometers and sounders to study the atmosphere and surface of Mars; and solar cosmic-ray, gamma-ray, and energy monitors. A mass spectrometer was to analyze samples of the surface of Phobos that were to be vaporized by a laser aboard the spacecraft. The lander included a television camera and a seismometer, and the hopper had an X-ray fluorescence spectrometer, among other instruments.

Preparations continued for the U.S.'s Mars Observer mission, scheduled to be launched in September 1992 by a Titan III rocket. Mars Observer was the first of a new line of spacecraft intended to be built from spacecraft originally designed for other missions. In this case its design was based on the RCA Satcom communications satellite, and it would use components from RCA weather satellites. However, NASA's concern that none of its few planetary missions be allowed any risk of failure had by early 1989 driven the cost of the mission from $60 million to $120 million.

Mars Observer was to spend one Martian year (687 Earth days) studying the "red planet" from orbit. A low-resolution camera would map the whole planet, and a high-resolution camera would observe only selected areas because of the spacecraft's limited transmitting capability. An array of spectrometers would map the mineral content of the surface and the chemistry and dust content of the atmosphere. A telemetry package would be added to relay data from French balloon-borne instrument packages that would be deployed by Soviet missions planned for the same time period.

Like Venus, Mars is fascinating because it is Earthlike in many respects. In particular there are indications that liquid water once carved the face of the planet, raising the possibility of life on Mars.

Jupiter. The Galileo orbiter-and-probe mission was the second planetary flight planned by the U.S. in 1989 and the one that had been awaiting launch the longest. It had been scheduled to fly in May 1986, but the *Challenger* disaster in January of that year not only grounded its launch vehicle, the space shuttle, but canceled the Centaur upper stage that would have boosted it away from Earth. (NASA ultimately decided that the Centaur's hydrogen fuel was not safe enough to be carried on a manned vehicle.) Having to make use of existing stages, NASA finally decided to go to Jupiter by way of the inner solar system; gravity assists at Venus, Earth, and then Earth again (plus some of its own maneuvers) would gradually redirect the orbit into the outer solar system while using a lower-power upper stage to launch the spacecraft. This trajectory required some alterations because the craft would go closer to the Sun than originally planned and would have to operate for six years before reaching its destination.

The mission was designed to analyze the chemistry, structure, and dynamics of Jupiter's atmosphere and the chemistry and shape of Jupiter's moons. Because Jupiter's great mass (318 times that of Earth) had kept it from losing its lighter elements, it was also believed to hold some clues to the origins of the solar system.

Galileo was scheduled for launch in October 1989 aboard the space shuttle. It would fly past Venus on Feb. 19, 1990, then past Earth on Dec. 12, 1990, and again on Dec. 6, 1992. Although long, this route would offer the first opportunity to take comprehensive space-physics measurements from inner to outer solar system with a single set of instruments.

Arrival at Jupiter was set for Nov. 29, 1995, six years after launch. About 150 days before arrival the probe would be activated and released from the main spacecraft to coast on its own; Galileo would then alter its trajectory slightly to miss Jupiter. On the inbound leg it would fly within 1,000 km (620 mi) of the volcanic moon Io and use yet another gravity assist to slow down in preparation for insertion into an orbit around Jupiter.

The probe would enter the atmosphere of Jupiter at 173,000 km/h (108,000 mph) and be subjected

to a rapid deceleration for about four seconds. A minute later a parachute would be deployed, and the probe would spend the next 75 minutes descending through the atmosphere and taking measurements of temperature, pressure, density, cloud particles and droplets, lightning, and the ratio of helium to hydrogen. Data would be relayed through the main spacecraft orbiting Jupiter, some 200,000 km (124,-000 mi) above. At a pressure equal to 10–20 times sea-level pressure on Earth, the probe would soon collapse.

An engine module aboard the orbiter, meanwhile, would insert it into an orbit that, with some further maneuvers, would take it past at least one of the Galilean moons (Io, Callisto, Europa, or Ganymede) on each orbit. Galileo's solid-state television camera would provide extremely high-resolution images of the surface of the moons and the cloud tops of Jupiter. Other instruments would take measurements of the intense plasma and radiation belts around Jupiter. Galileo was scheduled to operate around the planet for at least 22 months.

The first Jupiter probe, Pioneer 10, continued to set new records as the most distant man-made object. After 17 years in space, it was more than 6.7 billion km (4.2 billion mi) from Earth.

Neptune. Voyager 2 was to make the last major stop on its grand tour of the solar system when it flew past Neptune and Triton in August. The Voyager 1 and Voyager 2 spacecraft, both launched in 1977, initially were targeted for Jupiter (1979) and Saturn (1980 and 1981). Their continued good health allowed two unique mission extensions. The trajectory of Voyager 1 was altered to allow it to fly high out of the plane of ecliptic (the plane of the Earth's orbit, along which most planets lie) in order to explore that region of the solar system. Small changes to the trajectory of Voyager 2 allowed it to fly past Uranus (January 1986) and Neptune.

By May 1988 Neptune was starting to loom in the Voyager 2 cameras; the planet itself, still 1.1 billion km (700 million mi) away, filled an image measuring 8 × 8 pixels (a pixel is a picture element) out of the available 800 × 800-pixel screen. The planet appeared bluish green because methane in the atmosphere absorbs red light. Methane, however, constitutes less than 3% of the atmosphere; the rest is colorless hydrogen and helium. Triton, Neptune's largest moon, required less than one pixel on the screen and appeared reddish yellow as a result of methane-related organic compounds on its surface or in the atmosphere. Its surface may be covered by methane ice floating in a sludge of organic compounds.

Voyager's closest encounter with the planet was to be on Aug. 25, 1989. To ensure the fidelity of data transmitted from more than 4.3 billion km

(2.7 billion mi) away (4 hours 6 minutes at the speed of light), engineers developed a dual-processor technique for transmitting images to Earth. Both of Voyager's data processors were to be used, one to compress the images and the other to send them. On the Earth's surface the radio telescopes at the Very Large Array, Socorro, N.M., were to be joined electronically with Deep Space Network antennae to reduce the chance of losing any data.

Future missions. The only other approved deep-space mission as of early 1989 was the Ulysses solar polar mission of the European Space Agency (ESA), to be launched by the space shuttle in October 1990. In order to fly over the unexplored poles of the Sun, the craft was to be launched toward Jupiter and then make a gravity-assisted turn over that planet's north pole. This would place it on a trajectory that would pass over the Sun's south pole in April 1994 at an altitude of more than 320 million km (200 million mi).

Two new spacecraft projects were proposed by NASA in its 1990 budget plan released in January 1989—the Cassini/Huygens to Saturn and its moon Titan and the Comet Rendezvous Asteroid Flyby (CRAF). The two missions had been requested as a combined "new start" so that NASA could save costs by building two nearly identical Mariner Mark II spacecraft together rather than building them separately. Only the scientific packages for the two vehicles would differ from one another.

Cassini/Huygens, like the Galileo mission, would place a main spacecraft in orbit around the primary body and drop an atmospheric probe. For Cassini/Huygens the atmospheric probe would be targeted for Titan, the largest moon of Saturn. The dual name for the mission was derived from its international nature. NASA would develop the orbiter, named for Gian Domenico Cassini (1625–1712), who discovered the dark gap between rings A and B of Saturn plus four of the planet's moons; the ESA would develop the probe, named for Christiaan Huygens (1629–95), who discovered Titan and the true shape of Saturn's rings.

Because of the mass of the spacecraft and the lack of high-powered launch vehicles, Cassini/Huygens would take 6½ years to reach Saturn with the aid of gravity assists from Earth and Jupiter. It would be launched in April 1996 by a Titan-Centaur. En route it would fly past two asteroids and down Jupiter's magnetotail (that portion of the planet's magnetosphere extending away from the Sun), a region that was poorly explored by other spacecraft. Upon arrival at Saturn in October 2002, Cassini would be injected into an 85-day orbit. Near the end of its first orbit, it would release the Huygens probe to Titan. Many astronomers believed that the surface of Titan is covered by seas or lakes of liquid ethane

and methane, with a chemistry that may resemble that of primeval Earth.

CRAF would be launched into the asteroid belt in August 1995 and then fly past Earth in July 1997 for a gravity assist. This would retarget it for a flyby of 449 Hamburga, an 86-km (55-mi)-wide carbonaceous asteroid, in January 1998. The most exciting phase of the mission would begin in August 2000, when CRAF arrived at Comet Kopf, discovered in 1906. Because Kopf's closest approach to the Sun in its 6.46-Earth-year orbit is only 235 million km (146 million mi), it would not have been "weathered" quite as much as Halley's and other comets that plunge closer. CRAF would fly in formation with Kopf for almost 2⅔ years. At one point it would come within ten kilometers (six miles) of the ten-kilometer-wide nucleus, fire a small instrument-laden penetrator into the asteroid's surface, and then back away. A gamma-ray spectrometer in the probe would analyze the chemistry of the comet about one meter (3.3 ft) below the surface; other instruments would measure temperatures and the strength of the surface at impact. Meanwhile, the main spacecraft would fly around the comet, taking pictures and measurements of gas composition and electric and magnetic fields; it would also fly up and down the length of the comet tail to sample activities there. The primary mission would end in March 2003 as the comet receded toward the orbit of Jupiter. As a possible grand finale the spacecraft itself might land on the surface of the comet for closeup observations.

Advanced missions beyond these were outlined by a special commission convened by the National Research Council. Its report, *Space Science in the Twenty-First Century—Imperatives for the Decades 1995–2015*, emphasized the need for a special focus on missions for understanding Mars as well as the solar system as a whole. Mars missions advocated by the commission included a rover to traverse the planet's surface and a rocket stage to return to Earth with samples of soil and rock. Other proposals were a lunar geoscience orbiter, a Mercury orbiter/lander, and multiple flyby and rendezvous missions to asteroids and comets.

—Dave Dooling

Transportation

The rapid advances in the electronic communication of data during recent years were revolutionizing many transportation functions, including scheduling, routing, pricing, and operations of all carrier modes—airlines, buses, pipelines, railroads, trucks, and ships. This progress in electronic data interchange (EDI) was facilitating the use of intermodal transport and providing shippers with faster and more accurate

A McDonnell Douglas MD-80 makes its first test flight with a new type of fan-bladed, fuel-efficient engine on April 13, 1989, from Edwards Air Force Base in California. The ultrahigh-bypass engine has two sets of six-bladed counterrotating propfans.

data on rates, shipment tracking, and billing. A roadblock was the lack of standardization among the EDI systems, which prevented widespread computer-to-computer exchange of data.

An international transportation group working with the United Nations submitted for that organization's approval the first of a number of standardized communications proposals that covered such items as shipping instructions, rates, and cargo status. The group was under strong pressure to achieve standardization because of efforts to unite 12 European nations into an integrated common market by 1992.

The Canadian government, in cooperation with its different transport modes, started a program for developing a single national EDI system. The government was contributing $400,000 to the project, and another $560,000 was to come from private members of the implementing entity, Canadian Standard Interchange Facility (Cansif), which claimed that the potential cost savings from faster movement of goods were "monumental." Cansif said that it was attempting "to develop a national system that conforms with international procedures."

The largest shipper in the world, the U.S. Department of Defense (DOD), announced the start of an EDI program that would handle bids for a share of its $7 billion annual transport service bill. The rapid exchange of information resulting from the standardization of the way the department's 28,000 annual bids are submitted and processed should benefit both DOD and the carriers.

American President Companies—an ocean, rail, and truck carrier based in Oakland, Calif.—reported that it would install electronic tracking tags on 10,500 containers, 9,700 chassis, 250 trucks, and 240 double-stack railcars. The $2 million project was to take place despite the lack of agreement on an in-

ternational standard—the reason other carriers were delaying similar action.

Each tag contained a small transmitter, costing about $35, that could provide a range of information when passing a sensor that was linked to a central computer system. If successful, the pilot program should provide instant data on the location of equipment en route, as well as information about its size, age, and ownership.

The transportation industry was expected to be one of the major beneficiaries of satellite communications because of the latter's ability to provide continuous information about the location of aircraft, ships, and land vehicles. The 54-nation International Maritime Satellite Organization (Inmarsat)—of which the U.S. and U.K. were the largest backers—was providing such information to more than 7,300 ocean vessels. These ships could be advised about current weather conditions, schedule and route changes, and port and customs data.

Because the organization formally asked its members to allow its satellites to be used for land-based communications, other modes, especially railroads and trucks, were expected to be large users of Inmarsat in the near future. Steady reduction in the cost of carrier-related communications equipment should also stimulate its installation.

Air transport. Airline analysts predicted that most airplanes entering service in the 1990s would be refined derivatives of aircraft introduced during the 1980s. They would include jumbo jets with larger seating capacities and with quieter and more powerful engines. The two-engine A-320 jet built by the European consortium Airbus Industrie was considered the latest new-generation, high-technology air transport and was regarded as a solid competitor to manufacturers in the United States.

421

reates' work confirmed an earlier hypothesis that a pair of chlorophyll molecules are involved in the initial photon absorption. It is believed that a similar pair of molecules exists in the reaction centers of green plants.

Huber, managing director of the Max Planck Institute for Biochemistry in Martinsried, West Germany, directed the structural analysis, which was conducted from 1982 to 1985. However, it was Michel's preliminary work, carried out over the four-year period from 1978 to 1982, that cleared the way for the scientists' award-winning achievement. Michel eliminated the greatest technical hurdle of the project by developing a means of isolating the reaction center (membrane-bound protein) and putting it into the form of large, well-ordered crystals, a task that had long challenged scientists in the field.

Membrane-bound proteins are particularly difficult both to separate from the cell membrane and to put into crystal form. Difficulties in isolating the proteins arose because the detergents used to dissolve the lipid cell membrane away from the protein tended to modify the structure of the protein itself. Then researchers developed a new detergent, octylglucoside, that solved the problem.

Crystallization of the protein posed a second challenge because membrane-bound proteins are not soluble in water, and water molecules played a critical role in the already well-established process of crystallizing water-soluble proteins. Unlike water-soluble proteins, however, membrane-bound proteins are, by their very nature, partly hydrophobic (literally, "water-fearing") and partly hydrophilic ("water-loving"). The hydrophobic part lies inside the cell and interacts with lipids; the hydrophilic part lies outside the cell and interacts with water. As a consequence of their dual nature, such proteins, when exposed to water, will not arrange themselves into regular crystal arrays, as will hydrophilic water-soluble proteins. Rather than using water, Michel used a substance whose molecules, like the protein itself, had both hydrophobic and hydrophilic elements. These molecules "cleaned" the detergents from the protein and took the place of water molecules in the crystal lattice.

Although one year earlier other scientists had also succeeded in crystallizing membrane-bound proteins, no one had been able to create three-dimensional crystals that were large enough to allow researchers to study the arrangement of the constituent atoms. Michel was the first to achieve that goal.

Michel began his collaboration with Deisenhofer and Huber in 1982. By 1985 the three researchers had succeeded in determining the exact arrangement of the more than 10,000 atoms composing the membrane-bound protein. Said the Nobel committee, "They are the first to succeed in unraveling the full details of how a membrane-bound protein is built up, revealing the structure of the molecule atom by atom." The scientists accomplished this feat by means of X-ray diffraction, a technique in which Huber is an internationally recognized expert. In this procedure scientists deduce the atomic structure of a crystal by analyzing the manner in which the crystal's atoms scatter a beam of X-rays.

Deisenhofer was born in Zusamaltheim, Bavaria, now in West Germany, on Sept. 30, 1943. He attended the Max Planck Institute for Biochemistry in Martinsried, West Germany, where he received his doctorate in 1974. He worked there until 1987, when he left to join the scientific staff at the Howard Hughes Medical Institute in Dallas, Texas.

Huber was born in Munich, West Germany, on Feb. 20, 1937, and received his doctorate from the Munich Technical University. In 1972 he took a position as head of the Max Planck Institute for Biochemistry, where he remained for four years. In 1976 he left to teach chemistry at the Technical University, returning to the institute in 1987.

Michel was born in Ludwigsburg, West Germany, on July 18, 1948. He received his doctorate in 1977 from the University of Würzburg. In 1979 he joined the research staff at the Max Planck Institute for Biochemistry, where he did his prizewinning work. In 1987 he became head of the institute's new division for biophysics in Frankfurt am Main.

Nobel Prize for Physiology or Medicine

The 1988 Nobel Prize for Physiology or Medicine was one of only a few in the history of the Nobel Prizes that have recognized researchers in the commercial drug industry. It was shared by two U.S. colleagues, Gertrude Elion and George Hitchings, and a British pharmacologist, Sir James Black, primarily for their revolutionary approaches to drug design, although the laureates were also recognized for their development of various essential drugs. Said the Nobel Committee, "[The three researchers] introduced a more rational approach based on the understanding of basic biochemical and physiological processes," and this approach "has had a more fundamental significance" than their development of individual drugs.

Since 1945 U.S. drug researchers Hitchings and Elion have worked together at the Burroughs Wellcome Research Laboratories in New York and North Carolina to formulate drugs that are custom-designed to attack only certain abnormal cells and disease-causing microorganisms in the human body. From the outset their method of formulating target-specific drugs based on a fundamental understanding of the body's chemistry represented a radical departure from the trial-and-error approach toward drug

Sir James Black *Gertrude Elion* *George Hitchings*

research taken by many of their colleagues. Over the more than 40 years that they have worked together, Elion and Hitchings have developed numerous medicines, including drugs for treating leukemia, gout, malaria, and autoimmune disorders. Black was similarly recognized for his rational approach to drug design and for his development of the two key medicines propranolol and cimetidine.

When Elion and Hitchings began their prizewinning work in the 1940s, most drug researchers set out to discover new drugs rather than design them. Researchers sought out natural compounds, randomly altered their chemical structures, and then applied the altered compounds to infected animals in hopes of finding a substance that would damage the infecting organism without causing excessive harm to the host animal.

Elion and Hitchings, on the other hand, began by examining the difference between the biochemistry of normal human cells and that of cancer cells, viruses, bacteria, and parasites. Specifically, they searched for differences in the way nucleotides are synthesized in the various cells. Nucleotides are the building blocks of nucleic acids, the substances that compose the genetic material of living cells. (DNA—the "genetic messenger"—and RNA are the two classes of nucleic acids.) When Elion and Hitchings identified such differences, they synthesized compounds that interfered with nucleotide synthesis in the unwanted cells by substituting a false component for one of those needed for synthesis. Thus, although the cells proceeded as though they were replicating themselves, they were unable to complete their reproduction because cells must duplicate their DNA—which is composed of nucleotides—in order to divide.

Not only were the drugs developed by the two researchers effective, they were also target-specific so that, unlike other drugs of the time, they left the host's normal cells undamaged. Two compounds that used this strategy of inhibiting nucleotide synthesis—6-mercaptopurine (6MP) and thioguanine—proved particularly effective in combating rapidly dividing cancer cells and are still used to treat acute leukemias.

The approach to research by Elion and Hitchings enabled them to develop drugs that combat some of humankind's most common diseases. Today a number of their compounds are included in the World Health Organization's list of humankind's most essential drugs. The two scientists formulated thioguanine and 6MP in the early 1950s. In 1957 they altered 6MP to produce a less toxic compound, azathioprine—the first immunosuppressive agent that made successful organ transplants possible. Although new immunosuppressive drugs have since been developed, azathioprine has been the drug most commonly used to control rejection of transplanted organs and is still used to treat various autoimmune disorders, such as rheumatoid arthritis.

In the early 1960s, as a result of further work on 6MP, Elion and Hitchings created allopurinol, a drug that inhibits the synthesis of uric acid. It became a standard drug for treating gout, which is caused by the deposition of uric acid in and around the joints. Allopurinol is also used to treat kidney stones and to prevent kidney damage from an excess buildup of uric acid in patients undergoing treatment for cancer.

Elion and Hitchings also developed a group of drugs that proved effective in treating various infectious diseases by interfering with the synthesis of

433

nucleotides in the infecting organisms. These drugs include the antimalarial compound pyrimethamine and the drug trimethoprim, used to treat malaria and, in combination with other substances, as an antibiotic to treat infections of the urinary and respiratory tracts. In 1977 work done by the researchers led to the development of acyclovir, the first drug to prove effective against viral herpes. Other scientists used the principles established by Elion and Hitchings to formulate azidothymidine, the only drug approved in the United States as of early 1989 for the treatment of AIDS.

Black's prizewinning research began in the 1950s while he was working as a senior pharmacologist with the British firm Imperial Chemical Industries. He set out to develop a drug that would relieve angina pectoris, the spasms of deep pain felt in the chest when the heart does not receive sufficient oxygen. At the time conventional drugs to treat angina acted by increasing the amount of oxygen that could reach the heart. There was a second class of drugs emerging, however, whose action was based on a theory proposed by the U.S. scientist Raymond Ahlqvist in 1948. In an attempt to explain why the natural hormones epinephrine and norepinephrine (also known as adrenaline and noradrenaline, respectively) could cause smooth muscle (such as that in the heart) to contract at some times and to relax at other times, Ahlqvist suggested that the hormones acted through two isolated target areas in the heart muscle. He called these areas alpha and beta receptors and suggested that the hormones exerted their actions by stimulating these receptors, which in turn triggered the heart to contract or relax. Thus, the receptors acted as mediators between the hormones themselves and the effect those hormones ultimately had on the heart.

Black set out to find a way of blocking the beta receptors, which, when stimulated, cause the heart rate to quicken and increase the strength of heart contractions, thus increasing the heart's demand for oxygen. Angina pectoris results when this increased demand for oxygen is not met. Black reasoned that a beta blocker would lessen the stimulating effect of the hormones, thereby reducing the heart's oxygen demand and relieving anginal pain. In 1964 he succeeded in designing the beta-blocking drug propranolol, the drug currently used to treat angina, reduce mortality among heart-attack survivors, lower high blood pressure, and relieve migraines. Although other beta blockers had been developed before Black designed propranolol, his was the first that acted systematically and achieved widespread clinical acceptance.

A decade later, as a researcher at a British laboratory of SmithKline Beckman, Black used a similar strategy to develop a drug that blocks the histamine receptors in the stomach lining. Histamine plays a role both in respiratory allergies and in stimulating the production of gastric acid in the stomach. Overproduction of gastric acid can cause stomach ulcers. Researchers were puzzled by the fact that the antihistamines used to treat respiratory allergies were not effective in treating ulcers. Black suggested that, just as there were two types of receptors—alpha and beta—in the heart, there might also be two different types of histamine receptors: so-called H_1 receptors in the respiratory tract, which could be blocked by antihistamines, and H_2 receptors in the stomach lining, for which no blocking drug had yet been developed. By modifying the structure of histamine, Black succeeded in synthesizing a drug, cimetidine, that blocks the H_2 receptors, thereby inhibiting gastric acid production and allowing stomach ulcers to heal. Marketed under the brand name Tagamet, cimetidine became the best-selling drug in the world and provided the first nonsurgical alternative for treating gastric ulcers.

Black was born in Uddingston, Scotland, on June 14, 1924. He received a medical degree in 1946 from the University of St. Andrews, where he became an assistant lecturer in physiology. He took a teaching position with the University of Malaya in 1947 and remained there until 1950, when he returned to Scotland to teach at the University of Glasgow. He joined Imperial Chemical Industries as a senior pharmacologist in 1958. In 1964 Black became head of biologic research for Smith Kline & French Laboratories (a subsidiary of SmithKline Beckman) in Welwyn Garden City, England. In 1973 he returned briefly to the academic world as professor and head of the department of pharmacology at University College in London. He left in 1978 to become director of therapeutic research at Wellcome Research Laboratories in Kent. Black was knighted in 1981. In 1984 he became a professor of analytic pharmacology at King's College Hospital Medical School, University of London.

Elion was born on Jan. 23, 1918, in New York City. In 1937 she earned a bachelor's degree in biochemistry from Hunter College, New York City, and for the next seven years she worked in several laboratories and taught high-school chemistry and physics. In 1941 she received a master's degree from New York University. Elion joined the Burroughs Wellcome labs in 1944 and started her long collaboration with Hitchings a year later. Although she began a doctorate program at Brooklyn Polytechnic Institute while working at Wellcome, she left the program when she learned that she would have to give up her job for full-time study in order to earn a degree. She became emerita scientist with the Wellcome Research Laboratories in Research Triangle Park, N.C., in 1983. In addition to consulting for

Burroughs Wellcome, Elion served on the National Cancer Advisory Board, on the board of the World Health Organization, and as a research professor at Duke University, Durham, N.C.

Hitchings was born on April 18, 1905, in Hoquiam, Wash. He received his bachelor's and master's degrees from the University of Washington, and in 1933 he earned a Ph.D. in biochemistry from Harvard University, where he remained as an instructor until 1939. For the next three years he taught at Western Reserve University, Cleveland, Ohio (now Case Western Reserve University). In 1942 he joined the Burroughs Wellcome Research Laboratories in Tuckahoe, N.Y. He became emeritus scientist with the Wellcome Research Laboratories in Research Triangle Park, N.C., in 1975.

Nobel Prize for Physics

Three U.S. physicists—Leon Lederman, Melvin Schwartz, and Jack Steinberger—received the 1988 Nobel Prize for Physics for work they did while at Columbia University, New York City, in the early 1960s. The three scientists were recognized for two achievements: the production of the first laboratory-made beam of high-energy neutrinos and the discovery of a previously unknown type of particle, the muon neutrino. Neutrinos are elusive subatomic particles, with no electric charge and essentially no mass, that travel at the speed of light.

The results of the laureates' landmark experiment, done at the Brookhaven National Laboratory, Long Island, N.Y., had far-reaching consequences for particle physics. High-energy neutrino beams have become a basic research tool in the study of subatomic particles and nuclear forces. The physicists' second achievement, the discovery of the muon neutrino, played a central role in the formulation of the currently accepted theory in physics describing the relationships between the various fundamental particles that make up all matter.

The prizewinning experiment was prompted by a problem that stumped many physicists of the day: how to study the so-called weak force, or weak interaction, at high energies. The weak force is one of the four basic forces in nature (the other three are the gravitational, electromagnetic, and strong interaction). It manifests itself in certain forms of radioactive decay and in reactions between the lightest subatomic particles. It had resisted efforts at in-depth study because scientists had been unable to devise an experiment that could separate the effects of the weak force from the much stronger effects of the electromagnetic and strong forces.

It was Melvin Schwartz, then a graduate student of Steinberger, who first proposed that the researchers create a beam of high-energy neutrinos to probe the weak force. Schwartz reasoned that neutrinos were ideally suited for the task because they are influenced exclusively by the weak force and no other.

Because neutrinos are unaffected by the other fundamental forces, however, they rarely interact with other forms of matter and so are extremely difficult to detect. (It has been estimated that from a sample of ten billion neutrinos traveling through matter for a distance equal to the Earth's diameter, only one neutrino would interact with some particle of that matter.) Although scientists knew that the neutrinos' probability of interacting, via the weak force, rises in proportion to their energy, they had not invented a way of creating a beam of high-energy neutrinos. Neutrinos are produced naturally in certain radioactive-decay processes but at such low energies, in such small numbers, and with such scattered trajectories that they are of little use as tools in laboratory research.

Leon Lederman

Melvin Schwartz

Jack Steinberger

The Nobel Foundation, Stockholm

CERN photo

The solution proposed by the three researchers required an elaborate apparatus that was at the time the largest ever used in a physics experiment. Its purpose was to increase the statistical probability of neutrino interactions by creating a beam containing hundreds of billions of neutrinos and then sending the beam through a detector. In order to produce a beam of sufficient energy and intensity, the scientists used the Alternating Gradient Synchrotron particle accelerator at Brookhaven—which had been designed to be the most powerful accelerator in the world. The accelerator produced high-energy protons that were then fired at a beryllium target. The bombardment of the beryllium produced a stream of particles, including particles called pions (pi mesons) that, as they traveled, decayed into muons (mu mesons) and neutrinos. The stream of particles from the beryllium target was passed through a steel barrier 13.4 m (44 ft) thick. This barrier filtered out all particles but the neutrinos. A pure neutrino beam emerged from the steel barrier and entered a ten-ton aluminum spark chamber, in which a few of the neutrinos interacted with the aluminum atoms to leave trails of sparks.

The Brookhaven experiment was designed to answer a critical question, known as the two-neutrino question, that had arisen in theories of the weak force. Some theoreticians had suggested that there were two types of neutrinos: those produced when a pion decays to a muon (the reaction used to create the experimental neutrino beam) and those produced during beta decay in which a neutron changes to a proton by emitting an electron and a neutrino. The neutrinos in the incoming beam were unmistakably of the former, muon, type. If they had been identical to the latter variety, then when they reacted with other matter in the aluminum detector, they would have created roughly equal numbers of electrons and muons. In the Brookhaven experiment only muons were produced, indicating the existence of two distinct types of neutrinos and resolving the two-neutrino question. By virtue of their association with muons, the newly discovered neutrinos were named muon neutrinos.

The discovery of the muon neutrino led theorists to hypothesize that elementary particles fall into distinct but parallel "families." Theorists have used these family classifications to develop a scheme, called the standard model, for classifying all fundamental particles. The laureates' experiment played a crucial role in establishing this standard model.

Lederman was born in New York City on July 15, 1922. He received his doctorate in physics from Columbia University in 1951 and joined the faculty at Columbia, where he has been a full professor since 1958. Lederman has also served as U.S. representative to the International Committee on Future Accelerators and, from 1967 to 1970, as a member of the high-energy physics advisory panel to the Atomic Energy Commission. He was director of Nevis Laboratories in Irvington, N.Y., from 1962 to 1979 and from 1979 to 1989 was director of the Fermi National Accelerator Laboratory in Batavia, Ill.; for the 1989 *Yearbook of Science and the Future* he wrote a feature article about the laboratory. In 1989 he became a professor of physics at the University of Chicago.

Schwartz was born on Nov. 2, 1932, in New York City. In 1958 he earned a Ph.D. in physics from Columbia University, where he remained as a faculty member until 1966. That year he became a professor of physics at Stanford University. While on the Stanford faculty, Schwartz founded Digital Pathways, Inc., a small company in Mountain View, Calif., that designed computer-security systems. In 1983 Schwartz left Stanford to become full-time chairman and chief executive of the company.

Steinberger was born in Bad Kissingen, Germany, on May 25, 1921. He immigrated to the United States in 1934. His first degree, from the University of Chicago, was in chemistry, but during World War II Steinberger turned to physics while working at the Radiation Laboratory at the Massachusetts Institute of Technology. After the war he returned to the University of Chicago, where for his Ph.D. in physics he studied muons and showed that the muon decays into an electron and two neutrinos (one of which would later be demonstrated in his prizewinning work with Lederman and Schwartz to be the muon neutrino). After his graduation in 1948, Steinberger taught at the University of California at Berkeley until 1950 and then at Columbia University until 1971. In 1968 he became a staff physicist at the European Laboratory for Particle Physics (CERN) in Geneva.

—Carolyn D. Newton

Britannica Awards

Britannica Awards for 1989, honoring exceptional excellence in the dissemination of learning, were presented to five persons. Two of them, a British physicist and a British ethologist, were engaged in scientific research.

Although many medals and prizes mark original contributions to the world's sum of knowledge, the Britannica Awards, presented for the first time in 1986, celebrate both exceptional skills in imparting learning to others and a passion for its dissemination. Candidates for the awards are nominated by members of Britannica's Board of Editors and its Editorial Advisory Committees, drawn from the faculties of great universities in the United States, Canada, Japan, Australia, the United Kingdom, and continental Europe.

Jane Goodall

Goodall, Jane. British ethologist Jane Goodall's studies of chimpanzees in the wild made great contributions to the knowledge of human evolution as well as primate behavior. Born April 3, 1934, in London, she dreamed of being able to observe animals in their native state. Although an excellent student, she left school at age 18 to work until she could save enough money to go to Africa. When she reached her savings goal, she went to Kenya and came into contact with the anthropologist Louis S. B. Leakey, who hired her as his secretary. Under Leakey's supervision she held appropriate odd jobs, and eventually Leakey suggested that she try a long-term study of chimpanzees.

In 1960 she established her base on Lake Tanganyika within the Gombe Stream Game Reserve, where a band of some 100 chimpanzees lived freely but with government protection from poachers. Over the years her minute observation of the chimps' behavior and social life broke much new ground, including the notable revelations that these apes use crude tools and that, far from being exclusively herbivorous, they kill and eat insects, fowl, and even smaller simians.

A few years after the start of her study, *National Geographic* magazine sent a photographer, Baron Hugo van Lawick, to Kenya to record her work. He and Goodall were married in 1964. They were later divorced, and she married Derek Bryceson, a member of Tanzania's parliament and director of the country's national parks.

In 1965 she was awarded a Ph.D. from the University of Cambridge. From 1970 through 1975 she was visiting professor of psychiatry and human biology at Stanford University. Her writings, several of which were illustrated by her first husband, include *My Friends the Wild Chimpanzees* (1967), *Innocent Killers* (1970), *In the Shadow of Man* (1971), *The Chimpanzees of Gombe* (1986), and *My Life with the Chimpanzees* (1988).

Hawking, Stephen. Despite devastating physical handicap, Stephen Hawking not only was generally acknowledged to be Einstein's successor as the world's preeminent living theoretical physicist but also showed himself a superb communicator to lay readers of extremely difficult physical concepts. Hawking was born Jan. 8, 1942, in Oxford, England. From childhood his intelligence was almost intuitive in its instant grasp of the way things worked. He had concluded that astronomy would be his specialty before he graduated from University College, Oxford, in 1962. While pursuing graduate studies at the University of Cambridge, where he earned a Ph.D. in 1966, he became afflicted with amyotrophic lateral sclerosis, a progressive, incurable neuromuscular disease. With support from his tutor and the language student whom he married in 1965, he refocused his life and adapted with nearly superhuman determination to his growing physical immobilization.

Hawking's numerous contributions to physics—particularly in relativity theory, quantum mechanics, and the physics of black holes—earned him many high honors. In 1974 the Royal Society elected him one of its youngest fellows. He became professor of gravitational physics at Cambridge in 1977 and two years later was appointed Cambridge's Lucasian professor of mathematics, the position once held by Isaac Newton. His publications include *General Relativity: An Einstein Centenary Survey* (1979), *Superspace and Supergravity* (1981), and *The Very Early Universe* (1983). His *A Brief History of Time: From the Big Bang to Black Holes* (1988) was notable for its comprehensibility to nonscientists. In this edition of the *Yearbook of Science and the Future* he is the author of the feature article "The Arrow of Time."

Stephen Hawking

AWARD	WINNER	AFFILIATION
ARCHAEOLOGY		
MacArthur Prize Fellow Award	Anna C. Roosevelt	American Museum of Natural History, New York, N.Y.
MacArthur Prize Fellow Award	Susan I. Rotroff	Hunter College, New York, N.Y.
MacArthur Prize Fellow Award	Rita Wright	College of William and Mary, Williamsburg, Va.
ARCHITECTURE		
Arnold W. Brunner Memorial Prize	Arata Isozaki	Tokyo, Japan
Franklin Pierce Brown Medal	Marvin A. Mass	Cosentini Associates, New York, N.Y.
Gold Medal of the American Institute of Architects	Joseph Esherick	Esherick, Homsey, Dodge & Davis, San Francisco, Calif.
National Medal of Science	George W. Housner	California Institute of Technology, Pasadena
Pritzker Architecture Prize	Gordon Bunshaft (Retired)	Skidmore, Owings & Merrill, New York, N.Y.
Pritzker Architecture Prize	Oscar Niemeyer (Retired)	Rio de Janeiro, Brazil
Prix de Rome	Jacques Rousseau	Montreal, Quebec
ASTRONOMY		
Dannie Heineman Prize for Astrophysics	David L. Lambert	University of Texas, Austin
Henry Draper Medal	Riccardo Giovanelli	Arecibo Observatory, Puerto Rico
Henry Draper Medal	Martha P. Haynes	Cornell University, Ithaca, N.Y.
Klumpke-Roberts Award	Joseph Chamberlain	Adler Planetarium, Chicago, Ill.
MacArthur Prize Fellow Award	Noel M. Swerdlow	University of Chicago, Ill.
CHEMISTRY		
Anselme Payen Award	Bengt Rånby (Emeritus)	Royal Institute of Technology, Stockholm, Sweden
Arthur C. Cope Award	William S. Johnson (Emeritus)	Stanford University, Calif.
Arthur C. Cope Scholar Award	Norman L. Allinger	University of Georgia, Athens
Arthur C. Cope Scholar Award	Scott E. Denmark	University of Illinois, Urbana
Arthur C. Cope Scholar Award	Marye Anne Fox	University of Texas, Austin
Arthur C. Cope Scholar Award	Jeremy R. Knowles	Harvard University, Cambridge, Mass.
Arthur C. Cope Scholar Award	Jerrold Meinwald	Cornell University, Ithaca, N.Y.
Arthur C. Cope Scholar Award	Larry E. Overman	University of California, Irvine
Arthur C. Cope Scholar Award	Andrew Streitwieser, Jr.	University of California, Berkeley
Arthur C. Cope Scholar Award	Barry M. Trost	Stanford University, Calif.
Arthur C. Cope Scholar Award	George M. Whitesides	Harvard University, Cambridge, Mass.
Chemical Sciences Award of the National Academy of Sciences	Ronald C. D. Breslow	Columbia University, New York, N.Y.
Distinguished Service in the Advancement of Inorganic Chemistry	Neil Bartlett	University of California, Berkeley

AWARD	WINNER	AFFILIATION
Garvan Medal	Kathleen C. Taylor	General Motors Research Labs.
Gregori Aminoff Prize	Isabella L. Karle	Naval Research Laboratory, Washington, D.C.
Heisenberg Prize	J. N. Onuchic	São Paulo, Brazil
Inorganic Chemistry Award of the American Chemical Society	Malcolm H. Chisholm	Indiana University, Bloomington
Ipatieff Prize	Alexander M. Klibanov	Massachusetts Institute of Technology, Cambridge
James Flack Norris Award	William von Eggers Doering (Retired)	Harvard University, Cambridge, Mass.
Martin J. Buerger Award	George Jeffrey	University of Pittsburgh, Pa.
National Medal of Science	Elias J. Corey	Harvard University, Cambridge, Mass.
Nuclear Chemistry Award of the American Chemical Society	Ronald D. Macfarlane	Texas A & M University, College Station
Perkin Medal	James F. Roth	Air Products & Chemicals, Allentown, Pa.
Peter Debye Award	Gabor A. Somorjai	University of California, Berkeley
Polymer Chemistry Award of the American Chemical Society	William R. Krigbaum	Duke University, Durham, N.C.
Priestley Medal	George C. Pimentel	University of California, Berkeley
Roger Adams Award	George A. Olah	University of Southern California, Los Angeles
Robert A. Welch Award	Richard B. Bernstein	University of California, Los Angeles

EARTH SCIENCES

Alexander Agassiz Medal	Cesare Emiliani	University of Miami, Coral Gables, Fla.
Arthur L. Day Medal	Claude J. Allègre	University of Paris VII
Carl-Gustaf Rossby Research Medal	Richard J. Reed	University of Washington, Seattle
Charles A. Whitten Medal	James C. Savage	U.S. Geological Survey, Menlo Park, Calif.
Charles L. Mitchell Award	Gilbert B. Clark	National Oceanographic and Atmospheric Administration, Miami, Fla.
Clarence Leroy Meisinger Award	Daniel Keyser	State University of New York, Albany
Cleveland Abbe Award for Distinguished Service to Atmospheric Sciences	George J. Haltiner (Emeritus)	Naval Postgraduate School, Monterey, Calif.
Cleveland Abbe Award for Distinguished Service to Atmospheric Sciences	Edwin Kessler	University of Oklahoma, Norman
Gold Medal of the U.S. Geological Society	Claude J. Allègre	University of Paris VII
Harry H. Hess Medal	A. G. W. Cameron	Harvard College Observatory, Cambridge, Mass.
John Adam Fleming Medal	Donald A. Gurnett	University of Iowa, Iowa City
Jule G. Charney Award	Eugene M. Rasmusson	University of Maryland, College Park

AWARD	WINNER	AFFILIATION
Louis J. Battan Author's Award	Craig F. Bohren	Pennsylvania State University, University Park
MacArthur Prize Fellow Award	Charles Archambeau	University of Colorado, Boulder
MacArthur Prize Fellow Award	John G. Fleagle	State University of New York, Stony Brook
MacArthur Prize Fellow Award	Raymond Jeanloz	University of California, Berkeley
Maurice Ewing Medal	Klaus Wyrtki	University of Hawaii, Honolulu
Outstanding Contribution to the Advance of Applied Meteorology	Norman A. Phillips (Retired)	National Oceanographic and Atmospheric Administration, Washington, D.C.
Penrose Medal	Robert S. Dietz	Arizona State University, Tempe
Special Award of the American Meteorological Society	Joseph O. Fletcher	National Oceanographic and Atmospheric Administration, Rockville, Md.
Walter H. Bucher Medal	Arthur H. Lachenbruch	U.S. Geological Survey, Menlo Park, Calif.
William Bowie Medal	Walter H. Munk	Scripps Institution of Oceanography, La Jolla, Calif.

ELECTRONICS AND INFORMATION SCIENCES

AWARD	WINNER	AFFILIATION
Award for Initiatives in Research	John K. Ousterhout	University of California, Berkeley
National Medal of Science	Ralph E. Gomory	IBM Corp.
National Medal of Technology	Robert H. Dennard	IBM Corp.
National Medal of Technology	Harold E. Edgerton	EG&G Corp., Cambridge, Mass.
Quantum Electronics Award	William B. Bridges	California Institute of Technology, Pasadena

ENERGY

AWARD	WINNER	AFFILIATION
Japan Prize (1988)	Georges Vendryes	Atomic Energy Commission, France

ENVIRONMENT

AWARD	WINNER	AFFILIATION
Award for Excellence in Science	Ruth Patrick	Academy of Natural Sciences, University of Pennsylvania, Philadelphia
Climate Institute Award	John Chafee	U.S. Senate
Climate Institute Award	Roger Revelle	University of California, San Diego
Commander of the Brazilian Order of Rio-Branco	Thomas E. Lovejoy	Smithsonian Institution, Washington, D.C.
Creative Advances in Environmental Science and Technology	James G. Anderson	Harvard University, Cambridge, Mass.
Distinguished Service Award of the American Institute of Biological Sciences	Donald E. Stone	Duke University and Organization for Tropical Studies, Durham, N.C.
Henry Medal	David Challinor (Retired)	Smithsonian Institution, Washington, D.C.
Japan Prize (1989)	Frank S. Rowland	University of California, Irvine
J. Paul Getty Wildlife Conservation Prize	Perez Olindo	Kenyan Department of Wildlife Conservation and Management

AWARD	WINNER	AFFILIATION
MacArthur Award	Simon A. Levin	Cornell University, Ithaca, N.Y.
MacArthur Prize Fellow Award	Philip J. DeVries	Austin, Texas
R. Bruce Lindsay Award	Hene J. Busch-Vishniae	University of Texas, Austin
Right Livelihood Award	Friends of the Earth	Malaysia
Right Livelihood Award	Jose Lutzenberger	Brazil
Tyler Prize for Environmental Achievement	Bert Bolin	University of Stockholm, Sweden; International Meteorological Institute, Stockholm

FOOD AND AGRICULTURE

Advancement of Application of Agricultural and Food Chemistry	John M. Bremner	Iowa State University, Ames
Bio-Serv Award in Experimental Animal Nutrition	Kirk Klasing	University of California, Davis
Borden Award in Nutrition	James A. Olson	Iowa State University, Ames
Charles Porter Award	George A. Somkuti	U.S. Department of Agriculture
Charles Thom Award	William E. Sandine	Oregon State University, Corvallis
Conrad A. Elvehjem Award for Public Service in Nutrition (1989)	Helen A. Guthrie	Pennsylvania State University, University Park
Conrad A. Elvehjem Award for Public Service in Nutrition (1988)	R. Gaurth Hansen (Emeritus)	Utah State University, Logan
Cyrus Hall McCormick Jerome Increase Case Gold Medal Award	Wesley F. Buchele	Iowa State University, Ames
Distinguished Scientist of the Year Award	Thomas J. Sexton	U.S. Department of Agriculture
Distinguished Scientist of the Year Award	Richard F. Wilson	U.S. Department of Agriculture
John Deere Medal	Glenn O. Schwab (Emeritus)	Ohio State University, Columbus
Joseph B. Goldberger Award in Clinical Nutrition	Edwin L. Bierman	University of Washington, Seattle
Kishida International Award	Lyle G. Reeser (Retired)	Caterpillar Inc., Peoria, Ill.
Lederle Award in Human Nutrition	Janet C. King	University of California, Berkeley
Osborne and Mendel Award (1988)	George A. Bray	University of Southern California, Los Angeles
Osborne and Mendel Award (1989)	Robert J. Cousins	University of Florida, Gainesville
Mead Johnson Award	Alfred H. Merrill, Jr.	Emory University, Atlanta, Ga.
MacArthur Prize Fellow Award	I. Garth Youngberg	Institute for Alternative Agriculture, Greenbelt, Md.
Wilder Medal	R. C. Lamb	Geneva, N.Y.
World Food Prize	Robert F. Chandler, Jr. (Retired)	International Rice Research Institute, Los Banos, Philippines; Asian Vegetable Research and Development Center, Taiwan

LIFE SCIENCES

Albert Lasker Basic Medical Research Award	Thomas R. Cech	University of Colorado, Boulder
Albert Lasker Basic Medical Research Award	Philip A. Sharp	Massachusetts Institute of Technology, Cambridge

Scientists of the Year

AWARD	WINNER	AFFILIATION
Award for Scientific Reviewing	Eric R. Kandel	Columbia University, New York, N.Y.
Award in Molecular Biology	Kiyoshi Mizuuchi	National Institutes of Health, Bethesda, Md.
Award in Neurosciences	Seymour S. Kety	National Institutes of Health, Bethesda, Md.
Award in Neurosciences	Louis Sokoloff	National Institutes of Health, Bethesda, Md.
Award of Excellence of the American Fisheries Society	Clark Hubbs	University of Texas, Austin
Bader Award	Jeremy R. Knowles	Harvard University, Cambridge, Mass.
Bicentennial Medallion of the University of Pittsburgh	Mary E. Clutter	National Science Foundation, Washington, D.C.
Bicentennial Medallion of the University of Pittsburgh	Herbert Boyer	University of California, San Francisco; Genentech, Inc.
Biological and Medical Sciences Award	Frank H. Ruddle	Yale University, New Haven, Conn.
Daniel Giraud Elliot Medal	Jon E. Ahlquist	Ohio University, Athens
Daniel Giraud Elliot Medal	Charles G. Sibley (Emeritus)	Yale University, New Haven, Conn.; San Francisco State University, Calif.
Darbaker Prize	David Garbary	St. Francis Xavier University, Antigonish, Nova Scotia
Delmer S. Fahrney Medal	Peter H. Raven	Missouri Botanical Garden, St. Louis
Enrico Fermi Award	Richard B. Setlow	Brookhaven National Laboratory, Upton, N.Y.
Gairdner Foundation International Award	Michael J. Berridge	Cambridge University, England
Gairdner Foundation International Award	Thomas R. Cech	University of Colorado, Boulder
Gairdner Foundation International Award	Robert J. Lefkowitz	Duke University, Durham, N.C.
Gairdner Foundation International Award	Yasutomi Nishizuka	Kobe University, Japan
Gilbert Morgan Smith Medal	Ruth Sager	Harvard Medical School and Dana-Farber Cancer Institute, Boston, Mass.
Jacob K. Javits Award	John M. Russell	University of Texas Medical School, Galveston
Jeanette Siron Pelton Award	Scott D. Russell	University of Oklahoma, Norman
Jessie Stevenson Kovalenko Medal	Maclyn McCarty (Emeritus)	Rockefeller University, New York, N.Y.
Lewis S. Rosenstiel Award	Shinya Inoué	Marine Biological Laboratory, Woods Hole, Mass.
Lawrence Memorial Award	John V. Freudenstein	Cornell University, Ithaca, N.Y.
MacArthur Prize Fellow Award	Marvin P. Kahl	Sedona, Ariz.
MacArthur Prize Fellow Award	Naomi E. Pierce	Princeton University, N.J.; University of Oxford, England
Merit Award of the Botanical Society of America	Aubrey W. Naylor	Duke University, Durham, N.C.

AWARD	WINNER	AFFILIATION
Merit Award of the Botanical Society of America	Richard E. Schultes	Harvard Botanical Museum, Cambridge, Mass.
Merit Award of the Botanical Society of America	T. Elliot Weier	University of California, Davis
Moet Hennessy-Louis Vuitton Prize	Herbert W. Boyer	University of California, San Francisco
Moet Hennessy-Louis Vuitton Prize	Stanley N. Cohen	Stanford University, Calif.
National Medal of Science	Konrad E. Bloch	Harvard University, Cambridge, Mass.
National Medal of Science	Michael S. Brown	University of Texas, Dallas
National Medal of Science	Stanley N. Cohen	Stanford University, Calif.
National Medal of Science	Joseph L. Goldstein	University of Texas, Dallas
Outstanding Researcher Award of the American Society for Horticultural Science	George C. Martin	University of California, Davis
Repligen Award	Robert H. Abeles	Brandeis University, Waltham, Mass.
Richard Lounsbery Award	Richard Axel	Columbia University, New York, N.Y.; Howard Hughes Medical Institute, Bethesda, Md.
Robert Allerton Award	Peter H. Raven	Missouri Botanical Garden, St. Louis
Troland Research Award	Eric I. Knudsen	Stanford University, Calif.
USX Foundation Award in Molecular Biology	H. Robert Horvitz	Massachusetts Institute of Technology, Cambridge

MATHEMATICS

AWARD	WINNER	AFFILIATION
Applied Mathematics and Numerical Analysis Award	Alexandre J. Chorin	University of California, Berkeley
Copley Medal	Sir Michael Atiyah	University of Oxford, England
Crafoord Prize	Pierre Deligne	Institute for Advanced Study, Princeton, N.J.
Crafoord Prize	Alexandre Grothendieck	University of Montpellier, France

MEDICAL SCIENCES

AWARD	WINNER	AFFILIATION
Albert Lasker Clinical Medical Research Award	Vincent P. Dole	Rockefeller University, New York, N.Y.
Albert Lasker Public Service Award	Lowell P. Weicker, Jr.	U.S. Senate
Alfred P. Sloan Jr. Prize	Yasutomi Nishizuka	Kobe University, Japan
Bristol-Myers Award for Distinguished Achievement in Cancer Research	George W. Santos	Johns Hopkins University, Baltimore, Md.
Bristol-Myers Award for Distinguished Achievement in Neuroscience Research	Tomas Hökfelt	Karolinska Institute, Stockholm, Sweden
Bristol-Myers Award for Distinguished Achievement in Neuroscience Research	Walle J. H. Nauta	Massachusetts Institute of Technology, Cambridge
Bristol-Myers Award for Distinguished Achievement in Neuroscience Research	T. P. S. Powell	University of Oxford, England

443

Scientists of the Year

AWARD	WINNER	AFFILIATION
Bristol-Myers Award for Distinguished Achievement in Pain Research	Patrick D. Wall	University College, London
Charles F. Kettering Prize	Sam Shapiro (Emeritus)	Johns Hopkins University, Baltimore, Md.
Charles F. Kettering Prize	Philip Strax	University of Miami, Coral Gables, Fla.
Charles S. Mott Prize	Alfred G. Knudson	University of Pennsylvania and Fox Chase Cancer Center, Philadelphia
Distinguished Service Award of the American Medical Association	Eben Alexander, Jr. (Retired)	Bowman Gray School of Medicine, Wake Forest University, Winston-Salem, N.C.
Doerenkamp-Zbinden Foundation Award	Adriana Albini	National Institutes of Health, Bethesda, Md.
Doerenkamp-Zbinden Foundation Award	Yukihide Iwamoto	National Institutes of Health, Bethesda, Md.
Doerenkamp-Zbinden Foundation Award	Hynda Kleinman	National Institutes of Health, Bethesda, Md.
Doerenkamp-Zbinden Foundation Award	George Martin	National Institutes of Health, Bethesda, Md.
Front-Runner Award	Mathilde Krim	American Foundation for AIDS Research, New York, N.Y.
G. H. A. Clowes Award	Isaiah J. Fidler	University of Texas M. D. Anderson Cancer Center, Houston
Gairdner Foundation International Award	Albert Aguayo	McGill University, Montreal, Quebec
Gairdner Foundation International Award	Michael A. Epstein	University of Oxford, England
Japan Prize (1988)	Isao Arita	Kumamoto National Hospital, Japan
Japan Prize (1989)	Elias J. Corey	Harvard University, Cambridge, Mass.
Japan Prize (1988)	Frank Fenner (Emeritus)	Australian National University
Japan Prize (1988)	Robert C. Gallo	National Institutes of Health, Bethesda, Md.
Japan Prize (1988)	Donald A. Henderson	Johns Hopkins University, Baltimore, Md.
Japan Prize (1988)	Luc Montagnier	Pasteur Institute, Paris
March of Dimes/Colonel Harland Sanders Award	Victor A. McKusick	Johns Hopkins University, Baltimore, Md.
Maxwell Finland Award	C. Everett Koop	U.S. Department of Health and Human Services
National Medal of Science	Maurice R. Hilleman	Merck and Co.
National Medal of Science	Rosalyn S. Yalow	Mount Sinai School of Medicine, New York, N.Y.
National Medal of Technology	Raymond Damadian	Fonar Corp., Melville, N.Y.
National Medal of Technology	Paul C. Lauterbur	University of Illinois, Urbana
Potamkin Prize	Robert D. Terry	University of California, San Diego
Professional Engineers Gold Medal	John Smith	Hospital for Sick Children, Toronto, Canada; University of Toronto
Sarah L. Poiley Memorial Award	Saul Krugman	New York University, New York, N.Y.

AWARD	WINNER	AFFILIATION
Scientific Achievement Award of the American Medical Association	John G. Morrison	Piedmont, Calif.
Selman A. Waksman Award in Microbiology	Bernard D. Davis	Harvard Medical School, Boston, Mass.
William Beaumont Award	Peter O. Kohler	University of Texas, San Antonio
Wolf Prize	Henri-Gery Hers	Catholic University of Louvain, Belgium
Wolf Prize	Elizabeth Neufeld	University of California, Los Angeles

OPTICAL ENGINEERING

C. E. K. Mees Medal	Kenneth M. Baird (Retired)	National Research Council, Canada
Charles Hard Townes Award	Arthur Ashkin	AT&T Bell Laboratories
Charles Hard Townes Award	Daniel J. Bradley (Emeritus)	Trinity College, Dublin, Ireland
David Richardson Medal	Erik Anthon	Optical Coating Laboratory, Santa Rosa, Calif.
Frederic Ives Medal	C. Kumar N. Patel	AT&T Bell Laboratories
Joseph Fraunhofer Award	Parameswaran Hariharan	Commonwealth Scientific and Industrial Research Organization, Australia
Maria Goeppert-Mayer Award	Bonny L. Schumaker	Jet Propulsion Laboratory, California Institute of Technology, Pasadena
Max Born Award	Dietrich Marcuse	AT&T Bell Laboratories
R. W. Wood Prize	Daniel R. Grischkowsky	IBM Corp.

PHYSICS

Achievement in Physics Medal	Erich Vogt	Tri-University-Meson Facility, University of British Columbia, Vancouver
American Institute of Physics Science Writing Award	Michael Riordan	Stanford University, Calif.
Applied Mathematics and Numerical Analysis Award	Martin D. Kruskal	Princeton University, N.J.
Award for Scientific Reviewing	Sidney Coleman	Harvard University, Cambridge, Mass.
Bertram Eugene Warren Award	Robert Birgeneau	Massachusetts Institute of Technology, Cambridge
Bertram Eugene Warren Award	Paul M. Horn	IBM Corp.
Chevalier de l'ordre national du merite	Jean Saudinos	French National Saturne Laboratory, Saclay
Dannie Heineman Prize	Julius Wess	University of Karlsruhe, West Germany
Dannie Heineman Prize	Bruno Zumino	University of California, Berkeley
Davisson-Germer Prize	John L. Hall	University of Colorado, Boulder
Dirac Medal	Efim S. Fradkin	Lebedev Physical Institute, Moscow
Dirac Medal	David Gross	Princeton University, N.J.
Elliott Cresson Medal	Edward N. Lorenz	Massachusetts Institute of Technology, Cambridge

AWARD	WINNER	AFFILIATION
Enrico Fermi Award	Victor F. Weisskopf	Massachusetts Institute of Technology, Cambridge
Ernest Orlando Lawrence Memorial Award	Mary Gaillard	University of California, Berkeley; Lawrence Berkeley Laboratory
Ernest Orlando Lawrence Memorial Award	Richard T. Lahey, Jr.	Rensselaer Polytechnic Institute, Troy, N.Y.
Ernest Orlando Lawrence Memorial Award	Chain T. Liu	Oak Ridge National Laboratory, Tenn.
Ernest Orlando Lawrence Memorial Award	Gene McCall	Los Alamos National Laboratory, N.M.
Ernest Orlando Lawrence Memorial Award	Alexander Pines	University of California, Berkeley; Lawrence Berkeley Laboratory
Ernest Orlando Lawrence Memorial Award	Joseph S. Wall	Brookhaven National Laboratory, Upton, N.Y.
Excellence in Plasma Physics Research Award	Fritz Wagner	Max-Planck-Institut für Plasmaphysik, West Germany
Francesco Somaini Award	Carlo Castagnoli	Turin, Italy
Fujiwara Prize	Tetsuji Nishikawa	Kō Enerugi butsurigaku Kenkyūjo (KEK), Japan
Gentner-Kastler Prize	Andre Neveu	European Laboratory for Particle Physics (CERN)
Gold Medal of the Acoustical Society of America	Cyril M. Harris	Columbia University, New York, N.Y.
Gold Medal of the Weizmann Institute of Science	Herwig Schopper	European Laboratory for Particle Physics (CERN)
Hewlett-Packard Europhysics Prize	J. Georg Bednorz	IBM Research Laboratory, Zürich, Switz.
Hewlett-Packard Europhysics Prize	K. Alex Müller	IBM Research Laboratory, Zürich, Switz.
Howard N. Potts Medal	Sir Charles W. Oatley	University of Cambridge, England
Italgas Prize	Theodor Hänsch	Max Planck Institute for Quantum Optics; University of Munich, West Germany
J. J. Sakurai Prize	Stephen L. Adler	Institute for Advanced Study, Princeton, N.J.
James Clerk Maxwell Prize	Bruno Coppi	Massachusetts Institute of Technology, Cambridge
MacArthur Prize Fellow Award	Helen T. Edwards	Fermi National Accelerator Laboratory, Batavia, Ill.
MacArthur Prize Fellow Award	Robert S. Shaw	University of Illinois, Urbana
Max Planck Medal	Valentine Bargmann	University of Karlsruhe, West Germany
National Medal of Science	D. Allan Bromley	Yale University, New Haven, Conn.
National Medal of Science	Paul C. W. Chu	University of Houston, Texas
National Medal of Science	Joseph B. Keller	Stanford University, Calif.
National Medal of Science	Walter Kohn	University of California, Santa Barbara
National Medal of Science	Norman F. Ramsey	Harvard University, Cambridge, Mass.
National Medal of Science	Jack Steinberger	European Laboratory for Particle Physics (CERN)

AWARD	WINNER	AFFILIATION
Paul Dirac Medal and Prize	John Stewart Bell	European Laboratory for Particle Physics (CERN)
Prix Robin	Claude Itzykson	Center for Nuclear Studies, Saclay, France
Purple Ribbon Medal	Yoshio Yamaguchi	International Committee for Future Accelerators; International Union for Pure and Applied Physics
Robert R. Wilson Prize	Donald W. Kerst (Emeritus)	University of Wisconsin, Madison
Rutherford Medal and Prize	John D. Dowell	University of Birmingham, England
Rutherford Medal and Prize	Peter Kalmus	Queen Mary College, University of London
Shock Compression Award	Robert G. McQueen	Los Alamos National Laboratory, N.M.
Shock Compression Award	Melvin H. Rice	S-Cubed, San Diego, Calif.
Shock Compression Award	John M. Walsh	Los Alamos National Laboratory, N.M.
Stuart Ballantine Medal	John M. J. Madey	Stanford University, Calif.
Thibaud Prize	Daniel Froidevaux	European Laboratory for Particle Physics (CERN)
Tom W. Bonner Prize	Raymond Davis, Jr.	University of Pennsylvania, Philadelphia
U.S. Particle Accelerator School Prize	Ilja M. Kapchinskii	Soviet Institute for Theoretical and Experimental Physics
U.S. Particle Accelerator School Prize	Andrew M. Sessler	Lawrence Berkeley Laboratory, Calif.
U.S. Particle Accelerator School Prize	Vladimir A. Teplyakov	Soviet Institute for High Energy Physics
William F. Meggers Award	Ugo Fano (Emeritus)	University of Chicago, Ill.
W. K. H. Panofsky Prize	Charles Y. Prescott	Stanford Linear Accelerator Center, Calif.
Wolf Prize	Stephen W. Hawking	University of Cambridge, England
Wolf Prize	Roger Penrose	University of Oxford, England

PSYCHOLOGY

National Medal of Science	Eric R. Kandel	Columbia University and New York State Psychiatric Institute, New York, N.Y.
Troland Research Award	John T. Cacioppo	Ohio State University, Columbus

SPACE EXPLORATION

National Air and Space Museum Trophy	Harold Masursky	U.S. Geological Survey, Flagstaff, Ariz.
Robert J. Collier Trophy	Richard M. Truly	U.S. Navy

TRANSPORTATION

Frank G. Brewer Trophy	John D. Odegard	University of North Dakota, Grand Forks
National Air and Space Museum Trophy	Paul B. MacCready, Jr.	AeroVironment Inc., Pasadena, Calif.
National Medal of Technology	Clarence L. (Kelly) Johnson	Lockheed Corp., Burbank, Calif.
Wright Brothers Memorial Trophy	Sam B. Williams	Williams International Corp.

AWARD	WINNER	AFFILIATION
SCIENCE JOURNALISM		
American Institute of Physics Science Writing Award in Physics and Astronomy	Richard Preston	New York, N.Y.
James T. Grady-James H. Stack Award for Interpreting Chemistry for the Public	Robert Kanigel	Baltimore, Md.
MISCELLANEOUS		
MacArthur Prize Fellow Award	Alan Walker	Johns Hopkins University, Baltimore, Md.; National Museum of Kenya
National Medal of Science	William O. Baker	AT&T Bell Laboratories
National Medal of Science	Daniel C. Drucker	University of Florida, Gainesville
National Medal of Science	Milton Friedman	Stanford University, Calif.
National Medal of Science	Willis M. Hawkins	Lockheed Corp.
National Medal of Technology	Arnold O. Beckman	SmithKline Beckman Corp., Irvine, Calif.
National Medal of Technology	Edwin H. Land	Polaroid Corp., Cambridge, Mass.
Philip H. Ward, Jr., Medal	Harold A. Sorgenti	ARCO Chemical Co.
Public Welfare Medal of the National Academy of Sciences	David Packard	Hewlett-Packard Co.
Vannevar Bush Award	Glenn T. Seaborg	University of California, Berkeley
Westinghouse Science Talent Search	1. Christopher M. Skinner	Hall High School, Little Rock, Ark.
	2. Jordan S. Ellenberg	Winston Churchill High School, Potomac, Md.
	3. Richard H. Christie	Penfield High School, Penfield, N.Y.
	4. Stacy E. Benjamin	Francis Lewis High School, Flushing, N.Y.
	5. Sharon C. Posey	North Carolina School of Science and Mathematics, Durham
	6. Allene M. Whitney	Capital High School, Helena, Mont.
	7. Kevin N. Heller	Half Hollow Hills High School West, Dix Hills, N.Y.
	8. Andrew W. Jackson	Roxbury Latin School, West Roxbury, Mass.
	9. Andrew J. Gerber	Midwood High School, Brooklyn, N.Y.
	10. Divya Chander	Pascack Valley High School, Hillsdale, N.J.

Obituaries

Alvarez, Luis Walter, (June 13, 1911—Sept. 1, 1988), U.S. experimental physicist, won the 1968 Nobel Prize for Physics for his work with liquid-hydrogen bubble chambers, which he used to detect the reactions of resonance particles, subatomic particles that have extremely short lifetimes and occur only in high-energy nuclear collisions. Alvarez, who earned a B.S. (1932), M.S. (1934), and Ph.D. (1936) from the University of Chicago, joined (1936) the faculty of the University of California at Berkeley. He became professor of physics in 1945 and served in that capacity until 1978. While conducting research at the Massachusetts Institute of Technology during the 1940s, Alvarez developed a radar beam narrow enough to be used by a ground technician to guide a fog-enshrouded airliner in for landing.

Luis Walter Alvarez
Lawrence Berkeley Laboratory,
University of California

Besides the development of the ground-controlled landing approach system, Alvarez also devised linear radar antennas and a method for aerial bombing using radar to locate targets. During World War II he worked at the Los Alamos (N.M.) Laboratory, where he helped develop the atomic bomb, and after the war he designed the first proton linear accelerator. At the Lawrence Berkeley Laboratory, Alvarez was dubbed the "prize wild-idea man" because his scientific pursuits were so varied. In one of these efforts, he used cosmic rays in an attempt to find hidden treasure chambers at the Chephren pyramid at Giza, Egypt. The detectors placed under the pyramid, however, did not illuminate an area that contained less stone, and thus there was little likelihood of a hidden chamber. With his son Walter, Alvarez developed an impact theory proposing that the mass extinction of dinosaurs, together with hundreds of other species, took place some 65 million years ago when an asteroid or a comet struck the Earth.

Anderson, Herbert Lawrence (May 24, 1914—July 16, 1988), U.S. nuclear physicist, was a member of the team of 40 scientists who, on Dec. 2, 1942, in the basement of Stagg Field at the University of Chicago, achieved the first man-made self-sustaining nuclear chain reaction and thus was instrumental in ushering in the nuclear age. He was credited with designing and building the uranium and graphite pile used to conduct the experiment. Anderson, who earned a Ph.D. in physics from Columbia University, New York City, in 1940, was the first graduate student and the chief assistant of Enrico Fermi. Anderson helped design and construct Columbia's first particle accelerator, a 94-cm (37-in) cyclotron. While working on the Manhattan Project for the production of the first atomic bomb, Anderson was credited with developing a method for purifying uranium that was crucial to the success of the project. In 1944 he joined Fermi in New Mexico and served as group leader (1944–46) of the Los Alamos scientific laboratory, where the first atomic bomb was constructed. After returning to the University of Chicago as a professor, he helped design and build the university's 4.32-m (170-in), 460-MeV synchrocyclotron, the most powerful accelerator of its time. From 1958 to 1963 Anderson served as director of the Enrico Fermi Institute for Nuclear Studies, and in 1983 he was awarded the Enrico Fermi Award, the U.S. Department of Energy's highest scientific tribute, "for his pioneering collaboration with Enrico Fermi in demonstrating the emission of neutrons in fission at Columbia University; for his essential role in constructing the first chain-reacting piles; for his work on production and determination of properties of tritium and helium-3." Anderson succumbed to berylliosis, a lung disease he contracted while conducting atomic experimentation using beryllium and radon.

Barragán, Luis (1902—Nov. 22, 1988), Mexican architect, celebrated the simplicity and intense colors of the Mexican landscape with minimalist gardens and urban dwellings that used the inherent beauty of nature as a backdrop. After earning a degree in civil engineering from the University of Guadalajara, Barragán turned to architecture and adopted the theory set forth by landscape architect Ferdinand Bac, who used the environment of the garden as a focal point. After traveling in Spain, where he marveled at the Alhambra, a walled-in Moorish garden with fountains of running water, and in Greece, where he admired the simplicity of common village dwellings, Barragán returned to Mexico and fashioned his own designs. An intensely private man, he was not prolific and was little known outside his country because he routinely refused commissions. Barragán's most hailed designs included the Plaza de las Fuentes, El Pedregal, in Mexico City and the Satellite City Towers, Queretaro Highway, Mexico City (with Mathias Goeritz). His own San Cristobal residence in Mexico City was noted for its magnificent and serene garden. In 1980 Barragán was the recipient of the Pritzker Prize, one of architecture's most respected international honors.

Bourne, Geoffrey (Nov. 17, 1909—July 19, 1988), Australian anatomist and nutritionist, as an international authority on nutrition wrote widely renowned historical overviews on hunger, notably *Nutrition and the War* (1940) and *Starvation in Europe* (1943), but was more closely identified with his extraordinary work with primates while serving (1962–78) as director of the Yerkes Regional Primate Center at Emory University in Atlanta, Ga., which houses one of the largest collections of apes in the world. Bourne appeared on U.S. television and described, on the "Johnny Carson Show," how he taught chimpanzees to communicate by typing on a computer; he popularized his studies in such works as *Ape People* (1971), *Primate Odyssey* (1974), and *Gentle Giants: The Gorilla Story* (1975). After earning a B.Sc. (1931) and D.Sc. (1935) from the University of Western Australia, he worked as an anatomist and a biochemist in Australia before teaching histology at the University of London and physiology at the University of Oxford, where he earned a Ph.D. in 1943. During World War II he served as a nutritional adviser to the British forces in Burma and rose to the rank of lieutenant colonel. He was reader in histology at London Hospital Medical College (1947–57) before immigrating to the U.S. to become professor and chairman of anatomy at Emory University in 1957. After retiring as director of Emory's primate center in 1978, he became vice-chancellor and professor of nutrition at St. George's University School of Medicine in Grenada. He was in charge of medical students there when a coup by a revolutionary council precipitated an invasion by U.S. military forces in 1983.

Burk, Dean (March 21, 1904—Oct. 6, 1988), U.S. chemist, conducted pioneering research while working (1939–74) at the National Cancer Institute, New York City, as a chemist and from 1948 as chief of cytochemistry at the institute's laboratory. Burk earned both a B.S. (1923) and a Ph.D. (1927) from the University of California at Berkeley, and during the following two years studied at University College, London; the Kaiser Wilhelm Institute, Berlin; and Harvard University. He joined (1929) the staff of the U.S. Department of Agriculture and worked in its fixed-nitrogen research laboratory until 1937. Burk served as professor of biochemistry at Cornell University Medical College, New York City, from 1939 to 1941. His research on photosynthesis earned him the Hildebrand Prize in 1952, and in 1965 he received the Gerhard Domagk Prize for the development of a technique for detecting the difference between a normal cell and a cell damaged by cancer. Burk was also a discoverer of biotin, one of the B-complex vitamins, and he was credited with codeveloping the prototype of the nuclear magnetic resonance scanner, an imaging device.

Cool, Rodney Lee (March 8, 1920—April 16, 1988), U.S. physicist, was instrumental in establishing the existence of quarks, subatomic particles that are fundamental building blocks of matter; he spent much of his professional career attempting to define their properties. Cool, who earned his B.A. degree from the University of South Dakota in 1942, gained both his M.A. (1947) and Ph.D. (1949) in physics from Harvard University. In 1949 he joined Brookhaven National Laboratory, Upton, N.Y., as a research physicist; he rose to become associate director there in 1966. At Rockefeller University, New York City, he established in 1970 an experimental physics group that conducted experiments at CERN (the European Laboratory for Particle Physics) in Geneva. There, Cool and other experimental physicists examined the properties of quarks by attempting to observe one in a free state, a feat not yet accomplished, and by trying to obtain experimental evidence for the existence of a "top" quark.

Cournand, André Frédéric (Sept. 24, 1895—Feb. 19, 1988), French-born physician, shared the 1956 Nobel Prize for Physiology or Medicine with Dickinson W. Richards and Werner Forssmann for their discoveries concerning heart catheterization and circulatory changes. Cournand, who graduated from the Sorbonne in 1915, served in the French Army before completing his medical studies at the University of Paris. In 1930 he immigrated to New York City to study chest diseases with Richards at Bellevue Hospital, and the two perfected a method of catheterization using the heart catheter invented by Forssmann, who in 1929 had demonstrated how a catheter could be maneuvered through a vein in his elbow into his heart. This procedure enabled physicians to examine the diseased human heart and to make more accurate diagnoses of underlying anatomic defects. In 1934 Cournand joined the faculty of the College of Physicians and Surgeons of Columbia University, New York City, a post he held until 1964, when he became emeritus professor of medicine. He and Richards continued to collaborate on improvements in diagnosis and theory until the latter's death in 1973.

Dart, Raymond Arthur (Feb. 4, 1893—Nov. 22, 1988), Australian-born anatomist and paleoanthropologist, was credited with having found the link between apes and humans with his 1924 identification of an early human fossil skull in Africa. Though his announcements were received skeptically by fellow scientists, who then believed that humans had evolved in China, the correctness of Dart's *Australopithecus africanus* ("South African ape") species was later proved. Subsequent African discoveries by such anthropologists as Phillip Tobias, the Leakey family, and Donald Johanson underscored Dart's work and indicated that the creatures he identified lived more than two million years ago. Dart graduated with honors in biology from the University of Queensland (1913), received his M.D. from Sydney University (1917), and served as a captain in the Australian Army Medical Corps in Europe (1917–19). He was senior demonstrator in anatomy at University College, London, in 1919–20 and 1921–22, spent a year in the U.S. as a Rockefeller Foundation fellow (1920–21), and returned to London as a lecturer in histology (1921–22). He then served as both professor of anatomy (1923–58) and medical faculty dean (1926–43) at the medical school of the University of the Witwatersrand, Johannesburg. The skull Dart tagged as early human was from a cave near Taung, a village at the edge of the Kalahari Desert, 644 km (400 mi) southwest of Johannesburg; it was kept at the Transvaal Museum in Pretoria. After World War II Dart led expeditions that opened other major African fossil sites. Since 1966 he had been a visiting professor at the Institute for the Study of Human Potential in Philadelphia. In addition to many scholarly articles, he wrote *Adventures with the Missing Link* (1959), an autobiography.

Davies, John Grant (Nov. 5, 1924—Sept. 16, 1988), British astronomer, was a pioneer in the development of radio astronomy. In the 1950s he designed the drive system that guided the 2,000-ton Jodrell Bank radio telescope, located near Manchester, England, so that it achieved the precise motion needed for studying the heavens. The 76-m (250-ft)-diameter telescope was for several years the only instrument capable of tracking spacecraft on deep-space missions. Educated at the universities of Cambridge and Manchester, Davies joined Bernard Lovell at the Jodrell Bank laboratories of the latter school in 1947 and became a member of the university's physics department the following year. In his first important research he derived the precise orbits of meteors by studying the characteristics of the radar echoes from ionized meteor trails. In so doing he demonstrated that all meteors were moving in closed orbits around the Sun and that none originated in interstellar space. He later was a leader of a group of scientists who linked seven radio telescopes located between Jodrell Bank and Cambridge into an array with a resolution equal to that of a telescope more than 160 km (100 mi) in diameter.

Feynman, Richard Phillips (May 11, 1918—Feb. 14, 1988), U.S. theoretical physicist, shared with Julian S. Schwinger and Shinichiro Tomonaga the 1965 Nobel Prize for Physics for redefining the basic principles of quantum electrodynamics. The trio worked independently, and Feynman ingeniously constructed simple diagrams, now called Feynman diagrams, to represent graphically interactions of particles. Feynman earned a Ph.D. in physics from Princeton University in 1942 and was immediately

Richard Phillips Feynman
AP/Wide World

recruited to work on the atomic bomb project, first at Princeton (1942–43) and then at Los Alamos, N.M. (1943–45). Together with Hans Bethe, Feynman devised a top secret formula for predicting the energy yield of a nuclear weapon; their calculations remained classified. He joined the faculty at Cornell University, Ithaca, N.Y., in 1945 and stayed there until 1950, when he became professor of physics at the California Institute of Technology. He remained there for the rest of his professional career. Among Feynman's greatest scientific achievements was his use of a mathematical approach to formulate a theory for liquid helium, which helped physicists understand its many properties. His work with Murray Gell-Mann resulted in a theory that accounted for most of the phenomena associated with the so-called weak interaction of subatomic particles, and he later provided an explanation for the behavior of electrons in high-energy collisions. Feynman became a highly successful author in 1985 with his best-selling autobiography, *Surely You're Joking, Mr. Feynman!*, and in 1986 he became known to the general public as a member of the presidential commission investigating the space shuttle explosion. During a simple yet illuminating demonstration, he placed one of the shuttle's O-ring seals, the critical seals in the rocket booster, in a glass of ice water and squeezed it with a small clamp. Its failure to spring back into shape demonstrated that the rings were not resilient enough to maintain their shape after being subjected to cold. He maintained that this simple experiment could have averted the shuttle disaster. He received the Albert Einstein Award in 1954 and was the author of a highly regarded physics text, *Lectures on Physics* (3 vol., 1963–65).

Ford, Edmund Brisco (April 23, 1901—Jan. 22, 1988), British geneticist, was a leading figure in the study of the genetics of natural selection and was the founder of the science of ecological genetics. While attending the University of Oxford (1923–27), he conducted research with Julian Huxley on the genetic control of growth in freshwater crustaceans and with R. A. Fisher on genetic adaptations found in natural populations. Ford combined genetic experiments in the laboratory with quantitative observations of butterfly and moth populations in nature. His techniques, which included marking and recapturing animal specimens in the wild to estimate population change, became basic to what he called ecological genetics. In 1940 Ford speculated that genetic polymorphisms (consistent variations between members of a single species) are maintained when the variations are equally advantageous to the species. He applied this theory to the four human blood groups (A, B, AB, and O) in 1945 and theorized that the groups are balanced by their susceptibilities to different diseases. Ford joined the Oxford faculty in 1927, serving as director of the genetics laboratory (1952–69) and professor of ecological genetics (1963–69), and became emeritus professor in 1969. His books include *Butterflies* (1945), *Ecological Genetics* (1964), and *Genetics and Adaptation* (1976).

Gollan, Frank (July 1, 1909—found dead Oct. 6, 1988), Czechoslovak-born physician, was credited with isolating the MM poliomyelitis virus, a breakthrough that helped other scientists develop a polio vaccine. Gollan, who suffered from polio as a child, was determined to find a cure for the crippling disease. He fled Prague in 1938, when the Nazis occupied Czechoslovakia, and settled in Cleveland, Ohio. Gollan earned an M.D. degree from the Technical University of Prague in 1934 and studied in Paris and Zürich, Switz., before immigrating to the United States. He successively served as a surgeon with the U.S. Public Health Service (1945–46), assistant professor of physiology at the University of Minnesota (1946–48), and professor at Antioch College, Yellow Springs, Ohio (1948–52). During the early 1950s Gollan invented the first heart-lung machine used in open-heart surgery. He joined the radioisotope unit at the Thayer Veterans Administration Hospital, Nashville, Tenn., and served as director of research there from 1955 to 1960. From 1960 until his retirement, he was chief of radioisotope services at the Veterans Administration Hospital in Coral Gables, Fla.

Heinlein, Robert Anson (July 7, 1907—May 8, 1988), U.S. science-fiction writer, was a prolific author and master of the genre who produced such cult classics as *Starship Troopers* (1959), *Stranger in a Strange Land* (1961), *The Moon Is a Harsh Mistress* (1966), and *I Will Fear No Evil* (1970). Though many of his novels provoked controversy because of dire speculations about future societal changes, they were superb in the scientific realm, predicting the coming of the atom bomb, nuclear power plants, the water bed, moving sidewalks, and an electronic space defense shield. Heinlein, who took up writing when tuberculosis cut short his naval career, began writing science-fiction stories for *Astounding Science*

Robert Anson Heinlein
AP/Wide World

Fiction magazine before graduating to the *Saturday Evening Post* and elevating science fiction to a new sophistication. Some of his early novels captured the imagination with their vision of space travel becoming a commonplace occurrence, while later novels broke the traditional molds of science fiction by exploring the future while questioning present values. Among these works are *Rocket Ship Galileo* (1947), *Revolt in 2100* (1953), *Friday* (1982), *Job: A Comedy of Justice* (1984), and *The Cat Who Walks Through Walls: A Comedy of Manners* (1985). Heinlein was the recipient of a number of prizes, among them an unprecedented four Hugo awards.

Hull, Harvard Leslie (Oct. 23, 1906—Oct. 1, 1988), U.S. scientist and inventor, was dubbed the "father of the hot lab" in the early 1940s for developing a safe process for separating radioactive materials. Hull began working on the Manhattan Project, the program that led to the creation of the atomic bomb, while serving (1943–46) as director of process improvement for the electromagnetic separation of uranium-235 at the Tennessee East Corp., Oak Ridge, Tenn. Hull graduated with distinction from Nebraska Wesleyan University in 1927 and earned a Ph.D. in physics from Columbia University, New York City, in 1933. That same year he joined Sperry Gyroscope Co., in Brooklyn, N.Y., as a project engineer and served as research engineer (1935–40) there until he was named director of remote control development. Three years later he began working on the Manhattan Project. From 1946 to 1949 he served as associate director of Argonne National Laboratories near Chicago and was also director of remote control engineering there. From 1957 to 1977 Hull served as president of Hull Associates, an electronics consulting firm.

Kaiser, Emil Thomas (Feb. 15, 1938—July 18, 1988), Hungarian-born biochemist, conducted pioneering research on synthetic enzymes. Unlike other researchers, who attempted to discover new but scarce enzymes, Kaiser concentrated on adapting readily available ones into more useful and versatile catalysts, and he also made advances in discovering the physical and biologic properties of proteins and peptide hormones. His approach revolutionized synthetic chemistry. After earning his Ph.D. in organic chemistry from Harvard University in 1959, Kaiser taught chemistry at various universities before joining the faculty at the University of Chicago in 1963. He served as Louis Block professor there (1981–84) and later conducted studies at Rockefeller University, New York City. Kaiser isolated a naturally occurring peptide that prevents the formation of kidney stones and produced a more active form of a peptide hormone involved in the regulation of blood calcium. The latter hormone was useful in the treatment of Paget's disease and other bone disorders. His process for isolating and purifying enzymes also had applications for industrial technology. Kaiser, the editor of a number of books on synthetic chemistry, was elected to the National Academy of Sciences in 1987.

Murray, Henry Alexander (May 13, 1893—June 23, 1988), U.S. psychologist, developed a theory of human personality based on an individual's inborn needs and the ways people interact with one another and with the physical and social environment. Murray, who majored in history at Harvard University, earned an M.D. in 1919 from Columbia University's College of Physicians and Surgeons, an M.A. in biology from Columbia, and a Ph.D. in biochemistry from the University of Cambridge in 1927. His interest in psychology was sparked when he began reading the works of the eminent psychologist Carl Jung. He later visited Jung and credited him and Sigmund Freud with influencing his own work. With no formal training he began teaching psychology at Harvard University in 1927, and from 1929 to 1938 he served as director of the Harvard Psychological Clinic. One of Murray's most important contributions to analytical psychology was the development of the Thematic Apperception Test, which became an important tool in evaluating personality. By showing a person a series of 20 pictures, each depicting a different dramatic event which the subject was asked to interpret, Murray was able to evaluate personality, since studies proved that individuals are likely to interpret events according to their own experiences or those of family or friends. He published his most important work, *Explorations in Personality*, in 1938, and after his retirement from Harvard in 1962 he continued to lecture and devote much of his time to the study of the works of Herman Melville. At the time of Murray's death he was preparing a book that was tentatively titled *A Melville Mosaic: Morsels from the Unpublished Biography*.

Panofsky, Hans Arnold (Sept. 18, 1917—Feb. 28, 1988), U.S. atmospheric scientist, conducted important research on the lowest 91 m (300 ft) of atmosphere and was especially concerned that the chlorine atoms in fluorocarbon gases or oxides of nitrogen from fertilizer would destroy large portions of the ozone layer, which is needed to intercept harmful rays from the Sun. Panofsky earned a B.A. from Princeton University in 1938 and a Ph.D. in astronomy from the University of California at Berkeley in 1941. He served on the faculties at Wilson College, Chambersburg, Pa. (1941–42), New York University (1942–51), and Pennsylvania State University (1952–82). After his retirement in 1982 he continued to teach classes at the University of California at San Diego. Some of his other studies explored the atmospheric circulation of Jupiter, sunspots, climatic change, and the interpretation of satellite data. He also devised theories of wind flow over complex terrain and suggested how air turbulence can be a factor in causing airplane crashes. In 1965 he was the recipient of the Meisinger Award given by the American Meteorological Society, and in 1976 he was awarded the Carl-Gustaf Rossby Research Medal.

Raymond, Albert L. (Feb. 12, 1901—July 17, 1988), U.S. biochemist, served as senior vice-president and director of research for G. D. Searle & Co., a pharmaceutical firm, during the years in which many major drug discoveries—Dramamine, the motion sickness medication; the Pill (Enovid), a steroid hormone that suppresses ovulation; and aspartame, an artificial sweetener marketed as NutraSweet—were made. After earning a Ph.D. (1925) from the California Institute of Technology, Raymond joined the Rockefeller Foundation in New York City; he remained there until he joined G. D. Searle in 1934. Raymond became director of research two years later and quickly climbed the corporate ladder, becoming vice-president in 1945 and a director in 1947. Under his creative leadership other important drugs were developed, including Lomotil, used to curb diarrhea; Aldactone, used frequently by internists; and Flagyl, for vaginal infections. Nevertheless, it was probably the discovery of the Pill, which was first marketed in 1957 for menstrual dysfunction and in 1960 as a contraceptive, that had the most revolutionary impact.

Richter, Curt Paul (Feb. 20, 1894—Dec. 21, 1988), U.S. psychobiologist, drew on psychology, physiology, neurology, and psychiatry to investigate behavioral and biochemical interrelationships that can affect sleep, jet lag, stress reactions, and the onset of diseases; he was credited with introducing the concept of biorhythms and of the "biological clock," a term he coined in a paper he wrote in 1927 while serving as director of the Henry Phipps Psychiatric Clinic at Johns Hopkins University, Baltimore, Md., from 1922 to 1957. Richter's studies at the Technische Hochschule in Dresden, Germany, were interrupted with the advent of World War I.

He returned to the U.S. and in 1917 earned a B.S. from Harvard University and in 1921 a Ph.D. from Johns Hopkins, where he joined the faculty the following year. Besides directing the psychobiology laboratory there, he became professor of psychobiology in 1957; he retired from that post in 1960, although he continued to work in the laboratory until 1988. Throughout his career Richter was dedicated to the experimental study of animal and human behavior. For many of his experiments he used domesticated or laboratory rats and studied the differences between them and rats found in the wild. His work led to the discovery of an effective rat poison and to firsthand observations on the phenomenon of "sudden death" in animals and humans. The results of some of his experiments were published in *Biological Clocks in Medicine and Psychiatry* (1965).

Ruben, Samuel (July 14, 1900—July 16, 1988), U.S. inventor, as director of his own laboratory for more than 60 years (1923–85), masterminded significant contributions to electrochemistry and applied electrochemical engineering; he registered more than 300 patents, notably one for the alkaline battery. After graduating from high school Ruben worked to help support his family and, with the encouragement of Columbia University (New York City) physics professor Bergen Davis, he attended lectures at the university and gained access to its physics library. Ruben established Ruben Laboratories in New Rochelle, N.Y., and in the early 1920s produced the solid-state rectifier, which converted regular household electric current for use in radios. Until that time radios were powered by lead-acid storage batteries, which, if dropped, destroyed carpets and furniture. Ruben also invented the dry electrolytic capacitor, a small device that stored electricity and radically reduced the cost and size of radios. His many discoveries also included the dry electrolytic condenser, which for decades was used in nearly every radio and television set and in the starters of most electric motors; several hundred million condensers were produced annually. His invention of the "seven-second tube" radically reduced the warm-up period needed for the vacuum tubes then used in radio transmission. During World War II Ruben advanced military technology by designing the sealed mercury battery, which was impervious to temperature extremes and maintained its voltage at full strength throughout its use. The battery was ideally suited for walkie-talkies, mine detectors, and various pieces of communications equipment. Ruben later invented a compact mercuric-oxide dry-cell battery that had wide applications and was used in the manufacture of such products as electronic watches, Earth satellites, and heart pacemakers. He was awarded honorary Ph.D.'s from Columbia, from Butler University (Indianapolis, Ind.), and from the

Polytechnic Institute of New York. In 1965 he was hailed as inventor of the year by George Washington University, Washington, D.C., and he was the recipient of the Acheson Medal of the Electrochemical Society and the Longstreth Medal of the Franklin Institute.

Ruska, Ernst August Friedrich (Dec. 25, 1906—May 27, 1988), German electrical engineer, won the Nobel Prize for Physics in 1986 for the invention of the electron microscope. Ruska garnered half the award for his work, while Gerd Binning and Heinrich Rohrer shared the other half of the prize for developing the scanning tunneling microscope. Ruska studied engineering at the Technical University of Munich (1925–27) and at the Technical University of Berlin (1927–34), where he engaged in electron microscopy research. Earlier studies indicated that

Ernst August Friedrich Ruska
AP/Wide World

the resolving power of a conventional microscope was limited by the wavelength of visible light, and so Ruska's team theorized that a highly focused beam of electrons (which have a much shorter wavelength) would achieve a higher magnification and yield far greater detail. The team developed a rough prototype in 1931 using two electromagnetic lenses to magnify the electron image. In 1933 Ruska unveiled an electron microscope that permitted magnification far greater than a light microscope could achieve. As a research engineer with Siemens-Reiniger-Werke AG from 1937, Ruska perfected the first commercially available electron microscope (1939). He remained at Siemens until 1955, when he became director of the Institute for Electron Microscopy at the Fritz Haber Institute of the Max Planck Society. Ruska also taught electronic optics and microscopy at the Technical University of Berlin from 1949.

Steptoe, Patrick Christopher (June 9, 1913—March 21, 1988), British physician, was best known as the doctor who, together with British physiologist Robert Edwards, perfected in vitro ("test tube") fertilization of the human egg. The process involved extracting an egg from a woman's ovary using a procedure called laparoscopy, fertilizing the egg with

Patrick Christopher Steptoe
AP/Wide World

sperm in a glass container, and then returning the embryo to the womb, where, barring any problems, it developed normally. Their research resulted in the birth (July 25, 1978) of a perfectly formed baby girl, Louise Brown, the world's first "test-tube baby." Steptoe and Edwards were later credited with more than 1,000 such births including Louise Brown's younger sister. After graduating in 1939 from the University of London's St. George's Hospital Medical School, Steptoe joined the Royal Navy Volunteer Reserve, serving as a surgeon until his ship was sunk and he was taken prisoner by the Italians (1941). After his release in 1943, he returned to London to study obstetrics and gynecology. In 1951 he was named senior obstetrician and gynecologist at a hospital in Oldham, where he conducted research on sterilization and infertility. In 1967 he published the authoritative *Laparoscopy in Gynaecology* and the following year formed a partnership with Edwards. Steptoe became expert in using the laparoscope, a narrow tube through which optical fibers are threaded. He used the instrument to help Edwards harvest human eggs to be fertilized outside the womb. Their work, conducted in Steptoe's Centre for Human Reproduction at Oldham, raised a number of serious ethical questions. The two quietly collaborated until April 1978, when the news that a baby had been conceived outside the womb made headlines. Steptoe, who had been battling cancer for several years, died the day before he was to be made a Commander of the Order of the British Empire.

Tinbergen, Nikolaas (April 15, 1907—Dec. 21, 1988), Dutch-born British zoologist, shared the 1973 Nobel Prize for Physiology or Medicine with Konrad Lorenz and Karl von Frisch for their work in ethology, the study of animal behavior under natural conditions. Tinbergen was particularly noted for his research on social patterns among sea gulls and for his development of comprehensive and ingenious experiments that provided scientific tests for sociobiological theories. Tinbergen, whose older brother, Jan, won the 1969 Nobel Prize for Economics, grad-

uated (1932) from the University of Leiden and taught there (1933–49) except for a two-year period during World War II when he was imprisoned by the Nazi occupation forces. In 1949 he became a lecturer in the University of Oxford's newly formed department of animal behavior; he was named professor of animal behavior in 1966 and professor emeritus in 1974. Tinbergen applied to humans many of his findings on aggression, communication, and courtship behavior in animals, and in the 1970s he devoted most of his time to the study of autism in children. His many influential books include *The Study of Instinct* (1951), *The Animal in Its World: Explorations of an Ethologist, 1932–72* (1972–73), and *Autistic Children: New Hope for a Cure* (1983). He was also a skilled nature photographer and an award-winning documentary filmmaker.

Uhlenbeck, George Eugene (Dec. 6, 1900—Oct. 31, 1988), Dutch-born physicist, codiscovered with Samuel A. Goudsmit the electron's spin, a revolutionary finding that proved to be vital in understanding the nature of atoms. Uhlenbeck and Goudsmit were working on their Ph.D. degrees at the University of Leiden, when, in 1925, after ascertaining that electrons rotate about an axis, they theorized that an electron spins. In 1927 Uhlenbeck joined the faculty of the University of Michigan as an instructor in physics. He went back (1935) to The Netherlands as a professor at the State University of Utrecht but returned (1939) to the University of Michigan as professor of theoretical physics. From 1943 to 1945 he helped in the development of radar while working at the Radiation Laboratory at the Massachusetts Institute of Technology. In 1960 he was appointed professor and physicist at the Rockefeller Institute (later Rockefeller University), a post he held until his retirement in 1974. An expert on the theory of atomic structure and quantum mechanics, statistical mechanics, the kinetic theory of matter, and nuclear physics, Uhlenbeck published many influential papers on those subjects. He was the recipient of the National Medal of Science in 1977 and was cowinner of the Wolf Prize in 1979.

Vineberg, Arthur Martin (May 24, 1903—March 26, 1988), Canadian heart surgeon, developed in 1950 the Vineberg procedure, a surgical method of revascularizing the heart by transplanting the left internal mammary artery into the heart wall in order to provide an alternate blood flow to the heart when blockages caused by atherosclerosis threaten to stifle circulation. Later Vineberg improved his technique by also transferring to the heart tissue that is rich in blood vessels, taken from around the intestines. This tissue then develops new vascular connections with the heart muscle. Vineberg earned an M.S. (1928) and a Ph.D. (1933) in physiology from McGill University in Montreal. He studied in Paris and New

York City before joining the staff of the Royal Victoria Hospital in Montreal, where in 1957 he was named head of the department of cardiac surgery. Vineberg was the author of *How to Live with Your Heart: The Family Guide to Heart Health* (1975), and at the time of his death he was preparing *The Complete Guide to Heart Health*.

Felix Wankel
AP/Wide World

Wankel, Felix (Aug. 13, 1902—Oct. 9, 1988), German engineer, invented the revolutionary Wankel rotary engine, unique because it contained a rotor in the shape of a curved equilateral triangle in place of the moving pistons in standard internal-combustion engines. Wankel showed a natural understanding of mechanisms and invented the Wankel engine without knowing how to drive a car or having earned an engineering degree. He sold scientific books to finance a small engineering workshop and to pay for correspondence courses and night classes. Wankel specialized in the sealing problems of conventional engines. He was hired (1933) by the Daimler-Benz Co. but was soon fired. Wankel then worked (1934–36) for Bayerisch Motorenwerke (BMW), where he developed an airplane engine with rotary valves that replaced conventional valves, resulting in a lighter, more efficient configuration. In 1936 the German Air Ministry learned of his work and sought to enlist his skills for the Third Reich; Wankel reportedly persuaded Hermann Göring to build the Wankel Test Institute on the shores of Lake Constance in exchange for his continued research on pistonless, rotary engines. French occupation forces destroyed (1945) the institute, imprisoned Wankel for a short time, and forbade him to continue his work. In 1951 he joined NSU Motor Works, which produced his rotary automobile engine (1957). Many major corporations attempted to produce Wankel's engine; most successful were the Mazda automobile corporation in Japan and the Norton motorcycle company in Britain. Wankel received an honorary doctorate in engineering from the Technical University of Munich in 1969 and the Bavaria Order of Merit in 1973.

Williams, Roger John (Aug. 14, 1893—Feb. 20, 1988), U.S. biochemist and nutritional scientist, was best known to the scientific community for the discovery and synthesis of pantothenic acid, a water-soluble growth-promoting vitamin that was identified in 1941 as one of the 14 acids essential to animal metabolism. Williams was eager to establish chemical anthropology as a scientific study, and in his article "Chemistry Makes the Man," he advocated the study of the unique chemical composition of an individual. He also conducted studies on nutrition and how nutrients affect health, aging, psychological disorders, alcoholism, and mental retardation. Together with his brother Robert, who isolated vitamin B-1, he was awarded in 1941 the Charles Frederick Chandler Medal for research in biochemistry. After earning his Ph.D. in 1919 from the University of Chicago, Williams served as professor at the University of Oregon and Oregon State College (now Oregon State University). In 1939 he joined the faculty at the University of Texas at Austin, where he remained until his retirement in 1971. He founded the university's Clayton Foundation Biochemical Institute in 1940 and remained director there until 1985. Some of Williams's most influential writings include *An Introduction to Organic Chemistry* (1927), *Nutrition and Alcoholism* (1951), *Biochemical Individuality* (1956), *and Physicians' Handbook of Nutritional Science* (1975).

Wright, Sewall (Dec. 21, 1889—March 3, 1988), U.S. geneticist, together with British scientists R. A. Fisher and J. B. S. Haldane, founded population genetics, the study of both experimental and theoretical consequences of Mendelian genetics (the scientific study of heredity in accordance with Mendel's laws) on the population level. His experimental work included investigations of the effects of inbreeding and crossbreeding among guinea pigs in order to improve stock, and he later used these animals to correlate the effects of gene action on coat color. He was most prominently identified with his concept of genetic drift, termed the Sewall Wright effect, which propounds that in small isolated populations the few individuals possessing a rare gene may not pass it on, and a new species may result without natural selection playing a role. Wright also developed a mathematical foundation to synthesize the 19th-century theories of Charles Darwin, the father of evolution, and Gregor Mendel, the founder of genetic investigation. After Wright earned his Ph.D. in zoology from Harvard University (Sc.D., 1915), he conducted experimental work in animal genetics at the U.S. Department of Agriculture (1915–25) before serving on the faculties of the University of Chicago (1926–54) and the University of Wisconsin (1955–60). Wright wrote his masterpiece, *Evolution and the Genetics of Populations*, when he was 79.

Contributors to the Science Year in Review

D. James Baker *Earth sciences: Oceanography.* President, Joint Oceanographic Institutions Inc., Washington, D.C.

Fred Basolo *Chemistry: Inorganic chemistry.* Morrison Professor of Chemistry, Northwestern University, Evanston, Ill.

Harold Borko *Electronics and information sciences: Information systems and services.* Professor, Graduate School of Library and Information Science, University of California, Los Angeles.

John M. Bowen *Medical sciences: Veterinary medicine.* Associate Dean for Research and Graduate Affairs and Professor of Pharmacology and Toxicology, College of Veterinary Medicine, University of Georgia, Athens.

Keith J. Bowman *Materials sciences: Metallurgy.* Assistant Professor of Materials Engineering, Purdue University, West Lafayette, Ind.

D. Allan Bromley *Physics: Nuclear physics.* Henry Ford II Professor of Physics, Yale University, New Haven, Conn.

Paul J. Campbell *Mathematics.* Professor of Mathematics and Computer Science, and Director of Academic Computing, Beloit College, Beloit, Wis.

Douglas E. Comer *Electronics and information sciences: Computers and computer science.* Professor of Computer Science, Purdue University, West Lafayette, Ind.

Dave Dooling *Space exploration.* D² Associates, Freelance Science Writing and Aerospace Consulting, Huntsville, Ala.

F. C. Durant III *Electronics and information sciences: Satellite systems.* Aerospace Historian and Consultant, Chevy Chase, Md.

Robert G. Eagon *Life sciences: Microbiology.* Franklin Professor of Microbiology, University of Georgia, Athens.

Robert L. Forward *Physics: General developments.* Science consultant, Forward Unlimited, Malibu, Calif.

Richard S. Glass *Chemistry: Organic chemistry.* Professor of Chemistry, University of Arizona, Tucson.

Richard L. Gordon *Energy.* Professor of Mineral Economics and Director of the Center for Energy and Mineral Policy Research, Pennsylvania State University, University Park.

David Guise *Architecture and civil engineering.* Professor of Architecture, City College of New York, and private practice of architecture, New York, N.Y.

Stig B. Hagstrom *Physics: Condensed-matter physics.* Professor and Chairman of the Department of Materials Science and Engineering and Director of Center for Materials Research, Stanford University, Stanford, Calif.

Robert Haselkorn *Life sciences: Molecular biology.* F. L. Pritzker Distinguished Service Professor, Department of Molecular Genetics and Cell Biology, University of Chicago, Ill.

Lawrence W. Jones *Physics: High-energy physics.* Professor of Physics, University of Michigan, Ann Arbor.

John Patrick Jordan *Food and agriculture: Agriculture.* Administrator, Cooperative State Research Service, U.S. Department of Agriculture, Washington, D.C.

Lou Joseph *Medical sciences: Dentistry.* Senior Science Writer, Hill and Knowlton, Inc., Chicago.

George B. Kauffman *Chemistry: Applied chemistry.* Professor of Chemistry, California State University, Fresno.

study of the images drawn from whatever nature affords most soft and delicate, by rays of light. Mr. Paul Delaroche readily replies to the question.

In a note written at our request, the celebrated artist asserts that the processes employed by Mr. Daguerre "carry certain essential conditions of the art to such a degree of perfection, that they will become, for even the most skilful painters, a subject of study and observation." What he was particularly struck with in the photographic drawings, is that the "finish, which is of a most inconceivable richness, is in no way discordant with the body of the picture, and in no way spoils the beauty of the general effect." "The correction of the outlining," adds Mr. Delaroche, "and the precision of forms are as perfect as they can be, in Mr. Daguerre's drawings. The painter will find in this process a quick mode of making collections for study, which he might not be able to obtain elsewhere, without great loss of time, with much trouble, and much less success, whatever degree of talent he might possess." Having refuted, by excellent arguments, the opinion of persons who have imagined that photography would be hurtful to artists, and particularly to engravers, Mr. Delaroche concludes his observations with the following reflection:—"In the whole, the admirable discovery of Mr. Daguerre is an immense service rendered to the fine arts.". . .

One of the members only of your committee has seen the artist operate, and has operated himself. It is therefore on the personal responsibility of that deputy that we are able to entertain the Chamber with the Daguerreotype, as regards the conveniency of the apparatus. There is not one of the different branch operations of the Daguerreotype that every body cannot perform, even without any knowledge of drawing or of chemistry, and even with as much success as Mr. Daguerre himself.

The very short space of time in which the operation may be performed, is what has perhaps seemed the most astonishing: scarcely more than ten minutes are required during the dark days of the winter season to take a view of a monument, of a quarter of a city, etc.

In summer, when the sun shines in all his glory, half that time only will be requisite. In southern climates, two or three minutes at most will be sufficient. But it is important to observe, that the ten or twelve minutes of the winter season, the five or six minutes of summer, the two or three minutes of the southern regions, express only the time during which the sheet of plating must receive the image through the lens.

To this, therefore, must be added the time taken to unpack the apparatus and to arrange the camera obscura, to prepare the metal sheet, that of the operation by which the image must be rendered inaccessible to the effects produced upon it by irruption of light. The time employed altogether in these various operations may amount to thirty minutes or three quarters of an hour. . . .

The preparation on which Mr. Daguerre operates is a reactive, much more liable to the effects of light than any that has hitherto been made use of. The rays of the moon, we do not say naturally but condensed in the focus of a lens of the largest size, never produced any perceptible physical effect. The sheets of plated metal prepared by Mr. Daguerre on

"Still Life," taken by Daguerre of part of his studio, dates from 1837 and is the earliest known daguerreotype in existence.

Collection de la Societe Francaise de Photographie, Paris

Notre Dame Cathedral and the historical center of Paris served as another subject for Daguerre's early photography. The daguerreotype image is thought to have been made in 1838 or 1839.
Gernsheim Collection, Harry Ransom Humanities Research Center, University of Texas at Austin

the contrary become so white, when exposed to the same light and to the subsequent operations, that we may really hope to make a photographic map of our satellite. That is to say that in a few minutes one of the longest, most minute and delicate labours of astronomy may be effected.

An important branch of the science of observation and calculation, the one that treats of the intensity of light, *Photometry*, has hitherto made but little progress. Physical experimenters have succeeded in determining the comparative intensity of two lights near each other, and which they can see simultaneously; but none have yet found a perfect method to effect the comparison when the latter condition does not exist; when the experimenter operates on a light now visible and on a luminary that will not be visible until and after the first will have disappeared.

The artificial lights of comparison, to which, in the cases we have alluded to above, the observer is obliged to have recourse, are but very seldom permanent, or as fixed as could be desired; but very seldom, and particularly when the intensity of the light of the stars is to be tried, are our artificial lights sufficiently white. It is for this reason that there is a great difference between the determinations of comparative intensity of the sun and of the moon, of the sun and of the stars, given by equally skilful

astronomers; it is for this reason that the sublime consequences of the latter comparisons, relative to the humble position of our sun amidst the thousands of millions of suns, of which the firmament is set, are still enveloped in a sort of mystery, even in the writings of the boldest authors.

We will not hesitate then to assert that the system of reaction discovered by Mr. Daguerre will hasten the progress of one of the branches of science which does the most honour to human knowledge. By its aid, the natural philosopher may in future proceed by absolute intensities. He will compare lights by their effects. If he deem it useful, he may obtain with equal facility a print of the dazzling rays of the sun, of those, three hundred thousand times weaker, of the moon, and of the rays of the stars. These prints he will make of equal intensity, either by weakening the strongest light, by an excellent method, resulting from recent discoveries, but which it is not proper to detail here, or by letting the most powerful rays act during a second only, for instance, and letting the action of the others last half an hour. However when observers apply a new instrument to the study of nature, what they have hoped to attain is always trifling in comparison to the succession of discovery which the instrument itself gives rise to. In this case, more chance should be placed on what is unexpected. . . .

as the hour of the day, have their influence on the length of the operation. The most favourable time is between 7 and 3 o'clock; and the result, acquired in June and July, in 3 or 4 minutes, will require 5 or 6 minutes in May and August, 7 or 8 in April and September, and so on in proportion as we enter into the winter season. This is but a general *aperçu* for objects in a favourable light, for it sometimes happens that 20 minutes are but sufficient in the most favourable months, when the objects are nearly in the shade. . . .

The advice given for the layer is also applicable here. You must hasten to submit the proof as soon as it leaves the camera obscura to the 4th operation. There must not be more than an hour's interval, and success is much more certain when the operation is commenced immediately.

Fourth Operation. The requisites for this operation are:—

A bottle containing at least two pounds of mercury;
A lamp with spirits of wine;
The apparatus as in *plate* 5, *fig.* 1, 2, and 3;
A long-necked glass funnel.
The mercury is to be poured through the funnel into the capsule which is at the bottom of the apparatus, in sufficient quantity to cover the ball of the thermometer. This will take about two pounds, and when this has been done no other light must be used than a wax-candle.

You must now withdraw the small plank on which is fixed the plate of the apparatus, *plate* 3, *fig.* 4, which preserves it from coming into contact with the light, and this small plank is placed between the grooves of the black plank, *plate* 5, *fig.* 1; the black plank is then replaced in the apparatus on the wedges which keep the metal underneath, sloping in an angle of 45 degrees, so that it can be seen through the glass; the cover of the apparatus is then closed very gently to prevent the pressure of the air from raising up any part of the mercury.

When everything is arranged thus, it is necessary to light the lamp, to place it under the capsule containing the mercury, and to keep it there till the thermometer, the ball of which is in the mercury, indicates a heat of 60 degrees centigrade, when the lamp must be removed; if the thermometer has risen rapidly it will continue to ascend without the aid of a lamp, but it must not be allowed to exceed 75 degrees.

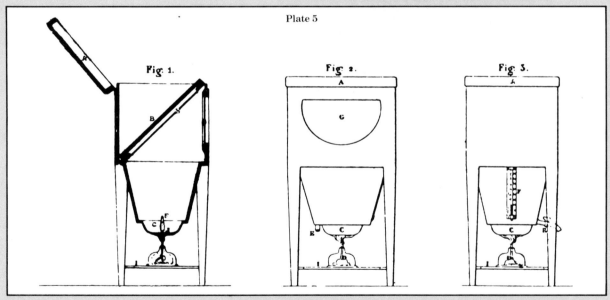

Plate 5

Plate 5 represents the same apparatus in three different points of view.

Fig. 1. A section of the apparatus.

Fig. 2. A front view of it.

Fig. 3. The same viewed from the side of the thermometer.

A. The lid of the apparatus.

B. A black board with grooves, to receive the board H, with the plate.

C. The capsule containing the mercury.

D. The lamp for spirits of wine.

E. A small cock introduced in one of the angles, and through which the mercury is drawn of by inclining the apparatus.

F. The thermometer.

G. A glass through which the drawings are viewed.

H. The board with the band and the drawing-plates.

I. A stand for the lamp which is affixed to the ring K, so that it should be exactly in the middle of the capsule.

The whole of the inside of the apparatus should be varnished black.

The imprint of the natural image exists on the plate, but it is not visible,—some minutes pass before it begins to appear, and this can be ascertained by looking through the glass by means of the wax light, but you must avoid doing this for any length of time, or it would otherwise leave traces on the plate. The proof must be left till the thermometer has descended to 45 degrees; it is then to be withdrawn and this operation is over.

When the objects have been placed in a strong light, and the light has been allowed to act too long in the camera obscura, this operation is terminated before the thermometer descends to 45 degrees; this can be ascertained by looking through the glass.

After every operation, it is essential to wipe thoroughly the interior of the apparatus, to remove the small layer of mercury which is generally to be found there. The black plank must also be well wiped, so that no mercury remain there. When the apparatus has to be packed up in order to go any distance, the mercury in the capsule should be replaced in the bottle, which is done by sloping the box to make it run out by the little cock placed for that purpose.

The proof may now be examined in a weak light, to ascertain whether success has been complete. It is removed from the little plank by taking off the four small metallic bands, which must be carefully cleaned with pummice-stone and water after every proof. The necessity of this arises, not only from their having been covered with a layer of iodine, but from their having also received the image. The

plate is then placed in the box with grooves, *plate* 2, *fig.* 3, until it undergoes the 5th and last operation, which need not take place immediately, for the proof can be preserved without any alteration whatever for several months, provided it be not looked at too often and exposed to broad day-light.

Fifth Operation. The fifth operation is for the purpose of removing from the plate the iodine, which otherwise, on the proof being exposed to light for too long a period, would undergo decomposition and destroy it.

This operation requires:—

Water saturated with common salt, or a weak solution of the hyposulphite of pure soda;

The apparatus described *plate* 6, *figs. 4 and 4 bis;*

Two copper pans tinned . . .;

A kettle of distilled water. . . .

To remove the layer of iodine, fill a large wide-mouthed bottle one-fourth part with common salt, and then fill it up with clear water. Shake the bottle now and then to make the salt dissolve. When the water is completely saturated, filter it through blotting-paper, to make it perfectly clear and limpid. To avoid making this liquid every time, a large quantity can be made at once—it will keep good in bottles well-corked.

Pour some salt water into one of the pans until it be about three centimetres deep, and fill the other pan with clean common water. Make both of these hot, but do not allow them to boil. Instead of the

. . . Fig. 3. A small tinned hook of copper, which is used to lift the plate from the pans, to shake it, and draw it out more easily.

Fig. 4. Represents an apparatus in tin varnished, to wash the drawings, which are then placed under the square rule D.

E. Thickness to retain the water which runs from the pipe C. . . .

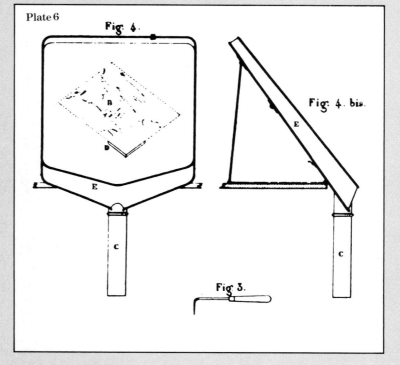

Plate 6
Fig. 4.
Fig. 4. bis.
Fig. 3.

The first commercial daguerreotype cameras were built by Alphonse Giroux, a relative of Daguerre's wife, but their design was soon copied by others. The one shown, an original Giroux bearing his seal, dates from 1839.
Science Museum, London

solution of common salt, the hyposulphite of pure soda can be employed, and this last solution is better than the preceding one, because it removes the iodine immediately, a result which does not always occur with the solution of common salt, especially when the proofs are of some standing. The operation is the same for both solutions: the hyposulphite does not require being warmed, and a smaller quantity will do, as it is necessary only that it should cover the plate at the bottom of the pan.

Dip the plate first into the pan containing common water; do not cease holding it, and take it out immediately, for it is merely requisite that the surface of the plate be made wet; and then, before it can dry at all, dip it in the salt water. If the plate were not dipped in common water previously to its being dipped in the salt water or the hyposulphite solution, indelible spots would be made. To facilitate the action of the salt water, or of the hyposulphite, on the iodine, the plate must be shaken, without being taken out of the liquid, by means of the tinned copper hook, (*plate* 6, *fig.* 3,) which is passed underneath the plate, which is to be raised and lowered several times. When the yellow colour has entirely disappeared, the plate is removed, and it is to be taken by the two extremities by pressing the hands against the thicknesses (to prevent the fingers touching the proofs) and dipped immediately into the first pan of clean water.

Then take the apparatus (*plate* 6, *fig.* 4 *and* 4 *bis*) and the kettle, (*plate* 6, *fig.* 5), which must be quite clean and have had some distilled water boiled in it. Remove the plate from the pan of water and place it immediately on the sloping board, (*plate* 6, *fig.* 4); and then, without allowing it to dry, pour on the surface, and by the top of the plate, the distilled water, very hot, but not boiling, so that the water may fall like a sheet on the whole extent of the proof, and carry off with it the whole solution of common salt or of hyposulphite, which is already weakened by the immersion of the plate in the first pan. . . .

After this washing, the proof is finished, and nothing remains to be done but to preserve it from dust and the vapour that might tarnish the silver. The mercury which sketches the images is in part decomposed; it sticks to the silver and withstands the water poured on it, but cannot bear any rubbing.

To preserve the proofs, they should be placed under glass and glued—this makes them unalterable, even if exposed to the sun. . . .

Institutions

of

Science

TSUKUBA

Japan's City for Science

by Tetsuzo Kawamoto

Some 60 kilometers northeast of Tokyo the Japanese have established a center for scientific research and development. In 25 years it has become home to 47 national institutions and some 6,500 researchers.

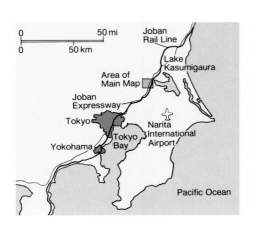

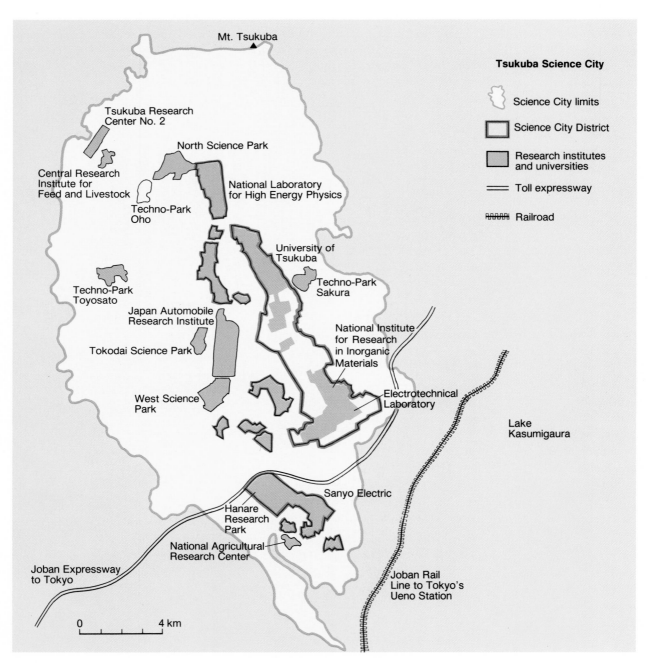

Mt. Tsukuba

Tsukuba Science City

Science City limits

Science City District

Research institutes and universities

Toll expressway

Railroad

Tsukuba Research Center No. 2

North Science Park

National Laboratory for High Energy Physics

Central Research Institute for Feed and Livestock

Techno-Park Oho

University of Tsukuba

Techno-Park Sakura

Techno-Park Toyosato

Japan Automobile Research Institute

National Institute for Research in Inorganic Materials

Tokodai Science Park

Electrotechnical Laboratory

West Science Park

Lake Kasumigaura

Sanyo Electric

Hanare Research Park

National Agricultural Research Center

Joban Expressway to Tokyo

Joban Rail Line to Tokyo's Ueno Station

0   4 km

Since the Japanese government decided to form Tsukuba Science City in 1963, a quarter of a century of planning and an investment of approximately 1.5 trillion yen have gone into its development as a national project. In Tsukuba Science City 47 national institutions under 10 ministries and agencies have moved from Tokyo or been newly established. Thirty of these are government research institutes, such as the Electrotechnical Laboratory. The other 17 include the University of Tsukuba and the National Laboratory for High-Energy Physics. There are approximately 6,500 researchers, of whom 2,500 hold Ph.D. degrees.

More than 30% of the 89 government research laboratories within Japan are concentrated in Tsukuba. Approximately 4,500 researchers work there. Since the total number of researchers in government research institutes in Japan is 10,200, more than 45% of them are in Tsukuba. The total budget for government research institutes in Tsukuba in 1989 was 74 billion yen, which was 48% of the total budget of 155 billion yen for all government research institutes in Japan.

Recently, many private research institutes have been striving to establish scientific contacts with the government laboratories. A number of the private institutes, specializing in general chemistry, pharmaceuticals, microcomputers and electronics, and materials and general construction, decided to relocate to Tsukuba Science City. There were also several large companies from other countries.

Tsukuba Science City is located 60 kilometers northeast of Tokyo and 40 kilometers northwest of the New Tokyo International Airport. (One kilometer = about 0.62 mile.) There is really no place called Tsukuba Science City; that is the name used as a matter of convenience during the planning. As an administrative district, Tsukuba Science City consists of Tsukuba city and Kukizaki town. Tsukuba Science City covers an area of about 28,560 hectares. (One hectare = about 2.47 acres.) This is about half the size of the 23 districts that make up Tokyo. Physically, Tsukuba consists of highlands 20–30 meters above sea level and lowlands that have been built up from small rivers such as the Sakura and Yata. (One meter = about 3.3 feet.) The surrounding area is rich in natural beauty, with Lake Kasumigaura to the east and Mt. Tsukuba (876 meters) with its twin peaks to the north.

TETSUZO KAWAMOTO is Chief Operating Officer of the Tsukuba Research Consortium, Tsukuba, Japan.

(Top) Overview of Tsukuba Science City is photographed from the tower of the Meteorological Research Institute. Mt. Tsukuba can be seen in the background at the far left.

(Top) Makoto Iwafuji/Newton Magazine, Kyoikusha

(Overleaf) Electric wave-testing equipment at the Tsukuba Space Center is used to check the quality of satellite antennas employed in electrical wave experiments. The many protrusions—electrical wave absorbers made of polyurethane foam—are designed to remove electrical wave reflections and thereby ensure high-precision tests.

Photograph, Makoto Iwafuji/Newton Magazine, Kyoikusha

Tsukuba Science City is divided into the Science City District and the Peripheral Development District. In the Science City District, government research institutes, universities, and housing for employees have been constructed. The Science City District covers about 2,700 hectares, extending about 18 kilometers from north to south and about 6 kilometers from east to west. In the Peripheral Development District of 25,850 hectares surrounding the Science City District, private companies' research laboratories and high-tech industries have been developing rapidly. At the same time, however, efforts were being made to preserve the rich agricultural land and natural environment of the area. The population of Tsukuba Science City (as of 1983) was about 160,000, with 45,000 living in the Science City District. In 1985 the International Science and Technology Expo '85 took place in Tsukuba. Some 20 million people from Japan and abroad visited the exposition.

Origins

The plan that eventually led to Tsukuba Science City did not start as a plan for a science city but evolved over the years. It stemmed originally from a need to curb the rapid overcrowding of Tokyo in the early 1960s, to promote advanced science and technology for the Japanese economy by providing a new research environment, and to increase the number of students who would go on to higher educational institutions. The three concerns were integrated by the Construction Act for Tsukuba Science City of 1970, and the plan to build a science city in the wide-open area of Tsukuba was established.

As the core of the Tsukuba project, 47 national research institutes and universities were to be relocated from Tokyo and its surrounding area to the Tsukuba Science City District. The government research institutes and universities needed approximately 1,500 hectares. Tsukuba Science

International Science and Technology Expo '85 was held at Tsukuba Science City in 1985. Approximately 20 million people from Japan and many other countries attended the exposition.

476

City was designed for a population of 100,000 people from the government research institutes and universities, including employees, their families, and university students. The Peripheral Development District was designed to contain the private research institutes and high-tech industries, calling for an additional population of about 120,000 people (including the 80,000 people who already lived there).

Land-utilization plan

The land-utilization plan for the Science City District established the mixed commercial-residential zone and the residential zone in the city's center. Government research institutes and universities were located in the area around the center.

The government research institutes and universities are grouped into five zones according to their specialized fields of activity: the higher education and training zone, the construction zone, the science and engineering zone, the biological and agricultural zone, and the common use zone. The University of Tsukuba, which has the highest population and largest land area in Tsukuba, lies just to the north of the city's center.

National Institutions in Tsukuba Science City

Institution	Research	Administration	Total	Institution	Research	Administration	Total
Higher Education and Training Group				Electrotechnical Laboratory	559	134	693
University of Tsukuba	1,548	1,972	3,520	Industrial Products Research Institute	103	25	128
University of Library and Information Science	59	83	142	National Research Institute for Pollution and Resources	248	82	330
National Laboratory for High Energy Physics	300	277	577	Meteorological Research Institute	143	36	179
National Education Center Annex	—	40	40	Aerological Observatory	8	30	38
Tsukuba Botanical Garden National Science Museum	13	7	20	Meteorological Instruments Plant, Japan Meteorological Agency	—	22	22
Tsukuba College of Technology	—	—	—				
Tsukuba International Center, Japan International Cooperation Agency	—	14	14	**Biological and Agricultural Group**			
				Tsukuba Life Science Center, The Institute of Physical and Chemical Research	11	17	28
Tsukuba International Agricultural Training Center, Japan International Cooperation Agency	—	22	22	Tsukuba Primate Center for Medical Science, National Institute of Health	7	3	10
				Tsukuba Medicinal Plant Research Station, National Institute of Hygienic Sciences	5	7	12
Construction Group				National Agricultural Research Center	213	120	333
National Research Center for Disaster Prevention	77	40	117	National Institute of Agrobiological Resources	152	103	255
NTT Tsukuba Field Engineering Development Center	125	20	145	National Institute of Agroenvironmental Sciences	166	64	230
Geographical Survey Institute	170	740	910	National Institute of Animal Industry	122	100	222
Public Works Research Institute	312	167	479	Fruit Tree Research Station	119	105	224
Building Research Institute	120	54	174	National Research Institute of Agricultural Engineering	75	38	113
				National Institute of Sericultural and Entomological Science	130	90	220
Science and Engineering Group				National Institute of Animal Health	156	162	318
National Research Institute for Metals, Tsukuba Laboratories	84	16	100	National Food Research Institute	110	27	137
National Institute for Research in Inorganic Materials	119	46	165	Tropical Agriculture Research Center	71	23	94
Tsukuba Space Center, National Space Development Agency of Japan	100	114	214	Forestry and Forest Products Research Institute	213	52	265
The National Institute for Environmental Studies	177	73	250	Tsukuba Office, Secretariat of Agriculture, Forestry and Fisheries Research Council	—	97	97
Tsukuba Administration Office, Agency of Industrial Science and Technology	—	72	72	Tsukuba Center for Seeds and Seedlings	8	—	8
National Research Laboratory for Metrology	128	94	222				
Mechanical Engineering Laboratory	219	64	283	**Common Use Facilities**			
National Chemical Laboratory for Industry	282	78	360	Tsukuba Center for Institutes	—	5	5
Fermentation Research Institute	71	17	88				
Research Institute for Polymers and Textiles	104	23	127				
Geological Survey of Japan	243	124	367	**Total (47 institutes)**	6,870	5,499	12,369

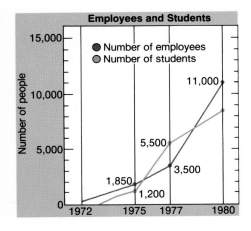

Employees and Students

Number of people

● Number of employees
○ Number of students

15,000

11,000

10,000

5,500

5,000

1,850

3,500

1,200

0

1972　1975　1977　1980

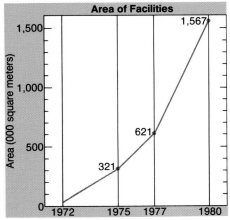

Area of Facilities

Area (000 square meters)

1,567

1,500

1,000

621

500

321

0

1972　1975　1977　1980

The Tsukuba Research Center for the Ministry of International Trade and Industry is located just to the south of the city's center.

A unique characteristic of the Science City District is the large percentage of land dedicated to government research institutes and universities. This area amounts to about 1,500 hectares, twice as large as the housing district. This ratio is unusual for Japanese cities.

In order to develop the 2,700 hectares of the Science City District, 1,800 hectares had to be bought from 2,600 different landowners. Buying this land was a difficult task. Buying large contiguous pieces was even more difficult. The sites purchased were mainly Japanese red pine forests. This was because, beginning about 1970, the use of fuel oil became popular in the nearby area. Thus, the pine forests were no longer important as a source of energy. As a result, the land procurement was targeted mainly at these forests. This resulted in the basic shape of the city being determined by the distribution pattern of the forests.

City growth

Tsukuba was a "custom-ordered city," and the choice of institutions to be relocated was very important. The Japanese Cabinet made four different selections of institutions to be moved to Tsukuba over the years. In 1967, 36 institutions were selected, and 43 were chosen in 1972, 1973, and 1975. The fact that the Cabinet met four times, and that different institutions were presented as candidates each time, reflects how agonizing the decisions were. According to the decision of the Cabinet in 1961 regarding the transfer of government offices, institutions to be moved from Tokyo were those that did not have to be located in Tokyo to carry out their functions. In 1963 a request was issued to the vice-ministers of each Cabinet ministry and agency to submit the names of institutions to be moved, the required acreage for the new site, and the date of moving. Thus, the institutes to be established in Tsukuba were selected by simply assembling candidates from each ministry.

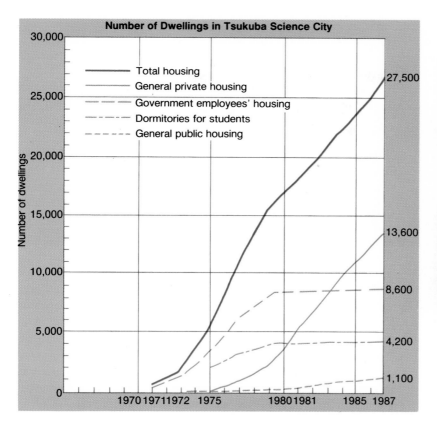

Number of Dwellings in Tsukuba Science City

Number of dwellings

- —— Total housing
- —— General private housing
- — — Government employees' housing
- —·— Dormitories for students
- - - - General public housing

30,000
25,000
20,000
15,000
10,000
5,000
0

27,500
13,600
8,600
4,200
1,100

1970 1971 1972 1975   1980 1981   1985 1987

It was not easy to move researchers and their families from Tokyo. Strong, even passionate, resistance developed among many, who had already established comfortable lives in Tokyo and its suburbs. If an institute moved, all employees would also have to move. To help allay their fears, the government promised high-quality research facilities and good schools and housing. In the end, however, some researchers chose to stay at Tsukuba during the week and return home to Tokyo on weekends.

The first institute to move was the National Institute for Research in Inorganic Materials. It started its research in Tsukuba in 1972. An

Housing for research workers and their families was built in a planned residential district (opposite page). A meal is enjoyed in the home of a Tsukuba research worker (above). Walkway (left) is one of many that connect parks with main public buildings in the Science City District.

(Opposite page) T. Watanabe—Orion Press

479

"Round greenhouse" (right) at the Tropical Agriculture Research Center provides an environment for studying tropical crops. Some 120 different kinds of plants are grown in the climate-controlled building. The Tsukuba Center Building (below) is a general information center and also provides sleeping accommodations. A laser radar (opposite page, top) at the National Institute for Environmental Studies can survey the degrees of air pollution within a radius of 50–60 kilometers, which includes the skies over Tokyo. It emits pulsed light in infrared and green wavelengths. Computer graphic (opposite page, right) was produced at the National Research Institute of Agricultural Engineering. The locations where landslides occurred are displayed in blue, and the magnitudes of the landslides are calculated and computer-processed from data obtained from soil sampled at the landslide locations.

Photos, Makoto Iwafuji/Newton Magazine, Kyoikusha

additional nine institutions had begun working there by 1975. These included the University of Tsukuba, the National Laboratory for High-Energy Physics, the Tsukuba Space Center (National Space Development Agency of Japan), the National Institute for Environmental Studies, the Tropical Agriculture Research Center, the Aerological Observatory, the National Education Center Annex, and the Meteorological Instruments Plant. At that time the number of employees was 1,850, the number of students was 1,200, and the total area of the facilities was 32 hectares.

Between 1975 and 1977 six more institutes began their work at Tsukuba. These included the National Research Center for Disaster Prevention, NTT Tsukuba Field Engineering Development Center, the National Research Institute for Metals, the National Research Institute of Agricultural Engineering, the National Institute of Agrobiological Resources, and the Tsukuba Botanical Garden, National Science Museum. Soon afterward, 15 more institutes joined the group at Tsukuba. At that time the number of employees grew to 3,500, the number of students 5,500, and the total area of the facilities 62 hectares. From 1977 to 1980 the remaining institutes moved to Tsukuba. The total number of

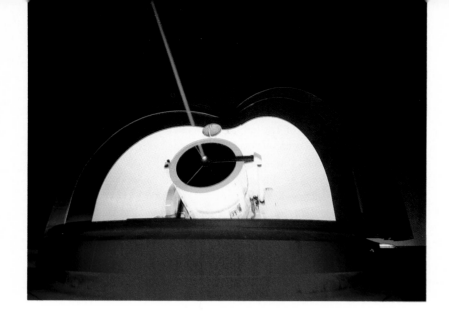

employees reached about 11,000, the total number of students 8,500, and the total area of the facilities 157 hectares.

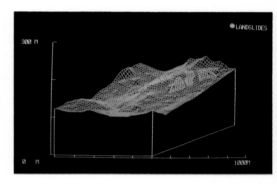

Private-sector institutes began locating chiefly in the Peripheral Development District about 1982, and five science parks were created there. The first to be developed was the Tokodai Science Park, where some 28 companies were operating on 41 hectares in early 1989 and where another 8 had decided to locate. Following this, the Tsukuba North Science Park (128 hectares), the Tsukuba West Science Park (102 hectares, the former International Science and Technology Expo '85 site), and the Tsukuba Techno-Park Toyosato (69 hectares) were created. In the Tsukuba North Science Park, 10 companies were operating, and another 7 companies had decided to locate there; in the Tsukuba West Science Park, 2 companies were operating, and another 13 were planning to locate there; and in the Tsukuba Techno Park Toyosato, 3 companies had begun operations, and another 26 were expected to follow. In 1989 the Tsukuba Techno-Park Oho (41 hectares) and the Tsukuba Techno-Park Sakura (66 hectares) were under development.

In addition, some private companies located their research institutes in the Peripheral Development District outside of the established science parks. A small (five-hectare) science park, Tsukuba Research Park Hanare, was created within the Science City District. Six private companies were operating there, and three more were expected to join them. The demand by private industry for sites in Tsukuba continued to be strong. The total number of employees in the private sector was about 3,100.

Basic urban facilities

Included among the basic facilities of Tsukuba Science City are the main streets, which have been developing steadily over the years. From 1977 to 1980 eight main streets, extending for a total length of 57 kilometers, were opened to traffic. Three streets run from north to south and five from east to west. The largest streets contain six lanes of traffic and also have wide sidewalks, bicycle lanes, and parkways to separate the

481

sidewalks from the streets. The streets were positioned lower than the residential lots to minimize sound pollution and to allow for pedestrian bridges.

In the central parts of the city and residential district, networks of pedestrian walkways connect residential areas with research institutes, universities, cultural facilities, and parks. The development of the walkways was delayed considerably, and they opened in about 1985.

The maximum planned water supply is 100,000 tons per day, with 60,000 tons per day for use by research institutes and universities and 40,000 for household use. The bulk of the water supply comes from Lake Kasumigaura. The urban sewage system was designed to treat rainwater and wastewater separately. Raw sewage is treated at the water-purification center near the Tone River and discharged into the river. Laboratory wastewater is treated at each research institute until it reaches a predetermined level of quality and then is discharged into the urban sewage system. Special contaminated laboratory wastewater is treated separately at each research institute and cannot be discharged into the urban sewage system. The treatment systems for the wastewater at research institutes are classified into three types—physical, chemical, and biologic. This treatment system is based on guidelines by the Science and Technology Agency and may be the most advanced treatment system for wastewater from research institutes in the world.

Housing and living conditions

Before construction of the research institutes and universities, housing for employees of government research institutes and universities received utmost priority. As a result, by 1989 there was no shortage of high-quality housing. Between 1971 and 1977 housing for 8,500 government

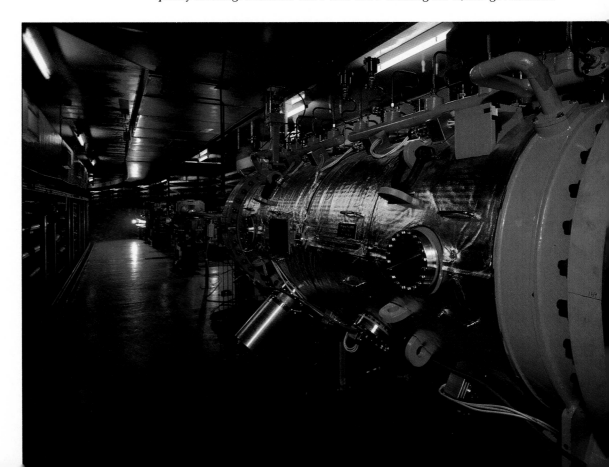

employees was completed in the planned residential district. After 1976 some 5,500 private residences were built in the private residential area. Most of the private residences are dormitories for students, but there is also some company housing.

Three high schools, six junior high schools, eight primary schools, and seven kindergartens were provided in the new city as the population increased. Many of these schools initiated unique educational programs. At the Takezono East Primary School, for example, research was being conducted in cooperation with the University of Tsukuba on the use of computers for teaching the compulsory curriculum.

There are 93 parks and green areas within the Science City District, covering approximately 100 hectares. This amounts to 10 square meters (108 square feet) of parks and green area per person in the planned population. Doho Park (20 hectares) has a world-class solar-heated pool and gymnasium. Many of the parks have tennis courts. A network of pedestrian walkways connects Doho Park and other parks to main public buildings in the Science City District. These extend for a total distance of 50 kilometers and are used by bikers as well as walkers.

Originally, the medical services available in the city were poor. However, Tsukuba University Hospital opened in 1976 and the Tsukuba Medical Center with an emergency hospital in 1985. Several private hospitals and many clinics have also opened in recent years.

In accordance with the construction plan for each residential district, four small shopping centers were developed. Originally, the quantity and quality of the existing shopping centers were not sufficient. Beginning in 1980, however, small- and medium-sized supermarkets and many

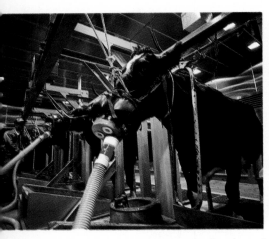

The entire interior wall surface of the zootron (above) at the National Institute of Animal Industry is covered with stainless steel plates so that the wall surface temperatures will instantly respond to changes in room temperature and also to protect the surfaces from corrosion caused by animal excretions. At the Geographical Survey Institute (below) coded cartographical information such as marks, lines, and/or points of location is being memorized by a computer as part of an effort to make maps by means of automated cartography.

Photos, Makoto Iwafuji/Newton Magazine, Kyoikusha

restaurants opened. Just before 1985, when the International Science and Technology Expo '85 was held, a large shopping facility (5½ hectares) that included department stores, movie theaters, and restaurants opened in the city center. In addition, the Tsukuba Center Building was developed with a hotel and concert hall.

After 1987 it was possible to travel directly from Tsukuba Science City to the Tokyo train station by highway bus. The time from Tsukuba to Tokyo is about 1½ hours. Bus routes within Tsukuba Science City have been gradually expanding since 1973, although in early 1989 most people still depended on private automobiles.

Current research

Tsukuba Science City is an attractive place for researchers for a variety of reasons. Because of their high density within a small area, researchers in different laboratories can make contact with one another by car in about 10 to 20 minutes. Tsukuba is also designed in such a way that most people who work in the institutes live in the city. Thus, they have many chances to make friendships through neighborhood activities, hobbies and sports, and alumni associations or even at restaurants. Even if their fields are not related, they are likely to know the others' workplaces and specialized areas and the present status of their research.

The most distinguishing feature with respect to research in Tsukuba Science City may be the concentration within a small area of many large-scale and up-to-date research facilities. These include a large-scale (15 × 15-meter) shaking table for earthquake simulation, a platform that can be hydraulically controlled to simulate ground movement in an earthquake and can accommodate buildings up to eight stories high, a full-scale fire-testing laboratory, three large-scale atmospheric diffusion wind tunnels, a natural environment simulator, a smog chamber, a large-scale outdoor river model test yard, and a large-scale hydraulics laboratory for modeling mixing and diffusion processes in reservoirs and lakes.

There are three laser radars for the remote measurement of atmospheric pollutants or the ozone layer and a tall steel tower for mete-

orologic observation. For work in high-energy physics there is a 30-GeV (billion electron volt) electron-positron colliding beam accelerator and a 500-MeV (million electron volt) electron linear accelerator (the Electrotechnical Laboratory). Metrologists and geophysicists have three large-scale testing tunnels for long-distance optical measurements, and researchers in acoustics are provided with an acoustics room that has the highest performance in the world.

The city contains observation networks for studying the activity of the Earth's crust, including three deep-borehole observation systems (2,300 meters–3,510 meters deep), around Tokyo for earthquake prediction studies in the Kanto and Tokai districts. The data from each observation site are automatically fed to the National Research Center for Disaster Prevention, where they are analyzed.

There are large-scale facilities for material analysis by ultrahigh-voltage, high-resolution electron microscopy. Instruments for studying material syntheses under ultrahigh pressure are also available.

"Gene bank" at the National Institute of Agrobiological Resources (above) preserves plant seeds for long periods of time at a temperature of −10°C and a relative humidity of 30%. Rotational experimentation apparatus at the Meteorological Research Institute (left) simulates complex meteorological phenomena.

Photos, Makoto Iwafuji/Newton Magazine, Kyoikusha

During the development of Tsukuba the conditions were ideal for the creation of such first-class facilities. One reason was that the Japanese government had good financial resources during the 1960s because of the nation's expanding economy. In addition, a new system for obtaining construction funds was proposed. This new system generated the funds for the research facilities by sale of the land in Tokyo owned by each institution. Many research institutes were located in high-priced zones in the central part of Tokyo. A second reason was that the sudden development of a huge market for equipment in Tsukuba prompted private industry to strive to supply the newest and best equipment and facilities. However, such facilities may become outdated quickly, and their renewal is an important problem confronting Tsukuba.

Tsukuba Science City is operating at the frontier of science and technology in Japan. The spectrum of research in Tsukuba is quite broad, including the Earth sciences, earthquake and disaster prevention, environmental protection, agricultural science and technology, materials science and technology, and high-energy physics, among others.

Since the high-temperature superconductors were discovered in 1986, many researchers throughout the world have participated in a race to find and develop more of these materials. Because of the quantity and quality of researchers and their enthusiasm, many advances in the synthesis of high-temperature superconductors have been made by researchers in Tsukuba. Among them are Hiroshi Maeda's discovery of new high-temperature bismuth superconductors, Fujio Izumi's structure determinations for high-temperature oxide superconductors, and Hideo Ihara's development of high-temperature oxide superconductors.

Using ultrahigh pressure, materials scientists have synthesized artificial diamonds as large as ten millimeters in diameter. Other diamonds were synthesized by vapor deposition. Tsukuba researchers developed a new method for preparing aromatic polyimide thin films by vacuum deposition polymerization. Other achievements included the development

of a superconducting magnet with the world's highest magnetic field, a solar cell made of amorphous silicon, robot guide dogs that can recognize obstacles and help blind people walk the streets safely, and the isolation and functional analysis of the highly active hypertension-causing protein, endothelin.

Scientific communication

In the early years there were few researchers working in the same field at Tsukuba. Thus, the pattern of communication was most often that of one researcher contacting another one directly. In 1978 the Tsukuba Center for Institutes (TCI) of the Science and Technology Agency was established, and two years later the Liaison Council for Research and

Fire-resistant door at the Building Research Institute (opposite page) is tested for resistance to heat and impacts and for heat insulation capability. In a freeze dryer at the Patent Microorganism Depository of the Fermentation Research Institute (left) microorganisms are preserved in ampoules. They appear white when protective agents are added to them. Below, "Melspider III," a robot that can move along wall surfaces without any need of support, is adjusted at the Mechanical Engineering Laboratory. Engineers are working to develop a suction mechanism that will allow the robot to adhere unerringly even to rough wall surfaces.

Photos, Makoto Iwafuji/Newton Magazine, Kyoikusha

Other Institutes of Tsukuba Science City was set up. The TCI provides a place for mutual contact and exchange among researchers as well as for facilitating the dissemination of information related to science and technology. The Liaison Council is composed of directors from about 70 research institutions in Tsukuba Science City (including private industry research institutes). It aims to promote mutual cooperation among the institutions in Tsukuba Science City.

As researchers working in the same field became more numerous, communication between scientists in the same field and among researchers in many fields increased. Informal research meetings, such as on heat transfer, applied Earth science, catalysis, electron microscopy, and insects, started among researchers from different institutes who worked in the same field. From 1981 the importance of such communication in Tsukuba was recognized by the Exploratory Research for Advanced

Technology program (ERATO) sponsored by the government. ERATO projects consist of government, university, and industry researchers, including scientists from other nations, under the guidance of a project leader. From about 1980 the Joint Government-Industry Program began. In this program 600 researchers from private industry work together with government researchers at government institutes for a period of one or two years.

Communication among researchers in different fields is difficult because of different scientific approaches and vocabulary. However, if such communication can be successfully carried out, it can be of tremendous value. It can help researchers gain new insight into their research and thus increase the opportunities and chances for success. Furthermore, the creation of new interdisciplinary fields becomes possible. This may be possible only in such a place as Tsukuba.

The Tsukuba Research Consortium (TRC) was established by eight independent high-tech corporations in 1980 and began operation in 1983. TRC aims to promote strong relations among the eight firms in order to foster the development of new industrial technologies. It also carries out programs that involve the various research sectors within Tsukuba and with other research institutions within Japan and in other countries. Many researchers from government institutes and universities go on a regular basis to TRC, where they can discuss their work with scientists from the corporations.

Plans and prospects for the future

The first phase of the Tsukuba Project, the relocation of national laboratories, researchers, and their families in a relatively short time, is considered a success. The second phase (which began in 1986) should see a settling down of government employees and their families and an expansion of the concept of Tsukuba Science City. With the increasing importance of Tsukuba and also the rising cost of land, it is essential to expand the original plan for the city. Tsukuba Science City was chosen recently by the National Land Agency to be a center for various business functions now based in Tokyo. Consequently, a new railway line, the "Joban-Shinsen," was proposed to run directly between Tokyo and Tsukuba, and a Tokyo metropolitan belt highway was envisioned to connect Tsukuba, Narita International Airport, and Hachioji, an important suburb of Tokyo. In addition, a new "Greater Tsukuba" plan was under development by the National Land Agency.

Beyond the overall planning for the city, there is a need to strengthen and make even more vibrant the scientific community within Tsukuba. The influx of private companies and researchers from other countries has helped to broaden the scientific base of Tsukuba. Now it is important to build on that base. Goals for the future are to foster a stimulating and intellectual atmosphere, to establish networks between researchers and within the scientific community, to pursue exhaustively individual technological fields, and to create new technologies by synthesis and fusion among various existing fields of technology.

488

Index

This is a three-year cumulative index. Index entries for review articles in this and previous editions of the *Yearbook of Science and the Future* are set in boldface type, *e.g.,* **Archaeology**. Feature articles appear under the article title and are identified as such. Entries to other subjects are set in lightface type, *e.g.,* radiation. Additional information on any of these subjects is identified with a subheading and indented under the entry heading. Subheadings in quotes refer to feature articles on that topic. The numbers following headings and subheadings indicate the year (boldface) of the edition and the page number (lightface) on which the information appears. The abbreviation "*il.*" indicates an illustration.

> **Archaeology 90**–288; **89**–278; **88**–321
> field research **89**–278
> honors **88**–478
> "New Light on the Maya" **88**–204

All entry headings are alphabetized word by word. Hyphenated words and words separated by dashes or slashes are treated as two words. When one word differs from another only by the presence of additional characters at the end, the shorter precedes the longer. In inverted names, the words following the comma are considered only after the preceding part of the name has been alphabetized. Names beginning with "Mc" and "Mac" are alphabetized as "Mac"; "St." is alphabetized as "Saint." Examples:

> Lake
> Lake, Simon
> Lake Placid
> Lakeland

u

Acknowledgments

17, 23   Illustrations by Pawel Bodytko

31, 36   Illustrations by Richard A. Roiniotis

63   (Bottom) James P. Crutchfield

70   (Top) James P. Crutchfield

94   Illustration by Anne Hoyer Becker

97   From *An Introduction to Pollen Analysis,* by Gunnar Erdtman, Chronica Botanica Company,
Waltham, Mass., 1943; Almqvist och Wiksell Forlag AB, Stockholm

121   Adapted from "A Comparison of Relict Versus Equilibrium Models for Insular Mammals of the Gulf of Maine,"
K. L. Crowell, *Biological Journal of the Linnean Society,* vol. 28, pp. 37–64, 1986; © 1986 The Linnean Society of London

124   Adapted from "Species-Area Relationship and Its Determinants for Mammals in Western North American National Parks,"
W. D. Newmark, *Biological Journal of the Linnean Society,* vol. 28, pp. 83–98, 1986; © 1986 The Linnean Society of London

129, 139   Illustrations by Curtis E. Hardy

168, 310   From "Molecular Manipulation Using a Tunnelling Microscope," J. S. Foster, J. E. Frommer, and P. C. Arnett, reprinted
by permission of *Nature,* vol. 331, no. 6154, pp. 324–326, Jan. 28, 1988, © Macmillan Magazines Ltd.

214, 215, 218, 219, 220   Illustrations by John L. Draves

281   Adapted from information obtained from NOAA

282   Adapted from "Evidence for Global Warming in the Past Decade," P. D. Jones, T. M. L. Wigley, *et. al.,* reprinted
by permission of *Nature,* vol. 332, no. 6167, p. 790, April 28, 1988, © Macmillan Magazines Ltd.

362   From "A Novel Free-Living Prochlorophyte Abundant in the Oceanic Euphotic Zone," S. W. Chisholm, *et. al.,* reprinted
by permission of *Nature,* vol. 334, no. 6180, pp. 340–343, July 28, 1988, © Macmillan Magazines Ltd.

410   From "Atomic Resolution Imaging of Adsorbates on Metal Surfaces in Air: Iodine Adsorption on Pt(111)," B. C. Schardt,
S-L Yau, F. Rinaldi, *Science,* vol. 243, no. 4894, cover and pp. 1050–1053, Feb. 24, 1989, © 1988 AAAS

N ow there's a way to identify all your fine books with flair and style. As part of our continuing service to you, Britannica Home Library Service, Inc. is proud to be able to offer you the fine quality item shown on the next page.

B ooklovers will love the heavy-duty personalized embosser. Now you can personalize all your fine books with the mark of distinction, just the way all the fine libraries of the world do.

T o order this item, please type or print your name, address and zip code on a plain sheet of paper. (Note special instructions for ordering the embosser). Please send a check or money order only (your money will be refunded in full if you are not delighted) for the full amount of purchase, including postage and handling, to:

Britannica Home Library Service, Inc.
Attn: Yearbook Department
Post Office Box 6137
Chicago, Illinois 60680

(Please make remittance payable to: Britannica Home Library Service, Inc.)

IN THE BRITANNICA TRADITION OF QUALITY...

PERSONAL EMBOSSER

A mark of distinction for your fine books. A book embosser just like the ones used in libraries. The 1½″ seal imprints "Library of _____" (with the name of your choice) and up to three centered initials. Please type or print clearly BOTH full name (up to 26 letters including spaces between names) and up to three initials.
Please allow six weeks for delivery.

Just **$20.00**

plus $2.00 shipping and handling

This offer available only in the United States.
Illinois residents please add sales tax

Britannica Home Library Service, Inc.